Incomplete Data in Sample Surveys

Volume 2
Theory and Bibliographies

Incomplete Data in Sample Surveys

Incomplete Data in Sample Surveys

Volume 2
Theory and Bibliographies

Panel on Incomplete Data
Committee on National Statistics
Commission on Behavioral and Social Sciences
    and Education
National Research Council

Edited by

William G. Madow
Committee on National Statistics
National Research Council
National Academy of Sciences
Washington, D.C.

Ingram Olkin
Department of Statistics and School of Education
Stanford University
Stanford, California

Donald B. Rubin
Department of Statistics and Department of Education
University of Chicago
Chicago, Illinois

1983

ACADEMIC PRESS
A Subsidiary of Harcourt Brace Jovanovich, Publishers
New York   London
Paris   San Diego   San Francisco   São Paulo   Sydney   Tokyo   Toronto

ACADEMIC PRESS, INC.
111 Fifth Avenue, New York, New York 10003

United Kingdom Edition published by
ACADEMIC PRESS, INC. (LONDON) LTD.
24/28 Oval Road, London NW1 7DX

Library of Congress Cataloging in Publication Data

Main entry under title:

Incomplete data in sample surveys.

Includes index.
Contents: v. I. Report and case studies -- v. 2.
Theory and bibliographies -- v. 3. Proceedings of the
symposium.
1. Sampling (Statistics)--Addresses, essays, lectures.
2. Social surveys--Response rate--Addresses, essays,
lectures. I. Madow, William G. (William Gregory),
Date   . II. Nisselson, Harold. III. Olkin, Ingram.
IV. National Research Council (U.S.). Panel on Incomplete
Data.
HA31.2.I52 1983   001.4'225   82-20591
ISBN 0-12-363902-6 (v. 2)

PRINTED IN THE UNITED STATES OF AMERICA

83 84 85 86   9 8 7 6 5 4 3 2 1

PANEL ON INCOMPLETE DATA IN SAMPLE SURVEYS

Ingram Olkin, Chair; Department of Statistics and School of Education, Stanford University

Barbara A. Bailar, Statistical Standards and Methodology, Bureau of the Census, U.S. Department of Commerce

Barbara A. Boyes, Office of Survey Design, Bureau of Labor Statistics, U.S. Department of Labor (deceased; member until March 1981)

Arthur P. Dempster, Department of Statistics, Harvard University

Robert M. Elashoff, Department of Biomathematics, University of California, Los Angeles

Robert L. Freie, Estimates Division, Statistical Reporting Service, U.S. Department of Agriculture

Louis Gordon, Office of Energy Information Validation, Energy Information Administration, U.S. Department of Energy (resigned, September 1979)

Robert M. Groves, Survey Research Center, University of Michigan

Morris H. Hansen, Westat, Inc.

Harold Nisselson, Westat, Inc.; Statistical Standards and Methodology, Bureau of the Census to 1979

Richard A. Platek, Census and Household Survey Methods Division, Statistics Canada

Donald B. Rubin, Department of Statistics and Department of Education, University of Chicago

Frederick J. Scheuren, Statistics of Income Division, Internal Revenue Service, U.S. Department of the Treasury

Joseph H. Sedransk, Department of Mathematics, State University of New York at Albany

Monroe G. Sirken, Office of Mathematical Statistics, National Center for Health Statistics, U.S. Department of Health and Human Services

William G. Madow, *Study Director*
M. Haseeb Rizvi, *Staff Officer*
Barbara A. (Booker) Malone, *Administrative Secretary*

(Biographical sketches of panel members and staff appear in the Appendix to Part I.)

COMMITTEE ON NATIONAL STATISTICS (1981–1982)

Stephen E. Fienberg, Chair; Departments of Statistics and Social Science, Carnegie-Mellon University

Jean D. Gibbons, Department of Management Science and Statistics, University of Alabama

Zvi Griliches, Department of Economics, Harvard University

Clifford Hildreth, Center for Economic Research, University of Minnesota

Nathan Keyfitz, Department of Sociology, Harvard University; Department of Sociology, Ohio State University

Leslie Kish, Institute for Social Research, University of Michigan

Gary G. Koch, Department of Biostatistics, University of North Carolina

Paul Meier, Department of Statistics, University of Chicago

Lincoln E. Moses, Department of Statistics and School of Medicine, Stanford University

Ingram Olkin, Department of Statistics and School of Education, Stanford University

Burton H. Singer, Department of Mathematical Statistics, Columbia University

Judith M. Tanur, Department of Sociology, State University of New York, Stony Brook

Edward R. Tufte, Departments of Political Science and Statistics, Yale University

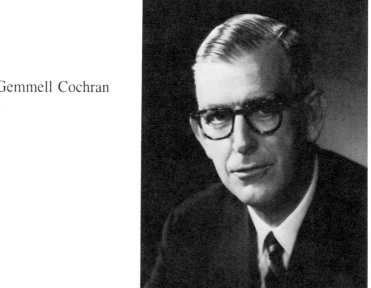

William Gemmell Cochran
1909–1980

This report is dedicated to the memory of William Gemmell Cochran, a man of warmth, wit, and wisdom who enriched the lives of all who knew him and a major contributor to the development of sampling theory as well as other areas of statistics.

Bill Cochran was born in Rutherglen, Scotland, and received degrees from Glasgow University and Cambridge University. During and after his academic work, he served as a statistician at the Rothamsted Experimental Station in England. During World War II, he was on the faculty of Iowa State College, and he also worked with the statistical research group of Princeton University on problems of naval warfare. Beginning in 1946, he was, successively, associate director of the Institute of Statistics at the University of North Carolina, head of the Department of Biostatistics at The Johns Hopkins University, and professor of statistics at Harvard University. In 1976 he became professor emeritus at Harvard.

In addition to his full academic life, Bill was an active member of many professional organizations. He served as president of the Institute of Mathematical Statistics (1946), the American Statistical Association (1953), The Biometric Society (1954), and the International Statistical Institute (1967–1971). He was elected honorary fellow of the Royal Statistical Society in 1959, and he was elected to the National Academy of Sciences in 1974. Bill was awarded a Guggenheim Fellowship in 1964, and in 1967 he received the S. S. Wilks Medal of the American Statistical Association for his many contributions to the advancement of the design and analysis of experiments and their value for military research.

Bill was involved in the early work of the panel, and we acknowledge his contribution as a participant in our discussions and as a colleague in the field of survey research.

Contents

Part I   Introduction

1   Introduction
Arthur P. Dempster and Donald B. Rubin

2   Historical Perspective
William G. Cochran

Part II   Selected Topics in Data Collection

3   Introduction   29
Joseph H. Sedransk

4   Callbacks, Follow-Ups, and Repeated Telephone Calls
P. S. R. S. Rao

5   The Impact of Substitution on Survey Estimates
David W. Chapman

6   Quota Sampling
Benjamin F. King

Part IV Weighting and Imputation Methods

12 Conceptual Issues in the Presence of Nonresponse
Donald B. Rubin

13 Weighting Adjustment for Unit Nonresponse
H. Lock Oh and Frederick J. Scheuren

14 An Overview of Hot-Deck Procedures

Barry L. Ford

15 Using Multiple Imputations to Handle Nonresponse
in Sample Surveys

Thomas N. Herzog and Donald B. Rubin

Part V Imputation Methodology: Total Survey Error

16 Introduction   249
Richard Platek and Gerald B. Gray

17 Imputation Methodology
Richard Platek and Gerald B. Gray

18 Hypothetical Example with Imputation Procedures
Richard Platek and Gerald B. Gray

19 Appendixes to Part V
Richard Platek and Gerald B. Gray

Part VI   Superpopulaton Models for Nonresponse

20   Introduction
Roderick J. A. Little

21   The Ignorable Case
Roderick J. A. Little

Part VII   Bibliographies

Contributors

Numbers in parentheses indicate the pages on which the authors' contributions begin.

Bengt Bogeström (479), Statistics Sweden, National Central Bureau of Statistics, S-11581 Stockholm, Sweden

David W. Chapman (45), Statistical Research Division, Bureau of the Census, U.S. Department of Commerce, Washington, D.C. 20233

William G. Cochran[1] (11), Department of Statistics, Harvard University, Cambridge, Massachusetts 02138

Arthur P. Dempster (3), Department of Statistics, Harvard University, Cambridge, Massachusetts 02138

Lawrence Emrich[2] (73), Department of Mathematics, State University of New York at Albany, Albany, New York 12246

Barry L. Ford (185), U.S. Department of Agriculture, Washington, D.C. 20250

Gerald B. Gray (249, 255, 295, 311), Census and Household Survey Methods Division, Statistics Canada, Ottawa, Ontario K1A 0T6, Canada

Larry V. Hedges (417), Department of Education, University of Chicago, Chicago, Illinois 60637

Thomas N. Herzog (209), U.S. Department of Housing and Urban Development, Washington, D.C. 20024

Benjamin F. King (63), School of Business Administration, University of Washington, Seattle, Washington 98195

[1]Deceased.

[2]Present address: Computing Research Section, Roswell Park Memorial Institute, Buffalo, New York 14263.

Monica Larsson (479), Statistics Sweden, National Central Bureau of Statistics, S-11581 Stockholm, Sweden

Roderick J. A. Little[3] (337, 341, 383), World Fertility Study, London, England

Lars Lyberg (479), Statistics Sweden, National Central Bureau of Statistics, S-11581 Stockholm, Sweden

William G. Madow (93), Committee on National Statistics, National Research Council, National Academy of Sciences, Washington, D.C. 20418

H. Lock Oh (143), Division of Economic Research, Office of Research and Statistics, Social Security Administration, Washington, D.C. 20009

Ingram Olkin (417), Department of Statistics and School of Education, Stanford University, Stanford, California 94305

Richard Platek (249, 255, 295, 311), Census and Household Survey Methods Division, Statistics Canada, Ottawa, Ontario K1A 0T6, Canada

P. S. R. S. Rao (33, 97), Department of Statistics, University of Rochester, Rochester, New York 14627

Donald B. Rubin[4] (3, 123, 209), Research Statistics Group, Educational Testing Service, Princeton, New Jersey 08540

Frederick J. Scheuren[5] (143), Office of Research and Statistics, Social Security Administration, Washington, D.C. 20009

Joseph H. Sedransk (29), Department of Mathematics, State University of New York at Albany, Albany, New York 12222

Bahadur Singh[6] (93, 107), Department of Mathematics, Illinois State University, Normal, Illinois 61761

Monroe G. Sirken (81), Office of Mathematical Statistics, National Center for Health Statistics, Hyattsville, Maryland 20782

[3]Present address: Department of Biomathematics, University of California, Los Angeles, Los Angeles, California 90024

[4]Present address: Departments of Statistics and Education, University of Chicago, Chicago, Illinois 60637.

[5]Present address: Statistics of Income Division, Internal Revenue Service, Washington, D.C. 20224.

[6]Present address: Department of Mathematical Sciences, Memphis State University, Memphis, Tennessee 38152.

Preface

Incompleteness of data occurs for a variety of reasons and in a variety of statistical contexts. When sample surveys are done, units that should be included among those from which a sample is selected may not be included; units selected for the sample may not respond; responding units may not respond to all items; and unit or item responses may be unusable. Each of these factors results in incompleteness. Although discussions of incompleteness have appeared in the sample survey literature for many years, concern with incompleteness and the volume of publications on theoretical aspects of nonresponse have been increasing.

The Panel on Incomplete Data, established by the Committee on National Statistics within the Commission on Behavioral and Social Sciences and Education of the National Research Council, was organized in 1977 because work in the field had reached a point at which it seemed desirable to make a comprehensive review of the literature on survey incompleteness in sample surveys and to explore ways of improving the methods of dealing with it. Initial planning for the study was undertaken by the Committee on National Statistics, with support provided by a consortium of federal statistical agencies. Funding for the work of the panel was provided by the National Science Foundation, the Social Security Administration, and the U.S. Department of Energy.

The panel's main task in the initial stages was to delineate the areas that should be included in the study. As a result of its deliberations, the panel decided that, in addition to a report, major parts of its work would consist of case studies and an exposition of theory dealing with incompleteness. The panel also planned a symposium to provide an opportunity to augment the range of topics discussed in the case studies and theory parts, which would permit new developments to be incorporated into its work. An annotated bibliography of important papers in the field was planned and a bibliography on nonresponse was later added. The panel's work is published in three volumes: the first includes the report of the panel and the case studies; the second includes the papers on theory and two bibliographies; and the third consists of the proceedings of the Symposium on Incomplete Data.

All members of the panel participated fully in the panel's work, including decisions about and preparation of parts of the report. In organizing its work, the panel designated three subpanels, on theory, on case studies, and on computer programs. The theory subpanel, chaired by Donald B. Rubin and with members Arthur Dempster, Robert M. Elashoff, Richard Platek, Ingram Olkin, Frederick Scheuren, and Joseph Sedransk, was responsible for preparing the theory part of Volume 2. The case studies subpanel, chaired by Harold Nisselson and with members Barbara Bailar, Barbara Boyes, Robert Elashoff, Robert Freie, Robert Groves, Morris Hansen, Ingram Olkin, Richard Platek, and Monroe Sirken, was responsible for preparing Part II of Volume 1. The computer programs subpanel, chaired by Joseph H. Sedransk and with members Ingram Olkin, Joseph I. Naus of Rutgers University, and Gordon T. Sande of Statistics Canada considered algorithms for dealing with missing data. The annotated bibliography was prepared by Lawrence V. Hedges of the University of Chicago and Ingram Olkin. The late William G. Cochran of Harvard University (to whom these volumes are dedicated) and Roderick J. A. Little of Datametrics Research, Inc. met with the panel on several occasions and contributed to the drafting of the panel's work. A steering committee consisting of Harold Nisselson, Ingram Olkin, Richard A. Platek, Donald B. Rubin, and Frederick J. Scheuren coordinated the project after the overall planning had been completed.

The panel relied heavily on its staff, William G. Madow, study director; M. Haseeb Rizvi, staff officer; and Barbara A. Malone, administrative secretary. In addition, the panel had the steady support and advice of Edwin D. Goldfield, executive director, and Margaret E. Martin, former executive director, of the Committee on National Statistics.

Drafts of the theory papers were reviewed by Professor Carl H. Särndal of the University of Montreal and Professor J. N. K. Rao of Carleton University; drafts of the case studies were reviewed by Professor Graham Kalton of the University of Michigan. I am indebted to them for their detailed and helpful suggestions.

A draft of the panel's report was also reviewed by three sets of reviewers within the National Research Council; I wish to express my thanks and appreciation for their comments.

In any venture of this magnitude the burden must naturally fall on a few shoulders. In the present instance, William G. Madow served not only as the study director, coordinating all the panel's activities and projects, but also provided intellectual guidance to authors on both theoretical and practical statistical issues. He was an author of many parts and a friendly critic of others. This project could not have been completed without his herculean efforts and constant help. It is hard to imagine how the project might have fared without him, and the panel wishes to acknowledge his efforts with special thanks.

Ingram Olkin, Chair
Panel on Incomplete Data

Contents of Volumes 1 and 3

Volume 3

Proceedings of the Symposium

PART I

Introduction

CHAPTER 1

Introduction

Arthur P. Dempster
Donald B. Rubin

1. ACKNOWLEDGMENTS AND OVERVIEW OF PANEL'S ACTIVITIES

The volume on the theory of handling nonresponse in sample surveys is the primary product of the theory subpanel of the Panel on Incomplete Data. The theory subpanel consisted of Donald B. Rubin (chairman), Arthur P. Dempster, Richard A. Platek, Frederick J. Scheuren, Joseph H. Sedransk, and Ingram Olkin (chairman of the full panel). In addition to the members of the subpanel, William G. Cochran and Roderick J. A. Little made substantial contributions at subpanel meetings. Furthermore, without continuous inspiration and guidance from Panel study director William G. Madow, this volume would never have been completed. Although each chapter is individually authored, many people offered criticisms and comments, which were reflected in subsequent revisions. We wish to express our gratitude to these critics, both on the panel and external to it.

Our subpanel was most fortunate to have the advice and encouragement of William G. Cochran, who, despite ill health, attended many meetings where plans were laid and draft materials reviewed. Cochran completed his chapter for the volume before his death on March 29, 1980. We are especially fortunate to have this document, written with typical Cochran directness and clarity, because Bill was an integral participant during the nearly 50 years of rapid development of the field of sample surveys, dating from his collaboration with Frank Yates at Rothamsted in the 1930s, and continuing with positions at Iowa State, Princeton, North Carolina, Johns Hopkins, and Harvard universities.

INCOMPLETE DATA
IN SAMPLE SURVEYS
Volume 2, Part I

During this time, he taught leaders in the field, wrote key books and papers, and provided distinguished leadership to studies and organizations of national and international importance.

Two other volumes are being produced by the Panel on Incomplete Data. The Case Study Subpanel chaired by Harold Nisselson has prepared Volume 1 consisting of studies of several large-scale surveys that have made deliberate efforts to deal with missing data. The case study and theory volumes complement but do not depend on each other. Under the direction of William G. Madow, a Symposium on Incomplete Data in sample surveys sponsored by the panel was held in August, 1979 in Washington, D.C. The symposium proceedings form a third volume of the panel's work, presenting specific current research papers that build on the basic material included here. The summary report of the panel is bound with the case studies volume. A selected annotated bibliography and a more extensive bibliography on nonresponse and related issues are bound with this volume as the final two parts.

A Theory of Current Practice was originally planned to serve as the basis for a short course on handling nonresponse in sample surveys, similar to 2-day courses conducted in series with the annual meetings of the American Statistical Association. As the chapters developed, it became clear that the complete volume would turn out to be too extensive and diverse for one such short course. Within each of the six nonbibliographic parts, however, the notation and the level of statistical and mathematical sophistication are relatively uniform. Consequently, each of these parts could serve as the basis for a short course on specific aspects of handling nonresponse. The entire volume could serve as the basis for a second graduate course in sample surveys. Knowledge of sampling obtainable from texts such as Cochran (1977) or Hansen, Hurwitz, and Madow (1953) is assumed of the reader.

Part I of this volume, in addition to the present introductory chapter, has a background chapter by William Cochran presenting a historical perspective on the emergence of the problem of nonresponse and of methods for handling it. Part II, coordinated by Joseph H. Sedransk, deals with data collection methods designed to reduce or alleviate problems of nonresponse. Individual chapters were authored by Sedransk, Rao, Chapman, King, Emrich, Sirken. We are fortunate to have received these informative contributions on field methods from statistcans with both applied experience and theoretical knowledge. Part III contains an introductory chapter by Madow and Singh and chapters by Rao and by Singh on frequentist and Bayesian methods for double sampling.

The fourth part of the volume presents theoretical foundations for practical methods of analyzing survey data with nonresponse, including the weighting and imputation methods widely used in major surveys conducted by government and private survey organizations. Individual chapters were written by Rubin, Oh and Scheuren, Ford, and Herzog and Rubin. Part V, by Platek and Gray, considers imputation methodology in a total survey error context.

The sixth part of the volume is by Little and presents likelihood methods for nonresponse. In this part, the reader is assumed to be familiar with the mathematical statistics of likelihood methods, for example, at the level presented in Cox and Hinkley (1974). There is some overlap between the materials in Parts IV and V; however, Part V is more general than Part IV, which concentrates on simple survey situations without response error.

Part VII is an annotated bibliography on nonresponse compiled by Olkin and Hedges; only selected material is covered in this part. Part VIII is a more extensive bibliography on nonresponse and related issues, but without annotations; it was compiled by Bogestrom, Larsson, and Lyberg.

This volume contributes to the theory and practice of handling nonresponse in sample surveys by discussing most of the fundamental mathematical statistical concepts that are needed to state and understand precisely the nonresponse problem, and by summarizing many of the current practices for handling nonresponse. Such a combination of mathematics and practice is always desirable in statistics and very desirable in a presentation of current knowledge of theory and methods for handling nonresponse, a problem rarely addressed by mathematical statisticians but constantly faced by practicing statisticians.

2. THE ROLE OF STATISTICAL THEORY IN HANDLING NONRESPONSE

The theories of some current practices for handling nonresponse in sample surveys presented here address both the design of surveys to minimize nonresponse and the analysis of surveys with nonresponse. However, any method of adjusting for incomplete data is dependent upon assumptions that are unverifiable using only the data at hand. As efforts summarized in the companion case study and symposium volumes make clear, there are usually systematic differences between respondents and nonrespondents and no statistical technique can be relied upon to adjust for all differences. Consequently, the ideal way to handle nonresponse is to obtain complete data. As a practical matter, however, some nonresponse remains after all efforts deemed cost-effective by the survey maker have been completed.

Therefore, it is both desirable to minimize nonresponse by design and necessary to adjust for the residual incomplete data by analysis, recognizing that no adjustment can fully compensate for the missing data. The solutions resulting from such adjustment are nearly always more sensitive to untestable assumptions concerning models than we would like.

In order to create a picture of what can and cannot be learned from currently available theory, the Subpanel decided to review theoretical developments already in place; it was expected that lacunae would appear that researchers would then fill in. In fact, the temptation was so great to fill gaps that a few newer developments are included in the volume, even though they have not benefited much from evaluation by experience.

Two kinds of nonresponse or incomplete data are addressed: unit nonresponse and item nonresponse. Unit nonresponse occurs when a unit included in the sample or census fails to provide usable information. For example, the sampled unit may refuse to be interviewed or fail to mail in a questionnaire. Item nonresponse occurs when a sampled unit provides usable responses to some items but not to others. For example, the unit may refuse to respond to income items but is willing to respond to all other items. Although the distinction between unit and item nonresponse is useful, in some cases it can be blurred. For example, if several sampling instruments are used, unit nonresponse on one of the instruments would be item nonresponse in the context of the entire survey.

A third type of incomplete data, undercoverage, occurs when a unit in the target population is omitted from but should have been included in the survey frame, and thus has no possibility of being included in the sample. The Panel decided early after its inception to focus its attention on the problems of item and unit nonresponse, primarily because undercoverage is so difficult a topic and its inclusion would have made the review too large. This decision is not meant to suggest that undercoverage is a less important problem than unit or item nonresponse. For some survey applications, problems of incomplete data due to undercoverage may be far more serious than problems of incomplete data due to unit or item nonresponse.

Design-based theory of the kind traditionally used by survey statisticians is represented in chapters such as those by Scheuren and Oh and by Platek and Gray. One distinction between these chapters is that Platek and Gray take an unconditional approach, calculating unconditional frequency properties of procedures, whereas Oh and Scheuren take a conditional approach, calculating conditional frequency properties of procedures as a means of drawing inferences. The conditional inference approach is similar in some ways to the likelihood/ Bayesian methods of drawing inferences discussed by Rubin and by Little.

In order to stimulate further interactions of theoreticians and practitioners, we have included chapters by Little on techniques that use standard parametric models and Bayesian techniques typically not employed by survey practitioners. We hope that other parts of this volume will also stimulate cooperation between mathematical and practicing statisticians, and so lead to new pragmatic techniques for handling nonresponse.

In order to compensate for incompleteness of data, one can modify the analysis, and one can seek to obtain more complete data. In general, both procedures will be only partially successful. Parts II and III of this volume primarily cover currently available technology for the latter approach, whereas, Parts IV–VI are concerned primarily with analysis of incomplete data. Both strategies should be deployed by many surveys, and their effects on the reduction of total survey error should be considered in the allocation of limited survey resources. Analysis is essential since the best collection efforts will leave residual incompleteness, often substantial residual incompleteness. Nevertheless, when data are incomplete, the performance of any data collection scheme and analysis procedure is invariably somewhat reliant on unverifiable assumptions.

3. OUTLINE OF VOLUME

The short chapters that make up Part II describe some major classes of current data collection methods for reducing nonresponse. Some of the reports describe techniques and what is known about their performance, and others provide basic theory for the complete designs which result from planned follow-up procedures. Part III, on double sampling, includes discussion of both design and analysis. These data collection techniques deserve their place before analysis techniques because only by making the data more complete can the dependence of the analyst for judgments about the nature and size of biases due to incompleteness be reduced.

Part IV presents a package in which the first and last chapters present discussions of how the problem could be handled without concern for allocation of resources. Chapter 12 by Rubin formulates the problem in both Bayesian and non-Bayesian terms. Both formulations result in the same basic message: if the population can be partitioned using observable characteristics so that the probability of missing data is constant within these recognizable parts, then adjustments can, in principle, be based on the data alone, subject to the usual limitations due to finiteness of samples; but if the probability of missingness depends on intrinsically unavailable information, which is moreover correlated with response, then appropriate adjustments can be made only by guessing at the effects of the unobservable biasing factors. The concluding chapter, by Herzog and Rubin, makes suggestions for improving current practice by means of multiple imputations, where, at the user's discretion, prior assessments of the effects of unobservable factors may be included.

Part IV also contains a chapter by Oh and Scheuren on weighting methods, and a chapter by Ford on hot-deck imputation methods. The basic idea of weighting is that different expansion factors should be applied to sample totals in subsets of the data, the factors being inversely proportional to the fractions missing in the subset, in order to correct for bias in the estimate of the population total. As Oh and Scheuren note, the resulting bias adjustment is less than perfect if residual nonrandomness of missingness is operating within subsets; they point out that much of current practice is oriented to applying this tool with as much skill as possible and then acting as though the adjustment is adequate, with little, if any, discussion of either the assumptions or possible resulting biases.

Oh and Scheuren write from the randomization theory perspective. They emphasize that even though the sample is selected by a physical randomization process, the weighting-class theory they discuss requires that missing units or items be designated by a *hypothetical* randomization process within strata or weighting classes. Also, there can be substantial practical differences between adjustment strategies from the randomization and Bayesian perspectives: whereas the randomization hypothesis leads to corrections that create hypo-thetical missingness probabilities defined over cross-classifications, a Bayesian adjustment strategy conditions on the observed counts within each cell and creates the estimated cell means over the cross-classified array. Further comparison and evaluation of Bayesian and non-Bayesian approaches is badly needed in this area.

Many ingenious imputation strategies are reviewed by Ford. The idea of imputation is both seductive and dangerous. It is seductive because it can lull the user into the pleasurable state of believing that the data are complete after all, and it is dangerous because it lumps together situations where the problem is sufficiently minor that it can legitimately be handled this way and situations where standard estimators applied to real and imputed data have substantial biases.

Hot-deck procedures, which impute items from a systematically or randomly chosen available sample unit, obviously incorporate artificial individual-to-individual variation into final estimates, and hence have more variance than estimates based on the imputation of sample averages of appropriate weighting classes. Although appropriate estimates of population totals or averages from artifically completed samples can be computed from the standard complete-data formulas, the same cannot be said for estimates of the variances of such estimates. Appropriate estimates of variance from samples completed by a hot-deck procedure must reflect the actual responding sample size before imputation, and estimated variances from samples where means are imputed must be adjusted to compensate for the reduced sample variance due to insertion of a constant imputed value. Estimates based on averages of existing data are equivalent to estimates based on existing and imputed data when imputed values are sample averages. By thus avoiding imputation, one may avoid the pitfalls of defining-inappropriate estimates of variances from real and imputed values.

In the fourth chapter in Part IV work by Rubin suggests that multiple imputation can be used to assess variability introduced by imputation methods. Estimates can be found by averaging over standard estimates from each of several imputations, and the variance of such an average can be estimated by summing between and within imputation components. Rubin further suggests that imputation techniques should attempt to approximate a Bayesian ideal by drawing at random from a posterior distribution of the missing data, and he even suggests incorporating variability among Bayesians by making the multiple imputations follow a distribution of Bayesians. Practical implementation is still in the developmental state, but Rubin's methods promise a flexible set of tools for the future. Herzog's example in this same chapter illustrates the kind of efforts needed to create multiple imputations and possible advantages.

Part V is devoted to an extensive treatment by Platek and Gray of imputation for nonresponse. Their model assumes that units have probabilities of responding. These probabilities may depend on the particular survey and the environment in which it is made as well as on the unit itself. They write from the frequentist standpoint of how the design might perform under repeated use and choose for a criterion total expected squared error. Total error includes the traditional design-based sampling error, and also squared bias and variance from nonresponse and from erroneous response. The response is assumed univariate so that unit and item nonresponse are equivalent. The properties of several basic imputation schemes are compared under a very general sampling design. A simple numerical example is included to show how the theory easily produces numerical comparisons from information about nonresponse probabilities and response error bias and variance.

As noted earlier in connection with Oh and Scheuren's chapter and Ford's chapter, the theoretical analysis in Part V depends on probabilistic modeling beyond that implicit in the randomization of the original design. Although the earlier chapters assume that probabilities of missingness are constant within weighting classes, the Platek and Gray theory posits probabilities of nonresponse and distributions of response errors for each unit. These probabilities are not known. In order to use the theory, it is necessary to specify numerically or to estimate these hypothetical probabilities. The theory can provide useful insights to practitioners wishing to assess different possible design choices before carrying out a survey, and similar insights about, say, weighting versus random hot-deck adjustment procedures when nonresponse at particular levels is anticipated. Advocates of more Bayesian data analysis and inference may feel more development is needed for this frequency theory to be relevant to analysis because the required probabilities of missingness must be adequately estimated from the data or fixed from prior considerations, and simple estimators based on true plus imputed data must be justified in terms of efficiency.

In order to introduce theoretical analyses of efficiency and robustness of estimators, one must make use of the parametric forms or models on which mathematical statistics thrives. These models include normal assumptions about population distributions and response errors, linear models as used in regression and analysis of variance, and log-linear and logistic models for counted data. To most theoretical statisticians, it is important that the future interactions between theory and practice include the insights which such models can provide.

The three chapters in Part VI, by Little, review the current literature on incomplete data in the framework of parametric models. The first chapter is an introduction. The second chapter treats the case in which missingness can be assumed to be at random (i.e., ignorable), and where efficiency aspects of estimation are reasonably well understood in the light of recent developments related to exponential family sampling models. In his third chapter, Little edges toward the future by considering models which explicitly allow for the most worrisome effect of missingness, namely, the bias that remains because response remains correlated with missingness even after the best efforts at poststratification. Substantial theoretical development in this direction is possible, and Little will have performed a very useful service if this review encourages prompt interaction between theory and practice to take advantage of the new theoretical work.

4. FINAL COMMENTS

The theoretical presentations in the volume are largely within the context of simple random sampling. Real-world complex surveys are only briefly addressed, and the complications and possibilities for improved procedures in panel and longitudinal surveys are not considered. Nevertheless, principles underlying the handling of nonresponse are addressed because the same basic issues arise in both simple and complex cases. Of course, all of the crucial computational tasks can be much more demanding in more complex surveys, even when using standard techniques such as weighting adjustments and hot-deck imputations.

In order to implement the newer theoretical ideas being proposed for the analysis of incomplete data, such as multiple imputations and likelihood methods, flexible computing is needed. Computing hardware and software have made striking advances in recent years, and in many ways, statistical theory and practice have yet to take full advantage of these new computing tools. In fact, the basis of most methods currently used to adjust for nonresponse originated at a time when computing facilities were quite primitive. We expect that newer techniques for handling incomplete data will push the boundaries of current statistical computing systems, but we also expect that as these boundaries are pushed they will be found to be rather flexible. Moreover, we expect that the emergence of new statistical techniques relying on powerful yet available computing environments will effect real improvements in the handling of nonresponse in sample surveys.

REFERENCES

Cochran, W. G. (1977). *Sampling Techniques*. New York: Wiley.
Cox, D. R., and Hinkley, D. V. (1974). *Theoretical Statistics*. London: Chapman and Hall.
Hansen, M. H., Hurwitz, W. N., and Madow, W. G. (1953). *Sample Survey Methods and Theory* (Vols. 1 and 2). New York: Wiley.

CHAPTER 2

Historical Perspective

William G. Cochran*

1. INCOMPLETE DATA

In censuses and in almost all sample surveys, a number of different variables are measured on all selected units. The incomplete or missing data with which this report deals are generally of two types. Sometimes, none of the variables is measured for a unit or subunit—the mail questionnaire was not returned, the interviewer could not find anyone at home, and so on. This type of miss will be called a *unit nonresponse*. Alternatively, most of the questions for a unit are answered, but for certain questions either no answer is given or the answer is judged to contain a gross error and is deleted during editing. Usually, such questions are ones that are sensitive, e.g., questions that concern income, or ones for which the respondent does not have the information. This type of miss is called an *item nonresponse*.

The most obvious consequence of nonresponse is that a smaller sample of data is available for making the estimates than was originally planned. In addition, there is often reason to believe that as a group nonrespondents differ systematically from respondents. As Deming (1950) expressed it with regard to human populations, "The people who do not respond are in some ways and in varying degrees different from them that do." Thus, in making estimates from the available respondent data, the sampler may face biases that are essentially unknown in size and direction.

---

* Professor Cochran died on March 29, 1980. This chapter is published as he left it except for the listing of the references and minor editorial changes resulting from subsequent rearrangements of the contents of this volume.

INCOMPLETE DATA
IN SAMPLE SURVEYS
Volume 2, Part I

2. SOME EARLY WORK ON UNIT NONRESPONSES

Discussions of the problem of nonresponse and of some possible methods for handling it seem to have first appeared in the 1930s and 1940s—the same period during which many of the standard techniques and results in probability sampling were developed.

The method of quota sampling, discussed in Part II, by King is an early example of a group of methods whose objective is to cut down or eliminate nonresponse when the sample data are being collected in the field. Quota sampling was developed by Cherington, Roper, Gallup, and Crossley as a means of saving field costs in taking stratified samples for public opinion surveys. This method formally avoids unit nonresponse by not requiring that any specific respondents be questioned. Instead, the interviewer is told merely how many persons who fall in each of a set of strata must be interviewed. The strata are usually cells of a multiple classification intended to be recognizable in the field by the interviewer—often a classification by variables like sex, color, geographic residence, plus age and income by broad classes. The method may involve some waste time in the field in partial interviews of people until the interviewer learns that they do not fall into any stratum in which respondents are still needed, and, of course, the method abandons random selection within strata.

Incomplete data are encountered in randomized experiments as well as in sample surveys, and the development of methods for making estimates of the effects of the treatment from experiments with missing data also began in the 1930s. The technique most widely used for this purpose in field experiments is worth noting. This technique, due to Yates (1933), applies the standard least squares model for the analysis of the complete results of field experiments to the incomplete data that are present. Yates does this by "filling in" or imputing values for all the missing observations by formulas such that the standard analysis of the completed data gives the same estimates as the least squares analysis of the incomplete data. The advantage of this approach is that investigators who know only how to analyze complete data can use Yates's method, while others may prefer to apply the least squares analysis directly to the incomplete data that are present. The same choice may be made in a number of sample survey problems. Thus, Hartley (1958) shows how to adapt the "fill-in" technique to finding maximum likelihood estimates of parameters from incomplete random samples of data for discrete distributions.

Since this approach might be able to handle many problems with incomplete data, the question of when the approach is valid is important. The approach does not require that the units (plots, subjects, etc.) for which data are missing are a random subsample of the units in the experiment. For every missing unit it requires a knowledge of the treatment and block, or more generally of the values of all background variables that enter into the prediction of the yield on the unit in the least squares equations. Furthermore, the fact that an observation is missing must be known to be unrelated to the size of the experimental error that would have arisen on this unit. In other words, the "miss" must be attributable to outside causes and not in any way to the yield on the unit. For instance, this assumption is satisfied in a field experiment for a corner plot that is in a rather exposed place and is trampled by a cow. It is not satisfied when two replicates of variety 3 are battered to the ground in a thunderstorm and are missing (not harvested), if variety 3 is known to have weak stalks. Finally, note that the results of the analysis of the incomplete data are conditional on the set of background variables for the missing observations.

A realization that standard methods can be applied to the incomplete data that we have does not, however, dispose of the statistical problems created by missing data in such cases. In randomized experiments, missing observations almost always make the analysis of the results more complicated for the experimenter. A number of papers have been written to present convenient methods of performing the statistical analyses, at first on desk machines and later for computer programs, given various configurations of missing data. With certain configurations, it has been found that some treatment contrasts that are of interest cannot be estimated from the incomplete data. New problems in statistical theory were encountered, for example, in finding out what can be estimated when data are missing, and in the extension of covariance adjustment to this case.

3. METHODS USING CALLBACKS

With human populations, one method of cutting down nonresponse rates is to make repeated attempts to contact each sample respondent and have the questions answered. Thus Deming (1944) writes, "Call-backs on a subsample of those people not at home on the first call must be made until results are obtained. In continuing surveys covering identical units, some method of substitution must be worked out for units that cease to exist. If a mailed questionnaire is used, there must be unrelenting follow-up by mail, telephone, and telegraph; and, finally, if necessary, by personal interview of a subsample of those unmoved by less expensive devices." Deming notes that the idea of callbacks on a subsample of initial nonrespondents was presented by W. N. Hurwitz in 1943 at a seminar of the Graduate School of the Department of Agriculture.

Hansen and Hurwitz (1946) published the theory covering the subsampling of nonrespondents for a random sample. They had in mind surveys in which the first contact was made by mail, followed by an interview subsampling of the nonrespondents (with, I suppose, some rule about the required number of callbacks). Describing their paper they write, "Personal interviews generally elicit a substantially complete response, but the cost per schedule is, of course, considerably higher than it would be for the mail questionnaire method. The purpose of this paper is to indicate a technique which combines the advantages of both procedures."

Later in the same paper, Deming (1944) writes, "Studies in the removal of the biases that arise in cheap methods of collecting data ... are worthy of the best efforts of statisticians. However complicated the theory of sampling may appear to be, the problem of predicting biases is by comparison much more complicated and less developed. There are as yet no theories of bias in any way comparable to the ones of sampling. There is an open field here for the joint efforts of statistician and psychologist."

In this connection it was realized around this time that examination of the numbers of completed questionnaires and of the mean responses obtained in successive calls could give valuable information about the effectiveness of callbacks and about the sizes and directions of the biases produced by failure to call back. Several papers published during 1939–1944 on nonresponse bias and the use of callbacks may be cited—Stanton (1939), Rollins (1940), and Hilgard and Payne (1944). In their discussion of the use of callbacks, Clausen and Ford (1947) give an example of a mailed questionnaire with two follow-ups. The response variable was the percentage of veterans in school or in training for postwar jobs. The initial sample size was 14,606, the response rate after three mailings being 88%. Table 1 shows the mean responses (percent of veterans in school or training) at each mailing, the percentage of the initial sample who replied to each mailing, and the cumulative percents. The percentage in school or training declined steadily in the first three waves, so that reliance on early returns would have overestimated this percentage. From Table 1 an estimate of the percent in school or training can be made for the final 12% of nonrespondents by plotting the response data against the cumulative percent response and making the estimate by judgment or by some kind of regression method. Clausen and Ford's estimate for this final group is 25% in school or training. In turn, this leads to a weighted estimate of the population mean that attempts to correct for nonresponse bias, namely, $[(.54)(42) + (.23)(25) + (.11)(29) + (.12)(25)] = 35\%$ in school or training. Hendricks (1948, 1949) has discussed this technique.

TABLE 1

Percent of Veterans in School or Training in Three Successive Mailings

	First mailing	Second mailing	Third mailing	Estimate for nonrespondents
Percentage in school or training	42	25	29	(25)
Percentage of initial sample who replied	54	23	11	12
Cumulative response (%)	54	77	88	100

On a related topic, the recent book by the psychologists Rosenthal and Rosnow (1975) summarizes the results of many investigations of the characteristics of those who volunteer, as compared with those who decline to volunteer, as subjects in research studies on human behavior and learning. The book estimates how the use of volunteers biases conclusions drawn from the studies.

From analyses of callback data, samplers learn about the sizes and directions of biases with different questions and different types of populations. It is usually found that respondents in a population are more intelligent, better educated, more interested in the questions, and are less embarrassed or threatened by the questions. A sampler might be able to predict from such data roughly the biases to be expected and the costs per completed interview at successive calls, particularly in repetitive surveys of the same population for the same items. These data may permit the construction of models for the effects of different calls that lead to the appraisal of different callback policies from a cost–benefit viewpoint. For instance, Deming (1953) gives methods (based on a model) that provide a specified mean square error in the estimated population total at minimum cost. With a binomial response variate, Birnbaum and Sirken (1950a,b) use the fact that the error in an estimated proportion is always bounded to determine the initial sample size and number of callbacks that make the absolute error of estimate in the sample proportion $\leq \delta$ with probability $1 - \alpha$ at minimum expected cost.

The major reviews by Yates (1946) and Mahalanobis (1946) of their work on the development of sample surveys did not discuss the handling of nonresponse problems, perhaps because nonresponse is rare in crop-cutting surveys. Yates did, however, criticize quota sampling, stating that "such a method may very easily introduce serious biases." In the discussion following Yates's paper, Hartley proposed another method for reducing biases due to missing data. He began by calling attention to the biases caused by the omission of "not at home" households in probability samples:

> Now, it is well known that if these "nobody in" households are left out, the remainder of the original sample is seriously biased. For instance, there will be an unduly low proportion of housewives with part- or full-time work, an unduly high proportion of young children, an unduly low proportion of "queuers," and many other misrepresentations. A classic example of this bias is mentioned by Professor Bradford Hill in his book, *Principle of Medical Statistics*. The example is the Ministry of Health report on the influenza pandemic of 1918. In this enquiry houses which were found closed at the time of the visit had to be ignored.

Hartley noted that repeated callbacks at "not-at-home" households would cut down the nonresponses, but commented, "whatever the success of the method, it is bound to be very laborious." He therefore proposed for consideration a cheaper alternative. Make a single call, but ask additional questions whose purpose is to find out, for the "at home" households, the proportion of the time of interviewing during which an adult will be found at home. The sample responses are then stratified by these proportions of time at home. The stratum weights are estimated from the sample proportions, and the form of estimate appropriate to stratified sampling is used. This proposal does not produce data for the not-at-homes, but the stratified estimate might prove to have less bias than the sample mean, and the method should indicate those variables for which the responses are correlated, and those for which they are not correlated, with the proportion of time spent at home. Hartley's proposal led to the Politz–Simmons methods (1949, 1950).

In his reply, Yates (1946) doubted whether Hartley's methods, though ingenious, would be very satisfactory in practice. As an alternative that would also reduce the amount of calling back, Yates proposed subsampling "the houses for which say more than one call-back is required, selecting say 50 percent of such houses for further calls, subsequently doubling the contribution of this 50 percent to the total sample." This is, of course, one version of the method described by Hansen and Hurwitz (1946).

4. ITEM NONRESPONSE

In all but the most recent work on data with item nonresponses, the approach has been to analyze the available incomplete data. As with randomized experiments, this analysis does not require the assumption that units with item nonresponses are a random subsample of the original data. The probability that an item is missing may depend on the values of other items for the unit.

But given these values the probability must be constant. For instance, the probability that income is unreported in a survey may depend on the sex, age, and educational level of the respondent. But if for males of a given age and educational level those with unusually high incomes are those who do not report incomes for one reason or another, analysis of the incomplete data will be subject to bias.

In the earliest paper on item nonresponses, Wilks (1932) considers a random sample from a bivariate normal distribution. In n_{12} observations, X_1 and X_2 are both measured, in n_{10} observations, X_1 is measured but X_2 is missing, while in n_{02} observations, X_2 is measured but X_1 is missing. Wilks finds maximum likelihood estimates of the parameters μ_1, μ_2, σ_1, σ_2, and ρ, and gives the large-sample formulas for the variances and covariance of $\hat{\mu}_1$ and $\hat{\mu}_2$. He notes that his estimates are not particularly simple and devotes a substantial part of the paper to studying the efficiencies of simpler estimates of the five parameters. For instance, if the n_{02} units in which X_1 was missing were a random subsample, we might use the mean of all the $n_{12} + n_{10}$ measured values of X_1 as an estimate of μ_1.

A more general concept developed by Wilks is that of the joint efficiency of a set of estimates. He defines this as the reciprocal of the determinant of the matrix of the large-sample variances and covariances of the estimates, following the approach by Fisher. He proves that this quantity is a maximum when the estimates are maximum likelihood estimates. This concept of efficiency is useful in Wilks's work in that he can calculate the relative efficiencies of the sets of simpler estimates that he and the reader might cor^ der using, so that the reader knows what penalty is being paid for simplici_.

No extensions of Wilks's work appeared until the 1950s. For more than 2 multivariate normal variates, Matthai (1951) showed how to write down the equations leading to the maximum likelihood estimates of the population means and to the information matrix, but did not discuss practical methods of solution.

Lord (1955) considers a trivariate normal sample in which X_1 is missing in a subsample of size n_{023}, while X_2 is missing in a sample of size n_{103}. The original sample size is $n = n_{023} + n_{103}$, so that X_3 is measured for all such data, leaving eight parameters μ_1, μ_2, μ_3, σ_1, σ_2, σ_3, ρ_{13}, and ρ_{23} to be estimated. Lord obtains explicit estimates. A device that he uses is to estimate first σ_3, $\sigma_{1\cdot3}$, $\sigma_{2\cdot3}$, $\beta_{1\cdot3}$, and $\beta_{2\cdot3}$, which uniquely determine σ_1, σ_2, σ_3, ρ_{13} and ρ_{23}, where the notation $\sigma_{1\cdot3}$, $\beta_{1\cdot3}$, etc., is the usual one for linear regressions on one independent variate.

Edgett (1956) develops the maximum likelihood estimates of the nine parameters in a trivariate normal in which X_1 is missing in part of the sample.

Anderson (1957) presents an approach that produces the maximum likelihood estimates for any number of variates, given certain patterns of missing data. In the simplest pattern of this type, the variates can be arranged in order so that for any unit in which X_2 is measured, so is X_1 and X_2, and so on. The approach depends on the fact that the likelihood factorizes into the marginal distribution of X_1; the conditional distribution of X_2 given X_1; the conditional distribution of X_3 given X_1 and X_2; and so on. It follows that μ_1 and σ_1 are estimated from the univariate distribution of X_1 in the whole sample since X_1 has no misses, while μ_2, σ_2, and ρ_{12} are estimated from the part of the sample in which X_1 and X_2 are measured and the part in which X_1 alone is measured, using the same technique as in double sampling with regression, and so on. As illustrations of this approach, Anderson works out the solutions given by Lord and Edgett for their trivariate problems. (Wilks's problem does not have Anderson's pattern of missing data.)

A different method proposed by Buck (1960) is also of interest. This method employs multiple regression rather than maximum likelihood and uses the set of observations for which all items are measured to substitute predicted or imputed values for all missing items on any units. For instance, if X_1 and X_4 are missing on a unit, the predicted value X_1 for this unit is obtained from the regression of X_1 on $X_2, X_3, X_5, \ldots, X_k$ in the sample in which all items are measured by substituting the known values of $X_2, X_3, X_5, \ldots$, for the unit in question. With a random sample the estimated population mean for the item is the mean of the observed and predicted values of this item for all the sample members. The matrix of sample mean squares and products, calculated from observed and predicted values, requires some adjustment in order to remove biases. This matrix is needed for regression calculations applicable to the whole sample.

5. NOTES ON THIS VOLUME

5.1. Part II: Selected Topics in Data Collection

Three of these techniques have been mentioned. On callbacks, data on the number of respondents found at successive calls are given from several sources, and Durbin and Stuart's (1954) data on the relative costs of obtaining a completed interview at successive calls are given in the chapter by Rao in Part II. The model and strategy from which to make cost–benefit studies of different call-back policies, developed by Deming with further work by P. S. R. S. Rao, is described with an illustration.

Some surveys allow substitution of a different respondent if the intended respondent cannot be contacted or refuses. This substitution is, of course, a departure from strict probability sampling, and usually the substitution rule is designed in the hope that the substitute will be similar to the respondent wanted. The chapter by Chapman describes substitution rules and gives a number of surveys in which the substitute data could be compared with that from the original respondents. The conclusion is that substitutions may reduce but do not eliminate respondent bias and probably work best when the sampling units are small in number, and a good deal of information about them is known with which to find good substitutes. No theory about substitutes seems to have been developed.

For quota sampling, studies of its performance relative to probability sampling have been made in the book by Stephan and McCarthy (1958). A combination of probability sampling and quota sampling has been developed by Sudman (1967), in which probability sampling is used down to the block level in the selection of the sample, and the quota method is introduced only in selecting people within blocks. The chapter by King in Part II gives a critique of the quota sampling method and examples of its current use by two sampling organizations.

In another area, the chapter by Emrich in Part II includes an account of the randomized response method. In this method, designed to encourage responses to sensitive questions, one of two questions is given to each respondent, and the interviewer does not know which one. This encourages respondents to answer, since they are not revealing sensitive information to the respondent.

One method of expanding the number of respondents who can supply desired information is network sampling (chapter by Sirken in Part II). The linkage rule that defines the possible respondents may be based on kinship, friendship, or proximity to the household. With these rules, the number of sources that can give information about a selected sample member, and hence the probability of being a respondent, varies from member to member, so that weighted estimates of population totals are required. The chapter by Sirken describes the kind of intended respondents for whom network sampling was produced, presents the theory, including costs, and gives its application to the problem of coverage (data missing because the sampling units in question are not in the frame).

5.2. Part III: Nonresponse and Double Sampling

The chapter by Rao in Part III describes double sampling, gives the theory and an illustration, and includes the more realistic methods of Srinath (1971) and J. N. K. Rao (1973) for determining the size of the subsample. Included also are the extension of the method to more than one subsample and to the ratio and regression estimators. Bayesian work on double sampling is described in the chapter by Singh. This involves its application to the estimation of population proportions, sampling methods that draw two samples (one pilot and one main) from the respondents and two from the nonrespondents, and the Bayesian applications to the estimation of regression coefficients.

5.3. Part IV: Weighting and Imputation Methods

The chapter by Rubin presents the concepts and notation that will be used in considering nonresponse later in this part. At the beginning, the chapter describes the randomization and Bayesian approaches to sample survey theory in the absence of nonresponse. In the randomization approach used in most textbooks, the values of the responses in the population are regarded as fixed numbers with no specific frequency distribution. The frequency distribution of estimates of the population total is that generated by the set of random samples and their resulting estimates that the sampling plan can provide. This approach avoids the assumption of any models that the population values follow and may hope to obtain robust results. But in samples with missing data, some models must be constructed about the missing data in order to make estimates. The Bayesian approach to survey sampling, described by Rubin is model oriented. The responses are assumed drawn at random from some superpopulation model, while the nonresponses are also drawn from a superpopulation model that may be the same or different from the model for the responses. It is noted

that in large samples the inferences are approximately the same in the randomization and Bayesian approaches if the distribution of the population data
is normal under the Bayesian approach. The presence of nonresponse creates
difficulties under both systems, since the assumptions that must be made about
the distribution of the nonresponses are unverifiable. The Bayesian system may
be in better shape for this task, since it also is accustomed to making assumptions
about the distribution of the responses, but the practical details of its application
may be complicated.

A compromise approach to the problem of making inferences about the
population total is to use Bayesian methods to make a series of plausible
assumptions about the distributions of the responses that nonrespondents
would have given had they responded. By drawing from any model for nonrespondents, we can impute values for the missing data, complete the data, and
hence calculate 95% confidence intervals for the population mean. A series of
these imputations may be of two types—repeated drawings from the same
model and drawings from different models. Multiple imputations of this type
will reveal how variation in drawing from the same model and variation in
drawing from different models about nonresponse will affect the 95% intervals,
or more generally analyses made on the incomplete sample data. This idea of
multiple imputations, discussed in Chapter 15 in Part IV, can make us more
fully aware of the kinds of conclusions that can safely be drawn from analyses
of incomplete sample data and the extent to which they will vary because of
incompleteness.

In the second chapter in Part IV, Oh and Scheuren discuss weighting adjustments for nonresponse. Some introductory material is first given. In one group
of methods widely used in survey practice, the sample of respondents is partitioned into classes or strata by variables thought to be related to the probability
of unit nonresponse so that units in the same stratum have about the same
probability of being a nonrespondent. Then the assumption is made that this
probability is actually constant for all members of the same stratum.

In stratum h, let π_h be the probability that any unit is selected, and ϕ_h the
probability that the unit responds if selected. If $\hat{Y}_{hr}$ is the sample total of the
respondents in stratum h, the estimated population total for this group of
methods is

$$\sum_h \frac{1}{\pi_h \phi_h} \hat{Y}_{hr} = \sum_h W_h \hat{Y}_{hr},$$

where

$$W_h = 1/\pi_h \phi_h$$

is a *weighting* or *inflation* factor.

In different applications of this method, the best estimates of W_h that the
data provide are used. The simplest case is that of simple random sampling in

which the population totals N_h for the strata are known. Here, $\pi_h = n_h/N_h$, and we take n_{hr}/n_h as our estimate of ϕ_h, so that

$$\pi_h \phi_h = n_{hr}/N_h$$

and the estimated population total is

$$\hat{Y} = \sum_h N_h \hat{Y}_{hr}/n_{hr} = \sum_h N_h \bar{y}_{hr}.$$

Variants of the method depend on the nature of the classification. We shall discuss several in this section under the assumption that the original sample was a simple random one.

In the technique known as poststratification, the classification is made after the data have been collected. In such cases the N_h are rarely known.[1] If the original sample sizes n_h are known, we may estimate N_h by Nn_h/n, since in poststratification the sample distributes itself approximately proportionally in the strata. This gives

$$\hat{Y} = \frac{N}{n} \sum_h \left(\frac{n_h}{n_{hr}} \hat{Y}_{hr} \right) = \frac{N}{n} \sum_h n_h \bar{y}_{hr}.$$

For example, the estimator by Hansen and Hurwitz mentioned in Section 1.3 is of this type. There are two poststrata. Stratum 1 consists of those who respond to the first (mail) call, with sample size n_1. Stratum 2 has original sample size $n_2 = n - n_1$, though the interview sample actually taken is of size n_2/k, with sample mean $\bar{y}_2$. The estimator is

$$\hat{Y} = \frac{N}{n}(n_1 \bar{y}_1 + n_2 \bar{y}_2).$$

In the method of Bartholomew (1961), calls are made on *all* n_2 in stratum 2. Any nonrespondents at the second call are assumed to be a random subsample of the n_2, so that the estimator is the same as that of Hansen and Hurwitz except that $\bar{y}_2$ is replaced by $\bar{y}_{2r}$, the mean for the respondents at the second call.

Unless the N_h are known, poststratification suffers a loss of precision because the strata weights are estimated from sample data. In some applications, the poststrata are formed by cross-classifications on two variables. The N_{ij} in stratum (i, j) are not known, but one or both of the marginal totals $N_{i.}$ of $N_{.j}$ are known. In this event we may try to improve on the usual poststratification estimator

$$\hat{Y} = N \sum_{ij} \frac{n_{ij}}{n} \bar{y}_{ijr},$$

---

[1] When the N_h are unknown, this method also goes by the name of a "weighting-class" adjustment.

replacing it by the weighted estimator

$$\hat{Y} = N \sum_{ij} w_{ij} \cdot \bar{y}_{ijr},$$

where the w_{ij} are estimated from both the n_{ij} and the known marginal proportions $N_{i.}/N$ and $N_{.j}/N$. This method of estimation is known as *raking*. Some of its potential applications will be described.

Other information may be used to estimate the probability of response ϕ_h. In the Politz-Simmons method, only a single call is made. Interviewing takes place on the six evenings Monday to Saturday. Any respondent found at home is asked on how many of the other five weeknights he or she was at home at this time. If the answer is h nights, the quantity $(h + 1)/6$ is taken as an estimate of ϕ_h. The sample results are poststratified into six strata $(h = 0, 1, \ldots, 5)$. This method, of course, omits from consideration those out of the total sample of size n who are never found at home; hence, instead of an estimate of the form

$$\hat{Y} = \sum_h \frac{1}{\pi_h \phi_h} \hat{Y}_{hr}$$

the method uses a ratio-type estimator

$$\hat{Y} = N \frac{\sum \hat{Y}_{hr}/\hat{\phi}_h}{\sum 1/\hat{\phi}_h}.$$

In the chapter by Oh and Scheuren on weighting adjustments in Part IV, the emphasis has been placed on comparisons among alternative estimators of the population total in the presence of missing data. In particular, the case where there is no adjustment for nonresponse is compared to estimators based on three different assumptions about the probability of a response, namely, a constant probability, probability proportional to a known value of x_i, and probability proportional to an unknown x_i. These assumptions are usually applied within strata in a poststratified estimate. Sometimes the units can be grouped into a two-way classification such that the probability of response is proportional to $u_h v_k$ for a unit in the (h, k) cell of the classification. Estimates of the population total are made by raking, using the information available about the u_h and the v_k. Some recommendations for future study are given. An appendix gives adjustments to the Horvitz–Thompson estimate of the population corresponding to the three assumptions given above about the probability of a response. The biases, variances, and estimated variances of these estimates are given, with a numerical example at the end.

With weighting methods, estimates of population totals are made without filling in the answers that nonrespondents are assumed to have given if they had responded. For the simpler weighting methods, however, one can construct a method of imputing a value for each missing unit such that the population total, estimated from the completed sample data, agrees with the estimation by the weighting method. For example, suppose that in a stratum the probability of response is assumed constant. If n_r respond out of n selected, with sample total $\hat{Y}_r$ for the respondents, the usual weighting estimate of the population total is $N\hat{Y}_r/n_r$. This estimate can be obtained by imputing the value of $\bar{y}$ for each missing value. The chapter by Ford in Part IV gives an account of one of the most common imputation methods, known as the "hot-deck" method. In a hot-deck procedure, a sample reported value is substituted for the missing value: in a "cold-deck" procedure, the value substituted is not a sample value. Usually, the sample is first classified by background variables thought to be related to the probability of a miss, so that substitution of a member of the same class will introduce little bias. In a sequential hot-deck method, the class is first put in some kind of order, and the last reported sample value is substituted, or occasionally something more complex. The hot-deck methods in three large surveys are described. Some work on the variance of the methods is given. With a simple random sample of size n, suppose that m units are missing and $n - m$ report. If the m are missing at random, the variance of the mean of the reporters is $\sigma^2/(n - m)$. If a sample member is substituted for each miss, the variance of the sample mean is (with replacement)

$$V(\bar{y}_h) = \frac{\sigma^2}{n}\left[1 + \frac{m(2n - m - 1)}{(n - m)n}\right].$$

This variance is always greater than or equal to $\sigma^2/(n - m)$. The variance is slightly different in a sequential hot-deck method. The chapter concludes by describing five studies in which the hot-deck method has been compared with alternatives, such as weighting, ratio or regression, for estimating the population total or mean.

5.4. Part V: Imputation Methodology (Total Survey Error)

In Part V, totals and variances are provided for four methods of imputation—called zero substitution, weighting, duplication, and historical substitution—using the Horvitz–Thompson estimator modified to include the probability that a unit, if selected, will respond. Variance formulas are extended to cover two-stage sampling. A numerical illustration is given. All developments are within the contest of total survey errors including errors of response as well as sampling errors and errors of nonresponse.

5.5. Part VI: Superpopulation Models for Nonresponse

In Part VI, item and unit nonresponse are considered in the context of sampling from an infinite superpopulation. In the second chapter in Part VI, items or whole units are assumed to be missing at random. After preliminaries, methods of finding maximum likelihood estimates are discussed, including the most general patterns of missing data to which Anderson's method is applicable, iterative methods such as the EM algorithm for handling more general patterns of missing data, and two-way contingency tables and multinomial distributions with missing values.

In the third chapter in Part VI, the superpopulation model is extended to cover cases in which the responding units are not a random sample of the sampling units. As might be expected, the cases that can be covered are those in which the probability of nonresponse is a function of y, though it may also depend on other variables y_2 and y_3. Some examples of maximum likelihood estimates are given in such cases; also, a numerical illustration is shown, in which the population mean is estimated by maximum likelihood and by the sample mean.

REFERENCES

Anderson, T. W. (1957). Maximum likelihood estimates for a multivariate normal distribution when some observations are missing. *Journal of the American Statistical Association* 52: 200–203.

Bartholomew, D. J. (1961). A method for allowing for "not-at-home" bias in sample surveys. *Applied Statistics* 10: 52–59.

Birnbaum, Z. W., and Sirken, M. G. (1950a). Bias due to nonavailability in sampling surveys. *Journal of the American Statistical Association* 45: 98–111.

Birnbaum, Z. W., and Sirken, M. G. (1950b). On the total error due to non-interview and to random sampling. *International Journal of Opinion and Attitude Research* 4: 179–191.

Buck, S. F. (1960). A method of estimating missing values in multivariate data suitable for use with an electronic computer. *Journal of the Royal Statistical Society*, Series B, 22: 302–306.

Clausen, J. A., and Ford, R. N. (1947). Controlling bias in mail questionnaires. *Journal of the American Statistical Association* 42: 497–511.

Deming, W. E. (1944). On errors in surveys. *American Sociological Review* 9: 359–369.

Deming, W. E. (1950). *Some Theory of Sampling.* New York: Wiley.

Deming, W. E. (1953). On a probability mechanism to attain an economic balance between the result and error of non-response and the bias of non-response. *Journal of the American Statistical Association* 48: 743–772.

Durbin, J., and Stuart, A. (1954). Callbacks and clustering in sample surveys: An experimental study. *Journal of the Royal Statistical Society*, Series A, 117: 387–428.

Edgett, George L. (1956). Multiple regression with missing observations among the variables. *Journal of the American Statistical Association* 51: 122–131.

Hansen, M. H., and Hurwitz, W. N. (1946). The problem of non-response in sample surveys. *Journal of the American Statistical Association* 41: 517–529.

Hartley, H. O. (1958). Maximum likelihood estimation from incomplete data. *Biometrics* 14: 174–194.

Hendricks, W. A. (1948). Mathematics of sampling. *Virginia Agricultural Experimental Station* (special bulletin).

Hendricks, W. A. (1949). Adjustment for bias caused by nonresponse in mailed surveys. *Agricultural Economics Research* 1: 52–56.

Hilgard, E. H., and Payne, S. F. (1944). Those not at home: Riddle for pollsters. *Public Opinion Quarterly* 8: 254–261.

Hill, A. Bradford (1956). *Principles of Medical Statistics.* London: The Lancet Press.

Lord, F. M. (1955). Estimation of parameters from incomplete data. *Journal of the American Statistical Association* 50: 870–876.

Mahalanobis, P. C. (1946). Recent experiments in statistical sampling in the Indian Statistical Institute. *Journal of the Royal Statistical Society* 109: 325–370.

Matthai, A. (1951). Estimation of parameters from incomplete data with application to design of sample surveys. *Sankhyā* 2: 145–152.

Politz, A., and Simmons, W. (1949). An attempt to get the "not at homes" into the sample without callbacks. *Journal of the American Statistical Association* 44: 9–31.

Politz, A., and Simmons, W. (1950). Note on "An attempt to get the 'not at homes' into the sample without callbacks." *Journal of the American Statistical Association* 45: 136–137.

Rao, J. N. K. (1973). On double sampling for stratification and analytical surveys. *Biometrika* 60: 125–133.

Rollins, M. (1940). The practical use of repeated questionnaire waves. *Journal of Applied Psychology* 24: 770–772.

Rosenthal, R., and Rosnow, R. L. (1975). *The Volunteer Subject.* New York: Wiley.

Srinath, K. P. (1971). Multiphase sampling in nonresponse problems. *Journal of the American Statistical Association* 66: 583–586.

Stanton, F. (1939). Notes on the validity of mail questionnaire returns. *Journal of Applied Psychology* 23: 104–115.

Stephan, F. F., and McCarthy, P. J. (1958). *Sampling Opinions.* New York: Wiley.

Sudman, S. (1967). *Reducing the Cost of Surveys.* Chicago: Aldin.

Wilks, S. S. (1932). Moments and distribution of estimates of population parameters from fragmentary samples. *Annals of Mathematical Statistics* 3: 163–195.

Yates, F. (1933). The analysis of replicated experiments when the field results are incomplete. *Empire Journal of Experimental Agriculture* 1: 129–142.

Yates, F. (1946). A review of recent statistical developments in sampling and sample surveys. *Journal of the Royal Statistical Society* 109: 12–43.

PART II

Selected Topics in Data Collection

CHAPTER 3

Introduction

Joseph H. Sedransk

In many current sample surveys nonresponse rates are at unacceptably high levels. Thus, within budgetary constraints, it is imperative to decrease the amount of nonresponse and to reduce its impact.

Skillful use of "field" or "data collection" methods can mitigate the effects of nonresponse. Several of these methods are discussed in other chapters of Part II.

(1) Callbacks, follow-ups, and repeated telephone calls
(2) Impact of substitution on survey estimates
(3) Quota sampling
(4) Randomized response techniques
(5) Handling missing data by network sampling

Callbacks are in common use to reduce nonresponse rates and to decrease the resulting biases. The role of callbacks in reducing nonresponse rates is illustrated in the chapter by Rao (Chapter 2), which presents summaries of the results of several surveys conducted between the 1940s and 1978. Some of these results also exhibit the consequence of making estimates before a sufficient number of calls have been made. In addition, there is a description of the practical use of models to determine the optimal number of callbacks.

When a response cannot be obtained from one sampled unit, another unit may be substituted. In the chapter by Chapman, several types of substitution procedures are illustrated. Then, a listing of advantages and disadvantages of the "substitution" method is given. Finally, four studies which provide estimates of the bias associated with one or more substitution procedures are described. While none of these studies was carried out in an ideal manner, all

INCOMPLETE DATA
IN SAMPLE SURVEYS
Volume 2, Part II

indicated that substitution procedures do not eliminate the effects of non-response bias. However, this conclusion must be a guarded one because three of the four studies employed less common substitution procedures, and, in general, the biases could only be estimated. Two basic problems with any substitution procedure are that the acceptance of nonresponse may be greater if substitution is permitted, and substituted units may differ from the units for which they substitute. Thus substitution is more nearly like imputation than an increase in size of sample.

Quota sampling techniques permit rapid completion of surveys and may also reduce survey costs and decrease nonresponse rates. In the chapter by King, some quota sampling methods in current use are described and contrasted with full probability sampling procedures. The results of empirical studies are inconclusive: For some surveys and certain variables, serious biases in estimation occur when quota sampling is employed, while for other surveys and variables, the performance of quota sampling is acceptable. An unfortunate feature of some of the studies is the impossibility of determining with certainty the causes of failure of a particular quota sample, as, for example, in preelection prediction. The basic problem with quota samples is the dependence on the interviewer for the final selection of the sampling units; large biases will sometimes occur and the occurrences are not predictable.

When sensitive issues are to be included in a personal interview survey, use of a randomized response technique may decrease the amount of nonresponse and improve the accuracy of the estimates by reducing the response bias. In the chapter by Emrich, several randomized response techniques are described; and advantages and disadvantages of the general approach are cited. Some studies have been carried out to compare results from using a randomized response technique and other procedures such as (unmodified) personal interviews, telephone interviews, and self-administered questionnaires. Generally, randomized response is most effective when utilized in surveys in which highly sensitive topics (e.g., drug use, child abuse) are included; and least effective when the subject matter is only slightly sensitive or when the variables (e.g., voting behavior) refer to socially desirable traits. However, the generally favorable comparative performance of "randomized response" must be conditioned upon both the type of population and the variables being studied.

Network sampling has potential advantages over traditional sampling methods when individuals are missed by traditional sampling because their own households are unwilling or unable to provide information about them. With network sampling such individuals are linked to other households that would be more likely to report them. For example, questions on illicit drug use by friends appear to be less threatening and hence less subject to underreporting than questions on self-use of drugs. Network sampling would handle this problem by linking drug users to the households of their close friends. Appropriate theory for the use of network sampling is given in the chapter by Sirken.

In addition, there is a detailed description of an experiment to investigate the gains from using network sampling in single retrospective mortality surveys.

Finally, many other "field" or "data collection" considerations affect both the rate and type of nonresponse. Among these are (a) double sampling (discussed in Part III); (b) use of alternative (proxy) respondents; (c) the use of financial incentives; (d) the auspices under which the survey was conducted (e.g., governmental, university, or commercial); (e) the selection, training, and supervision of interviewers; (f) the length and wording of questionnaires and the context of questions; and (g) the mode of acquiring data (e.g., personal interview, telephone interview, self-administered questionnaire). Of these, only double sampling is discussed in this volume (Part III).

One problem with which this report does not deal is that of "curbstoning" or the "faked" interview, i.e., the cases in which the interviewer fills out the schedule or questionnaire without conducting the interview. To reduce the proportion of "faked" interviews, questionnaires are validated and are examined for impossible entries, internal consistency, and any signs that may indicate poor quality of interview or that no interview has occurred.

Statistical theory for many "data collection" methods is sparse. For most of the techniques there is no satisfactory theoretical basis for predicting the effect of any of the methods on the response rate and on the accuracy of the measurement process. For example, use of a single adult ("household respondent") to provide information about all adult members of the household might be expected to affect both the nonresponse rate and the accuracy of the data. However, there are no models (and accompanying theory) to permit comparison of this method with the alternative which requires each adult to respond for himself.

Therefore, methodological studies of "data collection" often have no theoretical formulation, but examine the effects of various data collection methods. Some studies were conducted with split samples, a different method applied to each part. Others consist of applying a particular method and subsequently carrying out a follow-up study of the entire population.

Caution is necessary in generalizing from these methodological studies. Many of the investigations have been carried out some time ago, and conditions may have changed substantially. Furthermore, some of the results may hold only for specific types of populations, for particular variables, for particular survey organizations, or for particular allocations of resources to surveys.

CHAPTER 4

Callbacks, Follow-Ups, and Repeated Telephone Calls

P. S. R. S. Rao

1. INTRODUCTION

In many surveys, callbacks have been found to be effective in reducing nonresponse rates and the resulting biases. In mail surveys, callbacks usually take the form of follow-up letters, but may involve telephone calls or personal interviews. In telephone surveys and personal surveys, repeated calls are the usual form of callbacks.

Stephan and McCarthy (1958), Kish (1965), and Jessen (1978) provide data from a number of callback surveys conducted in the United States. Durbin and Stuart (1954) present the results of a study in the United Kingdom which was based on a sample drawn from the Electoral Register from two boroughs, two large towns, and two small towns. Kanuk and Berenson (1975) review a number of studies involving the use of mail surveys and follow-up letters. Bailar and Lanphier (1978) critically examine the number of callbacks, response rates, and other relevant qualities of 36 surveys conducted during 1975 by government and private agencies. Wiseman and McDonald (1978) present data from 182 telephone surveys of 32 corporations, conducted during a 6-week period in 1978. (Note that articles describing various callback strategies occasionally appear in the *Journal of Marketing Research, Public Opinion Quarterly,* and the *Journal of Advertising Research.*) To illustrate the need for callbacks, data from three surveys are presented in Section 2. The average response rates of a number of surveys [Cochran (1977) and P. S. R. S. Rao (1966)] are also presented there. However, these rates may not be valid for surveys currently made, or for any particular survey. Current survey experience for the type of survey to be made

INCOMPLETE DATA
IN SAMPLE SURVEYS
Volume 2, Part II

should be sought; for instance, nonresponse at first call may be higher, nowadays, because of increased participation of women in the labor force.

A number of factors such as the demographic and socioeconomic characteristics of the interviewed, the strategies of the interviewer like scheduling the callbacks at a time convenient to the potential respondent, and the costs of obtaining the needed information affect the success of a callback policy. These are not discussed in detail in this chapter. Deming formulated a model, described in Section 3, that permits such information to be incorporated in survey design. He showed how biases and mean square error of estimates depend on probabilities of response in different categories by call.

Callbacks are time consuming and they are usually costly since additional effort is needed in locating the not-at-homes and in obtaining responses from the reluctant nonrespondents. Sharp and Feldt (1959) point out that three-fourths of the complete interviews were obtained only after three calls and "to achieve the 2,313 interviews necessary for an 87% response rate, a total of 7,743 calls was required." For any proposed survey, the procedures for making callbacks and the number of calls that should be made on selected units or respondents before classification as a nonrespondent should be part of the survey design. They may be modified if the early experience of the survey indicates this to be desirable. The method [see Cochran (1977, p. 373] for determining the optimal number of calls using Deming's model is presented in Section 4. The results of a study conducted by the author to determine the optimal number of calls for surveys are presented in Section 5. The response rates at the different calls used in this study are those found by the author in P. S. R. S. Rao (1966). The results of the study presented in Section 5 may not be valid for particular surveys. For example, there has been a tendency since the 1950s for nonresponse to increase (unless increased interviewing efforts are made) and for refusals to increase relative to total nonresponse. However, the results presented in that section should provide general guidelines for determining the optimal number of calls required for any proposed survey.

2. DATA FROM CALLBACK SURVEYS

For the sake of illustration, we present in Tables 1a–1c data from three studies. The response and nonresponse rates along with the total number of contacted individuals (respondents and non respondents) are presented in these tables. Note that the asterisk indicates an estimated value.

All three surveys show that the number of responses increases substantially as the number of calls or follow-ups increase. In each of the surveys, the estimate of the mean after the first call is far from the estimate after three calls. For the first survey (Army veterans), the estimate of 12.7% from the 88% responses after

TABLE 1a

Data from Clausen and Ford (1947) from a Mail Survey of Army Veterans
(Total Number: 14,606)

	Number of the mailing			Nonresponse	Total (responses and nonresponses)
	1	2	3		
Percentage of returns	54	23	11	12	100
Percentage "considering enrolling in school"	10	15	21	25*	14*

three calls is not far from Clausen and Ford's estimate of 14% obtained from the observed trend of the figures at the successive calls. For the second survey, the sample mean of 387 fruit trees after three mailings (total of 41% response) differs substantially from the mean of 290 for the 59% nonrespondents. For the third survey, response to the first call is high since women with young children are likely to be present when the interviewer visits their homes. For the first survey, the item mean is negatively correlated with the number of responses at the different calls, whereas the reverse is true for the third survey. In the third survey [see Hilgard and Payne (1944)], it was noted that the means of the demographic characteristics varied with calls whereas the means of the non-demographic items—for instance, whether they have a refrigerator or whether they have bought any new appliances—did not vary with calls. If there is a trend in the item means as the number of calls increases, one may use the "resistance function" approach [see Hendricks (1949)]. In this procedure, an appropriate function relating the sample mean $\bar{y}_i$ at the ith call to the number (i) of the call is fitted and the means for the later calls are predicted. In the callback model developed by Thomsen and Siring (see Volume 3) where the probability of finding a person at home is estimated by means of information concerning the number of calls made before he/she was found at home, the model is similar to

TABLE 1b

Data from Finkner (1950) from a Mail Survey of North Carolina Fruit Growers
(Total Number: 3,116)

	Number of the mailing			Nonresponse	Total (responses and nonresponses)
	1	2	3		
Percentage of returns	10	17	14	59	100
Average number of fruit trees per farm	456	386	340	290	329

TABLE 1c

Data from Hilgard and Payne (1944) from a Survey of Urban Households
through Personal Interviews (Total Number: 3,265)

	Number of the call				
	1	2	3 or more	Nonresponse	Total
Percentage of responses	63.5	22.2	14.3	0	100
Percentage of households having children under 2 years of age	17.2	9.5	6.2	0	13.9

that of Politz and Simmons (1949). In the model of Drew and Fuller (1981), the population is supposed to be "partitioned into k categories corresponding to the k values of a discrete random variable."

In addition, Hansen, Hurwitz, and Madow (1953) comment that although there were about 11 million responses to a mail survey on employment, the biases (due to nonresponse) in estimating the population parameters differed between men and women and between age groups; they also differed for varying characteristics within a given class. Similar observations were made by Sharp and Feldt (1959) from the results of the Detroit Metropolitan Area Survey.

Observations of this sort confirm the need for repeated calls on the initial nonrespondents and the not at homes, and exhibit the dangers of making predictions based on the earlier returns of a survey.

The averages given in Tables 2a and 2b are illustrative and may not be valid today or for any particular survey. Any survey maker should conjecture similar response rates based on experience if possible. For example, in urban areas, response rates achieving 85% completion by the second call are probably very rare today. Also nonresponse rates vary widely from survey to survey and over time.

Stephan and McCarthy (1958) provide data on 11 surveys and Table 2a presents averages of their data as given by Cochran (1977). P. S. R. S. Rao (1966)

TABLE 2a

Average Response Rates

	Percentage of responses at			
Type of respondent	First call	Second call	Third or later call	Percentage of nonresponses
Any adult (5 surveys)	70	17	8	5
Random adult (3 surveys)	37	32	23	8

Source: Cochran (1977, p. 365).

TABLE 2b

Average Response Rates in 21 Surveys

Type of respondent	Percentage of responses at			Percentage of nonresponses
	First call	Second call	Third or later call	
Any adult (3 surveys)	69.4	16.3	9.2	5.1
Random adult (12 surveys)	33.1	26.0	24.8	16.1
Specified adult (6 surveys)	51.7	23.7	13.7	10.9

Source: P. S. R. S. Rao (1966).

obtained data on 22 surveys, including those considered by Stephan and McCarthy, and averages of 21 of these surveys are summarized in Table 2b. For the averages in Table 2a, the 5 surveys in the "any adult" category include three surveys where "any 'responsible' adult" could respond, and two surveys where a "specified adult" (wife, farm operator) could respond. The random adult category includes 3 surveys where a respondent was selected at random from a list of adults.

No summary of surveys was made. The averages for each of the three categories in Table 2b were based on the numbers of surveys entered next to the name of the category. Thus the averages are based on small numbers of surveys and should be taken as illustrative rather than typical. (It is emphasized, however, that, in general, the best way to deal with nonresponse is to have as little as possible.)

The averages in Table 2b are computed from a variety of surveys (conducted before 1965), most of which are nationwide on characteristics such as attitudes toward further education, consumer finances, attitudes of consumers, voting behavior, political opinions, and opinions about public and private organizations, and labor movements. Similar averages can be found from data given in Kish (1965), Jessen (1978), and Kanuk and Berenson (1975). Three of the 36 surveys studied by Bailar and Lanphier (1978) had nonresponse rates of 75, 54, and 50% with 2, 4, and 5 callbacks, respectively. The response rates of the telephone surveys reported by Wiseman and McDonald (1978) were often under 40%. In Table 2b, the average response rate at the first call is lower for the random adult than for the specified adult. This discrepancy might have occured due to the subject matter of the relevant surveys. The averages in Tables 2a and 2b demonstrate the usefulness of callbacks in obtaining higher response rates; and also demonstrate the relation of "type of respondent" with time of response.

As these data show, surveys vary widely in percentages of respondents. The data in Tables 2a and 2b mask important sources of variability in respondent percentages. Different definitions of nonresponse may be used in different surveys. Also, nonresponse may be classified by category, e.g. not at home, repeated calls, refusals, and unable to communicate. The proportions of non-respondents in such categories also vary from survey to survey. Nonresponse ratios vary by type of survey, interviewer strategy, the conditions in which the survey is made, and the questionnaire used, as well as other variables.

3. DEMING'S MODEL FOR CALLBACKS

Factors such as type of respondent (i.e., "any," "random," or "specified"), demographic and socioeconomic characteristics of the respondent, cooperation of the interviewee and ingenuity of the interviewer, monetary incentives, and costs of callbacks are represented in Deming's model (1953). The population is assumed to consist of k response classes according to individuals' availability, willingness to respond, and interest in the subject matter of the survey.

Let $p_j (j = 1, \ldots, k)$ denote the proportion of the population in the jth class, and μ_j and σ_j^2 the mean and variance of the characteristic of interest, y. Thus, the population mean of y is $\bar{\mu} = \sum p_j \mu_j$. Let w_{ij} be the probability that a person in the jth class responds on or before the ith call. It is assumed that $w_{ij} > 0$, although the model can be modified to include persons that cannot be reached.

In the course of i calls, n_{ij} persons from the jth group are assumed to respond, and $\bar{y}_{ij}$ denotes their mean. It is assumed that $E(\bar{y}_{ij}) = \mu_j$; i.e., respondents and nonrespondents belonging to the jth class have the same mean μ_j. (This assumption will be satisfied, for instance, when the classes are considered to be homogeneous with respect to y.)

Suppose that if only one call was to be made the available budget would be enough to take a sample of size n_0. In a survey involving i calls, let n_i denote the number of interviews obtained during i calls and let $\bar{y}_i$ denote their mean. Note that $n_i = \sum n_{ij}$, $\bar{y}_i = \sum (n_{ij} \bar{y}_{ij}/n_i)$, and the values of n_{ij} and $\bar{y}_{ij}$ are not observed since the different classes are not identified. As shown by Deming, for a fixed n_i,

$$E(\bar{y}_i | n_i) = \frac{\sum w_{ij} p_j \mu_j}{\sum w_{ij} p_j} = \bar{\mu}_i, \tag{1}$$

which does not depend on n_i. Thus, the bias in $\bar{y}_i$ is

$$B(\bar{y}_i) = \bar{\mu}_i - \bar{\mu}. \tag{2}$$

The variance of $\bar{y}_i$ is [Deming (1953)]

$$V(\bar{y}_i | n_i) = \frac{\sum_j w_{ij} p_j [\sigma_j^2 + (\mu_j - \bar{\mu}_i)^2]}{n_i (\sum_j w_{ij} p_j)}. \tag{3}$$

Thus for a policy requiring i calls, the conditional mean square error of $\bar{y}_i$ is

$$\text{MSE}(\bar{y}_i | n_i) = V(\bar{y}_i | n_i) + (\bar{\mu}_i - \bar{\mu})^2. \tag{4}$$

The approximate unconditional MSE is obtained from (3) and (4) by replacing n_i in (4) by

$$E(n_i) = n_0(\sum_j w_{ij} p_j). \tag{5}$$

In any survey the w_{ij} may be defined to depend on information concerning the survey and the sample units, e.g., respondents acceptable to a given survey, the type of survey unit, if known, interviewing strategies such as hours of interviewing, information to be obtained from neighbors, and so on. More complex models than Deming's may be formulated to use such information to allocate effort on successive calls if justified by the quality of the information.

Utilizing (4), the following section describes the procedure of obtaining the optimal number of callbacks.

4. OPTIMAL NUMBER OF CALLS FOR A PROPOSED SURVEY

For any survey, the optimal number of the call at which the lowest MSE occurs should be determined in advance. The MSEs for the policies with i calls are obtained by substituting the expected sample sizes in (4). The optimal callback policy would correspond to the lowest of the MSEs. Using Deming's model, Cochran (1977) illustrates the method of determining the number of calls that should be attempted on the selected unit before classifying him as a confirmed or "hard-core" nonrespondent. This optimum should be worked out for presumed values of p_j, μ_j, σ_j^2, and w_{ij}. Since the relative costs at the second and later calls increase from the first call, the expected number of interviews decreases as the number of calls required by a callback policy increases.

Suppose that for the proposed survey, the cumulative response rates at the end of the first, second, and third calls are expected to be 50, 75, and 90%. Let the relative values of the "average cost per completed interview" be 100, 125, and 140. [Computation of these costs is explained in Cochran (1977) and Rao (1966).] If the budget is large enough to make $n_0 = 1000$ initial calls (if only one call is made), the expected number of interviews in the first call is $E(n_1) = 1000$ (.50) = 500. For the same total budget and two calls being made, the expected number of interviews is $E(n_2) = 500/1.25 = 400$. Similarly $E(n_3) = 500/1.40 = 357$. The MSEs for the policies with 1, 2, or 3 calls are obtained by substituting the expected sample sizes in (4). The optimal callback policy would correspond to the lowest of the three MSEs.

5. NUMBER OF CALLS REQUIRED FOR SURVEYS MET IN PRACTICE—RESULTS OF A STUDY

As has been noted earlier, the number of calls required in a survey to attain the lowest possible MSE for the estimator depends on the initial sample size, the type of respondent, the relative costs at the successive calls, and the biases and the variances. The results of a study conducted by the author to determine through Deming's model the optimal number of calls for surveys met in practice is briefly described here. As explained in Section 1, the results for any specific survey planned now would differ from the ones given here. Hence the figures presented in Tables 3 and 4 represent examples of the methodology of callbacks. These figures may also be used to find the optimal number of calls for a proposed survey; this optimal number should, of course, be modified on the basis of the users experience and the nature of the survey.

5.1. Choosing the Parameters of the Model

The average response rates found in 22 surveys for the three types of respondent have already been presented in Table 2b. Since the true values of the parameters can rarely be assessed, very little data on the biases at the successive calls are available. The study considered R, the difference between the mean at the first call and the mean of the combined results obtained up to the maximum number of calls made, as an indicator of the bias in estimating the characteristics under study. The value of R was found to be between 0 and .05 for binomially distributed variables, although in some instances it was found to be as high as .20.

TABLE 3

Optimal Number of Calls and the Range of Calls (in Parentheses)
with MSEs within 5% of the MSE at the Optimum

Cost increase	n_0				
	500	1000	2000	4000	8000
Mild	7	7	8	8	8
	(4–8)	(5–8)	(6–8)	(7–8)	(7–8)
Moderate	4	5	6	7	8
	(3–6)	(4–7)	(5–8)	(6–8)	(7–8)
Intermediate	4	4	5	7	8
	(2–5)	(4–6)	(4–8)	(5–8)	(6–8)
Steep	1	1	5	6	7
	(1)	(1–4)	(3–7)	(5–8)	(6–8)

TABLE 4

Optimal Number of Calls for Different Cost Increase and Ranges of Q

Optimal number of calls		Range of Q when the cost increase is			
		Mild	Moderate	Intermediate	Steep
Any adult	1–3	<.09	<.12	<.30	<.80
	4–6	.09–.35	.12–2.05	.30–2.90	.80–3.35
	7–8	>.65	>2.05	>2.90	>3.35
Specified adult	1–3	<.27	<.35	<.70	<2.25
	4–6	.27–1.00	.35–5.50	.70–10.00	2.25–10.00
	7–8	>1.00	>5.50	>10.00	>10.00
Random adult	1–3	<.45	<.65	<1.50	<4.30
	4–6	.45–1.20	.65–8.80	1.50–8.80	4.30–13.00
	7–8	>1.20	>8.80	>9.50	>13.00

For the study, a maximum of eight calls was considered, since the available data suggest that at most about 3% additional response may be obtained for policies requiring higher than eight calls. It was enough to consider only $k = 3$ classes to represent the response rates and the ranges of biases of the surveys.

The value of w_{ij} is chosen to be of the form $\left[w_j + (1 - w_j) \cdot (1 - \alpha_j^{i-1})\right]$, where w_j and α_j range from 0 to 1. The probability that a respondent in the jth class will respond at the first call is w_j. The value of $(1 - \alpha_j^{i-1})$ increases as i increases to 2, 3, ..., 8. This form of w_{ij} presumes the intelligent enquiry of the interviewer and the cooperation of the respondent. For each type of respondent the different sets of w_{ij} and p_j for the study were chosen to yield the response rates obtained in Table 2b.

The investigation was initially conducted for binomially distributed variables, and the results were extended to the case of the continuous variables. Several sets of $\mu = (\mu_1, \mu_2, \mu_3)$ were included in the study. They were chosen to represent populations with item means $\bar{\mu}$ between 10.5 and 89.5%, or, roughly, between 0 and 100%. These choices of w_{ij}, p_j, and μ adequately represented the biases observed in practice.

The effects of four types of relative costs, which represent a wide variety of practical situations, were examined. For the "mild cost increase," the relative costs were 100, 110, 120, 130, 140, 150, 160, and 170. This type of cost increase is believed to represent surveys on (1) individuals who are readily available for an interview, (2) banks, retail stores, hospitals, and companies and the like, from whom information may be obtained without much difficulty, and (3) educational and religious institutions that can be located easily. The relative costs for the "moderate cost increase," similar to those found by Durbin and Stuart (1954) in the British surveys, were 100, 112, 127, 151, 250, 350, 450, and 550. The relative costs for the "intermediate cost increase" were 100, 105, 150, 200, 300, 400, 500, and 600. This type of cost increase represents situations where the cost appreciates only after the second call—for instance, the survey in which the first and second calls are made by telephone or mail and the subsequent calls by personal interview. For the "steep cost increase," the relative costs ranged from 100 to 800 with an interval of 100. For example the "steep cost increase" could represent surveys conducted in remote villages.

For the study, the available budget was considered to be enough to take samples of size $n_0 = 500$, 1000, 2000, 4000, and 8000 under a one-call policy.

5.2.   Optimal Number of Calls

When the variable is qualitative and binomially distributed, the MSE in (4) takes the form

$$\text{MSE}(\bar{y}_i | n_i) = \frac{\bar{\mu}_i(1 - \bar{\mu}_i)}{n_i} + (\bar{\mu}_i - \bar{\mu})^2. \tag{6}$$

The values of $\bar{\mu}_i$ and $\bar{\mu}$ were computed for the selected values of w_{ij}, p_j, and μ. The value of n_i in (6) was replaced by the expected sample size, as described in Section 4. Finally, the MSE from (6) was computed for each one of the choices of the parameters and the call at which the MSE is the lowest was determined as the optimum. Summary results regarding the effects of the different factors are as follows:

(1)   The MSEs at the optimum are ranked (highest to lowest) as any adult, specified adult, and random adult. However, for a given sample size n_0, "cost increase," and μ, it turned out that there is very little difference in the optimal number of calls required for these different *types of respondents*.

(2)   The observation regarding the *type of cost increase* is rather obvious: the optimal number of calls usually decreases from the mild to the steep cost increase, for any fixed budget.

(3)   When the biases at the successive calls are fixed, an increase in the initial *sample size* decreases the variance and consequently the minimum value of the MSE will be obtained at a later call. Thus an increase in n_0 increases the number of calls required to reach the optimum.

(4)   The number of calls required to reach the optimum increases as the *bias* increases relative to the variance.

The figures averaged over the three types of respondent are given in Table 3. The range of calls that have MSE within 5% of the MSE at the optimum are also presented there. The following conclusions can be drawn regarding the *general optimum*:

Obviously, no single number of calls can be recommended for all the situations met in practice. If the cost increase is moderate and the budget leads to $n_0 < 1000$, about 3 or 4 calls are enough to reach the optimum. If the sample size can be increased to 2000, the optimum is reached at the fifth or later call for the same type of cost increase.

5.3. A Procedure for Determining the Optimal Number of Calls When the Variable Is Discrete or Continuous

As mentioned in Section 5.2, the optimal number of calls increases as the bias (at the end of the first or later call) increases relative to the variance and as the sample size increases. Thus, if we consider the bias B_1 at the end of the first call, the optimal number of calls increases as the bias ratio Q, where $Q = B_1^2/[\bar{\mu}(1 - \bar{\mu})/n_0]$ increases. The magnitude of B_1 depends on the type of respondent chosen for the survey, and it may be possible to obtain it from past experience or the results at the end of the first call. For a given value of Q, the optimal number of calls depends on the relative costs. From the results of the study, the optimal number of calls when Q falls within specific ranges are computed and presented in Table 4. The figures in this table are applicable to continuous variable when Q is taken to be the ratio of the squared bias to the variance of the mean. The cell entries in Table 4 are the ranges of Q which, as mentioned, may be estimated from past experience or may be guessed from the available information.

As an illustration for using Table 4 for determining the number of calls for a proposed survey, suppose that the average expenditure on an item is to be estimated and the budget is sufficient to take a sample of size 1000 if only one call is made. Suppose that it is specified that the housewife or the head of the household should be contacted to elicit the required information and that the cost increase is of the intermediate type since the first call would be through the mail, the second one through the telephone, and the third and later calls through personal interviews. If the population variance for the item in question is thought to be $S^2 = 2,500$ and the bias to be about \$4, Q will be equal to 6.4. From Table 4, the number of calls required should be between 4 and 6.

REFERENCES

Bailar, B. A., and Lanphier, C. M. (1978). *Development of Survey Methods to Assess Survey Practices.* Washington, D.C.: American Statistical Association.

Clausen, J. A., and Ford, R. N. (1947). Controlling bias in mail questionnaires. *Journal of the American Statistical Association* 42: 497–511.

Cochran, W. G. (1977). *Sampling Techniques.* New York: Wiley.

Deming, W. E. (1953). On a probability mechanism to attain an economic balance between the resultant error of non-response and the bias of non-response. *Journal of the American Statistical Association* 48: 743–772.

Drew, J. H., and Fuller, W. A. (1981). Modeling nonresponse in surveys with callbacks. *1980 Proceedings of the Section on Survey Research Methods*, American Statistical Association, Washington, D.C.

Durbin, J., and Stuart, A. (1954). Callbacks and clustering in sample surveys: An experimental study. *Jour. Roy. Stat. Soc.* A117: 387–428.

Finkner, A. L. (1950). Methods of sampling for estimating commercial peach production in North Carolina. North Carolina Agricultural Experiment Station Technical Bulletin 91.

Hansen, M. H., Hurwitz, W. N., and Madow, W. G. (1953). *Sample Survey Methods and Theory*, Vols. 1 and 2. New York: Wiley.

Hendricks, W. A. (1949). Adjustment for bias by non-response in mailed surveys. *Agric. Econ. Res.*, 1: 52–56.

Hilgard, E. R., and Payne, S. L. (1944). Those not at home:Riddle for Pollsters. *Publ. Op. Quart.* 8: 254–261.

Jessen, R. J. (1978). *Statistical Survey Techniques*. New York: Wiley.

Kanuk, L., and Berenson, C. (1975). Mail surveys and response rates: A literature review. *Journal of Marketing Research* 12: 440–453.

Kish, L. (1965). *Survey Sampling*. New York: Wiley.

Politz, A. N., and Simmons, W. R. (1949). An attempt to get the not-at-homes into the sample without call-backs. *Journal of the American Statistical Association* 44: 9–31.

Rao, P. S. R. S. (1966). A Study of Call-Back Policies in Sample Surveys. Technical Report No. 10. Harvard University and Office of Naval Research.

Sharp, H., and Feldt, A. (1959). Some factors in a probability sample survey of a metropolitan community. *American Sociological Review* 24: 650–661.

Stephan, F. F., and McCarthy, P. J. (1958). *Sampling Opinions*. New York: Wiley.

Wiseman, F., and McDonald, P. (1978). An empirical investigation of refusal rates in consumer surveys. *Proceedings of the Survey Research Section, American Statistical Association*, pp. 283–287.

CHAPTER 5

The Impact of Substitution
on Survey Estimates

David W. Chapman

1. INTRODUCTION

One procedure that is used in many surveys to "impute" for unit nonresponse is field substitution. Rather than imputing data from respondents or adjusting the weights of the respondents as is often done in surveys (see chapters by Oh and Scheuren and by Ford), population units not originally selected for the sample are used to replace eligible sample units that do not participate in the survey. In designing a substitution procedure, an attempt is generally made to arrange for substitutes that will have survey characteristics similar to those of the nonrespondents.

The remainder of this chapter is devoted to a discussion of some substitution procedures including an investigation of the impact of substitution on survey estimates. This investigation of substitution procedures does not include any consideration of the impact of faked interviews, often referred to as "curbstoning." The faked interview refers to a situation in which the interview does not occur, but the interviewer fills in a questionnaire, or some missing information on a partially completed questionnaire, and pretends that the interview occurred. To help reduce the frequency of occurrence of faked interviews, a substantial proportion of the questionnaires should be validated to verify that the interviews took place. The interviewers should be informed that validation will occur soon after the interviews have been conducted. The validation process should be convincing to the interviewers.

INCOMPLETE DATA
IN SAMPLE SURVEYS
Volume 2, Part II

2. METHODS OF SUBSTITUTION
FOR NONRESPONDENTS

In general, two basic types of substitution procedure are used:

(1) Selection of a random substitute
(2) Selection of a specially designated substitute

With a random substitution procedure, an additional population unit is selected on a probability basis to replace each nonrespondent. Usually the substitute for a particular nonrespondent is chosen from a restricted population subgroup (e.g., the same block, area, stratum, or group of strata from which the nonrespondent was selected). In such cases it is assumed that the characteristics of a substitute selected from a population subgroup will be more nearly like those of the nonrespondent than would the characteristics of a substitute selected from the entire population.

For many random substitution procedures, potential substitutes (i.e., alternative or backup units) are selected by a random procedure prior to the data collection phase of the survey. This avoids any delay and trouble that would be involved in selecting a substitute for a nonresponding sample unit after the data collection activities have begun. Also, more than one backup unit is usually selected for each sample unit to allow for nonresponding substitutes.

A procedure that uses specially designated substitute units identifies one or more backup units to provide substitutes, if necessary, for each sample unit. The intent, of course, is to specify substitute units that have characteristics similar to those of the nonrespondents (e.g., a geographic neighbor of a nonrespondent or a unit that has specified characteristics identical with or similar to those of the sample unit.)

A substitution procedure that is neither a procedure using random substitutes nor one using specially designated substitutes from the survey population is a procedure suggested for personal interview household surveys by Kish and Hess (1959). With their procedure, households that are nonrespondents after k calls in a given survey are replaced by households that were nonrespondents after k calls in *another*, similar survey conducted somewhat earlier. Substitute units may be selected by either a random or a specially designated substitution procedure. Biases may occur because of differences in the population and units not responding after k calls in the surveys. The replacement unit may be more like the original unit because both did not respond for k calls. Additional calls are then made at the replacement households. Kish and Hess suggest that in many cases such a procedure may be less expensive and may provide lower survey nonresponse as compared to a procedure that makes the additional follow-up calls at the nonrespondent households in the current survey.

When a substitution procedure is used, there will generally be some survey nonrespondents for which substitutes are not obtained. In such cases, substitution should be used in combination with another imputation procedure to account for all the nonrespondents.

Example 1.   An example of a random substitution procedure is one used in the National Longitudinal Study (NLS), sponsored by the National Center for Educational Statistics. This procedure, which is discussed in more detail later in this section, is described in a report by Williams and Folsom (1977). The first stage of the NLS sample design was the selection of probability sample of four secondary schools from each of 600 strata. Two of the four schools were randomly selected for the primary sample, while the other two were designated as backups (i.e., possible substitutes). If either one or both of the primary schools did not participate in the NLS, one or both of the backup schools were approached, as needed, to be sample substitutes. If attempts to obtain cooperation from the two backup selections in a given stratum failed, no other substitutes were used. In such cases weight adjustments were made to impute for nonresponding schools.

Example 2.   An example of a substitution procedure using specially designated substitutes is one used in the Michigan Survey of Substance Use, described by Sirken (1975). The sample design for this survey, which is discussed in more detail later in this section, was a multistage household sample of 2100 households. If the designated interviews were not completed after three calls at a household, the household was dropped from the sample and an attempt was made to obtain a substitute household. In total there were 700 nonrespondent households in the survey. The first household approached to be the substitute was the one directly to the right of the nonresponding household. If this attempt failed, the household to the left of the nonrespondent was approached. If this attempt also failed, other households were approached in some manner (not described by Sirken) until a substitute household was obtained.

Example 3.   An example of a substitution scheme involving both of the basic types of substitution procedure is one designed by Westat Research for a study carried out by the Educational Testing Service (1972, Chapter 3) for the National Center for Educational Statistics. The design for this study involved the selection of a systematic sample of two schools with probability proportional to a measure of size in each one of about 500 strata. At the same time that the two schools were selected, a systematic sample of eight additional schools was selected per stratum to be used as backup schools. The first four selected were designated as backups for one of the primary selections and the other four were designated as backups for the other primary selection. If a primary school declined to participate after numerous requests, a substitute was approached. (The school nonresponse rate was about 10%). The first priority substitute was that school, if any, that (1) was located in the same school district, (2) was placed in the same stratum, (3) had the same grade structure, and (4) had the closest enrollment size to that of the nonrespondent school. If this attempt failed, the four systematically selected backup schools were approached in a predesignated sequence. With this procedure the top priority backup school is a designated substitute, while the other backup schools are randomly selected schools. Using this substitution procedure (which was implemented by the Educational Testing Service's Berkeley, California, office), a substitute school was obtained for nearly every nonrespondent school.

2.1. Advantages and Disadvantages of Substitution Procedures

A criticism of substitution procedures that is often made is that substitution is of no help in reducing nonresponse bias, since the nonresponses are replaced by responses that are presumably like the responses already in the sample. This is an unfair criticism if directed solely at the use of substitution procedures, since all the methods used for nonresponse imputation, including weight-adjustment procedures, suffer from that same basic weakness: data for nonrespondents have to be supplied (imputed) from data provided by respondents. The key question regarding the worth of substitution procedures is whether the use of substitutes provides better proxy values for nonrespondents than those provided by alternative imputation procedures.

A specially designated substitution procedure often uses a substitute that is (1) a neighbor of the nonrespondent or (2) a listing that is adjacent to the nonrespondent on the sampling frame. Because of this proximity, this type of substitution procedure might provide better proxy values than would be obtained by using an imputation procedure that involves some type of "averaging" of the characteristics of a subclass of respondents. However, in cases in which some information is available about the nonrespondents, better proxy values might be available from sample respondents than from substitutes, since much more information is available about respondents than about potential substitutes. For example, if the race of a nonrespondent household is obtained, this information could easily be used for an imputation procedure that is based on the characteristics of respondents (e.g., a weight-adjustment procedure). However, when a substitute is obtained for a nonrespondent, it would generally not be possible to select a substitute of the same race as the nonrespondent.

Perhaps the type of survey for which the use of substitution is most appropriate is one that involves a deeply stratified, relatively small sample of population units.[1] Surveys of institutions (e.g., schools or hospitals) are often of this type, since a substantial amount of stratification information may be available for a population of institutions, and the cost per sample unit might be

---

[1] The potential advantage of the use of substitution in this situation was described to David W. Chapman by Joseph Waksberg of Westat Research during a telephone conversation in January 1979.

high enough to force the sample size to a minimum level. In such cases, a substitute for a nonrespondent might be available that is very similar to the nonrespondent with respect to a number of characteristics. However, for the type of weight-adjustment procedure often used, the weight-adjustment classes would generally have to be large enough (to avoid producing a nontrivial increase in survey variances) to include institutions with substantial variation in some characteristics. Consequently, in surveys of this type, the use of substitute institutions would tend to provide better imputations than would the type of weight-adjustment procedure that is often used.[2]

For surveys with large sample sizes and relatively little information about nonresponding units (e.g., a large household survey), the use of substitutes would probably not provide any improvement in terms of bias reduction over the use of weight-adjustment procedures. However, some reduction in survey variances would result due to an increase in sample size. In such cases the small reduction in survey variances may not be worthwhile if one considers the potential problems that could result.

There are two disadvantages that generally apply to substitution procedures. Perhaps the major disadvantage of the use of substitution is that the effort extended to obtain participation from originally selected units may not be as intense as it would if no substitutes were available. That is, an interviewer, and perhaps a research analyst, may view a backup unit as one that is just as good (or nearly as good) as the unit initially selected. This could lead to a higher level of nonresponse, which could produce greater biases in the survey results. If a substitution procedure is used, steps should be taken in the planning of the data collection procedures to ensure that the maximum effort is made to obtain responses from the original sample units. This should include validating a substantial proportion of the substitute units to verify that substitutes were needed.

The other disadvantage of the use of substitutes is that there is a tendency to ignore the level of substitution used when the survey response rate is reported. That is, since survey practitioners process substitute responses when survey estimates are computed as if the substitutes were selected in the original sample, there is a tendency to view the substitutes as originally selected units when response rates are calculated. In fact, in some surveys, a record of whether a respondent is a substitute is not easy to find. If the substitutes are treated as original sample selections for the calculation of the response rate, the survey response rate will, of course, be overestimated, and the potential for nonresponse bias will be underestimated.

There are also two advantages that apply to substitution procedures. The first advantage is that the sample will be balanced with respect to sample size per substitution class. This balance has certain practical advantages. For

---

[2] If a raking ratio adjustment procedure were used, the problem of requiring large weight-adjustment classes would be avoided. For a discussion of raking ratio estimation, including an extensive reference list, see H. Lock Oh and Fritz Scheuren (1978).

example, if a self-weighting sample is selected, the final sample will still be essentially self-weighting, since the most appropriate selection probability to use for a substitute unit is usually the probability that the unit had of being selected into the initial sample. Furthermore, if a two-per-stratum design were used in order to allow for variance estimation, there would still be two units per stratum if substitutes were selected from the same stratum.

The other advantage to the use of substitution, which has already been mentioned, is that it increases the survey sample size, and therefore reduces the variances of survey estimates.

Whenever substitutes are used in a survey, care should be taken (1) to keep accurate records of which units are substitutes, (2) to identify which data records are obtained from substitute units, (3) to report the level of substitution, and (4) to treat the substitutes as nonresponse cases when calculating the survey response rate.

3. SUMMARIES OF SOME RESEARCH INVESTIGATION OF THE IMPACT OF SUBSTITUTION ON SURVEY ESTIMATES

An extensive search of the survey research literature, both published and unpublished, has not uncovered any theoretical work relating to substitution. Perhaps this is because any model that is used to represent a substitution procedure would either be too complex to formulate or too simple to provide useful results. Specifically, a model used to represent a specially designated substitution procedure would have to be complex to reflect appropriately the relation between the characteristics of the substitutes and those of the nonrespondents or between those of the substitutes and those of the respondents.

On the other hand, a model representing a *random substitution* procedure within poststrata would be simple, since the random substitutes would have the same expected characteristics as the *respondents* in the poststratum from which substitutes are selected, although not necessarily the expected characteristics of nonresponding units. For example, if simple random sampling is used to select the initial sample and the substitutes from a stratum, the expected value of the resulting stratum sample mean would be the stratum population mean for *respondents*. The bias of this estimate is the difference between the stratum population mean for respondents and the overall stratum population mean. The bias of the stratum sample mean would be the same if a weight adjustment procedure were used, assuming that the stratum would be used as a weight-adjustment class. (However, the survey variances associated with the weight-adjustment procedure would be somewhat larger.)

For a random substitution procedure to provide estimates with lower nonresponse bias than those that would be provided by a weight-adjustment procedure, the substitution classes would have to be defined differently—presumably narrower—than would the weight-adjustment classes. These classes would have to be defined in such a way that the differences between the population means for respondents and nonrespondents within a class would be smaller on the average than the corresponding differences within a weight-adjustment class.

It was also difficult to find research involving empirical studies of the impact on survey estimates of substitution procedures. In particular, only four studies were discovered that provided estimates of the bias associated with one or more substitution procedures. Furthermore, only one of these studies included a *comparison* of the estimated effects (or biases) for a substitution procedure with the corresponding estimated effects (or biases) for one or more alternative imputation procedures. Unfortunately, the type of substitution procedure used in the comparative analysis was atypical and the scope of comparisons was rather limited.

The four studies discovered are summarized in the remainder of this subsection, with the comparative study being discussed last.

3.1. Study by Cohen (1955)

The primary objective of Cohen's study was to estimate the bias associated with a substitution procedure that he refers to as a "modified probability sample." Although his procedure could be used for other types of surveys, it is investigated by Cohen in the context of a household survey.

To use Cohen's substitution procedure, the basic household sample has to be selected in pairs of housing units—presumably pairs of neighbors. The number of pairs selected is equal to the target sample size. One unit of each pair of units is selected at random to be the primary selection, while the other unit is designated as the alternative or backup selection. A call is made first at the primary unit in an attempt to obtain an interniew. If an interview is obtained, the interviewer proceeds to the next pair. If an interview is not obtained on the first call, (s)he attempts to obtain an interview with the alternative unit. If an interview is completed with the alternative unit, the interviewer continues to the next pair. If an interview is not obtained, (s)he returns to the primary unit, then back to the alternative, continuing in this manner until an interview is obtained.

Cohen wanted to find out whether this modified probability sample, which would reduce field costs, would introduce a nontrivial amount of bias in the survey estimates.

Cohen based his investigation on a subset of data collected in a household survey conducted by the Bureau of Social Science Research (BSSR). A brief description of the BSSR survey will be given, followed by a description of how Cohen carried out his study using a subset of the BSSR sample.

The BSSR study was a household survey carried out in the Washington, D.C., metropolitan area. The purpose of the BSSR survey was to study the effects on the community of the purchase of the *Times-Herald* by the *Washington Post*. The BSSR selected an equally weighted, multistage sample of about 550 pairs of adjacent households.[3] From each sample household an attempt was made to interview one person aged 18 or more, selected randomly from the eligible household members.

To investigate the modified probability sample substitution procedure, Cohen could only use those pairs of households in the BSSR survey for which completed interviews were obtained from members of both households. For this restricted subset of the sample, which included 326 of the original 550 pairs, Cohen was able to simulate how the sample would be selected using the modified probability sample. This was possible since a record of the number of calls required to obtain an interview was recorded for the BSSR survey.

Cohen randomly designated one household in each of the 326 pairs to be the primary unit. Based on the number of calls required to obtain an interview for each of the two households in a pair, Cohen was able to determine which of the two households would be included in the "modified probability sample." Comparisons were then made between the primary probability sample of 326 households and the modified probability sample of 326 households. These comparisons were done in the second part of his analysis.

In the first part of his analysis he did paired comparisons tests to compare the early and late respondents with respect to 12 survey items (all 0–1 items). These tests were carried out only for the 209 pairs (of the 326 pairs) for which one of the units responded on an earlier call than the other. For the 12 items included Cohen found significant differences in the sample proportions for only two items:

(1)   Proportion not in the labor force (higher for early responders)
(2)   Proportion who reported reading the *Washington Daily News* (higher for late responders)

There were two other items for which the difference in sample proportions was almost significant at the 10% level:

(1)   Proportion that are heads of household (higher for late responders)
(2)   Proportion residing in households with heads who are professionally or technically employed (higher for early responders)

For these two paired samples none of the other eight sample proportions were significantly different at the 20% level. These proportions included, for example, the proportion with one or more children in a household, the proportion

---

[3] The sample was selected in pairs as a means of providing a mechanism for doubling the sampling rate for a special segment of the population for certain questionnaire items. This did not affect Cohen's study, however, since his analysis was based only on the questionnaire items asked of all persons in the survey.

male, the proportion with family income over $5000, and the proportion under 40 years of age.

The second part of his analysis involved calculating an estimate of bias attributable to use of his substitution procedure. For the set of 326 interview pairs, he calculated the unweighted sample proportions for 12 survey items using a "straight" probability sample (i.e., the 326 primary units) and also using the modified probability sample of 326 primary and backup units. The estimated proportion in the labor force was about .06 higher with the substitution procedure. The estimated proportion reading the *Washington Daily News* was about .03 lower with the substitution procedure. For the other 10 survey items, the estimated proportions using the two procedures were within .02 of each other.

It should be noted that Cohen was only able to compare primary and substitute units for those cases in which both members of a selected pair of households supplied completed interviews. This restricted population may provide different comparisons between primary and substitute units than would be provided by the entire target population. In particular, no comparisons can be made in his study of the characteristics of the substitutes and the characteristics of the nonresponding primary units being replaced.

Furthermore, the substitution procedure investigated by Cohen differs from those typically used. With most procedures, in order to minimize the nonresponse bias, more than one call is generally made at the primary unit before a backup unit is approached. In fact, as was indicated in Section 2.1, a strong effort to obtain an interview from the primary unit before approaching the substitute unit is highly recommended. The savings on field costs that would be obtained by the use of Cohen's modified probability sample may not be worth the nonresponse bias associated with the additional substitutes used.

3.2.   Study by Williams and Folsom (1977)

The study by Williams and Folsom of the Research Triangle Institute was done for the National Center for Educational Statistics (NCES). This study was based on data collected in the NCES sponsored National Longitudinal Study of the High School Class of 1972 (NLS). They attempted to measure the portion of bias in the first-year estimates that is attributable to school nonresponse.

The basic objective of the NLS was to determine what happens to students after they graduate from high school. Variables of interest included type and amount of additional education, vocational experience, plans, and attitudes. The NCES wished to relate this information to the students' personal and educational background. The full-scale NLS was begun in January 1972; and the first phase of the NLS, referred to as the basic year (BY) survey, ended in June 1973. The primary survey instruments for the BY survey were student, counselor, and school questionnaires, student test booklets, and students' school record information forms.

The sample design for the BY survey was a stratified two-stage probability sample with schools as the first stage and students as the second stage. The first stage primary sample consisted of the selection of 1200 schools—2 from each of 600 strata. Two additional schools were selected per stratum on a probability basis to serve as backups (potential substitutes) for the 2 primary selections. At the second stage, a sample of 18 students was selected from each cooperating school.

If either one or both of the primary schools selected from a stratum declined to participate, one or both of the backup schools were approached. In strata for which the 2 backup schools selected did not provide the substitutes needed, no additional units were approached. In total, 974 schools participated in the BY survey: 921 primary schools plus 53 substitutes. The student questionnaire was completed by 16,409 students. The nonparticipating primary schools for which substitutes were not obtained were accounted for in the estimation procedures by making adjustments in the weights of the cooperating schools.

From October 1973 through April 1974 the first data collection follow-up procedure (FFU) of the NLS was conducted. In additon to administering a questionnaire to students who participated in the BY survey, there was a complete follow-up of BY nonrespondent schools. A sample of persons who were seniors in 1972 was selected from each of these BY nonrespondent schools. The questionnaire administered to this sample of 1972 seniors included 14 questions about information initially requested in the BY survey. The FFU data gathered retrospectively from BY nonresponding schools allowed Williams and Folsom to make some estimates of bias in the BY survey estimates due to nonresponding schools.

In the FFU survey, 1300 sample schools completed FFU questionnaires: 1153 primary schools plus 131 backup schools plus 16 additional schools selected to account for an increase in the frame.[4] The FFU survey contained completed questionnaires from 21,350 students.

The main purpose of the study by Williams and Folsom was to estimate and analyze the part of the bias in the BY estimates that is attributable to *school nonresponse*. This included the effect on bias of the use of substitutes and of weight adjustments to account for nonrespondent schools. Other sources of bias in the BY estimates (e.g., student nonresponse in participating schools) were not investigated in their study. Estimates of the biases due to nonresponding schools were made for estimated totals and proportions for 35 student items. These estimates were calculated by comparing the BY estimates obtained from the BY survey data with the "best estimates" computed from the BY data and from the retrospective data obtained in the FFU survey from the sample of 1972 seniors in BY nonrespondent schools. For the BY survey about 20% of the

---

[4] The 1153 primary schools included those that participated in both the BY and FFU surveys and those that participated only in the FFU survey. The 131 backup schools included backup schools used as substitutes for both the BY and FFU surveys.

primary schools did not participate. However, after the FFU survey only 2% of the BY primary schools were still nonrespondents. Consequently, differences in the "best estimates" and BY survey estimates should reflect the impact on BY survey estimates of the use of substitutes and weight adjustments to adjust for the 20% of the primary schools that did not participate in the BY survey. Unfortunately, they were not able to separate the impact of the use of substitutes from the impact of the school nonresponse weight adjustments.

The 35 questionnaire items included in the analysis contained a total of 155 response categories (i.e., multiple choice type responses). Estimates of the bias in BY estimates of student totals[5] were calculated for all 155 categories. For each category the null hypothesis that there is no bias in BY estimates was tested against a two-sided alternative. For the 5% level of significance the null hypothesis of no bias was rejected 91 times out of 155. For these estimates the average estimate of school nonresponse bias in BY estimates is approximately a negative 5%.

Although there were some simplifying assumptions and approximations made in estimating the nonresponse biases, Williams and Folsom state on page 8 of their report that "the results are so consistent and dramatic it is doubtful that a more refined analysis would alter the conclusions."

3.3.   Study by Sirken (1975)

Sirken's investigation was based on data collected in the Michigan Survey of Substance Use, August 1974, sponsored by the Michigan Department of Health.

The Michigan Survey was a statewide, multistage, self-weighting probability sample of the noninstitutionalized population 13 years of age and older residing in Michigan during August 1974. The main objective of the survey was to estimate the number and proportion of persons in the population and in various subpopulations that used 16 types of substances (drugs) during the previous year.

There were 2100 households selected for the Michigan Survey. Half of the eligible persons in participating households were interviewed for the survey. If all the designated interviews for a sample household were not obtained after three visits, that sample household was discarded and a substitute household was approached. The prescribed pattern of substitution was to take the household to the right of the nonrespondent; then, if necessary, approach the household to the left. Only one call was made to a substitute household. In spite of this, a substitute household was obtained for each nonrespondent household. (Sirken's report did not indicate whether it was necessary in some

---

[5] An estimated total refers to the estimated number of students in the population who would respond in that category.

cases to contact more than the two adjacent neighbors to obtain a substitute, and if so, how this was done.)

Of the 2100 households selected, interviews were completed in 1400 households. Substitute households were obtained for the 700 nonparticipating households. In total, 2539 interviews were obtained in the Michigan Survey: 1552 from initially selected households, 839 from substitute households, and 148 that have unknown status. That is, about one-third of the survey responses came from substitute households.

Sirken compared some survey characteristics by three age categories for the following three groups of respondents:

(1)   Initially designated individuals who were interviewed on the first call
(2)   Initially designated individuals who were interviewed on the second or third call
(3)   Substitute individuals

The survey items used for the comparison of the three groups were the percentage of persons using (1) alcohol, (2) prescribed drugs, (3) nonprescribed drugs, and (4) illicit drugs in the past year. These comparisons indicated that the characteristics of the substitute persons were about the same as those initially designated persons interviewed on the first call. (This is not surprising since only one call was made at each substitute household.) For the oldest age group included in the analysis, 35 years and older, the characteristics of those persons interviewed on the second or third call were also about the same as for those interviewed on the first call and for those of the substitutes. However, for the youngest age group, 13–17 years of age, and for all four survey items, the substance use rate was higher for the persons interviewed on the second or third call than it was for substitutes and for persons interviewed on the first call. The same relation held for the middle-age group, 18–34 years of age, for two of the four survey items used in the comparison: percentages of use rates for alcohol and for illicit drugs.

A similar relation was observed between early and late respondents for a survey of Vietnam veterans [Wish, Robins, Helzer, Hesselbrock, and Davis (1978)]. They found a statistically significant difference between early and late respondents for the proportion of veterans experiencing various types of behavioral problems (e.g., alcohol abuse, arrests, unemployment, and divorce). In all cases the proportion experiencing the problem was higher for the late responders.

Based on the evidence in the Michigan Survey that the substance use rate increases as the number of required calls increases, Sirken suggests that the characteristics of the persons in nonresponding households might be closer to those of persons interviewed on the second or third call than to those of the substitute persons. Sirken shows that if this is the case in the Michigan Survey, there would be a negative bias of about 3 percentage points in the estimates of the substance use rates of alcohol and illicit drugs for both the 13–17 and 18–34 age groups.

Since the characteristics of the Michigan Survey nonrespondents were not known, there is no basis for evaluating the accuracy of Sirken's speculative estimates of bias. If survey data for at least some of the nonrespondents had been obtained, more objective estimates of bias associated with the substitution procedure could have been made.

3.4. Study by Durbin and Stuart (1954)

The investigation by Durbin and Stuart (1954) was a comparative study of alternative methods of coping with total questionnaire nonresponse. This study, which was carried out in six urban areas in Great Britain, was part of an experimental study planned and directed by a research group called the Survey Research Committee.

The frame (and presumably the population) from which the sample was selected for this study was the Electoral Register. A probability sample of 1260 names was selected for the sample, 360 from one of the six survey areas and 180 from each of the other five areas. Within each of these six areas, uniform selection probabilities were used. However, the uniform selection probability used to select registrants in one area was, in general, different from that used to select registrants in the other areas. These differential selection probabilities were not taken into account in the comparative analysis. That is, for calculating estimates the entire sample was treated as self-weighting.

The survey data were collected by personal interview. The questionnaire contained items which covered a variety of topics, including age, sex, marital status, employment characteristics, leisure activities, and smoking and drinking habits. The comparative analysis was based on estimated proportions for 32 of the questionnaire items.

There were seven methods of coping with nonresponse that were compared:

(a) and (b)   Make a maximum of (a) one call or (b) three calls and assume that the respondents constitute a probability sample from the total population.

(c)   Make an unlimited number of calls and assume that the respondents constitute a probability sample from the total population.

(d)   Make only one call and adjust the selection probability of each respondent to take into account the number of days in the previous 6 days that the respondent was home [i.e., the Politz–Simmons method, described by Politz and Simmons (1949)].

(e), (f), and (g)   Make a maximum of (e) one call, (f) two calls, or (g) three calls and obtain substitutes for the nonrespondents using a quota sampling procedure.

The substitution procedure described in (e)—with variations (f) and (g)—is rather unusual. Instead of selecting substitute individuals from the Electoral Register to replace nonrespondents, the nonrespondents are replaced by a quota sample. Although Durbin and Stuart do not give the details of how the quota sample was selected, they indicate that the interviews were conducted mostly outside the home and that the control factors for the quota sample were sex, age, and income class. An attempt was made to obtain the control factors for each sample person not interviewed on the initial call by requesting this information from other household members or, if necessary, from neighbors. The cell counts of the first-call nonrespondents for the three-way cross-classification of the control factors provided the quotas for the quota sampling for procedure (e). Quotas to be used for procedures (f) and (g) were obtained in an analogous way from cell counts made after two and three calls. Using this type of substitution procedure, many of the substitutes used may not even be listed on the sample frame (i.e., the Electoral Register), depending on exactly how the quota sample of replacements was selected.

Of the original sample of 1260 names, 80 were eventually classified as ineligible, leaving an eligible sample size of 1180 persons. The response rates after various numbers of calls are the following:

Number of calls	Number of responses	Response rate (%)
1	374	31.7
3	823	69.7
Unlimited	938	79.5

This table indicates that even with unlimited callbacks the survey response rate was only 79.5%. Substitutes from the quota sample were obtained for most, but not all, of the nonrespondents. (Durbin and Stuart do not give reasons for the apparent shortage of substitutes.) The number of substitutes obtained for the nonrespondents is given below for procedure (e)—substitution after one call—and for procedure (g)—substitution after three calls:

Substitution procedure	Number of respondents	Number of nonrespondents	Number of substitutes	Total number of interviews
(e) Substitution after one call	374	806	701	1075
(g) Substitution after three calls	823	357	259	1082

The 259 quota substitutes used in procedure (g) consisted of those among the 701 substitutes used in procedure (e) to replace first-call nonrespondents who remained nonrespondents after three calls. It seems that the total number of interviews for procedures (e) and (g) should have been the same. The discrepancy of seven interviews shown in the above table was not discussed by Durbin and Stuart.

The method of analysis used by Durbin and Stuart was to compare the estimates based on all the procedures to those obtained for the unlimited callback (U.C.) procedure. That is, the estimates based on the U.C. procedure were considered to be unbiased for this experiment, or at least to be the best estimates to use as a standard for comparison. This would have been a sound approach to making the comparisons if the response rate for the U.C. procedure had been closer to 100%. However, since the response rate for the U.C. procedure was only 79.5%, the method of comparison is not sound since the estimates based on the U.C. procedure might contain a substantial amount of nonresponse bias.

In particular, the method of comparison to the U.C. estimates is especially unfavorable toward the substitution procedures and the Politz–Simmons procedure. The substitution and Politz–Simmons procedures attempt to impute for all survey nonrespondents, not just for those who eventually become respondents using unlimited callbacks. Consequently, for the 32 questionnaire items included in the comparison analysis, all three substitution procedures and the Politz–Simmons procedure provide estimates that often vary considerably from those of the U.C. procedure. Of these four alternatives, procedure (g)—substitution after three calls—compares most favorably with the U.C. procedure.

There was not much of a pattern observed in the differences between the estimates based on the U.C. procedure and those based on the best substitution procedure (i.e., the procedure for which substitutions were used after three calls). Sometimes the estimated proportions were higher using the U.C. procedure, but other times they were higher for the three-call substitution procedure. It did appear, however, that the quota sample substitutes used after three calls constituted a somewhat younger, less affluent group than did the respondents who cooperated after three calls.

Of all six procedures being compared to the U.C. procedure in the comparative analysis [i.e., (a), (b), (d), (e), (f), and (g)], the one that provided estimates closest to those of the U.C. procedure was procedure (b)—making a maximum of three calls and assuming the respondents constitute a probability sample from the total population. The favorable appearance of the three-call procedure is not surprising since the three-call sample makes up 80% of the U.C. sample (i.e., 823 of the 938 U.C. respondents).

If the U.C. procedure has to be taken as a standard of comparison, then all the procedures compared should be geared to that level of response. That is, all the procedures should attempt to impute to the sample of 938 U.C. respondents and not to the total eligible sample of 1180 persons. If this had been done, the substitution procedures might have compared more favorably with the other procedures than they did.

Even though the substitution procedures included in the study may be somewhat better than they appeared in this experiment, it does not seem that the generation of substitutes from a quota sample is a very promising imputation method. This type of procedure could be difficult to apply to surveys of institutions, since it might be hard to obtain control factor information for quota substitutes. Also, it would be difficult to use in household surveys since the quota control factors for nonrespondents might be difficult to obtain in some surveys. Even if control factors could be obtained for household nonrespondents, it is questionable whether, in general, a replacement obtained from a quota sample would provide a better substitute than would a neighbor.

4. CONCLUSION

As was pointed out in the beginning of Section 3, there does not appear, at this time, to be any theoretical results available that would be helpful in evaluating the general usefulness of substitution procedures as a method for imputing for total questionnaire nonresponse. There appear to be some situations for which the use of a substitution procedure would be appropriate, and other situations for which such a procedure would not be wise.

Perhaps the only way that substitution procedures can be evaluated is through empirical investigations. Only four studies that investigated the impact of substitution on survey estimates have been uncovered. Although none of these studies was carried out under ideal conditions, they all seemed to indicate that substitution procedures do not eliminate the effects of nonresponse bias. This was perhaps best demonstrated in the Research Triangle Study for the National Center for Educational Statistics, described by Williams and Folsom (1977). This study indicated that there was consistently a negative 5% bias in a number of estimated totals that was attributable to the use of substitute schools and to school nonresponse weight adjustments.

The fact that substitution procedures do not seem to eliminate nonresponse bias does not imply that substitution procedures are inappropriate. It is probably true that there is no procedure available that can adequately correct nonresponse bias. In a study carried out by Westat Research for the National Center for Health Statistics, described by Chapman (1974), it was discovered that none of the six alternative weight-adjustment procedures that were compared could correct the nonresponse bias associated with a number of items in a medical history questionnaire.

To evaluate the usefulness of substitution procedures, empirical studies should be carried out that compare imputations based on substitutes with those based on alternative nonresponse procedures. In an ideal study, sample units would be declared nonrespondents after a specific number of calls (e.g., three). The substitution procedure being evaluated would then be applied to obtain substitutes for the nonrespondents. However, extensive efforts would continue to obtain cooperation from the nonrespondents. The data collection activities would proceed until all of the originally designated sample persons or institutions, except the hard-core refusals, were persuaded to participate in the survey. (An alternative method of obtaining the survey characteristics of the nonrespondents is to use administrative records.)

If this type of study were done, estimates based on the substitutes could be compared to estimates based on alternative weight-adjustment procedures with respect to how close the estimates are to those that are nearly free of nonresponse bias (i.e., those based on almost all of the sample). Until this type of study, or some variant of it, is carried out for a number of surveys of various types, it will be difficult to evaluate the use of substitution procedures as a method of imputing for nonresponse relative to alternative imputation methods.

REFERENCES

Bailar, Barbara A., Bailey, Leroy, and Corby, Carol (1978). A comparison of some adjustment and weighting procedures for survey data. In N. Krishnan Namboodiri (ed.), *Survey Sampling and Measurement*. New York: Academic Press.

Chapman, David W. (1975). An investigation of nonresponse imputation procedures for the health and nutrition examination survey. Prepared for the Division of Health Examination Statistics, National Center for Health Statistics; HEW, by Westat Research.

Cohen, Reuben (1955). An investigation of modified probability sampling procedures in interview surveys. M.A. thesis submitted to the graduate faculty of The American University, May 26, 1955.

Durbin, J., and Stuart, A. (1954). Callbacks and clustering in sample surveys: An experimental study. *Journal of the Royal Statistical Society*, Series A (General), Part IV pp. 387–410.

Educational Testing Service (1972). Anchor test study. Final report, prepared for the U.S. Office of Education, National Center for Educational Statistics. [Chapter 3 ("Sample Design") was prepared by Westat Research.]

Kish, Leslie, and Hess, Irene (1959). A "replacement" procedure for reducing the bias of nonresponse. *The American Statistician* 13: 17–19.

Oh, H. Lock, and Scheuren, Fritz (1978). Some unresolved application issues in raking ratio estimation. *1978 Proceedings of the Section on Survey Research Methods, American Statistical Association*, pp. 723–728.

Politz, A., and Simmons, W. R. (1949). An attempt to get the "not-at-homes" into the sample without callbacks." *Journal of the American Statistical Association* 44:9–31.

Sirken, Monroe (1975). Evaluation and critique of household sample surveys of substance use. *In* Alcohol and other drug use and abuse in the State of Michigan. Final report, prepared by the Office of Substance Abuse Services, Michigan Department of Public Health.

Williams, Stephen R., and Folsom, Ralph E., Jr. (1977). Bias resulting from school nonresponse: Methodology and findings. Prepared by the Research Triangle Institute for the National Center for Educational Statistics.

Wish, E. D., Robins, L. N., Helzer, J. E., Hesselbrock, M., and Davis, D. H. (1978). Monday morning quarterbacking on limiting call-backs: Evidence from a panel study of veterans. Presented at the annual meeting of the American Association of Public Opinion Research, Roanoke, Virginia, June 1978.

CHAPTER 6

Quota Sampling

Benjamin F. King

1. QUOTA SAMPLING DEFINED

To understand the way in which *quota sampling* may serve as a "solution" to the problem of missing data in sample surveys, one should first consider the method of *full probability sampling* of a target population of human individuals. For example, consider the adult occupants of housing units in a certain standard metropolitan statistical area (SMSA). In full probability sampling, a set of sample housing units is selected in a multistage (possibly stratified) design with probabilities proportional to size at various stages—e.g., Census tracts, followed by block groups, followed by blocks, down to the selection of housing units with known probabilities at the last stage. Within each sampled housing unit, a list is made of all adult occupants, and a single respondent is selected with known probability from that list. Callbacks or follow-up visits are made to housing units in which persons were not at home on earlier visits, and similarly, successive attempts are made to convert individuals who refused to cooperate with the interviewers when first approached. With sufficient callback visits it may be possible to obtain responses from a large enough proportion of the originally selected individuals that any effects on estimation from nonresponse are negligible. A number of techniques are used to correct for deficiencies in the frames at various stages, including errors in field listing of housing units, so that, if adequate resources in time and money are available, one may state that almost all of the target individuals in the population had a chance to be selected, that the selection rates can be calculated, and that most of those who were asked cooperated in the interview. Thus, the textbook theory of estimation of population characteristics can be applied, and, especially important, it is possible to

INCOMPLETE DATA
IN SAMPLE SURVEYS
Volume 2, Part II

calculate estimates of the mean square error of estimation for the purpose of making probability statements.

Suppose, however, that the survey research organization is faced with the problem of delivering the desired number of completed cases in only 2 weeks after the start of field operations. The administration of callbacks to achieve high response requires considerable calendar time—some people are hardly ever at home; others must return from vacation; many require several attempts at persuasion before they finally agree to be interviewed. Thus, if it were necessary to stop interviewing at the end of 2 weeks in a conventional full probability operation, it is likely that only 40 or 50% of the target cases would be completed, and it would be difficult to defend such a sample against allegations of bias. Furthermore the sample would not provide the numbers of interviews required for ultimate estimation and analysis.

Quota sampling, as it is practiced today, is a method that enables one to obtain a desired number of completed cases in a relatively short period of field time without the expense of callbacks. In the form with the least potential bias, referred to by Sudman (1967) as "probability sampling with quotas," the method involves drawing sampling locations down to the block level with exactly the same technique of multistage selection with probabilities proportional to size as in full probability sampling. Then, instead of field listing of housing units and probability sampling of households and persons contained therein, interviewers are allowed to fill quotas of respondents according to the availability of qualified subjects and whatever personal judgment may enter into the selection process. The quota controls, usually few in number for administrative feasibility, are set according to the most recent Census counts for the smallest area that immediately surrounds the sampling location. For example, an interviewer may be instructed to begin calling on households at a particular corner of a city block and proceed from door to door until five adult females and five adult males are interviewed. Not-at-homes and refusals are ignored by continuing to the next household where a cooperating individual may be found. With this procedure, it is possible that a cluster of 10 interviews, balanced with respect to sex, could be completed in a day or two. If greater control were desired, the sex strata could be broken down into age groups within sex, making the filling of quotas more time consuming, but forcing the demographic characteristics of the cluster to be more congruent with the characteristics of the immediately surrounding area.

It is these considerations that have led Cochran (1977) to describe quota sampling as "stratified sampling with a more or less nonrandom selection of units within strata."

Following are descriptions of the exact quota methods employed by two well-known survey research organizations:

1.   At the National Opinion Research Center of the University of Chicago (NORC) quota sampling is used at the Census block level with clusters of five

respondents for each block. Starting points for each cluster are selected within the same primary sampling units as the blocks or pseudoblocks that were listed for the NORC National Probability Sample (1978) drawn in 1972. To fill cluster quotas for persons 18 or older, interviewers are instructed to follow a serpentine pattern over adjacent blocks. They are required to canvass only after 3:00 P.M. on weekdays or during the weekend or holidays. In addition to sex quotas, there is an age control for males, with the break point at age 30, and the females are controlled for employment status. The main idea behind the additional controls within sex is to capture younger males and employed females who tend not to be so readily available for interview. The cluster quotas are set to be in proportional agreement (on the average) with the corresponding age, sex, and employment status for the tract or minor civil division containing the starting point for the cluster (the smallest Census area for which joint statistics are reported).

2. At the Gallup Organization, Inc., (1972) in Princeton, N.J., the starting locations for quota sampling are probabilistically selected in the same way as one would select for full probability sampling, just as at NORC. The procedures for subsequent stages of sampling are described in a design write-up for *Trends*, the personal interview omnibus survey of Gallup (1972):

> . . . In each cluster of blocks and each segment so selected, a randomly selected starting point is designated on the interviewer's map of the area. Starting at this point, interviewers are required to follow a given direction in the selection of households, taking households in sequence, until their assigned number of interviews has been completed. . . Within each occupied dwelling unit or household reached the interviewer asks to speak to the youngest man 18 or older at home, or if no man is at home, the oldest woman 18 or older. This method of selection within the household has been developed empirically to produce an age distribution by men and women separately which compares closely with the age distribution of the population. It increases the probability of selecting younger men, who are at home relatively infrequently, and the probability of reaching older women in the household who tend to be under-represented unless given a disproportionate chance of being drawn from among those at home. The method of selection among those at home within the household is not strictly random, but it is systematic and objective. . . Interviewing is conducted at times when adults, in general, are most likely to be at home, which means on weekends or if on weekdays, after 4:00 P.M. for women and after 6:00 P.M. for men. . . .

The description goes on to discuss a "Politz–Simmons" adjustment for times at home, and poststratification according to Census figures on educational attainment.

2. CRITICISM AND SHORTCOMINGS
OF THE METHOD

The fundamental criticism of quota sampling is that, in the absence of a full understanding of the selection mechanism that determines which individuals shall participate in the survey, it is difficult, if not impossible, to deal in conventional ways with the chance variability of estimates about parameters of interest in the target population. For example, tests of significance and confidence interval estimates must employ estimated standard errors (computed from the quota sample) which may be very different in magnitude from the root mean square errors about population parameters that are needed for meaningful inferences. In a sense, the problem is similar to that of frame deficiency and the bias of nonresponse in full probability sampling, but in the case of full probability sampling one can through careful examination of frames and monitoring of follow-up results put bounds on the biases that may result, whereas with quota sampling one can never be very sure of the extent of the deficiencies in coverage and the biases that ensue. Indeed, to be able to do so would probably eliminate whatever cost and time advantage there is in quota sampling.

Some of the principal sources of bias in this method are as follows:

a. *Differences in Respondent Availability.* Since no callbacks are employed, it is suspected that quota methods are biased against household occupants who are seldom at home. Although the controls discussed earlier are designed to correct this deficiency, the degree of success in that correction is unknown. Since, in principle, the problem can be corrected with a sufficient number of control strata, this problem is related to the following.

b. *Insufficient Control Strata.* With more control variables and quotas imposed on the interviewers, the sample can be brought into greater "alignment" with the target population, but the more detailed quotas would be more and more difficult to fill, and thus the relative speed advantage of quota sampling over full probability sampling would be lost. Furthermore, it is generally believed in the survey research community that interviewers can only handle a small number of quota controls without getting bogged down with tallying and becoming confused.

c. *Interviewer Selection Bias.* Except for instructions concerning age precedence, as in the description of the Gallup procedures above, the interviewers are given complete freedom of selection within the control strata that are specified. Thus it is possible that various biases, conscious and unconscious, are present in the determination of which doors to knock on, as well as which persons to interview. The choices could well be associated with respondent attitudes and characteristics.

d. *Incorrect Information on Stratum Sizes.* Within the fixed clusters that are assigned to each sampling point, the quotas are set in accordance with the

distribution of the control characteristics for the smallest immediately surrounding area—usually the tract, enumeration district, or minor civil division.
To the extent to which Census information is incorrect or outdated, biases can
result. Related to this problem is the fact that cluster sizes in quota sampling are
usually made equal in interviewer assignments, whereas if proper missed-
dwelling unit procedures are used in full probability sampling, the cluster sizes
will change according to growth or diminution in housing in the sampling
locations. Thus, quota sampling would not ordinarily reflect dramatic shifts in
the distribution of the population over the target area.

The effects of these and other possible biases are difficult to assess. It is not
clear that they are worse than some of the shortcomings that result from the
inability of survey organizations to carry out the principles of full probability
sampling to the letter, especially at a time when there is growing resistance to
interviewing, even when multiple callbacks and incentives are employed.

One problem that may occur in quota sampling is the faked interview. A
faked interview occurs when the interviewer, for whatever reasons, fills out or
completes a schedule instead of finding a respondent. It is essential to verify
that interviews do occur. The interviewers should know that validation will
occur and the validation process should be convincing to the interviewer.

3. EMPIRICAL COMPARISONS OF QUOTA AND FULL PROBABILITY SAMPLING

Immediately after the failure of the preelection pools to forecast the victory
of the incumbent President Harry S. Truman over Thomas E. Dewey in
November 1948, the Social Science Research Council appointed a committee of
statisticians and sociologists to study the technical procedures and methods of
interpretation that had been used. In the committee's report (Mosteller, Hyman,
McCarthy, Marks, and Truman, 1949), considerable attention is paid to the
method of selection of respondents used by the principal polling organizations—
almost uniformly quota sampling because of its time and cost advantages.
Although the full blame for the forecasting debacle is not attributed to
sampling—equally important was the failure of the pollsters to interpret the
undecided vote and to detect the shift in voter attitudes that occurred near the
end of the campaign period—it is observed that the quota methods tended to be
biased against the lower educational attainment classes and against isolated
rural dwellers. A particularly dramatic difference in results is shown in the table
(p. 95 of the report) describing two parallel samples, one by quota method and
one by a probability method, executed by the Washington State Public Opinion
Laboratory:

	Actual Washington State vote (%)	Probability sample (%)	Quota sample (%)
Dewey	42.7	46.0	52.0
Truman	52.6	50.5	45.3
Wallace	3.5	2.9	2.5

The table seems to show a clear superiority of the probability sample over the quota results, but the authors are careful not to generalize to all quota sampling because of contradictory results in other comparisons. Rather than recommending the cessation of quota sampling, the committee report calls for greater care in the design of the samples and in the training of interviewers. There is reason to believe that the committee report and the embarrassment of the general failure resulted in a general tightening up of procedures within the major polling organizations.

Stephan and McCarthy (1958) report the results of several experimental comparisons of the results of quota sampling and full probability methods, including the Washington State findings shown. In 1946, the National Opinion Research Center (NORC) fielded a quota sample with a set of questions that were almost identical to those asked in the area probability survey of the Monthly Report of the Labor Force by the Census Bureau. As reported by Stephan and McCarthy, the gross tabulations for the NORC survey and the Census survey were in close agreement. For finer comparisons it was difficult to separate the effects of sampling variability from the possible biases. In general, the quota results appear to be quite good, perhaps due to the relative complexity of the quota controls and the special care with which interviewers were instructed in preparation for the experiment. Other comparison studies reported by Stephan and McCarthy do not show such close agreement for the two methods. In tentative generalization, the authors suggest that the best results occur when rent quotas or small geographic area controls are used in place of less precise interviewer-determined classifications of socioeconomic status. In commenting on the carefully controlled experiments of Moser and Stuart (1953) in England, Stephan and McCarthy conclude their chapter on comparisons with this statement:

> ... the fundamental status of quota sampling, as far as evidence derived from direct comparisons is concerned, is left more or less as outlined. ... Instances of serious bias can be found; close agreement with check data or with probability sample results exists for many items; the sources of serious bias are frequently related to the socio-economic control; the actual allocation of bias among possible sources is extremely difficult; and it seems impossible to place quota sampling on a sound theoretical basis.

Sudman (1967) discusses the results of three NORC surveys dealing with attitudes toward matters concerning world tensions. The sequence consisted of a probability sample with callbacks in June 1963, followed by a quota sample in

December 1963, followed by another callback survey in June 1964. Comparisons were made for five questions that were asked exactly the same way each time. For these questions on world affairs the comparisons are ambiguous. As in some of the results reported by Stephan and McCarthy, it is impossible to identify discrepancies as due to sampling variation, true changes over time, or quota sampling biases. For the demographic variables, however, the callback and quota results are very close. The sex ratio for the quota sample is closer to the Census distribution, whereas the probability samples are deficient in males. However, the quota sample appears to be deficient in one- and two-member households, a not unexpected result. Sudman mentions in his closing sentence that NORC had plans to experiment with a control for household size in future surveys, but to this writer's knowledge, the experiments have never taken place.

Finally, in a recent experiment, NORC split the selected blocks in its General Social Survey for 1975 and 1976 into two subsamples and used full probability techniques with callbacks in half and quota methods of canvassing households in the other. Since the two methods were applied to persons living in the same localities at the same time, many of the possibly confounding variables for comparisons should have been controlled. Stephenson (1979) reports comparisons for a large number of demographic and attitudinal variables. He finds no important differences for the two methods except for the generally recognized bias against smaller households (which seems not to have much effect on other comparisons). He reports, however, a deficiency in employed males, which would indicate that the age control that is intended to correct this bias is not effective.

4. THEORETICAL METHODS FOR ESTIMATING BIAS

Two papers that have attempted to deal with the problem of estimating the bias in quota sampling and correcting for it within the same survey are those by Stinchcombe (1971) and King (1974). Stinchcombe's unpublished work proposes a resurvey of the sample blocks after quota methods have been applied. The resurvey would employ the same method of approach to the households as in the first pass. The purpose of the second and possibly subsequent passes over the sampling areas is to estimate the availability distribution of the target individuals—i.e., the sample picked up on the first pass consists of the most available, those on the second pass the next most available, etc. Assuming that variables of interest are correlated with availability and that the bias in estimation is a function of the association between the availability in quota sampling and the "true availability" that would be found in random selection, Stinchcombe proposes a method for estimation of that bias. The author admits to serious questions concerning the economic feasibility of the technique vis-à-vis full probability sampling with callbacks.

King, adapting a Bayesian model of biased measurement to the case of quota sampling versus full probability sampling, proposes a scheme in which the ultimate clusters in multistage sampling may be composed totally of quota observations, totally of observations involving callbacks, or some mixture of both types of measurement. He develops a formula for allocation of fixed resources between the two methods to minimize a quadratic loss function for the error in estimation of the mean of an unbiased measurement process—with the estimation of the bias in quota sampling a by-product of the procedure. For the cases studied, it appears that quota sampling is only economically desirable when the unbiased process is imprecise relative to the prior variance of the mean of that process and the prior correlation between the means of the unbiased and biased processes is very high. In plain language, one has to be fairly certain that the results between quota and full probability methods will be in agreement before quota sampling should be used.

5. SUMMARY

Because the estimation of biases and their control is difficult at best, it is unlikely that quota sampling will ever be theoretically justified as a method of avoiding the problem of missing data in sample surveys. It is, however, likely that quota sampling will continue to be used by reputable survey organizations as long as there is no prohibition against subjective assessment that the biases are small, and as long as there are no practical alternatives for fast surveys such as those required in preelection polling. The forecasting of voting behavior provides a unique opportunity for continual testing of the accuracy of the method, and when serious failures do occur (e.g., the debacle in forecasting the results of the British elections of 1970), it is usually found that the failure was due to some factor not immediately associated with quota methods—for example, shifts in voter attitudes at the last moment or unexpected bad weather.[1]

Care should be taken, however, to avoid the use of quota sampling if there is reason to believe that the variables of interest or the availability of the subjects

---

[1] One of the polls that preceded the 1970 general election, Marplan, was described in *The London Times* (July 21, 1970, p. 9) as using "recognized random sampling methods." It had the greatest prediction error of all of the polls. The most accurate forecast, predicting a close Conservative victory, was that of Opinion Research Centre, using quota methods. The British Gallup Poll also used quota methods, but it predicted a Labour lead of 7%.

The American Gallup Organization does not employ quota methods in its preelection polls, but rather, last-stage clusters of households are selected by systematic sampling with random starts. Since, however, callbacks are not used, only Politz–Simmons adjustments, the method cannot be called "probability sampling."

involved are associated with the demographic characteristics that will be represented disproportionately in quota sampling. Explicit modification of controls may correct the deficiencies, but if the target group is difficult to reach (e.g., young adults living alone) the additional controls may be economically no better than full screening with probability methods.

REFERENCES

Cochran, W. G. (1977). *Sampling Techniques.* New York: Wiley.

The Gallup Organization, Inc. (1972). The Design of the Sample for *Trends*, the Personal Interview Omnibus Survey. Princeton, N.J.

King, B. F. (1974). Surveys combining probability and quota methods of sampling. *Proceedings of the Social Statistics Section of the American Statistical Association.*

Moser, C. A., and Stuart, A. (1953). An experimental study of quota sampling. *Journal of the Royal Statistical Society* A116: 349–394.

Mosteller, F., Hyman, H., McCarthy, P., Marks, E. S., and Truman, D. B. (1949). *The Pre-Election Polls of 1948*, Bulletin 60. New York: Social Science Research Council.

National Opinion Research Center (1978). *General Social Surveys, 1972–1978: Cumulative Codebook*. Chicago: National Opinion Research Center.

Stephan, F. F., and McCarthy, P. J. (1958). *Sampling Opinions.* New York: Wiley.

Stephenson, C. B. (1979). Probability sampling with quotas: An experiment. *The Public Opinion Quarterly* 43(4): 477–496.

Stinchcombe, A. (1971). The Computation of Bias in Quota Samples. Unpublished.

Sudman, S. (1967). *Reducing the Cost of Surveys.* Chicago: Aldine.

CHAPTER 7

Randomized Response Techniques

Lawrence Emrich

The randomized response technique, first proposed by Warner (1965), was developed to obtain more reliable information concerning sensitive issues on sample surveys. It was hypothesized that greater respondent cooperation would be elicited through the use of a device which selects, by chance, one of two statements to which the respondent is to reply truthfully, without revealing this selection to the interviewer. The two statements are of the following forms: (1) I am a member of group A, and (2) I am not a member of group A. The respondent is instructed to answer "yes" or "no" to the statement selected by the randomizing device. Because the interviewer is unaware of the statement to which the respondent is replying, embarrassment and/or possible legal implications (as might arise in surveys concerning illegal activities such as drug abuse or child abuse) are avoided.

The randomizing device may be, for example, a box containing known proportions of white and black balls. The respondent would be instructed to select a ball at random, without allowing the interviewer to see which color was chosen; and to answer question (1) if a white ball was chosen and question (2) if a black ball was chosen. In this way, confidentiality is maintained.

More generally, let λ be the population proportion of yes answers, π be the true proportion of the population in (sensitive) group A, P be the (known) probability that the randomizing device chooses the sensitive question. Then

$$\lambda = P\pi + (1 - P)(1 - \pi).$$

From this relation, an unbiased estimate of π may be made (Warner, 1965).

Numerous modifications of Warner's original technique have been proposed. Horvitz, Shah, and Simmons (1967) suggested that respondents select

INCOMPLETE DATA
IN SAMPLE SURVEYS
Volume 2, Part II

one of two *unrelated* (rather than related) questions. In this case,

$$\lambda = P\pi_A + (1 - P)\pi_B,$$

where λ and P are defined as before, π_A is the true proportion of the population with (sensitive) attribute A, and π_B is the true proportion of the population with (nonsensitive) attribute B. If π_B is not known, two independent samples would be needed to estimate π_A and π_B, the population proportions in the two noncomplementary groups.

Folsom, Greenberg, Horvitz, and Abernathy (1973) modified this two sample technique further by using two nonsensitive questions. In the first sample, nonsensitive question (1) is asked directly while nonsensitive question (2) is used in the randomizing device while in the second sample, nonsensitive question (2) is asked directly and nonsensitive question (1) is used in the randomizing device.

Abul-Ela, Greenberg, and Horvitz (1967) also utilized more than one sample in a technique developed to obtain information on more than one sensitive issue at a time. It was shown that the technique could be used to estimate t population proportions, where at least 1 and not more than $t - 1$ of them involve sensitive topics.

A modification proposed by Greenberg, Abul-Ela, Simmons, and Horvitz (1969) avoided the nonsensitive question altogether. They suggested a randomizing device consisting of a box with known proportions of red, white, and blue marbles. The respondent would be asked to select a marble and to respond as follows: If a white marble is chosen, answer the (sensitive) question. If a blue marble is chosen, say "yes." If a red marble is chosen, say "no."

Further modifications and some technical investigations of the properties of the randomized response techniques may be found in Eriksson (1973) and Swensson (1976, 1977).

As with Warner's original technique, all of the above modifications were proposed with the intention of increasing the response rate while decreasing the response bias (due to untruthful answers) by preserving the confidentiality of the respondent when dealing with sensitive issues. As noted by Wiseman, Moriarty, and Schafer (1975–1976), socially undesirable responses are more likely to appear in a (confidential) mail questionnaire than in a personal interview survey. However, in many situations personal interviews are necessary because of the nature of the survey. The randomized response technique is highly suited for this situation.

The disadvantages of the technique are the increased cost of training interviewers in the technicalities of the technique and the increased time of the interview required to explain the technique to the respondent. The latter defect may cause a higher rate of refusals than would have occurred had the question been asked directly. Other disadvantages of the technique are noted by Berman, McCombs, and Boruch (1977) in a report on a study in which 72% of the respondents felt, to some degree, that the technique made telling the truth less important since random errors are already a part of the procedure. Further, the

TABLE 1

Highly Personal	Low Threat ←	Library card and voting behavior	Bankruptcy	Drunken driving	→ High Threat Total sample
	Face to face	100	50	50	200
	Random response	100	50	50	200
	Telephone	100	50	50	200
	Self-administered questionnaire	100	50	50	200
Impersonal					

authors hypothesized that the very use of the method suggests to the respondent that the subject matter of the question is highly personal even though the respondent might not have felt so had he been asked the question directly. The authors commented that in either case, response error would likely increase, nullifying the positive aspects of the technique.

Since a decrease in nonresponse is one of the major hypothesized advantages of the randomized response techniques, several studies have been carried out to determine the effect of the method, as compared to other methods, on the response rate.

Locander, Sudman, and Bradburn (1976), in a study carried out in Chicago, compared four interview techniques: face to face interview, telephone interview, self-administered questionnaire, and an unrelated question randomized response technique. Further, different "threatening" topics were considered concerning the ownership of a Chicago Public Library card, voter registration and voting behavior, involvement in bankruptcy, and being charged with drunken driving. Table 1 shows the study design. It was planned that there would be approximately 50 respondents per cell giving a total sample size of 800.

The four topics were chosen because, a priori, the authors felt that the level of "threat" would increase as one goes from a question on having a library card to one concerning being charged with drunken driving; and because results could be validated using public records.[1] Hence, the effect of the randomized response technique on both the response rate and on the response error could be determined.

In Table 2, the percentage of respondents and total sample size are given for each method of interview and each question (e.g., bankrupt or not). Unfortunately, the results are inconclusive. The telephone survey seemed more successful

---

[1] The authors note that the respondents in the face-to-face bankruptcy cell had all declared bankruptcy in the recent past. The respondents in the drunken-driving cells had all been recently charged with drunken driving. The respondents in the library card and voting behavior cells were drawn from a random sample and validated from Chicago Public Library and city voting records. (This was done after the questionnaire was administered.)

TABLE 2

Percentage of Completed Interviews by Method of Administration and Sample

	Sample			
Method	Library card and voting behavior	Bankruptcy	Drunken driving	Total
Personal	76.0	70.3	57.1	67.8
interview	$n = 125$	$n = 54$	$n = 63$	$n = 242$
Telephone	89.9	68.3	77.8	76.6
	$n = 109$	$n = 60$	$n = 63$	$n = 232$
Self-administered	75.4	59.3	47.5	60.7
questionnaire	$n = 114$	$n = 59$	$n = 61$	$n = 234$
Randomized	77.6	67.2	58.1	67.6
response	$n = 116$	$n = 55$	$n = 62$	$n = 233$
Total	79.7	66.2	60.1	
	$n = 464$	$n = 228$	$n = 249$	

than a personal interview or the randomized response technique, the latter two methods having similar results.

The results were just as inconclusive when the effect on response bias was considered. By validating the results using public records, an index of distortion of results was defined. The results shown in Table 3 represent the proportion of respondents in each cell who gave distorted answers.

One way of looking at the table, as suggested by the authors, is to note that response errors may be due either to overreporting a socially desirable act (owning a library card, being registered to vote, or voting in the primaries) or underreporting a socially undesirable act (bankruptcy or drunken driving). The authors conclude that the random response procedures are least effective in

TABLE 3

Proportion of Distorted Responses

	Threat				
Method	Voter registration	Library card	Bankruptcy	Vote in primary	Drunken driving
Personal interview	.15	.19	.32	.39	.47
	$n = 92$	$n = 93$	$n = 38$	$n = 80$	$n = 30$
Telephone	.17	.21	.29	.31	.46
	$n = 89$	$n = 97$	$n = 41$	$n = 77$	$n = 46$
Self-administered	.12	.18	.32	.36	.54
questionnaire	$n = 80$	$n = 82$	$n = 31$	$n = 74$	$n = 28$
Randomized	.11	.26	.00	.48	.35
response	$n = 61$	$n = 61$	$n = 26$	$n = 50$	$n = 23$

reducing overreporting of socially desirable acts and most effective in reducing underreporting of socially undesirable acts. However, this is only one interpretation of the results and the authors conclude that, from the findings, no method is superior to all other methods for all types of "threatening" questions.

Chi, Chow, and Rider (1972) investigated the incidence of induced abortion in Taiwan. A total of 2497 currently married women between 15 and 49 years of age were selected by a stratified probability sample in a county of Taiwan with approximately 100,000 eligible women. The usual face-to-face interview technique was used for 1246 of the women, while the remainder were interviewed using the randomized response technique with an unrelated question and known population proportion. Again, the results of this study are inconclusive: 88.89% of the interviews using the randomized response technique were completed, while 88.71% of the women in the complementary group completed the interview.

Goodstadt and Gruson (1975) employed the unrelated question technique (with unknown population proportion for the nonsensitive topic) in a survey concerning drug use among high school students. Upon examining the completion rates for the questions concerning drug use, the authors found a significantly greater probability for those in the randomized response group to satisfactorily complete the drug use question of interest: 13.3% of 421 students failed to complete the critical drug use question when asked directly, while 5.5% of 431 students in the randomized response group failed to complete the question. This overall difference in completion rates was significant at the .001 level. Further, in five of the six drug categories considered, the estimate of the frequency of drug use was higher in the randomized response group than in the direct questioning group. This seems to indicate not only an increase in response rate, but also a decrease in response bias.

Brown and Harding (1973) also employed the unrelated question technique with unknown population proportion in a study concerned with the nontherapeutic use of drugs in the military. The study, which included approximately 700 enlisted men and 320 junior officers, distributed among four major Army posts, compared the randomized response technique to an anonymously administered 62-item questionnaire.

In four of the five drug categories considered, the estimates of drug use among enlisted men were approximately the same for the questionnaire and the randomized response groups. The exception was the estimates of the use of barbituates, where the randomized response technique yielded a significantly higher estimate than the questionnaire (17% versus 10%).

The estimates of drug use among the officers, however, were consistently higher in the randomized response group. The results may indicate, at least for the officer data, the superiority of the randomized response technique.

In a study of illicit drug use in the Army, Brown (1975) compared a mail-back version of the randomized response technique with a conventional mail questionnaire. The randomized response questionnaire consisted of two sets of questions: Set A consisted of five nonsensitive questions, while set B contained five drug questions. The nonsensitive questions pertained to characteristics possessed by known proportions of the target subjects. The randomizing device was based on census data which indicate that almost exactly 8% of all births each year take place in November. The respondents were directed to answer the sensitive question if their mother was not born in November. Hence, a known percentage (92%) of the respondents answered the sensitive questions.

The results of the study indicate a superiority of the conventional questionnaire. The return rate was significantly higher for the conventional questionnaire (48%) than for the randomized response questionnaire (31%), while reported drug use rates were not significantly related to the method used.

Krótki and Fox (1974) studied a stratified cluster sample of 1045 Edmonton (Canada) women between 18 and 54 years of age in a comprehensive fertility study. The sample was divided into three subsamples. The first involved asking the respondent all fertility questions directly, including questions on abortion. In the second sample, respondents were asked the sensitive questions using the randomized response technique. The third group was given anonymous mail-back questionnaires.

There were seven "sensitive" topics in the questionnaire. The unrelated question technique was used for the randomized response group; the population proportions of the incidences of the unrelated questions being estimated by either census data or data obtained in the study itself.

The results show that the randomized response technique definitely increased response rates over the anonymous questionnaire, the former having a 95% completion rate, while the latter had a 73% completion rate. Unfortunately, the rate for the direct inquiry method was not given.

The importance of the randomized response technique in increasing response rates, however, may be questioned since a high percentage (68%) of the totality of the respondents, when asked, said that their friends would have answered a direct question on abortion.

Zdep and Rhodes (1976) utilized the randomized response technique of Folsom, Greenberg, Horvitz, and Abernathy (1973) involving two samples and two nonsensitive questions in a national probability sample of 2000 adults aged 18 and older concerning child abuse. They compared the results of this survey with another national probability sample conducted 8 weeks later. This later survey consisted of a split sample in which half of the respondents marked their answers on a form given to them by an interviewer, sealed it in an envelope, and then returned it to the interviewer, while the other half responded in a similar manner, but returned the envelope by mail to Opinion Research Corporation's headquarters.

The results of the two surveys are summarized in Table 4. Clearly, the randomized response technique (RRT) greatly improved the response rate as compared with either of the self-administered techniques.

The estimates of the percentage of child abusers which resulted from the three techniques also strongly favored the randomized response procedure

TABLE 4

Percentage of Usable Responses

Method	Refusals	Nonreturners	Percentage usable
RRT			
Sample 1	9	—	98
Sample 2	4	—	99
Self-administered and returned to interviewer	65	—	88
Self-administered and mailed back	—	117	75

(see Table 5). As the authors point out, for each of the self-administered surveys the estimates do not differ significantly from zero. This indicates that the subject matter was highly sensitive.

As may be seen from the above studies, the randomized response technique has varying amounts of effect on the response rate in sample surveys. It would appear that it is most effective when utilized in surveys in which the subject matter is highly sensitive and least effective when the subject matter is only slightly sensitive or socially desirable.

Other explanations of why the technique failed to increase the response rate in certain situations have also been proposed. These include the inability of the respondent to understand the technique, and the lack of trust in the confidentiality of the results. Folsom (1974) reports on a study concerned with drunken driving, the results of which seem to support this latter explanation. These drawbacks may possibly be overcome by better interviewer training.

TABLE 5

Method	Estimated percentage of abusers
RRT	15
Self-administered and returned to interviewer	3
Self-administered and mailed back	4

REFERENCES

Abul-Ela, Abdel-Latif A., Greenberg, Bernard G., and Horvitz, Daniel G. (1967). A multi-proportions randomized response model. *Journal of the American Statistical Association* 62 : 990–1008.

Berman, John, McCombs, Harriet, and Boruch, Robert (1977). Notes on the contamination method. Two small experiments in assuring confidentiality of responses. *Sociological Methods Research* 6: 45–62.

Brown, George H. (1975). Randomized Inquiry vs. Conventional Questionnaire Method in Estimating Drug Usage Rates through Mail Surveys. Human Resources Research Organization, Technical Report 75–14.

Brown, George H., and Harding, Francis D. (1973). A Comparison of Methods of Studying Illicit Drug Usage. Human Resources Research Organization, Technical Report 73–9.

Chi, I. C., Chow, L. P., and Rider, Rowland V. (1972). The randomized response technique as used in the Taiwan outcome of pregnancy study. *Studies in Family Planning* 3: 265–269.

Eriksson, Sven (1973). Randomized Interviews for Sensitive Questions. Ph.D. dissertation. University Institute of Statistics, Gothenburg, Sweden.

Folsom, Ralph E. (1974). A Randomized Response Validation Study: Comparison of Direct and Randomized Reporting of DWI Arrests. Research Center for Measurement Methods, Bureau of the Census.

Folsom, Ralph E., Greenberg, Bernard G., Horvitz, Daniel G., and Abernathy, James R. (1973). The two alternate questions randomized response model for human surveys. *Journal of the American Statistical Association* 68: 525–530.

Goodstadt, Michael S., and Gruson, Valerie (1975). The randomized response technique: A test on drug use. *Journal of the American Statistical Association* 70: 814–818.

Greenberg, Bernard G., Abul-Ela, Abdel-Latif A., Simmons, Walt R., and Horvitz, Daniel G. (1969). The unrelated question randomized response model theoretical framework. *Journal of the American Statistical Association* 64: 520–539.

Horvitz, D. G., Shah, B. V., and Simmons, Walt R. (1967). The unrelated question randomized response model. *Proceedings of the American Statistical Association, Social Statistics Section,* pp. 65–72.

Krótki, Karol J., and Fox, Bonnie (1974). The randomized response technique, the interview, and the self-administered questionnaire: An empirical comparison of fertility reports. *Proceedings of the American Statistical Association, Social Statistics Section,* pp. 367–371.

Locander, William, Sudman, Seymour, and Bradburn, Norman (1976). An investigation of interview method, threat and response distortion. *Proceedings of the American Statistical Association, Social Statistics Section,* pp. 21–27.

Swensson, Bengt (1976). Combined Independent Questions versus Randomized Response. Efficiencies under Equal Degree of Protection. Department of Statistics, University of Stockholm, Report No. 15.

Swensson, Bengt (1977). Survey measurement of sensitive attributes. Some contributions. Ph.D. dissertation. Department of Statistics, University of Stockholm.

Warner, Stanley L. (1965). Randomized response: A survey technique for eliminating evasive answer bias. *Journal of the American Statistical Association* 60: 63–69.

Wiseman, Frederick, Moriarty, Mark, and Schafer, Marianne (1975–1976). Estimating public opinion with the randomized response model. *Public Opinion Quarterly* 39: 507–513.

Zdep, S. M., and Rhodes, Isabelle N. (1976). Making the randomized response technique work. *Public Opinion Quarterly* 40: 531–537.

CHAPTER 8

Handling Missing Data
by Network Sampling

Monroe G. Sirken

1. INTRODUCTION

Network sampling offers design options that are not available in surveys based on traditional sampling. Sometimes these options can substantially improve the conduct of surveys for which traditional sampling is inefficient. In this report, we discuss network sampling as a strategy for handling missing data due to undercoverage and response errors in surveys based on traditional sampling.

Network sampling seeks to make household survey designs more efficient by utilizing information that individuals not necessarily residing in the same households are able to report about one another by virtue of their relations. In other words, individuals linked to one another by specified relations are made eligible to serve as informants for one another in the survey. The individual is linked to a group of related persons that are eligible to report him, and he belongs to each group of related persons, possibly including himself, that he is eligible to report. The grouping of related persons that he is eligible to report is called a cluster, and the grouping of related persons eligible to report him is called a network. A person's network and cluster may or may not contain the same individuals.

The essential differences between network sampling and traditional sampling are the network and cluster sizes. In traditional sampling, the size of the network and of the cluster is equal to one, as it would be, for instance, in household surveys based on de jure residence rules. In network sampling, on the other

INCOMPLETE DATA
IN SAMPLE SURVEYS
Volume 2, Part II

hand, the network and cluster sizes are not necessarily equal to one and they may vary in size from person to person.

Surveys based on network sampling have three versatile design features:

(1) Counting rules that define relationships making individuals eligible to serve as informants for one another in the survey

(2) Estimators that permit variation in network and cluster sizes

(3) Counting rule weights that adjust for variations in network sizes

Like most sample design options, network sampling is more advantageous under some conditions than others. It has potential advantages in the following circumstances or combinations of circumstances which typically present difficult, if not insurmountable, survey design problems for traditional sampling:

(a) Estimates are needed for small population domains (Nathan, Schmelz, and Kenvin, 1977; Sirken, 1970).

(b) Individuals have multiple links with enumeration units (Sirken, 1975).

(c) Individuals are reluctant (Fishburne and Cisin, 1980) or unable (Sirken, Royston, and Bridges, 1977) to provide information about themselves.

(d) The sampling frame is incomplete (Sirken, Giraubard, and LaValley, 1978b).

Design problem (a) implies large sampling errors and the other listed problems imply large nonsampling biases for traditional sampling. Problem (b) results in erroneously counting individuals more than once, and problems (c) and (d) result in some individuals not being counted at all. This paper focuses on missing data problems when the survey fails to enumerate individuals due to problems (c) and (d). The design effects of network sampling are discussed when these problems are present in sample surveys of rare populations.

In traditionally based sample surveys, individuals are uniquely linked to their respective de jure residences where they are eligible to be enumerated. Therefore, individuals that do not reside at households covered by the sampling frame are ineligible to be enumerated, and individuals that, for one reason or another, are not reported by their own households would also be missed. The strategy of network sampling is to adopt counting rules with the property of linking individuals to households that are covered by the frame, and that contain willing and able informants.

Network sampling handles the individuals that traditional sampling misses due to incomplete frames by adopting counting rules that link the missed individuals to households that are covered by the frame. For instance, individuals without fixed addresses, residing in missed households, or living in institutions would be missed by traditional sampling. In network sampling, the strategy is to link these individuals to knowledgeable informants, such as their relatives or friends, that reside in households that are covered by the frame.

Individuals that are missed by traditional sampling because their own households are unwilling or unable to report them are linked by network sampling to other households that would be more likely to report them. For instance, questions on illicit drug use by friends appear to be less threatening and hence less subject to underreporting than questions on self-use of drugs (Fishburne and Cisin, 1980). Hence, network sampling handles this problem by a counting rule that links heroin users to the households of their close friends. Questions about deceased persons offer another illustration. Households containing surviving relatives appear to be more knowledgeable informants for decedents than the decedent's former residences. Why this is so will be explained later.

The network estimator, its sampling variance, and the cost function of the survey based on network sampling are derived in Sections 2, 3, and 4 respectively. The sampling error effects of network sampling are discussed in Section 3 and the nonsampling error effects are discussed in Section 5.

2. THE NETWORK ESTIMATOR

Let $\Omega_I = \{I_1, \ldots, I_\alpha, \ldots, I_N\}$ represent a population of N individuals with a specified trait. Counting rule r is adopted for linking the I_α $(\alpha = 1, \ldots, N)$ individuals to households covered by the sampling frame, where they would be enumerable. Let G_{ij} denote the jth $(j = 1, \ldots, T_i)$ person that resides at the H_ith $(i = 1, \ldots, M)$ household listed in the sampling frame. The $T = \sum_{i=1}^{M} T_i$ persons covered by the frame are denoted Ω_F. The links between the I_α in Ω_I and the G_{ij} in Ω_F that are eligible to report them by rule r are specified by the indicator variable

$$_r\delta_{\alpha ij} = \begin{cases} 1 & \text{if } G_{ij} (i = 1, \ldots, M; j = 1, \ldots, T_i) \text{ is eligible} \\ & \text{to report } I_\alpha (\alpha = 1, \ldots, N) \text{ by rule } r \\ 0 & \text{otherwise.} \end{cases}$$

The number of persons in H_i $(i = 1, \ldots, M)$ eligible to report I_α $(\alpha = 1, \ldots, N)$ by rule r is $_rs_{\alpha i} = \sum_{j=1}^{T_i} {}_r\delta_{\alpha ij}$, and the number of persons in Ω_F eligible to report I_α by rule r is $_rs_\alpha = \sum_{i=1}^{M} {}_rs_{\alpha i}$. Denote by $_rN_{\bar{F}}$ the subset of the I_α in Ω_I for which $_rs_\alpha = 0$. These persons are not linked to in-scope households by rule r and hence would not be enumerated. Let $_rN_F = N - {}_rN_{\bar{F}}$.

A simple random sample of m out of M households is selected with replacements; $I_\alpha (\alpha = 1, \ldots, N)$ individuals eligible to be reported by the sample households are enumerated in the survey. The multiplicity estimator, one of several network estimators that have been proposed (Birnbaum and Sirken, 1965) to estimate N, is

$$\hat{N}_r = \frac{M}{m} \sum_{i=1}^{M} a_i({}_r\lambda_i), \tag{1}$$

where the Bernoulli variable

$$a_i = \begin{cases} 1 & \text{if } H_i \ (i = 1, \ldots, M) \text{ is sampled} \\ 0 & \text{otherwise,} \end{cases}$$

and the variate

$$_r\lambda_i = \sum_{\alpha=1}^{N} \sum_{j=1}^{T_i} {_r\delta_{\alpha ij}} w_{\alpha ij} \tag{2}$$

is the weighted sum of the $I_\alpha \ (\alpha = 1, \ldots, N)$ that are eligible to be reported by $H_i \ (i = 1, \ldots, M)$.

The multiplicity estimator is unbiased if the counting rule weights, the $w_{\alpha ij} \ (\alpha = 1, \ldots, N; i = 1, \ldots, M; j = 1, \ldots, T_i)$, satisfy the following conditions

$$\sum_{i=1}^{M} \sum_{j=1}^{T_i} {_r\delta_\alpha} w_{\alpha ij} = 1 \qquad (\alpha = 1, \ldots, N), \tag{3}$$

and the multiplicities, the s_α, satisfy the conditions

$$_r s_\alpha > 0 \qquad (\alpha = 1, \ldots, N). \tag{4}$$

Several kinds of counting rule weights that satisfy the conditions in (3) have been proposed (Sirken, 1972; Sirken and Royston, 1976). Each kind requires a somewhat different type of information about the networks. For instance, a weight that depends only on the number of persons eligible to report $I_\alpha \ (\alpha = 1, \ldots, N)$ is

$$w_{\alpha ij} = w_\alpha = 1/_r s_\alpha. \tag{5}$$

It is noteworthy that the multiplicity estimator in (1) requires the weights only for the reports of the I_α made by sample households. Hence, it is often feasible to collect the information needed to determine these weights from the sample households where the individuals are enumerated in the survey. Consequently, it is essential to evaluate the ability of the informants to provide this information for the individuals they are linked to by the counting rules. In the analysis that follows, it is assumed that the informants are error-free. In practice, however, this assumption may not be completely satisfied (Marks and Ockay, 1978).

3. SAMPLING VARIANCE

The sampling variance of $\hat{N}_r$ is

$$V(\hat{N}_r) = (M/m)V(\lambda_r), \tag{6}$$

where

$$V(\lambda_r) = \frac{1}{M} \sum_{i=1}^{M} ({}_r\lambda_i - \bar{\lambda}_r)^2.$$

To illustrate the design effect of network sampling on sampling errors, we make the following simplifying assumptions:

(a) Simple random sampling of households with replacement.
(b) $w_{\alpha i j} = 1/{}_r s_\alpha$ and ${}_r s_\alpha > 0$ ($\alpha = 1, \ldots, N$).
(c) $\sum_{\alpha=1}^{N} \sum_{j=1}^{T_i} {}_r \delta_{\alpha i j} \le 1$ ($i = 1, \ldots, M$).

Although SRS is not a realistic design for most population surveys, it is assumed here strictly as a matter of convenience. Assumption (c) implies that no more than one individual will be enumerable at a household, and that no individual will be enumerable more than once at a household. This strong assumption is most likely to be satisfied if $P = N/M$ is a small fraction. Under these assumptions,

$$V(\lambda_r) = P(K_r - P) = P(1 - P) - P(1 - K_r), \tag{7}$$

where

$$K_r = \frac{1}{N} \sum_{\alpha=1}^{N} 1/{}_r s_\alpha.$$

Since K_r is the inverse of the harmonic means of the s_α it follows that $1/\bar{s}_r \le K_r \le 1$, where $\bar{s}_r = (1/N) \sum_{\alpha=1}^{N} {}_r s_\alpha$. The second term on the right side of (7) represents the reduction in sampling variance due to network sampling since

TABLE 1

Estimates of K for Selected Family Networks by Age of the Person

Relationships included in the network	Age of person				
	All ages	Under 17	17–44	45–64	65+
Person and his children	.67	1.00	.62	.41	.49
Person and his siblings	.39	.44	.35	.37	.47
Person and his parents	.52	.34	.42	.76	.98
Person, his children and siblings	.30	.44	.26	.21	.28
Person, his parents and siblings	.26	.22	.21	.31	.46
Person, his children and parents	.34	.34	.29	.34	.48
Person, his children, siblings, and parents	.20	.22	.17	.18	.27

$K_r = 1$ for traditional sampling. Under the specified assumptions, the sampling error effect is never unfavorable because $K_r \leq 1$ for network sampling.

Estimates of K_r based on selected family counting rules are presented in Table 1 for age groupings of the population. These estimates, based on a national household sample survey (Royston, Sirken, and Bergsten, 1978), are presented to illustrate how K_r varies by type of counting rule and age of the person. In general, they should be used cautiously to determine the design effect of network sampling in Eq. (7) since assumption (c) may not apply.

4. EXPECTED COSTS

The expected field cost of a network survey based on sample size m and counting rule r is

$$C_r = mc_r,$$

where the unit cost

$$c_r = c_1 + \bar{R}_r(c_2 + \bar{s}_r c_3) \tag{8}$$

and

$\bar{R}_r = P\bar{s}_r =$ expected number of reports per household by rule r
$c_1 =$ cost of contacting a household
$c_2 =$ cost of enumerating a person
$c_3 = {}_r c_3 / \bar{s}_r$, where ${}_r c_3 =$ cost of determining the counting rule weight of an enumerated person by rule r.

Since $\bar{s}_r = 1$ and $c_3 = 0$ in surveys based on traditional sampling, the unit cost for traditional sampling is $c_t = c_1 + Pc_2$. Consequently, the unit cost is less for traditional than for network sampling. Nevertheless, network sampling may be more efficient than traditional sampling. Assume Eq. (8) for the cost function and Eq. (7) for the variance; then network sampling is more efficient than traditional sampling when the following inequality is satisfied:

$$K_r < 1 - (1 - P)(1 - \theta),$$

where $\theta = c_t/c_r$ ratio of the unit costs for traditional and network this sampling. If P/θ is small, this implies that network sampling enhances efficiency when $K_r < \theta$.

5. DESIGN EFFECTS OF NETWORK SAMPLING ON DATA COMPLETENESS

In this section we discuss two sources of underenumeration in household surveys:

(1) Undercoverage: Individuals are missed because they are ineligible to be enumerated at any in-scope households.

(2) Underreporting: Individuals are missed because they are not enumerated at households that are eligible to report them.

Although survey estimates are subject to these biases whether they are based on traditional sampling or on network sampling, sometimes the biases are appreciably less when based on network sampling.

Whether or not the I_α in Ω_I are reported by their eligible G_{ij} in Ω_F is viewed as a random process. Let

$$
{}_r\delta'_{\alpha ij} = \begin{cases} 1 & \text{if } {}_r\delta_{\alpha ij} = 1, \text{ and } I_\alpha \, (\alpha = 1, \ldots, N_F) \text{ is enumerated} \\ & \text{at } G_{ij} \, (j = 1, \ldots, T_i); \, i = 1, \ldots, M) \text{ by rule } r \\ 0 & \text{otherwise.} \end{cases}
$$

The multiplicity estimate of N in (1) may be written

$$
\hat{N}'_r = \sum_{\alpha=1}^{N} \sum_{i=1}^{M} \sum_{j=1}^{T_i} \delta'_{\alpha ij} w_{\alpha ij}, \tag{9}
$$

and its relative bias is

$$
\frac{1}{N} B(\hat{N}'_r) = \frac{1}{N} E(\hat{N}'_r) - 1 = -\left[(1 - g_r) + g_r(1 - h_r) \right], \tag{10}
$$

where $g_r = {}_r N_F/N = $ the fraction of the I_α in Ω_I that are linked to the G_{ij} in Ω_F by rule r and $h_r = E(\hat{N}'_r)/{}_r N_F = $ the expected fraction of the I_α linked to G_{ij} in Ω_F by rule r that are reported in the survey.

Recently, experiments were conducted in North Carolina to investigate the design effect of network sampling in single retrospective mortality surveys (Sirken and Royston, 1976). In surveys of this type, Ω_I represents the population of N persons that died during a calendar period preceding the survey, and Ω_F represents the T persons residing in the M households covered by the sampling frame when the survey is conducted. The findings that will be presented in this paper are based on a 12-month retrospective period. The survey adopts a counting rule that links the N deaths in Ω_I to the T persons in Ω_F that are eligible to report them. The survey experiments tested, among others, the three counting rules defined in Table 2. Traditional sampling is based on rule r_1, and rules r_2 and r_3 imply network sampling.

TABLE 2

Counting Rules Tested In The North Carolina Mortality Study

Counting rule	Definition
r_1	I_α ($\alpha = 1, \ldots, N$) is eligible to be enumerated at the household that was his former place of residence.
r_2	I_α ($\alpha = 1, \ldots, N$) is eligible to be enumerated at the households of his surviving spouse, siblings, and children residing in the county in which I_α formerly resided.
r_3	I_α ($\alpha = 1, \ldots, N$) is eligible to be enumerated at his former place of residence, and at the households of his surviving spouse, siblings, and children residing in the country where I_α formerly lived.

The effect of the three counting rules on the rates of undercoverage and underreporting of decedents in the age group 65–84 years is shown in Table 3. The combined error rate is less for each of the two network sampling options r_2 and r_3 than for traditional sampling r_1. About 15% of the deaths were missed by r_3, 22% by r_2, and 29% by r_1. Thus, r_3 represents the preferred counting rule. Virtually all of the difference between the counting rules is accounted for by the difference in the coverage rates, since the underreporting rates were about the same for the three rules.

All the noninstitutional deaths but none of the institutional deaths were eligible to be enumerated by r_1. Institutional deaths represented about 22% of all decedents in the age range 65–84 years. On the other hand, nearly two-thirds of the institutional deaths in this age group were survived by either a spouse, sibling, or child who, at the date of the survey, resided in the county in which the decedent formerly resided. Consequently, they were eligible to be enumerated by r_2 and r_3. The institutional deaths that were not survived by non-institutionalized relatives residing in the decedent's county were the only deaths

TABLE 3

Effect of Counting Rules[a] on Undercoverage and Underreporting of Decedents in Mortality Surveys: Decedents, 65–84 Years of Age

Counting rule	Proportion of deaths missed in the survey		
	Total: $(1 - g_r) + g_r(1 - h_r)$	Undercoverage: $(1 - g_r)$	Underreporting: $g_r(1 - h_r)$
r_1	.29	.22	.07
r_2	.22	.16	.06
r_3	.15	.08	.07

[a] See Table 2 for definitions of counting rules.

that were ineligible to be enumerated by r_3. They represented about 8% of all deaths. In addition r_2 failed to cover about 10% of the noninstitutional deaths that did not have surviving relatives in the decedent's county. It is noteworthy that the undercoverage by r_2 and r_3 was negligible when decedents in North Carolina were linked to their spouses, children, and siblings that resided anywhere in the United States.

About 7% of the deaths were not reported by households that were eligible to report them. The percentage was slightly higher for institutional deaths than for noninstitutional deaths. Whether the eligible household was the decedent's former place of residence or a household representing the residence of a surviving relative in the same county did not seem to affect the level of underreporting. However, about 70% of the descedents' former residences were occupied by surviving relatives and 30% were not. Only one death in 38 was not reported by a decedent's former residence that was occupied by surviving relatives. On the other hand, 4 deaths in 17 were not reported by decedents' former residences that were not occupied by surviving relatives. We suspect that percentage of underreporting by decedents based on traditional sampling, that is, based on r_1, would be substantially higher in other parts of the country than it was in North Carolina because smaller fractions of the decedents' former residences would be occupied by surviving relatives and smaller fractions of the decedents' former residences that were not occupied by their relatives would report the decedents in the survey.

REFERENCES

Birnbaum, Z. W., and Sirken, Monroe G. (1965). Design of sample surveys to estimate the prevalence of rare diseases: three unbiased estimates. *Vital and Health Statistics Series*, Series 2, No. 11, pp. 1–8.

Fishburne, P. M., and Cisin, Ira (1980). National survey on drug abuse: main findings: 1979. National Institute of Drug Abuse, p. 108.

Marks, Eli, and Ockay, Cathey (1978). A model for network (multiplicity): estimation of census undercoverage. *American Statistical Association, Proceedings of the Survey Methods Section*.

Nathan, Gad, Schmelz, Usiel, and Kenvin, Jay (1977). Multiplicity study of marriages and births in Israel. *Vital and Health Statistics Series*, Series 2, No. 70, pp. 1–64.

Royston, Patricia N., Sirken, Monroe G., and Bergsten, Jane (1978). Bias and sampling errors of mortality counts based on network surveys. *American Statistical Association Proceedings of the Social Statistics Section*.

Sirken, Monroe G. (1970). Survey strategies for estimating rare health attributes. *Proceedings of the Sixth Berkeley Symposium on Mathematical Statistics and Probability*, pp. 135–144.

Sirken, Monroe G. (1972). Variance components of multiplicity estimators. *Biometrics* 28(3): 869–873.

Sirken, Monroe G. (1975). Discussion of medical provider surveys of neurological conditions. *American Statistical Association Proceedings of the Social Statistics Section*, pp. 55–58.

Sirken, Monroe G., Graubard, Barry I., and McDaniel, Miriam J. (1978a). National network surveys of diabetes. *American Statistical Association Proceedings of the Social Statistics Section*.

Sirken, Monroe G., Graubard, Barry I., and LaValley, Richard W. (1978b). Evaluation of census population coverage by network surveys. *American Statistical Association Proceedings of the Social Statistics Section.*

Sirken, Monroe G., and Royston, Patricia N. (1976). Effect of selected survey design factors on the registered deaths reported in a single time retrospective household sample surveys. *American Statistical Association, Proceedings of the Social Statistics Section*, pp. 773–777.

Sirken, Monroe G., Royston, Patricia N., and Bridges, M. P. (1977). Counting rule bias in household surveys of deaths. *American Statistical Association Proceedings of the Social Statistics Section*, pp. 347–351.

PART III

Nonresponse and Double Sampling

CHAPTER 9

Introduction

William G. Madow and Bahadur Singh

Double sampling methods for dealing with nonresponse consist of selecting a probability sample of the population, attempting to interview the sample, and then selecting and interviewing a probability subsample of the nonrespondents. If all units in the subsample respond, no nonresponse bias will occur, but the variance of the estimator will be larger than if all originally selected units had responded. To eliminate (as much as possible) nonresponse in the subsample, a greater interviewing effort per unit is made for the subsample than for the original sample. In practice, some nonresponse will remain, but the nonresponse rate is usually sharply reduced. Three and higher stage samples for nonresponse can also be used, but limitations of time as well as cost effectiveness usually keep such designs from being used. Double sampling may be used after the initial interviewing effort or after one or more callbacks. At some point, one must decide whether to use additional callbacks, a final intensive callback effort, or double sampling. For a fixed budget and a requirement for completion within prescribed time limits, the decision will depend on the mean square error.

Part III consists of two chapters on dealing with nonresponse through double sampling, that is, by selecting a subsample of nonrespondents for an intensive interviewing effort. In the following chapter, P. S. R. S. Rao uses a probability sampling design approach, and in the chapter by Singh a Bayesian approach is used. Both chapters classify the N units in the population into respondent and nonrespondent strata. The respondent stratum consists of N_1 units that would respond, if selected, to the survey and the nonrespondent stratum consists of N_2 units that would not respond if selected, $N = N_1 + N_2$.

The distinctions between Chapters 10 and 11 are not in the problems discussed and the assumptions made to deal with nonresponse, but rather in the statistical formulations and the methods of inference, randomization (Chapter

INCOMPLETE DATA
IN SAMPLE SURVEYS
Volume 2, Part III

10) or Bayesian (Chapter 11). In the psd approach of Chapter 10, the characteristics of the units of the population are assumed to be constants and
randomness comes from the probability sampling plan.

In the Bayesian approach of Chapter 11, the unit characteristics are assumed
to be random variables having a joint distribution, the super-population distribution; randomness comes from the distribution and from the sample
selection procedure, if a probability sampling plan is used. In the psd approach,
previous knowledge is primarily embodied in the probability sampling plan. In
the Bayesian approach, previous knowledge is in the probability sampling plan,
if one is used (as in Chapter 11), and in the super-population distribution, which
is never exactly known and which may be poorly known. For example, in
Chapter 11 assumptions of normality and independence are made, but the
inferences do not depend on these assumptions being exactly correct. The inferences also are different. In psd, the probability sampling plan generates
distributions of estimators of population characteristics based on the possible
samples and their known probabilities of selection; for a given probability
sampling plan, the selected estimator is required to be design-consistent and
have smaller mean square error within cost restrictions than alternative estimators. The Bayesian approach results in posterior distributions of the characteristics being estimated conditional on the sampling plan, the selected sample,
and the characteristics of the sample. From these posterior distributions,
Bayesian confidence (probability) intervals can be obtained.

In Chapter 10, a random sample of n units is selected from the combined
population of N units. Of the n units, n_1 units turn out to have been selected
from the stratum of respondents and n_2 units from the stratum of nonrespondents; i.e., there are n_1 responding and n_2 nonresponding units. Then, a second-
stage sample consisting of the n_1 responding units and a subsample of m_2
of the n_2 nonrespondents is selected. Intensive efforts are made to obtain interviews from the m_2 units that did not respond in the first stage. This approach is
then a special case of double sampling. Estimators are defined and estimators of
sampling variance are obtained; also the additional problem of determining
optimal size m_2 of the subsample of respondents is considered.

Chapter 11 discusses a more general survey design for dealing with
nonresponse and applies Bayesian methods to obtain estimators and posterior
distributions. The more general design begins with a first-phase pilot survey
intended to make the resultant estimators more efficient than they might
otherwise be; this pilot survey could also be used in the psd approach. Another
part of the design assumes that the population is stratified or poststratified into
L classification strata and that the two strata (response, nonresponse are crossed
with these L strata. The more detailed stratification also could be incorporated
into the psd approach.

A pilot sample is selected in a first phase on the basis of which the units are
classified into the L classification strata where nonresponse may occur in each
stratum. The pilot sample is itself selected in the two stages discussed in connec-

tion with the psd approach so that information is obtained from a random sample of nonrespondents.

The information obtained in the first phase is used to determine the size of the first-stage sample in the second phase; the size of the second-stage sample of nonrespondents depends on the number of nonrespondents and statistical characteristics obtained in the first-stage sample of the second phase.

The second-phase sample is selected in the same two stages from the units not selected in the first stage. Thus, at the end of the two phases, data have been obtained from two samples each consisting of respondents and nonrespondents.

In the Bayesian approach, the N variables are assumed to be independent and the N_i variables within stratum i to be identically distributed with normal distributions, $i = 1, 2, \ldots, L$. Prior distributions of the resulting $2L$ parameters of the multivariate normal distribution and the $L - 1$ proportions of the population in the L strata are specified.

Based on this prior specification, the first-phase sample is used to obtain a posterior distribution of the parameters, which in turn is used as a prior distribution to obtain the posterior distribution of the parameters given both phases of the design. The latter distribution is used to obtain the predictive distribution of the values associated with the nonresponding and nonselected units of the population, which is used to obtain the posterior distribution of the population characteristics to be estimated. (The procedure can also be carried out in a single-phase sample relying on an assumed prior distribution of the parameters.) Optimal allocation of the sample is obtained by formulating a loss function depending on costs and on the design paramenters of the survey, and then choosing the values of the design parameters that minimize the expected loss.

CHAPTER 10

Randomization Approach

P. S. R. S. Rao

1. INTRODUCTION

When nonresponse occurs, the subsampling procedure of Hansen and Hurwitz (1946) is an alternative to callbacks and similar procedures. In this approach, the population of size N is assumed to be composed of two strata of sizes N_1 and $N_2 = N - N_1$, of "respondents" and "nonrespondents." The initial simple random sample of size n results in n_1 respondents and n_2 non-respondents. A subsample of size $m_2 = n_2/k$, where k (>1) is predetermined, is drawn from the n_2 nonrespondents and through intensive efforts information on y is assumed to be obtained from all of the m_2 units. In practice, it may not be possible to obtain information from all of the m_2 units and some adjustments to the estimates have to be made, accounting for the "hard-core" nonrespondents.

While Hansen and Hurwitz consider mail surveys for the initial attempt and personal interviews at the second stage, their procedure is applicable to any type of interviewing (e.g., telephone, personal interview).

The following sections describe the estimator for the population mean of y and its standard error, and the procedure for determining the values of n and k. The cases of stratification and ratio and regression estimation are also described. An extension of the above procedure by El Badry (1956) to more than two calls is presented. Most of the material in the following sections is contained in Cochran (1977).

INCOMPLETE DATA
IN SAMPLE SURVEYS
Volume 2, Part III

2. THE ESTIMATOR WITH DOUBLE SAMPLING

2.1. The Estimator and Its Variance

The estimator for the population mean $\bar{Y}$ of the finite population is

$$\hat{\bar{Y}} = w_1 \bar{y}_1 + w_2 \bar{y}_{2m}, \tag{1}$$

where $w_1 = n_1/n$ and $w_2 = n_2/n$. The sample mean $\bar{y}_1$ is based on n_1 observations and $\bar{y}_{2m}$ on m_2 observations.

The expected value of $\bar{y}_{2m}$ for a given first sample s, consisting of n_1 respondents and n_2 nonrespondents, is equal to $\bar{y}_2$, which is the mean of the n_2 units. Thus,

$$E(\hat{\bar{Y}}|s) = w_1 \bar{y}_1 + w_2 \bar{y}_2 = \bar{y}, \tag{2}$$

where $\bar{y}$ is the mean of the n sampled units. Clearly,

$$E(\hat{\bar{Y}}) = \bar{Y}. \tag{3}$$

From (2),

$$V[E(\hat{\bar{Y}}|s)] = \frac{(1-f)}{n} S^2, \tag{4}$$

where $f = n/N$ and $S^2 = \sum_1^N (y_i - \bar{Y})^2/(N-1)$ is the population variance. From (1),

$$V(\hat{\bar{Y}}|s;n_2) = w_2^2 \frac{(k-1)}{n_2} s_2^2 = w_2 \frac{(k-1)}{n} s_2^2, \tag{5}$$

where s_2^2 is the variance of the n_2 "nonrespondents." For a fixed value of n_2, the average of the variance in (5) is

$$E[V(\hat{\bar{Y}}|s;n_2)] = w_2 \frac{(k-1)}{n} S_2^2, \tag{6}$$

where S_2^2 is the variance of the N_2 units of the second stratum. Since $E(w_2) = W_2 = N_2/N$, from (6),

$$E[V(\hat{\bar{Y}}|s)] = W_2 \frac{(k-1)}{n} S_2^2. \tag{7}$$

Thus, from (4) and (7),

$$V(\hat{\bar{Y}}) = \frac{(1-f)}{n} S^2 + W_2 \frac{(k-1)}{n} S_2^2. \tag{8}$$

The second term on the right-hand side of (8) is the increase in variance due to the subsampling. As we expect, this increase will be small if the proportion of nonrespondents W_2 and their variance S_2^2 are small, and the subsampling fraction $(1/k)$ is large.

From the derivations of Cochran (1977) and J. N. K. Rao (1973), the estimator of this variance can be written as

$$v(\hat{\bar{Y}}) = \frac{(N-n)(n_1-1)}{N(n-1)} w_1 \frac{s_1^2}{n_1} + \frac{(N-1)(n_2-1) - (n-1)(m_2-1)}{N(n-1)} w_2 \frac{s_{2m}^2}{m_2}$$

$$+ \frac{N-n}{N(n-1)} \left[w_1(\bar{y}_1 - \hat{\bar{Y}})^2 + w_2(\bar{y}_{2m} - \hat{\bar{Y}})^2 \right], \tag{9}$$

where s_1^2 and s_{2m}^2 are the variances of the n_1 and m_2 units.

2.2.   Optimal Values of n and k

The cost of sampling is considered to be

$$C' = c_0 n + c_1 n_1 + c_2 m_2, \tag{10}$$

where c_0 is the initial cost for "setting up" the survey, c_1 is the cost per unit for obtaining the responses from the n_1 units and processing them, and c_2 is the cost per unit for contacting the subsampled units and for obtaining and processing responses from them. Usually c_2 is much larger than c_1, since additional effort is needed for contacting the nonrespondents and eliciting responses from them. From (10), the expected cost is

$$C = E(C') = \left(c_0 + c_1 W_1 + \frac{c_2 W_2}{k} \right) n. \tag{11}$$

Minimizing the expected cost for a prescribed value V for the variance in (8), or minimizing the variance for given C, is equivalent to minimizing $(V + S^2/N)C$. Thus, the optimal value of k is

$$k_{opt} = \left[\frac{c_2(S^2 - W_2 S_2^2)}{S_2^2(c_0 + c_1 W_1)} \right]^{1/2}. \tag{12}$$

From (12), we notice that the optimal size of the subsample is large if c_2 is small relative to $(c_0 + c_1 W_1)$ and S_2^2 is large relative to S^2. For a specified V, from (8) and (12),

$$n_{opt} = \frac{N[S^2 + (k_{opt} - 1)W_2 S_2^2]}{NV + S^2}$$

$$= n_0 \left[1 + \frac{(k_{opt} - 1)W_2 S_2^2}{S^2} \right], \tag{13}$$

where $n_0 = NS^2/(NV + S^2)$ is the sample size required when $W_2 = 0$. Similarly, for a fixed cost C,

$$n_{opt} = \frac{k_{opt}C}{k_{opt}(c_0 + c_1 W_1) + c_2 W_2}. \tag{14}$$

2.3. An Alternative Procedure for Determining the Size of the Subsample

Srinath (1971) and J. N. K. Rao (1973) suggest determining the size of the subsample as

$$m_2^* = \frac{n_2^2}{k^* n + n_2} = n \frac{w_2^2}{k^* + w_2} = m_2 \frac{k w_2}{k^* + w_2}, \tag{15}$$

where k^* is "some constant fixed in advance" and $m_2 = n/k$. From (1) and (15), for the variance of $\hat{\bar{Y}}$ we find that

$$V^*(\hat{\bar{Y}} \mid s; w_2) = w_2^2 \left(\frac{1}{m_2^*} - \frac{1}{n_2} \right) s_2^2 = \frac{k^*}{n} s_2^2, \tag{16}$$

$$E[V^*(\hat{\bar{Y}} \mid s; w_2)] = \frac{k^*}{n} S_2^2, \tag{17}$$

and from (4) and (17),

$$V^*(\hat{\bar{Y}}) = \frac{(1 - f)}{n} S^2 + \frac{k^*}{n} S_2^2. \tag{18}$$

For this method of choosing the size of the subsample, the cost function analogous to (10) is

$$C^{*\prime} = c_0 n + c_1 n_1 + c_2 m_2^*, \tag{19}$$

and from (19) the "expected cost" considered by Srinath (1971) is

$$C^* = (c_0 + c_1 W_1)n + c_2 \left(\frac{n W_2^2}{k^* + W_2} \right), \tag{20}$$

which is obtained by replacing w_2 and w_2^2 by W_2 and W_2^2. We note from (15) that m_2 is larger or smaller than m_2^* as k^* is larger or smaller than $(k - 1)w_2$. Similarly, from (8), (11), (18), and (20), we observe that $V(\hat{\bar{Y}})$ is smaller or larger than $V^*(\hat{\bar{Y}})$ and C is larger or smaller than C^* as k^* is larger or smaller than $(k - 1)W_2$.

Minimizing C^* for a given value V of $V^*(\hat{\bar{Y}})$ or minimizing $V^*(\hat{\bar{Y}})$ for a given value of C^*, from (18) and (20) we obtain the solution to the optimal value of k^* as

$$(k^*_{\text{opt}} + W_2)^2 = \frac{(S^2 - W_2 S_2^2) c_2 W_2^2}{S_2^2 (c_0 + c_1 W_1)}. \tag{21}$$

From (21), we find that

$$k^*_{\text{opt}} = (k_{\text{opt}} - 1) W_2. \tag{22}$$

For a specified value V for the variance, from (18),

$$n^*_{\text{opt}} = n_0 \left[1 + k^*_{\text{opt}} (S_2^2 / S^2) \right], \tag{23}$$

which is the same as n_{opt} of (13).

Similarly, for a specified C^*, from (20),

$$n_{\text{opt}} = \frac{C^*(k^*_{\text{opt}} + W_2)}{(c_0 + c_1 W_1)(k^*_{\text{opt}} + W_2) + c_2 W_2^2}. \tag{24}$$

2.4.   An Illustration

To compare the two procedures in Sections 2.2 and 2.3 for determining the sample sizes, consider the example of Hansen and Hurwitz (1946) in which $c_0 = .1$, $c_1 = .4$, and $c_2 = 4.5$. The required precision is that given by a simple random sample of 1000; i.e., $n_0 = 1000$ and $V = (N - n_0) S^2 / N n_0$. Suppose that it is assumed that S^2 and S_2^2 are equal.

If the value of W_2 is thought to be equal to .4, $k_{\text{opt}} = 2.83$ from (12), $k^*_{\text{opt}} = .728$ from (22), and $n_{\text{opt}} = n^*_{\text{opt}} = 1728$ from (13) and (23). The required "expected" size of the subsample is

$$m_{2\text{opt}} = n_{\text{opt}} W_2 / k_{\text{opt}} = 1728(.4)/2.82 = 245; \tag{25}$$

see Cochran (1977: 373). Similarly, from Srinath (1971: 585; Example 1),

$$m^*_{2\text{opt}} = n_{\text{opt}} \frac{W_2^2}{k^*_{\text{opt}} + W_2} = \frac{1728(.16)}{.728 + .4} = 245. \tag{26}$$

For the present case, both $m_{2\text{opt}}$ and $m^*_{2\text{opt}}$ are equal to 245. From (11) and (20), the expected cost is $1690.

Suppose that the true value of W_2 is equal to .6 instead of .4 as was thought earlier. With the earlier *computed values* of k_{opt} of 2.82 and k^*_{opt} of .728 and this value of .6 for W_2, from (8),

$$V(\hat{\bar{Y}}) = \left(\frac{1}{1728} - \frac{1}{N} \right) S^2 + \frac{(.6)(1.82)}{1728} S^2$$

$$= V + (.21/1000) S^2,$$

and from (18), $V^*(\hat{\bar{Y}}) = V$. However, from (11) and (20), $C = \$2108$ $C^* = \$2558$, respectively. Thus, with an *extra cost* the second procedure would provide the required precision although W_2 is equal to .6 instead of .4. We note that these total costs are obtained with $W_2 = .6$. With the increased budget of $2558 and $W_2 = .6$, from (12), $k_{opt} = 2.63$ and from (14), $n_{opt} = 1988$. With these values $V(\hat{\bar{Y}}) = V$. Thus, the first procedure also provides the required precision with the increased budget; however, it cannot be implemented, since it was not known initially that $W_2 = .6$.

On the other hand, if W_2 is equal to .2 instead of .4, with $k_{opt} = 2.82$ and $k^* = .728$, from (8),

$$V(\hat{\bar{Y}}) = V - (.21/1000)S^2.$$

and from (18), $V^*(\hat{\bar{Y}}) = V$. However, from (11), $C = \$1277$, and from (20), $C^* = \$1061$. Thus, with an extra cost the first procedure gives more precision than required.

The size of the subsample is given by n_2/k for the first procedure and by (15) for the second procedure. However, it should be chosen from (25) or (26) if the unconditional variance or the expected cost is to be minimized. Consequently, the size of the subsample depends on the unknown value of W_2. This illustration shows the difficulty of determining the size of the subsample when W_2 is not known exactly. The following procedure does not have that difficulty.

2.5. Size of the Subsample That Minimizes the Conditional Variance

From (4) and (6), the variance of $\hat{\bar{Y}}$ may be written as

$$V(\hat{\bar{Y}}) = \frac{(1-f)}{n}S^2 + E_{w_2}\left[\frac{w_2(k-1)}{n}S_2^2\right]. \tag{27}$$

When the value of W_2 cannot be guessed, Cochran (1977) suggests finding the values of n from (12) and (13) for a series of values of W_2 from zero to a "safe upper limit" and using the maximum value of n in this series as the optimal value. The value of n_2 is observed at the end of the initial survey. With these n and n_2 the optimal value of k can be obtained by prescribing an upper limit V_0 to the conditional variance $\{w_2(k-1)/n\}S_2^2$ in (27). This procedure will guarantee that for each sample s, $V(\hat{\bar{Y}})$ will not exceed $V = (1-f)S^2/n + V_0$. Unlike the procedures in Sections 2.2 and 2.3, this method determines the subsample size from the observed value of w_2.

2.6. Stratified Sampling

The population consists of L strata of sizes N_h ($h = 1, 2, \ldots, L$). In the hth stratum, N_{h1} is the size of the "respondent" and $N_{h2} = N_h - N_{h1}$ is the size of the "nonrespondent" stratum. The initial simple random sample of size n_h from the hth stratum results in n_{h1} respondents and $n_{h2} = n_h - n_{h1}$ nonrespondents. Subsequently, information on y is obtained on a subsample of size m_{h2} drawn randomly from the n_{h2} units. Let $\bar{y}_{h1}$ denote the mean of the n_{h1} respondents and $\bar{y}_{h2(m)}$ denote the mean of the m_{h2} subsampled units. The estimator for the population mean of y is

$$\hat{\bar{Y}} = \sum_{h=1}^{L} W_h \left\{ \frac{n_{h1}}{n_h} \bar{y}_{h1} + \frac{n_{h2}}{n_h} \bar{y}_{h2(m)} \right\}. \tag{28}$$

Let s denote the collection of the n_{h1} respondents and n_{h2} nonrespondents in the L strata. For a fixed value of n_h,

$$E(\hat{\bar{Y}}|s) = \sum_{h=1}^{L} W_h \left\{ \frac{n_{h1}}{n_h} \bar{y}_{h1} + \frac{n_{h2}}{n_h} \bar{y}_{h2} \right\}$$

$$= \sum W_h \bar{y}_h = \bar{y}_{st}, \tag{29}$$

say, where $\bar{y}_{h2}$ is the mean of the n_{h2} units and $\bar{y}_h$ is the mean of all the n_h units. From (29), $\hat{\bar{Y}}$ is clearly unbiased for the population mean $\bar{Y}$ and

$$V[E(\hat{\bar{Y}}|s)] = \sum W_h^2(1 - f_h) \frac{S_h^2}{n_h}, \tag{30}$$

where $f_h = n_h/N_h$ is the sampling fraction in the hth stratum.
From (28), for a fixed n_h,

$$V(\hat{\bar{Y}}|s) = \sum W_h^2 \left\{ \left(\frac{n_{h2}}{n_h} \right)^2 \left(1 - \frac{m_{h2}}{n_{h2}} \right) \frac{s_{h2}^2}{m_{h2}} \right\}, \tag{31}$$

where s_{h2}^2 is the variance of the n_{h2} units. Thus, from (30) and (31),

$$V(\hat{\bar{Y}}) = \sum W_h^2(1 - f_h) \frac{S_h^2}{n_h} + E_{m_{h2}, n_{h2}} \left\{ \sum W_h^2 \left[\left(\frac{n_{h2}}{n_h} \right)^2 \left(1 - \frac{m_{h2}}{n_{h2}} \right) \frac{S_{h2}^2}{m_{h2}} \right] \right\}, \tag{32}$$

where S_{h2}^2 is the variance of the N_{h2} nonrespondents.
The approaches of Cochran (1977) and Sedransk and Singh (1974) may be suitably adapted to determine the optimal values of $n = \sum n_h$ and the m_{h2}.

3. RATIO AND REGRESSION ESTIMATORS

Cochran (1977) gives expressions for the MSEs of the ratio and regression estimators when there is initial nonresponse and neither the characteristic of interest Y nor the auxiliary characteristic X is measured. However, both Y and

X are obtained from a subsample of size m_2 from the nonrespondents. The ratio estimator for $\bar{Y}$ is

$$\hat{\bar{Y}}_R = (\bar{y}/\bar{x})\bar{X}, \qquad (33)$$

where $\bar{X}$ is the population mean of X, $\bar{y} = w_1\bar{y}_1 + w_2\bar{y}_2$ as defined in (1), and $\bar{x} = w_1\bar{x}_1 + w_2\bar{x}_2$. The values of $(\bar{y}_1, \bar{x}_1)$ and $(\bar{y}_2, \bar{x}_2)$ are obtained from the first and second samples. The approximate MSE of this estimator is obtained from (8) by replacing S^2 and S_2^2 with S_d^2 and S_{2d}^2, which are the variances of $d_i = y_i - Rx_i$, where $R = \bar{Y}/\bar{X}$ for S_d^2 and $R = \bar{Y}_2/\bar{X}_2$ for S_{2d}^2. Note that S_d^2 is the variance of the entire population and S_{2d}^2 is the variance of the stratum of nonrespondents.

For the above type of nonresponse, a regression estimator for $\bar{Y}$ is

$$\bar{y}_{lr} = \bar{y} + b(\bar{X} - \bar{x}). \qquad (34)$$

The value of the regression coefficient b is obtained from the results of both samples. The approximate expression for the MSE of $\bar{y}_{lr}$ is obtained from (8) by replacing S^2 and S_2^2 by $S^2(1 - \rho^2)$ and $S_2^2(1 - \rho_2^2)$, where ρ is the correlation coefficient between X and Y for the entire population, and ρ_2 for the stratum of nonrespondents.

A number of alternative procedures of estimation may be suggested. For instance, $\bar{y}/\bar{x}$ in (33) may be replaced by $\hat{R} = w_1 r_1 + w_2 r_2$, where $r_1 = \bar{y}_1/\bar{x}_1$ and $r_2 = \bar{y}_2/\bar{x}_2$. Similarly, different methods for obtaining b in (34) may be suggested. Further investigation is needed to determine the appropriateness of these alternative methods.

4.   EXTENSION TO MORE THAN TWO ATTEMPTS

El-Badry (1956) extends the procedure of subsampling to more than two calls. The initial sample of size n results in n_1 responses and n_{12} nonresponses. A sample of size $m_{12} = n_{12}/K_1$ is attempted at the second call, which results in n_2 responses and n_{22} nonresponses. For the third call a sample of size $m_{22} = n_{22}/K_2$ is attempted. This process is continued, with the last $[(L + 1)\text{th}]$ attempt being made on a subsample of size $m_{L2} = n_{L2}/K_L$ from the n_{L2} nonrespondents. All of the m_{L2} units are assumed to respond. Let $t_1, t_2, \ldots, t_{L+1}$ denote the totals of the Y characteristic for the $n_1, n_2, \ldots, n_{L+1}$ respondents. Note that n_{L+1} is the same as m_{L2}. Let $W_{j2}(j = 1, 2, \ldots, L)$ denote the proportion of the population who would not respond at the end of the jth attempt, but may respond at a subsequent attempt, and let S_{j2}^2 denote their variance. An unbiased estimator for $\bar{Y}$ is

$$\hat{\bar{Y}} = (t_1 + K_1 t_2 + K_1 K_2 t_3 + \cdots + K_1 K_2 \cdots K_{L+1} t_{L+1})/n. \qquad (35)$$

The variance of this estimator is [see Srinath (1971)]

$$V(\hat{\bar{Y}}) = \frac{(1-f)}{n}S^2 + \frac{(K_1 - 1)W_{12}S_{12}^2}{n}$$

$$+ \frac{1}{n}\sum_{j=2}^{L}\left(\prod_{i=1}^{j-1} K_i\right)(K_j - 1)W_{j2}S_{j2}^2. \qquad (36)$$

In (36), S^2 is the variance for all the units in the population, as defined earlier. The optimal values of n and K_j can be determined as in the case of two attempts. It is easy to see that when $V(\hat{\bar{Y}})$ in (36) is required to equal V, the optimal size of the initial sample for predetermined K_j is given by

$$n_{opt} = n_0\left[1 + \frac{(K_1 - 1)W_{12}S_{12}^2}{S^2} + \frac{1}{S^2}\sum_{j=2}^{L}\left(\prod_{i=1}^{j-1} K_i\right)(K_j - 1)W_{j2}S_{j2}^2\right], \quad (37)$$

where $n_0 = NS^2/(NV + S^2)$ is the sample size required when $W_{12}, W_{22}, \ldots, W_{L2}$ are equal to zero.

REFERENCES

Cochran, W. G. (1977). *Sampling Techniques*, pp. 370–374. New York: Wiley.

El-Badry, M. A. (1956). A sampling procedure for mailed questionnaires. *Journal of the American Statistical Association* 51: 209–227.

Hansen, M. H., and Hurwitz, W. N. (1946). The problem of nonresponse in sample surveys. *Journal of the American Statistical Association* 41: 517–529.

Rao, J. N. K. (1973). On double sampling for stratification and analytical surveys. *Biometrika* 60: 125–133.

Sedransk, J., and Singh, B. (1974). Sample size allocation in two phase sampling. *Communication in Statistics* 3(11): 1025–1040.

Srinath, K. P. (1971). Multiphase sampling in nonresponse problems. *Journal of the American Statistical Association* 66: 583–586.

CHAPTER 11

Bayesian Approach

Bahadur Singh

1. INTRODUCTION

The sample survey theory and methods as put forth in the conventional textbooks in sampling theory, e.g., Cochran (1977), are based on the frequency definition of probability. A different approach is adopted by "Bayesian" statisticians. Here, statistical inference involves revision via Bayes theorem of initial ("prior") opinions in the light of relevant new information (i.e., sample data). The Bayesian approach has several advantages over the traditional sampling theory approach. First, there are occasions when available information about the parameters of interest (from pilot studies, similar previous studies, etc.) can be expressed in the form of a prior distribution. Bayes's theorem modifies this prior information through the likelihood function in a very natural fashion. Second, in some cases, Bayesian procedures yield inferential statements (e.g., point estimates) similar to those obtained from the use of the traditional sampling theory approach. However, for designing an investigation, the Bayesian approach offers a formal, coherent manner of incorporating available prior information. This is a particularly appealing consideration for the multitude of populations which are repeatedly sampled, since such repetitive sampling inevitably yields data useful (at least) for the careful planning of future studies.

In this section, we discuss from a Bayesian viewpoint inference problems concerning finite-population parameters when there is nonresponse. When there is a substantial amount of nonresponse in a sample survey, a common practice is to select a subsample of the nonrespondents and to obtain the desired data from this subsample by using more expensive measurement techniques. It is customary to assume that there are two strata of unknown sizes: Stratum 1

INCOMPLETE DATA
IN SAMPLE SURVEYS
Volume 2, Part III

consists of those units who would, if selected in the sample, supply the necessary information without recourse to additional measurement techniques; and stratum 2 is the complementary stratum of "nonrespondents." Since such a sampling procedure is a special case of the poststratification technique, this general case is considered first. The special case of inference problems concerning finite-population parameters when there is nonresponse is discussed in the subsequent sections.

In recent years, some research papers have appeared in the "Bayesian" literature on problems of making inferences concerning finite-population parameters such as means and proportions and regression coefficients. Some of the general references about inference for the finite-population mean are those of Ericson (1969), Palit and Guttman (1972), Guttman and Palit (1972a, 1972b), Rao and Ghangurde (1972), and Singh and Sedransk (1976). The problem of nonresponse has also drawn considerable attention. Bayesian inference about the population mean when there is nonresponse is discussed by Ericson (1967), Singh and Sedransk (1976, 1978b) and Rubin (1977). Inference concerning the population proportion in dichotomous processes when there is nonresponse is considered by Kaufman and King (1973), Singh (1974) and Gunel (1979). Finally, Singh and Sedransk (1975, 1978a) consider inference for regression coefficients in a multiple linear regression when there is nonresponse.

2. ESTIMATION OF THE FINITE-POPULATION MEAN

Singh and Sedransk (1976, 1978b) consider estimation of the mean $\bar{X}$ of a finite population of N distinguishable units as follows: Assume that it is desired to employ stratified sampling but that there is no list of the units in each stratum. Thus, a poststratification technique is adopted. It is assumed that the population is partitioned into L mutually exclusive and exhaustive strata with the strata boundaries fixed in advance of sampling and N_i (unknown) units belonging to stratum i ($\Sigma_{i=1}^{L} N_i = N$). Let X_{ij} denote the value of the random variable X for the jth unit in stratum i. Then, we can write the finite population mean $\bar{X}$ as

$$\bar{X} = \sum_{i=1}^{L} \pi_i \bar{X}_i, \tag{1}$$

where

$$\bar{X}_i = \sum_{j=1}^{N_i} \frac{X_{ij}}{N_i} \quad \text{and} \quad \pi_i = \frac{N_i}{N}.$$

A first-phase (pilot) simple random sample of size n' is drawn without replacement with n_i' units identified as members of stratum i ($\sum n_i' = n'$). Then, independent simple random subsamples of sizes $m_1', \ldots, m_L'$ ($0 \leq m_i' \leq n_i'$) are selected without replacement and the variate values $\mathbf{x}'_i = (x'_{i1}, \ldots, x'_{im'_i})^t$ are obtained. It is assumed that the distribution of $\mathbf{n}' = (n'_1, \ldots, n'_{L-1})^t$, conditional on $\boldsymbol{\pi} = (\pi_1, \ldots, \pi_{L-1})^t$, can be satisfactorily approximated by a multinomial distribution with parameters n' and $\boldsymbol{\pi}$.

For the second-phase sample, a simple random sample of size n is selected without replacement from the $(N - \sum n'_i)$ units in the population not selected in the first-phase sample. With n_i units found to be in stratum i ($\sum n_i = n$), independent simple random subsamples of sizes $m_i \geq 0$ ($i = 1, \ldots, L$) are selected without replacement from the $n_i + n'_i - m'_i$ ($i = 1, \ldots, L$) units available; and the variate values $\mathbf{x}_i = (x_{i1}, \ldots, x_{im_i})^t$ are obtained. It is assumed that the distribution of $\mathbf{n} = (n_1, \ldots, n_{L-1})^t$, conditional on $\boldsymbol{\pi}$, can be satisfactorily approximated by a multinomial distribution with parameters n and $\boldsymbol{\pi}$.

To illustrate the approach, Singh and Sedransk assume that, in stratum i, the X values $\{X_{i1}, X_{i2}, \ldots, X_{iN_i}\}$ are a random sample from a normal superpopulation[1] with unknown mean μ_i and precision h_i. The random samples across the strata are assumed to be independent. The superpopulation parameters

$$\boldsymbol{\mu}^t = (\mu_1, \ldots, \mu_L), \qquad \mathbf{h}^t = (h_1, \ldots, h_L)$$

are assumed to have independent, locally uniform prior distributions:

$$f(\boldsymbol{\mu}, \mathbf{h}) = \prod_{i=1}^{L} f(\mu_i, h_i) \propto \prod_{i=1}^{L} (1/h_i). \qquad (2)$$

It is further assumed that the prior $g(\boldsymbol{\pi})$ on $\boldsymbol{\pi}^t = (\pi_1, \ldots, \pi_{L-1})$ is independent of the prior distribution on $(\boldsymbol{\mu}, \mathbf{h})$ and is given by

$$g(\boldsymbol{\pi}) \propto 1/\{\pi_1 \pi_2 \cdots (1 - \sum_{i=1}^{L-1} \pi_i)\}. \qquad (3)$$

Using the model and the assumptions regarding the X values, and the priors (2) and (3), the posterior distribution of $(\boldsymbol{\pi}, \boldsymbol{\mu}, \mathbf{h})$ given the first-phase sample, say, f' is obtained in a straightforward manner. Combining the likelihood of $(\boldsymbol{\pi}, \boldsymbol{\mu}, \mathbf{h})$ (based on the second-phase sample) with the prior f', the posterior distribution of $(\boldsymbol{\pi}, \boldsymbol{\mu}, \mathbf{h})$ is obtained. From the predictive distribution of the unobserved components of $\mathbf{X} = (X_{i1}, \ldots, X_{iN_i}; i = 1, \ldots, L\}$ the posterior distribution and moments of $\bar{X}$ are obtained. [See Singh and Sedransk (1976, 1978b) for additional details.]

The loss is assumed to be given by

$$L(n, n_i, m_i, \mathbf{x}_i; i = 1, \ldots, L; Q', \bar{X}, \hat{\bar{X}}) = K(\bar{X} - \hat{\bar{X}})^2 + \sum_{i=1}^{L} c_i m_i + cn + C, \qquad (4)$$

where

$$Q' = (n', n'_i, m'_i, \mathbf{x}'_i; i = 1, \ldots, L).$$

[1] Other superpopulation assumptions are considered by Singh (1974).

The positive constant K represents the trade-off between errors of estimation and sampling costs. The fixed budget for the first-phase sampling is denoted by C, while the per unit costs of sampling at the second phase are c and c_i $(i = 1, \ldots, L)$. Here, c is the per unit cost (at the first stage of second-phase sampling) of sampling and identifying the units as to stratum membership; and c_i is the per unit cost in stratum i of subsampling and obtaining and processing the desired measurements.

The optimal point estimator of $\bar{X}$ and the optimal values of the m_i $(i = 1, \ldots, L)$ and n are obtained using an extensive form of analysis. Two simple approximations are developed for the optimal value of n, the total sample size in the second-phase sample.

Employing a model suggested by Hartley and Rao (1968), Rao and Ghangurde (1972) also consider estimation of the finite-population mean in stratified two-phase sampling. This model depends on an alternative definition of the likelihood. It is based on the assumption that the variable X is measured on a known scale of measurement so that X takes a finite set of values.

In stratum i, let $\mathbf{N}_i = (N_{i1}, \ldots, N_{iT_i})^t$, where N_{it} is the number of units having the measurement X_{it}, so that $N_i = \sum_t N_{it}$ ($i = 1, 2, \ldots, L$). In terms of the N_{it} the ith stratum mean is $\bar{X}_i = \sum_t N_{it} X_{it} / N_i$, and the overall population mean is $\bar{X} = \sum_i \sum_t N_{it} X_{it} / N$. The prior distribution on $(\mathbf{N}_1, \ldots, \mathbf{N}_L)$ is assumed to be "diffuse." It is further assumed that the prior on $(N_1, \ldots, N_L)$ is "diffuse" and is independent of the prior on $(\mathbf{N}_1, \ldots, \mathbf{N}_L)$.

Rao and Ghangurde (1972) consider two two-phase sample designs. One is similar to that described in this section. The other is to select a simple random sample of size n' from the entire population with n_i' units identified as belonging to stratum i. First-phase subsamples of sizes $\{m_i'\}$ are selected independently in the L strata. Second-phase subsamples of sizes $\{m_i\}$ are selected from the remaining $\{n_i' - m_i'\}$ units in the strata. In each case they give the optimal point estimator of $\bar{X}$, and those values of the m_i $(i = 1, \ldots, L)$ which minimize the preposterior expectation of the posterior variance of $\bar{X}$ subject to a fixed budget.

3. NONRESPONSE PROBLEM

In this section we consider inferences concerning

(i)   Estimation of the finite population mean (Section 3.1)
(ii) Estimation of the finite population proportion (Section 3.2)
(iii) Estimation of regression coefficients (Section 3.3)

when there is nonresponse.

We shall assume throughout that stratum 1 corresponds to the stratum of "respondents" and stratum 2 to that of "nonrespondents."

3.1. Finite Population Mean

For the estimation of the finite population mean when there is nonresponse, we can write

$$\overline{X} = \pi\overline{X}_1 + (1 - \pi)\overline{X}_2, \tag{5}$$

where $\pi = N_1/N$ is the (unknown) proportion of respondents in the population, and $\overline{X}_1$, $\overline{X}_2$ are, respectively, the strata means in the respondent and non-respondent strata.

The first-phase sample of size n' yields n_1' respondents and n_2' nonrespondents. It is assumed[2] now that $m_1' = n_1'$. That is, data are obtained from all respondents and from the m_2' nonrespondents ($0 \leq m_2' \leq n_2'$) subsampled from the n_2' initial nonrespondents. For the second-phase sample of size n there are n_1 respondents and n_2 nonrespondents. Data are obtained from all respondents ($m_1 = n_1$) and from the m_2 subsampled nonrespondents ($0 \leq m_2 \leq n_2$). This sample design consists of four samples; i.e., in each phase, there are samples of both "respondents" and "nonrespondents." However, the two first-phase samples are unnecessary if comparable prior information is available from other sources.

In the following discussion, we substitute the symbols (m', m) for (m_2', m_2) and assume the loss function given in (4) with the substitutions indicated earlier. The principal results from Section 2 are outlined for this important special case.

The optimal point estimator of $\overline{X}$ is the posterior mean of $\overline{X}$, and is given by

$$E''(\overline{X}|n, n_1, \mathbf{x}_1, m, \mathbf{x}_2, Q') = p''\bar{x}_{S1}'' + (1 - p'')\bar{x}_{S2}'' = \bar{x}_S'', \tag{6}$$

where

$$Q' = (n', n_1', \mathbf{x}_1', m', \mathbf{x}_2'),$$

$$n_1'' = n_1 + n_1', \qquad n'' = n + n', \qquad m'' = m + m', \qquad p'' = n_1''/n'',$$

$$\bar{x}_{S1}' = \sum_{k=1}^{n_1'} x_{1k}'/n_1', \qquad \bar{x}_{S2}' = \sum_{k=1}^{m'} x_{2k}'/m',$$

$$\bar{x}_{S1}'' = (n_1'\bar{x}_{S1}' + n_1\bar{x}_{S1})/n_1'', \qquad \bar{x}_{S2}'' = (m'\bar{x}_{S2}' + m\bar{x}_{S2})/m'',$$

with $\bar{x}_{S1}$ and $\bar{x}_{S2}$ defined by suppressing the primes in $\bar{x}_{S1}'$ and $\bar{x}_{S2}'$. The optimal value of m, m_o, is given by

$$m_o = \begin{cases} 0 & \text{if} & \varphi \leq 0 \\ (n - n_1 + n' - n_1' - m')\varphi & \text{if} & 0 < \varphi < 1 \\ n - n_1 + n' - n_1' - m' & \text{if} & 1 \leq \varphi, \end{cases} \tag{7}$$

---

[2] See Section 2 (second and third paragraphs) for the sample design and notation.

where

$$\varphi = \left[(1 - p'')\{v_2' v_2' K/(v_2' - 2)c_2\}^{1/2} - m'\right](n - n_1 + n' - n_1' - m')^{-1},$$

$$v_2' = m' - 1, \qquad v_2' v_2' = \sum_{k=1}^{m'} (x_{2k}' - \bar{x}_{S2}')^2.$$

Assuming that $m_o = (n - n_1 + n' - n_1' - m')\varphi$, it is clear that subsampling of nonrespondents should be increased as the proportion of "respondents" in the two samples decreases, the standard deviation (based on the pilot data) of the responses among nonrespondents increases, the per unit cost of sampling the nonrespondents decreases, and K increases.

The expression for the optimal value of n, n_o, is cumbersome. However there are two approximate values which may be used directly or as an initial starting point in a computer search for n_o.

The first approximation to n_o is developed by ignoring the restrictions that $m_o \geq 0$ and $m_o \leq n - n_1 + n' - n_1' - m'$ and then carrying out the pre-posterior analysis accordingly. Then, the approximation to n_o, n_A, is given by

$$n_A = \{KV'/(c + c_1 p')\}^{1/2} - n', \tag{8}$$

where

$$V' = n'\left\{\left(\frac{u' + p'^2}{n_1'}\right)\frac{v_1' v_1'}{(v_1' - 2)} + \frac{u' v_2' v_2'}{m'(v_2' - 2)} + u'(\bar{x}_{S1}' - \bar{x}_{S2}')^2\right\},$$

$$v_1' = n_1' - 1, \qquad v_1' v_1' = \sum_{k=1}^{n_1'} (x_{1k}' - \bar{x}_{S1}')^2, \qquad p' = n_1'/n',$$

$$u' = p'(1 - p')/(n' + 1).$$

If $n_A < 0$, take $n_A = 0$, while if $n_A > N - n'$, take $n_A = N - n'$.

The second approximation to n_o is developed by obtaining an upper bound on the expected loss function and then minimizing this expected loss with respect to n. The approximate optimal value of n, n_c, is given by

$$n_c = \left[KS'/\{c + p'c_1 + (1 - p')c_2\}\right]^{1/2} - n', \tag{9}$$

where

$$S' = n'\left[\{(u' + p'^2)v_1' v_1'/n_1'(v_1' - 2)\} + u'(\bar{x}_{S1}' - \bar{x}_{S2}')^2\right].$$

Rao and Ghangurde (1972) also discuss estimation of the finite-population when there is nonresponse. As before, stratum 1 is the stratum of "respondents," while stratum 2 is that of "nonrespondents." A first-phase (pilot) sample of size n' is drawn without replacement by SRS out of the N population units. Assuming n_1' responses, a subsample of size m' $(0 \leq m' \leq n' - n_1')$ is drawn without replacement by SRS out of the $n' - n_1'$ "nonrespondents." A second-phase (main) sample of size n is drawn using SRS without replacement out of the remaining $N - n_1' - m'$ units in the population. Assuming n_1 responses, a subsample of size m ($0 \le m \le n - n_1$) is drawn without replacement by SRS out of the $n - n_1$ "nonrespondents." Using the parameterization suggested by Hartley and Rao (1968) (see Section 2) the posterior distribution of (N_1, N_2) is obtained given the samples from both phases. Simple expressions for the optimal estimator of $\overline{X}$ and the optimal value of m are obtained.

Ericson (1967) presented the first results pertaining to estimation of the population mean when there is nonresponse. He, however, assumed sampling from infinite populations and strata variances known. Ericson (1967, Section 7) considers several generalizations of the basic model to handle "hard-core" nonrespondents.

3.2. Finite-Population Proportion

Kaufman and King (1973) consider the estimation of the population proportion of individuals who have a specified characteristic. Assume that each individual in the population is labeled "favorable" or "unfavorable," and, as usual, let $i = 1$ denote the stratum of respondents and $i = 2$ denote the complementary stratum of nonrespondents. It is first assumed that the population is infinite.

Let p_{fi} denote the joint probability that an individual belongs to stratum i and favors a given proposal, and let the marginal probability that an individual favors a given proposal be denoted by p_f; i.e., $p_{f1} + p_{f2} = p_f$. The other joint probabilities $\{p_{ui}\}$ and the marginal probability p_u are defined in an analogous manner. Further, let π denote the probability that an individual belongs to the respondent stratum. The above joint and marginal probabilities can be conveniently displayed in Table 1.

Instead of the parameterization given in Table 1, it is convenient to work with an alternative parameter set:

$p_{1 \cdot f}$ = the conditional probability of "response" given "favorable"
$p_{1 \cdot u}$ = the conditional probability of "response" given "unfavorable," with
$p_{2 \cdot f} = 1 - p_{1 \cdot f}$ and $p_{2 \cdot u} = 1 - p_{1 \cdot u}$; and
$p_{f \cdot 1}$ = the conditional probability of "favorable" given "response"
$p_{f \cdot 2}$ = the conditional probability of "favorable" given "nonresponse," with
$p_{u \cdot 1} = 1 - p_{f \cdot 1}$ and $p_{u \cdot 2} = 1 - p_{f \cdot 2}$.

TABLE 1

	Response 1	Nonresponse 2	
Favorable (f)	p_{f1}	p_{f2}	p_f
Unfavorable (u)	p_{u1}	p_{u2}	p_u
	π	$1 - \pi$	1

Then, the proportion of people in the entire population who would favor a given proposal p_f is given by

$$p_f = \pi p_{f \cdot 1} + (1 - \pi) p_{f \cdot 2}. \tag{10}$$

It is further assumed that the prior distribution on $(\pi, p_{f \cdot 1}, p_{f \cdot 2})$ is given by

$$f'(\pi, p_{f \cdot 1}, p_{f \cdot 2} | Q')$$
$$\propto \pi^{n'_1 - 1}(1 - \pi)^{n'_2 - 1} p_{f \cdot 1}^{n'_{f1} - 1}(1 - p_{f \cdot 1})^{n'_{u1} - 1} p_{f \cdot 2}^{n'_{f2} - 1}(1 - p_{f \cdot 2})^{n'_{u2} - 1}, \tag{11}$$

where $Q' = (n'_1, n'_2, n'_{f1}, n'_{u1}, n'_{f2}, n'_{u2})$. Assuming some restrictions on the prior parameters, two alternative forms of this prior distribution are discussed.

The sample design is single phase and it is of the following type: A random sample of size n is drawn from an assumed infinite population. Assuming n_1 responses (n_{f1} favorable, n_{u1} unfavorable), a random sample of fixed size m ($0 \le m \le n_2$) out of the n_2 nonrespondents is selected. Responses (m_f favorable) are assumed to be obtained from the m nonrespondents.

It is further assumed that (conditional on π) n_1 is distributed as binomial with parameters (n, π). Using the definitions of the joint, marginal and conditional probabilities given earlier the likelihood of $(\pi, p_{f \cdot 1}, p_{f \cdot 2})$ given the data (n, n_1, n_{f1}, m, m_f) is given by

$$l(\pi, p_{f \cdot 1}, p_{f \cdot 2} | n, n_1, n_{f1}, m, m_f)$$
$$\propto \pi^{n_1}(1 - \pi)^{n - n_1} p_{f \cdot 1}^{n_{f1}}(1 - p_{f \cdot 1})^{n_1 - n_{f1}} p_{f \cdot 2}^{m_f}(1 - p_{f \cdot 2})^{m - m_f}. \tag{12}$$

Combining the likelihood (12) with the prior (11), the posterior distribution of $(\pi, p_{f \cdot 1}, p_{f \cdot 2})$, say, f'', is obtained. The posterior mean and variance of p_f are obtained in a straightforward manner using (10) and the posterior distribution f''.

Kaufman and King (1973) perform the Bayesian analysis in two parts:

(i) In the first part, it is assumed that the main interest is to obtain the optimal estimator of p_f and the optimal value of m. To do this, it is assumed that the loss is given by

$$L(n, n_1, n_{f1}, m, m_f; p_f, \hat{p}_f, K, Q') = K(p_f - \hat{p}_f)^2 + c_2 m, \tag{13}$$

where $K = $ a positive constant which represents the trade-off between the errors of estimation and sampling costs and $c_2 = $ the per unit cost of sampling and processing the desired measurements from the nonrespondents.

As usual, the optimal point estimator of p_f is the posterior mean of p_f, say, $\hat{p}_{fo}$. An algorithm is given for obtaining the optimal value of m, m_o. Then the optimal loss is given by

$$L_1 = L_1(n, n_1, n_{f1}, m_o; \hat{p}_{fo}, K, Q') + c_2 m_o.$$

(ii) In the second part, it is desired to obtain the optimal value of n. It is assumed that the loss is given by

$$L_2 = L_1 + cn, \tag{14}$$

where c is the per unit cost of selection in the random sample.

Now the expectation of the loss (14) is taken with respect to the joint pre-posterior distribution of (n_1, n_{f1}) given n and Q'. The resulting loss is then minimized with respect to n to obtain the optimal value n_o. An algorithm is given for obtaining n_o.

Then the results are extended to the case of finite populations.

Gunel (1979) studies the multinomial model 2×2 contingency table data with some cell counts missing. He assumes a random sample of size n with n_1 responses and n_2 nonresponses. Of these n_1 responses, n_{f1} are found to be favorable and n_{u1} are unfavorable. Given this data (i.e., no classification of the nonrespondents), Gunel considers inference problems regarding

(i)   The test for a specified value of p_f (see Table 1)
(ii) The test of row–column independence
(iii) The test for specified values of (p_{f1}, p_{f2}) (see Table 1)

Kaufman and King (1973) also consider inference problems for dichotomous processes when there is no follow-up for nonrespondents. However, unlike Gunel, Kaufman and King consider the optimal choice of n.

3.3. Regression Models

In many situations researchers are interested in studying the relation between two or more variables. In this case, the researcher might wish to make inferences concerning the regression coefficients of a multiple linear regression. Singh and Sedransk (1975, 1978a) consider inferences about such regression coefficients when there is nonresponse. Rubin (1977) considers a related problem employing a multiple linear regression model. These two papers are now described.

Singh and Sedransk (1978a) assume that there is a single response variable X and r regressor variables $Z_1, \ldots, Z_r$. As before, $i = 1$ denotes the set of individuals in the given population who would, if sampled, "respond" to the given inquiry; and $i = 2$ denotes the complementary set of "nonrespondents." It is further assumed that π is the (unknown) proportion of respondents in the population. Singh and Sedransk (1978a) illustrate their approach by assuming that there are two multiple linear regressions, one for the "respondent" stratum and the other for the "nonrespondent" stratum:

$$x_{ij} = \bar{x}_i + \sum_{k=1}^{r} \beta_{ik}(z_{ikj} - \bar{z}_{ik}) + \epsilon_{ij}, \qquad i = 1, 2, \tag{15}$$

where $\bar{z}_{ik}$ and $\bar{x}_i$ are the sample means of the z_{ikj} and x_{ij} and the $\{\epsilon_{ij}\}$ are assumed to be independent with $\epsilon_{ij} \sim N(0, h_i^{-1})$.

Defining $\boldsymbol{\beta}_i = (\beta_{i1}, \ldots, \beta_{ir})^t$, it is assumed that the parameters $\{(h_i, \boldsymbol{\beta}_i);$ $i = 1, 2\}$ have independent, locally uniform prior distributions:

$$\prod_{i=1}^{2} f(\boldsymbol{\beta}_i, h_i) \propto \prod_{i=1}^{2} h_i^{-1}. \tag{16}$$

It is further postulated that the prior $g(\pi)$ on π is independent of the prior distribution on $\{(\boldsymbol{\beta}_i, h_i); i = 1, 2\}$ and is given by

$$g(\pi) \propto \{\pi(1 - \pi)\}^{-1}. \tag{17}$$

Distributional assumptions about the z_{ikj} are made when needed.

The first-phase (pilot) random sample of size n' yields responses

$$\mathbf{x}_1' = (x_{11}', \ldots, x_{1m_1'}')^t, \qquad \{\mathbf{z}_{1j}' = (z_{11j}', \ldots, z_{1rj}')^t, j = 1, \ldots, m_1'\}$$

from the $m_1' \equiv n_1'$ respondents.[3] Then a random subsample of fixed size m_2' $(0 \le m_2' \le n_2')$ is selected from the n_2' nonrespondents. With an assumed 100% response, the variant values

$$\mathbf{x}_2' = (x_{21}', \ldots, x_{2m_2'}')^t, \qquad \{\mathbf{z}_{2j}' = (z_{21j}', \ldots, z_{2rj}')^t, j = 1, \ldots, m_2'\}$$

are obtained. It is assumed that the distribution of the number of respondents m_1' can be satisfactorily approximated by (conditional on π) a binomial distribution with parameters n' and π.

The posterior distribution of $(\pi, \boldsymbol{\beta}_i, h_i; i = 1, 2)$ given the pilot data is derived in a straightforward manner using (15)–(17). In the sequel this posterior distribution f' is treated as a prior distribution on $(\pi, \boldsymbol{\beta}_i, h_i; i = 1, 2)$.

For the second-phase sample, a random sample of size n is selected (independently of the pilot sample) from the population. The sample design and notation are exactly as given for the first-phase sample except that here we suppress the primes $[$i.e., $\{m_i, \mathbf{x}_i, \mathbf{z}_{i1}, \ldots, \mathbf{z}_{im_i}\}$ replaces $\{m_i', \mathbf{x}_i', \mathbf{z}_{i1}', \ldots, \mathbf{z}_{im_i'}'\}]$.

Combining the likelihood from the second-phase sample with the prior f', we obtain the posterior distribution f'' of $(\pi, \boldsymbol{\beta}_i, h_i; i = 1, 2)$. As usual single primes refer to the first-phase (pilot) sample while double primes refer to the distribution posterior to samples from both phases.

It is assumed that joint inference about the regression coefficients (β_{1k}, β_{2k}) is of main interest and that the loss is given by

$$L = L(n, m_i, \mathbf{x}_i, \mathbf{z}_{i1}, \ldots, \mathbf{z}_{im_i}; i = 1, 2; \beta_{1k}, \beta_{2k}, \hat{\beta}_{1k}, \hat{\beta}_{2k}, K_1, K_2, K_3, Q')$$
$$= K_1(\beta_{1k} - \hat{\beta}_{1k})^2 + K_2(\beta_{2k} - \hat{\beta}_{2k})^2 + K_3(\beta_{1k} - \hat{\beta}_{1k})(\beta_{2k} - \hat{\beta}_{2k})$$
$$+ cn + c_1 m_1 + c_2 m_2 + C,$$

[3] See Section 2 (second and third paragraphs) for the sample design and notation.

where $Q' = \{n', m'_i, \mathbf{x}'_i, \mathbf{z}'_{i1}, \ldots, \mathbf{z}'_{im'_i}; i = 1, 2\}$, and the positive constants K_1, K_2 and K_3 represent trade-offs among the errors of estimation and sampling costs. The fixed budget for first-phase sampling is denoted by C, while the per unit costs of sampling at the second phase are c, c_1, and c_2. Here, c, c_1, and c_2, are, respectively, the costs of selecting the random sample, sampling and processing the responses of the "respondents," and sampling and processing the responses of the "nonrespondents."

The optimal point estimator of (β_{1k}, β_{2k}) and the optimal values of m_2 and n are obtained using an extensive form of analysis. The optimal point estimator of β_{ik} $(i = 1, 2)$ is given by the posterior mean of β_{ik},

$$E''(\beta_{ik}|n, m_i, \mathbf{x}_i, \mathbf{z}_{i1}, \ldots, \mathbf{z}_{im_i}; Q') = \hat{\beta}_{iko} = b''_{ik},$$

where

$$\mathbf{b}''_i = (\mathbf{S}_i + \mathbf{S}'_i)^{-1}(\mathbf{S}'_i\mathbf{b}'_i + \mathbf{S}_i\mathbf{b}_i),$$

$$\mathbf{S}'_i = \mathbf{Z}'^t_i\mathbf{Z}'_i,$$

$\mathbf{Z}'_i$ is an $(m'_i \times r)$ matrix with (l, k)th element $(z'_{ikl} - \bar{z}'_{ik})$, $\mathbf{1}$ is an $(m'_i \times 1)$ vector of unit elements, $\mathbf{b}'_i = (b'_{i1}, \ldots, b'_{ir})^t$ is any solution of the "normal equations"

$$\mathbf{b}'_i = \mathbf{Z}'^t_i(\mathbf{x}'_i - \mathbf{1} \cdot \bar{x}'_i),$$

$$Q' = \{n', (m'_i, \mathbf{x}'_i, \mathbf{z}'_{i1}, \ldots, \mathbf{z}'_{im'_i}); i = 1, 2\},$$

and $(\mathbf{S}_i, \mathbf{Z}_i, \mathbf{b}_i)$ are defined analogously to $(\mathbf{S}'_i, \mathbf{Z}'_i, \mathbf{b}'_i)$ by suppressing the single primes throughout.

To complete the preposterior analysis, we make some distribution assumptions about the z_{ikj}. Let

$$\mathbf{z}_{ij} = (z_{i1j}, \ldots, z_{irj})^t; \qquad j = 1, \ldots, m_i; \quad i = 1, 2.$$

First we assume that the $\mathbf{z}_{ij}, j = 1, \ldots, m_i$, are i.i.d. $N_r(\boldsymbol{\mu}_i, \boldsymbol{\Sigma}_i)$ where $\boldsymbol{\mu}_i$ and $\boldsymbol{\Sigma}_i$ are unknown parameters. It is further assumed that the parameters $\{(\boldsymbol{\mu}_i, \boldsymbol{\Sigma}_i^{-1}); i = 1, 2\}$ have independent, locally uniform prior distributions:

$$\prod_{i=1}^{2} f(\boldsymbol{\mu}_i, \boldsymbol{\Sigma}_i^{-1}) \propto \prod_{i=1}^{2} |\boldsymbol{\Sigma}_i^{-1}|^{-(1/2)(r+1)}.$$

Finally, it is postulated that the $\{\mathbf{z}'_{ij}\}$ have the same distributional structure as do the $\{\mathbf{z}_{ij}\}$.

The preposterior analysis is completed using the above assumptions on $\{z_{ijk}\}$. The optimal value of m_2, m_{2o}, is given by

$$m_{2o} = \begin{cases} 0 & \text{if} \quad \varphi \leq 0 \\ (n - m_1)\varphi & \text{if} \quad 0 < \varphi < 1 \\ n - m_1 & \text{if} \quad \varphi \geq 1, \end{cases}$$

where

$$\varphi = \frac{1}{(n - m_1)} \left[\left\{ \frac{K_2(v_2'v_2')}{c_2(v_2' - 2)} \cdot (m_2' - 1)(S_2')^{kk} \right\}^{1/2} - (m_2' - 2) \right],$$

$$v_2' = m_2' - p_2', \qquad p_2' = \text{rank } \mathbf{Z}_2' = \text{rank } \mathbf{S}_2' = r,$$

$$v_2'v_2' = (\mathbf{x}_2' - \bar{x}_2' \cdot \mathbf{1} - \mathbf{Z}_2'\mathbf{b}_2')^t(\mathbf{x}_2' - \bar{x}_2' \cdot \mathbf{1} - \mathbf{Z}_2'\mathbf{b}_2'),$$

and $(S_2')^{kk}$ is the (k, k)th element of $(S_2')^{-1}$.

Assume that $m_{2_0} = (n - m_1)\varphi$; it is clear that subsampling of nonrespondents should be increased as the standard deviation of the responses among nonrespondents increases, the per unit cost of sampling the nonrespondents decreases, and K_2 increases.

There is no simple analytical expression for the optimal value of n, n_0. Singh and Sedransk develop an approximation for n_0 by ignoring the restrictions that $m_{2_0} \geq 0$ and $m_{2_0} \leq n - m_1$ and then carrying out the preposterior analysis accordingly. Then, the approximation to n_0, n_A, is given by

$$n_A = \max\left[\{K_1 V'/(c + c_1 p')\}^{1/2} - n', 0 \right],$$

where

$$v_1' = m_1' - p_1', \qquad p_1' = \text{rank } \mathbf{Z}_1' = \text{rank } \mathbf{S}_1' = r,$$

$$v_1'v_1' = (\mathbf{x}_1' - \bar{x}_1' \cdot \mathbf{1} - \mathbf{Z}_1'\mathbf{b}_1')^t(\mathbf{x}_1' - \bar{x}_1' \cdot \mathbf{1} - \mathbf{Z}_1'\mathbf{b}_1'),$$

$$V' = n'\{v_1'v_1'(S_1')^{kk}/(v_1' - 2)\}, \qquad p' = m_1'/n',$$

and $(S_1')^{kk}$ is the (k, k)th element of $(S_1')^{-1}$.

In some circumstances one might wish to consider inference [see, e.g., Konijn (1962), Porter (1973)] concerning the pooled regression coefficients

$$\bar{\beta}_k = \pi\beta_{1k} + (1 - \pi)\beta_{2k}; \qquad k = 1, \ldots, r.$$

Singh and Sedransk (1975) have extended the methods discussed earlier to the case where inference about $\bar{\beta}_k$ is desired (and appropriate).

Rubin (1977) considers a related nonresponse problem as follows: A simple random sample of size n is selected from the finite population of N units, yielding n_1 responses and $n_2 = n - n_1$ nonresponses. Then the sample mean $\bar{x}_n$ of the dependent variable X is given by

$$\bar{x}_n = (1 - p)\bar{x}_1 + p\bar{x}_2,$$

where $\bar{x}_1$ and $\bar{x}_2$ are, respectively, the sample means of the dependent variable X in the respondent and nonrespondent strata and $p = n_2/n$ is the proportion of nonrespondents in the sample. It should be noted that $\bar{x}_2$ is not observable, since the n_2 observations are missing.

The model for the X values is assumed to be given by

$$x_{ij} = \alpha_i + \sum_{k=1}^{r} \beta_{ik}z_{ikj} + \epsilon_{ij}, \qquad i = 1, 2,$$

where the $\{z_{ikj}\}$ are the regressor variables and the observations on these are available for the respondents as well as the nonrespondents. Further, the $\{\epsilon_{ij}\}$ are assumed to be independent with $\epsilon_{ij} \sim N(0, \sigma_i^2)$.

Let $\delta_i = (\sigma_i^2, \alpha_i, \beta_{ik}; k = 1, \ldots, r)^t$; it is assumed that the components of the parameter δ_1 have independent, noninformative prior distributions. Combining the prior on δ_1 with the likelihood of δ_1 given the respondent data, the posterior distribution on δ_1 is obtained. This posterior distribution on δ_1 is now used to obtain the predictive distribution of $\mathbf{x}_2 = (x_{21}, \ldots, x_{2n_2})^t$. This predictive distribution is obtained by assuming that the nonrespondents' parameters are centered at the respondents' parameters with variability specified by "subjective" parameters. Then this resulting predictive distribution of $\mathbf{x}_2$ is used to make a "subjective confidence interval" for the sample mean $\bar{x}_n$.

REFERENCES

Cochran, W. G. (1977). *Sampling Techniques* (3rd ed.). New York: Wiley.

Ericson, W. A. (1967). Optimal sample design with non-response. *Journal of the American Statistical Association* 62: 63–78.

Ericson, W. A. (1969). Subjective Bayesian models in sampling finite populations (with discussion). *The Journal of the Royal Statistical Society, Series B (Methodological)* 31:195–233.

Gunel, Erdogan (1983). A Bayesian analysis of the multinomial model for a dichotomous response with nonrespondents. *Journal of the American Statistical Association* (in press).

Guttman, I., and Palit, C. D. (1972a). Optimal allocation for two phase stratified samples when the within stratum observations are correlated: A Bayesian approach. Technical Report #300, Department of Statistics, University of Wisconsin, Madison.

Guttman, I., and Palit, C. D. (1972b). Effect of auto-correlations on the optimum allocations in two-phase stratified sampling. Technical Report #301, Department of Statistics, University of Wisconsin, Madison.

Hartley, H. O., and Rao, J. N. K. (1968). A new estimation theory for sample surveys. *Biometrika* 55:547–559.

Kaufman, G. M., and King, B. (1973). A Bayesian analysis of nonresponse in dichotomous processes. *Journal of the American Statistical Association*, 68:670–678.

Konijn, H. S. (1962). Regression analysis in sample surveys. *Journal of the American Statistical Association* 57:590–606.

Palit, C. D., and Guttman, I. (1972). Bayesian distribution theory for two phase sampling under non-standard conditions. Technical Report #303, Department of Statistics, University of Wisconsin, Madison.

Porter, R. (1973). On the use of survey sample weights in the linear model. *Annals of Economic and Social Measurement* 2:141–158.

Rao, J. N. K., and Ghangurde, P. D. (1972). Bayesian optimization in sampling finite populations. *Journal of the American Statistical Association* 67:439–443.

Rubin, D. (1977). A method for formalizing subjective notions about the effect of nonrespondents in sample surveys. *Journal of the American Statistical Association* 72: 538–543.

Singh, B. (1974). Some contributions to the theory of nonresponse in sample surveys from a Bayesian view. Unpublished Ph.D. thesis, Department of Statistics, University of Wisconsin, Madison.

Singh, B., and Sedransk, J. (1975). Estimation of regression coefficients when there is nonresponse. Technical Report #25, Statistical Science Division, State University of New York at Buffalo.

Singh, B., and Sedransk, J. (1976). A two-phase sample design for estimating the finite population mean: Post stratification. Technical Report #39, Statistical Science Division, State University of New York at Buffalo.

Singh, B., and Sedransk, J. (1978a). Sample size selection in regression analysis when there is non-response. *Journal of the American Statistical Association* 73:362–365.

Singh, B., and Sedransk, J. (1978b). A two-phase sample design for estimating the finite population mean when there is nonresponse. In N. K. Namboodiri (ed.), *Survey Sampling and Measurement*, Chapter 10. New York: Academic Press.

PART IV

Weighting and Imputation Methods

Conceptual Issues in the Presence of Nonresponse

Donald B. Rubin

The purpose of this chapter is to introduce concepts useful for understanding the methods for handling nonresponse in sample surveys discussed in the subsequent chapters of this part of the volume. In order to establish notation and basic ideas, we begin with a discussion of inference in the absence of nonresponse, and then extend the development to include inference in the presence of nonresponse.

In the absence of nonresponse, two approaches to inference about finite population quantities from sample surveys can be distinguished, the *randomization approach* and the *model-based approach*. The randomization approach, which dominates current survey practice, treats values in the population as fixed, and inferences are derived from the distribution used to select units into the sample. The model-based approach, which dominates mathematical statistical literature, treats values in the population as random variables and inferences are derived from the model specified for these random variables. Probability sampling is not formally required under the model-based approach, although in practice it is strongly advisable in order to avoid sensitivity of inferences to unverifiable aspects of the model [see, for example, Rubin (1978a)].

Although the model-based approach to statistics is prevalent in many branches of statistics, it is not greatly favored by survey practitioners. The models commonly discussed in the statistics literature are insufficiently rich for the data from large surveys using complex sampling designs. Consequently, many survey practitioners feel that the potential biases from model misspecification outweigh the potential gains from efficient estimation if the model is true (Hansen, Madow, and Tepping, 1978). This assessment is not actually a criticism

INCOMPLETE DATA
IN SAMPLE SURVEYS
Volume 2, Part IV

of the model-based approach in principle, but rather a criticism of the technology currently available for its implementation.

In the presence of nonresponse, the randomization approach needs to be modified, since the known specification for the sampling mechanism (i.e., the mechanism that selects units into the sample) is no longer sufficient to derive inferences. Some assumption needs to be made about the *responding mechanism*, that is, the mechanism that governs which units in the sample respond and which fail to respond.

Commonly, the responding mechanism is assumed to be ignorable, a concept defined in this chapter; the weighting methods of the chapter by Oh and Scheuren and the hot-deck methods of the chapter by Ford, for example, assume that within certain subgroups of the sample, the responding mechanism can be regarded as another stage of random sampling. Randomization inferences are based on the distribution obtained by combining the known model for the sampling mechanism with such a postulated model for the responding mechanism. This approach is appropriately named "quasi-randomization" in the chapter by Oh and Scheuren, where the "quasi" refers to the implicit modeling of the responding mechanism which it involves. For simplicity, in this chapter, both the pure randomization and the quasi-randomization approaches are called the randomization approach.

The treatment of nonresponse in the model-based approach is conceptually more straightforward than in the randomization approach, since the model for the population values is simple extended to include the modeling of the responding mechanism. Inferences are based on the distribution derived from the joint model for (a) the population values, (b) the responding mechanism, and (c) the known sampling mechanism. This approach is developed in detail in Part VI of this volume: Chapter 20 deals with ignorable responding mechanisms and Chapter 21 deals with nonignorable responding mechanisms.

The discussion of the model-based approach in this chapter is Bayesian in the sense that inferences are made by calculating a posterior probability distribution of unknown values in the finite population given (a) known values in the population and (b) a priori specified models. Thus, the focus of discussion in this Bayesian approach is on the observable values in the finite population just as in the randomization approach. Much of the theory presented here is based on the missing data framework of Rubin (1976), which focuses on estimating parameters of a hypothetical superpopulation from which the finite population is drawn. A non-Bayesian model-based approach to inference is proposed by Royall (1968), where inferences are based on the mean squared error of estimators under repeated sampling from such a superpopulation. We find this approach harder to justify in finite-population sampling than the Bayesian perspective, since the former leads to inferences which are not conditional on the population of interest. However, in simple cases, the two approaches lead to similar answers in practice. Little and Rubin (see Volume 3,

Session VIII), in a discussion of Brewer and Särndal (see Volume 3, Session VIII), provide more arguments for the practical sufficiency of the dichotomous—randomization versus Bayesian—view of inference in finite-population surveys.

A review of the theory in the *absence* of nonresponse is given in Section 1. This discussion then leads to the consideration of theory in the *presence* of nonresponse given in Section 2. In order to focus on issues arising from nonresponse, we assume in Sections 1 and 2 a simple random sample with one variable Y whose mean $\overline{Y}$ we wish to know in a population of N units. Also, we assume that if Y is recorded for the ith unit, then its true value is always obtained without error, and this value is always the same. Many of the essential features of the nonresponse problem are present in this simple case. New issues that arise in more general surveys are briefly addressed in Section 3. The other chapters in Part IV deal with techniques for handling response. The chapter by Oh and Scheuren on weighting methods and the chapter by Ford on the hot deck are based largely on the randomization point of view; these two methods are standard methods currently used in large scale surveys. The technique of multiple imputations discussed in the chapter by Herzog and Rubin can be viewed as a method for approximating either the randomization or Bayesian approach in practice; although promising, this method is not standard practice at this time.

1. THEORY IN THE ABSENCE OF NONRESPONSE

This section presents the theory underlying randomization inference and Bayesian inference in the absence of nonresponse. In order to focus on essential issues, we assume that a simple random sample of n units is drawn from a population of N units with the objective of estimating the mean of a variable in the population. More general survey situations are briefly discussed in Section 3.

The material presented here on randomization inference is the standard approach presented in the classical books on sample surveys, such as Cochran (1977), Hansen, Hurwitz, and Madow (1953), and Kish (1965). The material on Bayesian inference is less well known among survey practitioners, although in fact quite old. For example, Bayesian methods were used by Laplace in 1820 to estimate the population of France (Cochran, 1978). The subjective Bayesian approach to surveys has been presented in Ericson (1969) and Lindley (1972). Another Bayesian approach, called "phenomenological" in Rubin (1978b,c) because of the focus on observables, is being followed here since it explicitly addresses sample design and nonresponse issues by including models for sampling and nonresponse in addition to the traditional Bayesian model for the distribution of the data.

1.1.   Notation in the Absence of Nonresponse

Suppose that there is one variable of interest in a sample survey and that this variable is the only one recorded for data analysis. The value of this variable for the ith unit in the population of N units is Y_i, where Y_i cannot be recorded unless the ith unit is included in the sample. Further suppose that the objective of drawing a sample is to estimate the mean value of the variable in the population $\bar{Y} = \sum_1^N Y_i/N$. The inferences for $\bar{Y}$ will be made using probability statements based on the observed values of Y_i in the sample.

Let the design vector $D = (D_1, \ldots, D_N)$ indicate sampled and unsampled units in the survey: $D_i = 1$ means that the ith unit is included in the sample; $D_i = 0$ means that the ith unit is not sampled, and thus Y_i cannot be observed. In the absence of nonresponse, $D_i = 1$ implies the Y_i is observed.

Throughout this part of the volume, we shall assume that the indices of the units have been assigned as a random permutation of $(1, \ldots, N)$ and thus are "noninformative" in the terminology of Godambe (1966). This assumption is nothing more than a notational convenience because any information in the units' labels or names can always be encoded as covariates. That is, if there exists auxiliary information available on the units and we wish to incorporate it in our survey design or data analysis, then this information should be used to create covariates. For example, suppose the units are people and the names of the people are considered to be informative because of indications of family ties and gender. Then indicator covariates can be defined to encode gender and family ties from the names of the people, and the indices can be assigned as a random permutation with no loss of information.

In order to focus on issues of nonresponse, we assume throughout the chapter that the survey is a probability sample—more precisely, an "unconfounded" probability sample in the sense to be indicated. In the case of only Y recorded, we mean by an unconfounded probability sample that all users of the survey will accept the probability model specifying that (a) the vector D is unconfounded with the vector $Y = (Y_1, \ldots, Y_N)$, that is, for each of the possible values of D, $\Pr(D|Y) = \Pr(D)$; and (b) each unit has positive probability of being sampled, that is, $\Pr(D_i = 1|Y) > 0$ for each i and all possible values of Y. If $\Pr(D|Y) \neq \Pr(D)$, the sample is said to be confounded, (i.e., is confounded with Y). If $\Pr(D_i = 1|Y) = 0$ for some i and some possible Y, the sample is said to be a nonprobability sample (i.e., some unit has zero probability of being sampled).

We call the model for $\Pr(D|Y)$ the sampling mechanism, where we use the noun "mechanism" rather than "model" to distinguish this model from the more usual statistical models applied to the distribution of the data Y. Both randomization and Bayesian methods of inference require specification of a sampling mechanism before inferences for $\bar{Y}$ can be drawn. If it is inappropriate to assume an unconfounded probability sampling mechanism, then some other specific sampling mechanism must be assumed; for example, a confounded probability sampling mechanism specifying that the probability of sampling the ith unit is a decreasing function of Y_i, such as for positive Y_i, $\Pr(D|Y) = \prod_{i=1}^{N} [\exp(-Y_i)]^{D_i} [1 - \exp(-Y_i)]^{1-D_i}$. Such a model might be appropriate for a quota survey where units with larger values of Y_i are less likely to participate.

Because we are assuming random indexing of units and a probability sampling mechanism, all samples of the same size are equally likely; that is, all D having the same value of $n = \sum_1^N D_i$ have the same probability of occurrence. It is common for n to be fixed a priori at the desired sample size; the resulting sample is called a simple random sample. In some cases, n is not fixed a priori. For instance, in Bernoulli sampling, the sampling of the units is effectively determined by the results of N independent tosses of a coin; e.g., if the coin has probability .2 of heads (for sampled), $\Pr(D|Y) = \prod_1^N (.2)^{D_i}(.8)^{1-D_i}$. With a probability sampling mechanism, nearly all practical inferences treat n as fixed at its observed value, and thus treat the sample as a simple random sample, with corresponding sampling mechanism

$$\Pr(D|Y) = \Pr(D) = \begin{cases} \binom{N}{n}^{-1} & \text{if } \sum_1^N D_i = n, \text{ where } n \text{ is fixed and} \\ & \text{known a priori} \\ 0 & \text{otherwise.} \end{cases} \quad (1)$$

Throughout Sections 1 and 2 of this chapter, we shall assume that Eq. (1) is the accepted specification for the mechanism that selects units to be included in the sample, the sampling mechanism. Consequently, in the context of these Sections, "probability sampling mechanism" implies "simple random sampling mechanism."

1.2. Further Model Specification in the Absence of Nonresponse

Having specified the sampling mechanism $\Pr(D|Y)$, an obvious question is whether to complete the probability specification by including a model for the marginal distribution of the vector Y. That is, should Y be treated as fixed but unknown or as a random variable? The randomization and Bayesian answers to this question are different, randomization inference treating Y as fixed and Bayesian inference treating Y as a random variable.

Randomization inference avoids specifying a model for the distribution of the data $\Pr(Y)$, because such a specification is often considered relatively subjective and questionable. The specification for the sampling mechanism is usually considered to be entirely acceptable and objective. Randomization inferences about $\bar{Y}$, since they are not based on a specification for the distribution of Y, ideally are intended to hold regardless of the distribution of Y; actually for most practice, relatively mild assumptions, based on the approximate normality of sample means, are required. Usually careful survey design will lead to sample means (in simple random samples or within strata) that are approximately normally distributed for any plausible Y.

Bayesian inferences, on the other hand, require and are sensitive to the specification of the model for the distribution of the data. However, one clear advantage of specifying a model for $\Pr(Y)$ is that direct probability statements can be made about the distirbution of $\bar{Y}$ given the observed values in the sample. That is, after observing D and the known values of Y_i, Bayesian inference, in contrast to randomization inference, treats these known values as the observed values of random variables and so draws inferences about the random variable $\bar{Y}$ by conditioning on these observed values.

1.3. Randomization Inference in the Absence of Nonresponse

Randomization inference treats Y as fixed and draws inferences for $\bar{Y}$ by considering the "randomization" distribution of a statistic S chosen to estimate $\bar{Y}$. The randomization distribution of S is defined to be the conditional distribution of S given Y, as specified by $\Pr(D|Y)$.

Specifically, there are three tasks that must be handled in order to draw randomization inferences about $\bar{Y}$:

(1) Define a statistic $S = S(Y, D)$, depending only on values Y_i such that $D_i = 1$, to be used to estimate $\bar{Y}$ (e.g., the sample mean of the Y_i).

(2) Analytically calculate properties of the randomization distribution of S, principally the mean and variance:

$$E(S|Y) = \sum_D S \Pr(D|Y),$$

$$\mathrm{Var}(S|Y) = \sum_D (S - E(S|Y))^2 \Pr(D|Y).$$

The summation is over the set of all possible design vectors D.

(3) Estimate the randomization distribution of S, e.g., find good estimators of its bias $E(S|Y) - \bar{Y}$ and its variance $\mathrm{Var}(S|Y)$.

If (a) the squared bias of S is negligible compared to its variance, (b) the variance of S is well estimated by the statistic $\hat{V}\mathrm{ar}(S|Y)$, and (c) the randomization distribution of S is approximately normal, then $S \pm 2\sqrt{\hat{V}\mathrm{ar}(S|Y)}$ includes $\bar{Y}$ in approximately 95% of the possible samples generated by $\Pr(D|Y)$. The observed value of this interval, i.e. the observed value of S plus and minus twice the square root of the observed value of $\hat{V}\mathrm{ar}(S|Y)$, is the 95% confidence interval for $\bar{Y}$ based on the statistics S and $\hat{V}\mathrm{ar}(S|Y)$.

With a simple random sample and no nonresponse, the usual statistic S for estimating $\bar{Y}$ is the sample mean

$$\bar{y} = \sum_1^N D_i Y_i/n = \sum_1^n y_i/n. \tag{2}$$

It is easy to show under the specification (1) for the sampling mechanism that $\bar{y}$ is unbiased for $\bar{Y}$:

$$E(\bar{y}|Y) = \sum \bar{y}\,\mathrm{Pr}(D|Y) = \sum_D \bar{y}\,\mathrm{Pr}(D) = \bar{Y}. \tag{3}$$

Similarly, the variance of $\bar{y}$ is given by

$$\mathrm{Var}(\bar{y}|Y) = \sum_D (\bar{y} - E(\bar{y}|Y))^2 \,\mathrm{Pr}(D) = \frac{V}{n}\left(1 - \frac{n}{N}\right), \tag{4}$$

where

$$(N-1)V = \sum_1^N (Y_i - \bar{Y})^2. \tag{5}$$

When n and N are moderately large, the distribution of the $\binom{N}{n}$ possible values of $\bar{y}$ generated by S is often approximately normal; this crucial result (cf. Madow, 1948) is based on the central limit theorem effect. Consequently, the distribution of the $\binom{N}{n}$ possible values of $(\bar{y} - \bar{Y})/\sqrt{(V/n)(1 - (n/N))}$ is approximately $N(0, 1)$, so that the interval

$$\bar{y} \pm 2\sqrt{\frac{V}{n}\left(1 - \frac{n}{N}\right)} \tag{6}$$

includes $\bar{Y}$ in approximately 95% of the possible samples.

In a particular sample, the value of $\bar{y}$ is known; however, V is a function of unobserved Y_i values, and so the interval (6) cannot be calculated in a particular sample. A second statistic, specifically

$$\hat{V} = \frac{1}{n-1}\sum_1^N D_i(Y_i - \bar{y})^2 = \frac{1}{n-1}\sum_1^n (y_i - \bar{y})^2 \tag{7}$$

is used to estimate V; it can be shown that $\hat{V}$ is unbiased for V. The two statistics $\bar{y}$ and $\hat{V}$ then form the basis of randomization inference for $\bar{Y}$.

Upon substituting the statistic $\hat{V}$ for V in (6), we have that with a simple random sample and moderately large n, the interval

$$\bar{y} \pm 2\sqrt{\left(\frac{N-n}{nN}\right)\hat{V}} \tag{8}$$

covers $\bar{Y}$ with approximate probability 0.95 in the frequency sense that in about 95% of the possible samples of size n, the interval given by (8) includes the fixed but unknown $\bar{Y}$.

1.4. Bayesian Inference in the Absence of Nonresponse

Bayesian methods for drawing inferences in sample surveys are conceptually different from randomization methods, but in practice can often lead to similar applied inferences. After specifying a model for the distribution of the data $\Pr(Y)$, the objective of the Bayesian approach is to calculate the posterior distribution of $\bar{Y}$, that is, the conditional distribution of $\bar{Y}$ given all observed values. In the absence of nonresponse, this distribution can be calculated from the conditional distribution of the unobserved components of Y, say Y_U, given the observed or known components of Y, say, Y_K, and the observed value of D. Having computed this distribution of Y_U, the distribution of the sum of the observed and unobserved Y values can be calculated, and hence the distribution of $\bar{Y}$ in the population.

In the case considered in this section with a simple random sample, no nonresponse and only Y recorded, the sampling mechanism is "ignorable" in that it does not affect the posterior distribution of Y_U. More explicitly, the sampling mechanism is ignorable if

$$\Pr(Y_U \mid Y_K, D) = \Pr(Y_U \mid Y_K), \tag{9}$$

where these probabilities are being evaluated at the observed values of Y_K and D. When the sampling mechanism is ignorable, inferences for $\bar{Y}$ follow from the model for $\Pr(Y)$, which is constant under permutation of the unit indices (i.e., is unit exchangeable) because the indexing of units is random.

As an example of the Bayesian approach in the case of this section, suppose we model $\Pr(Y)$ by specifying that the Y_i are independent and identically distributed (i.i.d.), where $f(.|\theta)$ is a common model for each Y_i and θ is a vector parameter having marginal prior distribution $p(\theta)$. Further, let $f(Y_i|\theta)$ be normal with mean μ and variance σ^2, $\theta = (\mu, \sigma^2)$, where $p(\theta) \propto \sigma^{-2}$. Then standard Bayesian calculations show that given Y_K,

$$(\bar{Y} - \bar{y}) \times \left(\left(\frac{N-n}{nN} \right) \hat{V} \right)^{-1/2}$$

is distributed as Student's t with $n-1$ degrees of freedom. Thus, with about 95% probability, $\bar{Y}$ lies in the interval

$$\bar{y} \pm 2 \sqrt{ \left(\frac{N-n}{nN} \right) \hat{V} },$$

effectively the same practical answer as given by randomization inference when n is large.

If a nonnormal model for $\Pr(Y)$ had been chosen, the inferences for $\bar{Y}$ would have been different in general. However, if the sampled Y_i are not violently nonnormal and the samples are reasonably large, the inference that the posterior distribution of $\bar{Y}$ is approximately normal with mean $\bar{y}$ and variance $[(N - n)/(nN)]\,\hat{V}$ can be justified from several perspectives that do not assume the i.i.d. normal model for Y_i (cf. Ericson, 1969; Pratt, 1965). The required Bayesian computations in such cases, however, can be quite demanding as these references make clear.

1.5. Comparing Randomization and Bayesian Inference in the Absence of Nonresponse

Although the randomization and Bayesian inferences for $\bar{Y}$ that we have presented are essentially the same, the logical paths leading to these inferences are very different. The randomization logic assumes that Y is fixed and that D is a random variable; thus, the sample mean $\bar{y}$ and sample variance $\hat{V}$ have a conditional distribution given Y. Under this distribution, the interval (8) includes $\bar{Y}$ in approximately 95% of the $\binom{N}{n}$ possible samples generated by D; the observed value of interval (8) is called a 95% confidence interval for $\bar{Y}$. The phenomenological Bayesian logic assumes that Y and D are both random variables, where D is fully observed and Y is only partially observed, and inferences about the unobserved values of Y, Y_U, are drawn by calculating the distribution of Y_U given the observed values of D and Y_K. In order to calculate this conditional distribution, a prior distribution must be placed over all random variables; thus a model must be specified for $Pr(Y)$ in addition to the model for $Pr(D|Y)$ required by both randomization inference and Bayesian inference. Given a probability sampling mechanism, the normal model for $Pr(Y)$ is a special model that leads the Bayesian to essentially the randomization answer for large n.

Advantages of the randomization approach relative to the Bayesian approach include (a) simplicity and (b) performance as advertised. That is, (a) the statistics $\bar{y}$ and $\hat{V}$ are simple to compute and (b) the probabilities are accurate large samples frequency statements about the proportion of times in long-run practice that the stated intervals will include $\bar{Y}$. Advantages of the Bayesian approach relative to the randomization approach in the simple case of this section include (a) its greater ability to model other (e.g., skew) distributions and so the potential to obtain more accurate probability intervals for $\bar{Y}$ and (b) intervals for $\bar{Y}$ that are direct probability statements about the likely value of $\bar{Y}$.

Because Bayesian inference is focused on being optimal given the model specifications, the Bayesian must always be concerned about the possibility of an inappropriate answer if the specified model is not a good reflection of reality. Randomization inference, on the other hand, avoids a particular model specification for $Pr(Y)$ and consequently tends to be suboptimal but more robust.

2. THEORY IN THE PRESENCE OF NONRESPONSE

We continue to assume that the survey is a simple random sample for values of Y, but we now allow the possibility of nonresponse. Specifically, let $R = (R_1, \ldots, R_N)$, where $R_i = 1$ indicates that the ith unit will respond if sampled for this survey and $R_i = 0$ indicates that the ith unit will not respond if sampled. If the ith unit is a nonrespondent, Y_i is not observed and so not recorded for data analysis. Let the vector $M = (M_1, \ldots, M_N)$ document the recording process for Y: $M_i = 1$ means that Y_i is recorded for data analysis, whereas $M_i = 0$ means that Y_i is not recorded; hence in this special case, when there is no nonresponse, $M = D$. More generally when there exists the possibility of nonresponse, Y_i can be missing for sampled as well as unsampled units; that is, $M_i = 0$ if $D_i = 0$, but for sampled nonrespondents, $D_i = 1$ and $M_i = 0$. Because $M_i = D_i R_i$, $i = 1, \ldots, N$, the use of both M and R is notationally redundant. However, it is convenient to have both indicators because R is only partially observed in a sample (being unknown for unsampled units), whereas both D and M are fully observed in a sample. Consequently, it is simpler notationally to assume that the values of D and M are known in a survey, and values of R_i only known from D_i and M_i.

This section begins with a discussion of the additional model specification needed in the presence of nonresponse and the sensitivity of inference to that model specification; then we discuss randomization inference and Bayesian inference in the presence of nonresponse. A concluding comment considers a compromise approach in which Bayesian methods are used to draw inferences about the values of the unobserved Y_i created by nonresponse and thereby to generate Bayesian distributions for the complete-data statistics that would have been used in the absence of nonresponse.

2.1. Additional Model Specification in the Presence of Nonresponse

As discussed in Section 1, both randomization inference and Bayesian inference require the specification of a sampling mechanism [i.e., a model for $\Pr(D \mid Y)$] in order to draw inferences about the values of Y in the population. When nonresponse is a possibility, both methods also require a model specification for $\Pr(M \mid D, Y)$ in order to draw inferences. In the trivial case of no possibility of nonresponse, we of course have $\Pr(M \mid D, Y) = 1$ if $M = D$ and 0 otherwise. If there is the possibility of nonresponse, though, the assertion that M always equals D is incorrect.

Because $M = R \cdot D$, one way to specify $\Pr(M \mid D, Y)$ is to specify $\Pr(R \mid D, Y)$, that is, specify the probability of the pattern of response given D and Y. It is often natural to think about the probability of response given Y, $\Pr(R \mid Y)$. (For example, it might be reasonable to model the probability of response in an income survey as decreasing with income.) Now by Bayes's theorem

$$\Pr(R \mid D, Y) = \Pr(R \mid Y)\Pr(D \mid Y, R)/\Pr(D \mid Y), \tag{10}$$

In the context of a simple random sample,

$$\Pr(D \mid Y, R) = \Pr(D) = \Pr(D \mid Y); \tag{11}$$

hence

$$\Pr(R \mid D, Y) = \Pr(R \mid Y), \tag{12}$$

Thus, it becomes natural to specify $\Pr(M \mid D, Y)$ by specifying $\Pr(R \mid Y)$, the probability of response given Y. By analogy with the model for $\Pr(D \mid Y)$, we call the model for $\Pr(R \mid Y)$ the responding mechanism, where as before, the noun "mechanism" is used to distinguish $\Pr(R \mid Y)$ from the Bayesian model for the distribution of the data $\Pr(Y)$. Specific models for the responding mechanism have received some attention, especially in economics literature; Chapter 22 in Part VI reviews some of these specific models.

In some cases, it is reasonable to assume $\Pr(R \mid Y)$ is a probability responding mechanism, more precisely, an unconfounded probability responding mechanism; that is, $\Pr(R \mid Y) = \Pr(R)$ and $\Pr(R_i = 1 \mid Y) > 0$ for all i and all possible Y. Since the indexing of units is random, $\Pr(R)$ takes the same value for all R with the same value of $\sum_1^N R_i$. Consequently, a probability responding mechanism, like a probability sampling mechanism, is a random choosing of Y_i. The uniform responding mechanism in the chapter by Oh and Scheuren is a probability responding mechanism.

More generally, it will not be reasonable to assume a probability responding mechanism for the sample as a whole because in general respondents differ from nonrespondents, and a confounded responding mechanism will be appropriate. Since there are no Y_i values observed for units with $R_i = 0$, the modeling of $\Pr(R \mid Y)$ must rely largely on prior assumptions, ideally based on familiarity with the content or the subject area of the survey and the "psychology" of the units of the survey [e.g., see Rosenthal and Rosnow (1975) for research on characteristics of the volunteer subject].

For an example exhibiting the need to rely on prior assumptions for the responding mechanism, suppose that half of the sampled units are nonrespondents and the respondents' Y_i values appear to be exactly the right half of a normal distribution. Which is a more appropriate estimate of $\overline{Y}$: the sample mean for respondents or the minimum observed Y_i for respondents? With a probability responding mechanism, the sample mean is appropriate, whereas if nonresponse occurs for smaller values of Y_i and the Y_i are known to be symmetrically distributed in the population, the minimum observed Y_i is more appropriate. The observed values of Y_i alone cannot discriminate between these alternatives, and consequently inferences will necessarily be sensitive to the choice of models.

2.2.   Sensitivity of Inference to Model Specification

If in a particular survey context there is no single accepted responding mechanism, then it is prudent for both the randomization inference advocate and the Bayesian inference advocate to perform data analyses under a variety of plausible responding mechanisms. If (a) inferences about $\bar{Y}$ vary in important ways as the models change and (b) the data cannot eliminate some models as inappropriate, then the conclusion must be that the data cannot support sharp conclusions about $\bar{Y}$ without further specification of the model for $\Pr(R \mid Y)$.

Even when there exists an accepted responding mechanism, randomization and Bayesian inferences can be difficult to draw. As an illustration, in the half-normal example, suppose we accept a model for $\Pr(R \mid Y)$ that specifies $R_i = 0$ if $Y_i < 100$. The essential problem is that both randomization and Bayesian inferences will depend on prior assumptions about the distribution of Y_i for units with $R_i = 0$, and these prior assumptions cannot be addressed by the observed data because there are no Y_i values observed when $R_i = 0$. Randomization inference is confronted with this fact rather directly because the probability content of a confidence interval depends upon the distribution of Y_i for non-respondents. Bayesian inference is confronted with this fact indirectly, via sensitivity of inferences to the specification of the distribution of the data $\Pr(Y)$; $\Pr(Y)$, together with the assumed responding mechanism $\Pr(R \mid Y)$, implies a distribution for the nonrespondents' Y_i values, and this implied distribution cannot be checked by the observed values of Y_i.

The potential sensitivity of inference to prior assumptions about the distribution of Y_i for nonrespondents is common to both randomization inference and Bayesian inference. The sensitivity of Bayesian inference to the specification for $\Pr(Y)$ is, in a sense, the equivalent of the inability of randomization inference to estimate the randomization distribution of statistics without making some assumptions about the distribution of $\bar{Y}$.

2.3.   Randomization Inference in the Presence
of Nonresponse

Although randomization inference principles can be stated when there is nonresponse, it can be quite difficult to apply these principles to reach inferences in practice. After specification of the responding mechanism, there are three tasks that must be handled:

(1)   Define a statistic $S = S(Y, D, M)$, depending only on values Y_i such that $M_i = 1$, to be used for estimating $\bar{Y}$ (e.g., perhaps a weighted mean of the Y_i with weights reflecting the probability of nonresponse as a function of Y_i).

(2)   Analytically calculate properties of the randomization distribution of S,

principally, the mean and variance:

$$E(S)|Y) = \sum_M \sum_D [S \times \Pr(M|D, Y) \Pr(D)] \qquad (13)$$

and

$$\mathrm{Var}(S|Y) = \sum_M \sum_D (S - E(S|Y))^2 \Pr(M|D, Y) \Pr(D). \qquad (14)$$

The summation is over the set of all possible missingness patterns M and designs D.

(3) Estimate the randomization distribution of S, e.g., find good estimators of its bias $(E(S|Y) - \bar{Y})$ and variance $\mathrm{Var}(S|Y)$.

If (a) the squared bias of S is negligible compared to its variance, (b)·the variance of S is well estimated by $\hat{\mathrm{V}}\mathrm{ar}(S|Y)$, and (c) the randomization distribution of S is approximately normal, then the observed value of S plus and minus twice the square root of the observed value of $\hat{\mathrm{V}}\mathrm{ar}(S|Y)$ will be considered a 95% confidence interval for $\bar{Y}$.

Even assuming an accepted specification for the responding mechanism, the remaining tasks can be formidable. Because the indexing of units is random, $\Pr(R|Y)$ is an exchangeable function of the (R_i, Y_i)—i.e., the function is the same for all permutations of the unit indices. Hence, a confounded responding mechanism, i.e., $\Pr(R|Y) \neq \Pr(R)$, implies that $\Pr(R|Y)$ varies with each Y_i for fixed $(Y_1, \ldots, Y_{i-1}, Y_{i+1}, \ldots, Y_N)$ and thus $\Pr(M|D, Y)$ varies with each Y_i. As a consequence, $E(S|Y)$ and $\mathrm{Var}(S|Y)$ calculated in task (2) will generally be functions that are difficult to estimate, as called for in step (3), because they will vary with all Y_i values, even those with $R_i = 0$ for which there are no observations. Furthermore, the approximate normality of the randomization distribution should be verified for the specification $\Pr(R|Y)$, statistic S, and plausible Y.

The formidable nature of the above tasks can be easily illustrated by a specific example. Consider the 50% response situation discussed earlier, with the observed data appearing right-half normal and the minimum observed value equal to 100. Suppose that $\Pr(R|Y)$ specifies that all units with Y_i less than ϕ will be nonrespondents and that all units with Y_i greater or equal to ϕ will be respondents, where ϕ is uniformly distributed between 0 and 10^6. Although $S = \min[Y_i|M_i = 1]$ (the minumum observed Y_i) seems to be a plausible estimator of $\bar{Y}$, the bias and variance of this estimator depend upon the distribution of Y_i for the nonrespondents, and consequently, no satisfactory randomization inferences can be drawn for $\bar{Y}$ without making some further assumptions about the distribution of Y_i for the nonrespondents. Specifically, in large samples under these models the statistic $\min[Y_i|M_i = 1]$ will nearly equal the median of the Y_i in the population; thus, the bias of $\min[Y_i|M_i = 1]$ for estimating $\bar{Y}$ is the difference between the median of the Y_i and $\bar{Y}$, which cannot be determined without adding some further prior assumptions about the distribution of Y in the population. Of course, if we are willing to assume that the distribution of Y is symmetric, then $\min[Y_i | M_i = 1]$ is nearly unbiased for $\bar{Y}$. However, in general, the randomization distribution of $\min[Y_i | M_i = 1]$ will be impossible to estimate without making rather strong assumptions about the distribution of Y_i for nonrespondents.

This simple example illustrates that it is generally difficult to carry forth the prescriptions for a valid randomization inference analysis even supposing (a) a probability sampling mechanism, (b) one variable in the survey, and (c) an accepted specification for the responding mechanism. Aside from analytic and computational problems, the need to rely on prior assumptions about the distribution of Y_i for nonrespondents tends to destroy the appealing distribution-free flavor of randomization inference.

There are, however, special cases of nonresponse for which randomization inference can be applied just as if there were no possibility of nonresponse. With a probability sampling mechanism and a probability responding mechanism, nonresponse is just like another level of random sampling. As a consequence, within randomization inference, M can play the role of D because M is independent of Y.

Specifically, let the statistic S be

$$\bar{y}_1 = \left(\sum_1^N M_i Y_i \right) \left(\sum_1 M_i \right)^{-1}, \tag{15}$$

the sample mean of Y for the responding units. Since $\bar{y}_1$ depends only on Y and M, its randomization distribution is determined by the model for $\Pr(M | Y)$. But with probability sampling and probability responding mechanism, that is, when $\Pr(D | Y) = \Pr(D)$ and $\Pr(R | Y) = \Pr(R)$, we have $\Pr(M | Y) = \Pr(M)$, and by the random indexing of the units, $\Pr(M)$ assigns equal probability to all values of M with the same value of $n_1 = \sum M_i$; hence, all cases with the same number of respondents are equally likely. If we consider n_1 fixed, then the randomization distribution of $\bar{y}_1$ is identical to the randomization distribution of the sample mean with no nonresponse and an intended sample size equal to n_1. Consequently, by conditioning on the observed value of n_1, randomization inference proceeds just as if a random sample of size n_1 were intended instead of a random sample of size $n = \sum D_i$. The relevant statistic is $\bar{y}_1 = \sum M_i Y_i / n_1$, rather than $\bar{y} = \sum D_i Y_i / n$, and the only effect of nonresponse is the loss of sample size from n to n_1. Hence, the resulting randomization inference is that the interval

$$\bar{y}_1 \pm 2 \sqrt{\frac{N - n_1}{n_1 N}} \, \hat{V}_1 \tag{16}$$

covers $\bar{Y}$ with approximately 95% probability, where $\hat{V}_1$ is the variance of the n_1 observed values of Y_i.

Of course, the interval (16) is generally not a 95% interval with confounded responding mechanisms, i.e., when $\Pr(R \mid Y) \neq \Pr(R)$. In the example given earlier, with only the largest half of the sampled values of Y_i observed, the interval would be nearly a 95% interval for the mean Y_i of *respondents* in the population, that is, for the mean of the *largest* 50% of the Y_i in the population.

2.4. Bayesian Inference in the Presence of Nonresponse

Because Bayesian inference requires a model for $\Pr(Y)$ in addition to the models for $\Pr(D \mid Y)$ and $\Pr(M \mid D, Y)$, it already has the available tools needed to draw inferences when confronted with nonresponse, assuming of course acceptable models for $\Pr(R \mid Y)$ and $\Pr(Y)$. Although computational problems may arise, Bayesian inference in principle calculates the posterior distribution of the unobserved Y values Y_U given the observed Y values Y_K and the observed values of D and M:

$$\Pr(Y_U \mid Y_K, D, M) = \frac{\Pr(Y)\Pr(D \mid Y)\Pr(M \mid D, Y)}{\int \Pr(Y)\Pr(D \mid Y)\Pr(M \mid D, Y)\, dY_U}, \tag{17}$$

With a probability sampling mechanism, $\Pr(D \mid Y) = \Pr(D)$, so that this posterior distribution becomes

$$\Pr(Y_U \mid Y_K, D, M) = \frac{\Pr(Y)\Pr(M \mid D, Y)}{\int \Pr(Y)\Pr(M \mid D, Y)\, dY_U}, \tag{18}$$

With additionally a probability responding mechanism, we have that $\Pr(M \mid D, Y) = \Pr(M \mid D)$, and thus,

$$\Pr(Y_U \mid Y_K, D, M) = \frac{\Pr(Y)}{\int \Pr(Y)\, dY_U} = \Pr(Y_U \mid Y_K). \tag{19}$$

Thus, with probability sampling and responding mechanisms, the sampling and responding mechanisms are ignorable in the sense that inferences about the distribution of Y in the population follow simply from the model for the distribution of the population data $\Pr(Y)$. Consequently, in this case, Bayesian inference is exactly as if a simple random sample of size n_1 had been intended with no nonresponse. Using the normal model for $\Pr(Y)$, the resulting inference is thus that the interval

$$\bar{y}_1 + 2\sqrt{\frac{N - n_1}{n_1 N}}\,\hat{V}_1$$

includes $\bar{Y}$ with 95% probability, which is essentially the same practical answer as generated by randomization inference in this case.

With a specific confounded responding mechanism and a specific model for $\Pr(Y)$, the Bayesian still has a straightforward mathematical path to inference using Eq. (18) rather than the simpler Eq. (19). However, the computational problems can be formidable. Furthermore, as we have warned earlier, Bayesian inference can be sensitive to the models being employed.

There are two general ways to specify the necessary models for $Pr(Y)$ and $Pr(M|D, Y)$ in this nonignorable case. First, we can specify the models by specifying $Pr(Y)$ and $Pr(R|Y)$ as suggested by Eq. (18). For example, $Pr(Y)$ could be the i.i.d. normal model discussed earlier, and $Pr(R|Y)$ could be the i.i.d. logistic regression model (such a model might be appropriate when the probability of nonresponse is thought to monotonically increase with Y). Because there are no units with $R_i = 0$ and Y_i observed, $Pr(R|Y)$ cannot be estimated directly by data, and the posterior distribution of Y_U can be very sensitive to prior specifications such as the normality of Y. Censored data models are of this type in that they specify the marginal distribution of Y, i.e., $Pr(Y)$, and the censoring process given values of Y, i.e., $Pr(R|Y)$. For examples, see Chapter 22 of this volume.

The second way to specify the necessary models confronts the model sensitivity more directly by modeling $Pr(R)$, $Pr(Y_i|R_i = 1)$, and $Pr(Y_i|R_i = 0)$. Suppose R is modeled as i.i.d. Bernoulli, where the probability that R_i equals 1 is estimated by the proportion of sampled units responding. Given $R_i = 1$, the Y_i are modeled as i.i.d. $N(\mu_1, \sigma_1^2)$, where the marginal (i.e., prior) distribution of (μ_1, σ_1^2) is proportional to σ_1^{-2}; μ_1, σ_1^2 are estimated by data from the sampled respondents. Given $R_i = 0$, the Y_i are modelled as i.i.d., $N(\mu_0, \sigma_0^2)$, where there are no data directly relevant to estimating μ_0, σ_0^2. The prior relation between respondents and nonrespondents is governed by the specification $Pr(\mu_0, \sigma_0^2|\mu_1, \sigma_1^2)$. Even assuming large samples so that the probability of being a respondent is effectively known and the respondents' parameter (μ_1, σ_1^2) is effectively known, inferences for $\bar{Y}$ will vary with the prior specification $Pr(\mu_0, \sigma_0^2|\mu_1, \sigma_1^2)$. Because of the potential sensitivity of inferences to this prior specification, ideally a variety of plausible nonresponse models should be tried in order to see how inferences vary with prior specifications unassailable by the data. For example, it would be interesting to see how inferences vary with the values of b and k in the above model with $\mu_0 = \mu_1 + b\sigma$ and $\sigma_0 = \sigma_1 k$. However, even with simple models such as this one, the computations required to perform an exact Bayesian analysis can be substantial.

2.5. Comparing Randomization and Bayesian Inference

Nonresponse can create severe problems for both randomization and Bayesian inference especially because of the absence of an accepted model for $Pr(R|Y)$, the responding mechanism. Both methods of inference require such a model in order to draw inferences, and the observed data alone cannot be used to assess the appropriateness of particular aspects of the specification of this model. Ideally therefore, inference should take place under a variety of plausible models. A special case of nonresponse which is relatively easy for both methods of inference occurs with a probability responding mechanism because then nonresponse is just like another level of probability sampling. Because of this desire to carry out analyses under a variety of models for the responding mechanism, computational ease is practically very important.

Given a specific confounded responding mechanism, Bayesian inference in principle has a straightforward prescription because it always requires a model for $\Pr(Y)$. From the specified models it can generate a distribution of Y_i values for the sampled nonrespondents and thereby for all unobserved Y_i values in the population. Randomization inference also requires assumptions about the distribution of Y_i for nonrespondents because the randomization distributions of statistics depend on functions of Y that cannot be estimated without making assumptions about the distribution of Y for nonrespondents. If some assumptions are to be made in any case, why not specify $\Pr(Y)$ and turn to Bayesian methods? One obvious answer is that much of the spirit of randomization inference is the desire to avoid specifying a particular model for Y, and the Bayesian's specification of a model for $\Pr(Y)$ does not necessarily lead to good inferences.

Even assuming satisfactory specifications for $\Pr(R \mid Y)$, both methods of inference generally face nontrivial computational problems. These computational barriers make the assessment of sensitivity of inference to different models expensive in practice.

2.6. A Compromise Approach

Because of the sensitivity of inference to assumptions about the process of nonresponse which are unassessable by the observed data, an important component of a satisfactory analysis in the presence of nonresponse is the display of sensitivity of inferences to these assumptions. That is, ideally inferences should be drawn under a variety of plausible models. However, the computational complexity of randomization and Bayesian inference under confounded responding mechanisms make this ideal difficult to attain in practice.

A compromise approach suggested by Rubin (1977) is computationally straight-forward relative to valid randomization and Bayesian inferences. This approach provides a display of the sensitivity of inferences under a variety of models for the responding mechanism. Furthermore, it is relatively simple to calculate an inference under a particular model for the responding mechanism that is approximately valid from the randomization and Bayesian perspectives.

In the compromise approach, models of the distribution of the data and the responding mechanism are used to generate a distribution for Y_i values that are missing because of nonresponse, and thereby to draw inferences for the complete-data statistics that would have been observed in the absence of nonresponse. More precisely, consider the standard complete-data statistics for drawing inference about $\bar{Y}$ in the absence of nonresponse: $\bar{y}$ and $\hat{V}$.

Under both randomization and Bayesian models of inference, $\bar{y} - \bar{Y}$ is considered to be approximately normally distributed with mean zero and variance $\hat{V}[(1/n) - (1/N)]$. When confronted with missing data, the statistics $\bar{y}$ and $\hat{V}$ are unknown. In the compromise approach, the focus remains on these complete-data statistics, but because they are unknown, a posterior distribution is generated for them using a Bayesian model for $\Pr(R \mid Y)$. For a variety of plausible models for $\Pr(R \mid Y)$, the posterior distributions of $\bar{y}$ and $\hat{V}$ should be evaluated to see how the complete-data statistics could vary under various specifications for nonresponse, and thus to see how the standard inference for $\bar{Y}$ could vary if the nonrespondents had responded according to the assumed models.

It may often be desirable to combine the posterior distribution of the complete-data statistics under one model with the complete-data inference about $\bar{Y}$ to obtain an inference about $\bar{Y}$ under the model for nonresponse. Assuming normal distributions, an obvious way to combine the posterior distribution and the complete-data inference is to let the center of the 95% interval be the expectation of the mean $\bar{y}$, and the variance be the sum of (a) the expectation of the variance $\hat{V}$ar plus (b) the variance of the mean $\bar{y}$. Ideally, this resulting compromise inference should be compared to the true Bayesian inference under the model specification and the randomization distribution of the resulting compromise inference should be evaluated. However, each of these efforts can be quite demanding.

Chapter 15 discusses the use of multiple imputations to simulate the posterior distribution of the complete-data statistics. The chapter by Herzog and Rubin also indicates senses in which the resulting compromise inference can be an approximately valid Bayesian inference and an approximately valid randomization inference.

3. ISSUES IN MORE GENERAL SURVEYS

In more general surveys, there may be different probabilities of selection for different units, subsampling of primary sampling units, covariates and stratification variables used for creating adjusted estimators, and other such complications discussed, for example, in Cochran (1977) and Hansen, Harwitz, and Madow (1953). There are many interesting and difficult issues in complicated surveys, even in those with no possibility of nonresponse. For instance, even randomization inference begins to rely on presumed relationships among variables when deciding among possible estimators. Also, in order to estimate variability of estimates, difficult computational issues arise which lead to methods such as balanced half-replication (McCarthy, 1966) in randomization inference and the simulation of posterior distributions in Bayesian inference.

The following chapters avoid these distracting issues by concentrating on simple cases. Although the cases are simple, many of the conceptual issues presented are relevant to more complicated surveys. The central new issue is stratifying (or classifying) units on the basis of covariates so that within each stratum nonrespondents and respondents can be assumed to be random samples from the same population, i.e., so that within each stratum, the responding mechanism is an unconfounded probability responding mechanism. Of course, it is virtually impossible to verify that any stratification has produced a situation wherein the response mechanism is an unconfounded probability response mechanism. Nevertheless, most applied procedures in use are based on such an assumption, that is, an assumption that the responding mechanism is ignorable.

Another new issue in complex surveys is the distinction between unit and item nonresponse. In a survey with only one variable of interest (i.e., when Y_i is scalar), there is no distinction between unit and item nonresponse. When Y_i is multivariate, there are important differences between unit nonresponse (all of Y_i is missing—the ith unit refused to participate) and item nonresponse (some components of Y_i are missing—the ith unit refused to answer income questions). Current practice in large surveys typically handles unit nonresponse by weighting methods and item nonresponse by imputation methods.

The weighting methods presented in the chapter by Oh and Scheuren are largely motivated by randomization considerations, although modeling arguments are relevant to some procedures, such as raking. For item nonresponse, weighting methods require a relatively careful new analysis for each question to be asked of the data; that is, the same simple modification in general can not be appropriately applied to all data analyses. One way to avoid such extra complications is to impute for each missing value, and so make the problem of nonresponse apparently vanish. A notable example of such a procedure is the hot-deck method discussed in the chapter by Ford. The hot deck, after creating a stratum for each nonrespondent, draws from the respondents' data in the stratum and thereby "fills in" the nonrespondent's missing values. Such imputation procedures do not fit well within the theoretical frameworks we have discussed, although in simple cases, adjustments to estimators based on imputed data can be made to obtain valid inferences, at least when assuming an unconfounded responding mechanism. (see, for example, Afifi and Elashoff, 1966). The technique of multiple imputations, discussed in the chapter by Herzog and Rubin, is designed to be a general-purpose method for obtaining valid inferences in practice. Multiple imputations also allow the evaluation of sensitivity of inference to models for the responding mechanism, an essential feature of a truly satisfactory study of the effect of nonresponse. Although the method of multiple imputations has promise for the future, currently it is not commonly used.

REFERENCES

Afifi, A. A., and Elashoff, R. M. (1966). Missing observations in multivariate statistics (Vol. 1). Review of the Literature. *Journal of the American Statistical Association* 61: 595–604.

Cochran, W. G. (1977). *Sampling Techniques*. New York: Wiley.

Cochran, W. G. (1978). Laplace's ratio estimator. In H. A. David (ed.), *Contributions to Survey Sampling and Applied Statistics*, pp. 3–10. New York: Academic Press.

Ericson, W. A. (1969). Subjective Bayesian models in sampling finite populations (with discussion). *Journal of the Royal Statistical Association*, Series B, 31: 195–233.

Godambe, V. P. (1966). A new approach to sampling from finite populations. *Journal of the Royal Statistical Society*, Series B, 28: 310–328.

Hansen, M. H., Hurwitz, W. N., and Madow, W. G. (1953). *Sample Survey Methods and Theory* (Vols. 1 and 2). New York: Wiley.

Hansen, M. H., Madow, W. G., and Tepping, B. (1978). On inference and estimation from sample surveys. *American Statistical Association Proceedings, Section on Survey Research Methods*, pp. 82–107.

Kish, L. (1965). *Survey Sampling*. New York: Wiley.

Lindley, D. V. (1972). *Bayesian Statistics, A Review*. Society for Industrial and Applied Mathematics.

Madow, W. G. (1948). On the limiting distributions of estimates based on samples from finite universes. *Annals of Mathematical Statistics* 19: 535–545.

McCarthy, P. J. (1966). Replication: An approach to the analysis of data from complex surveys. *Vital and Health Statistics*, PHS Publication No. 1000-Series 2; No. 14. Public Health Service.

Pratt, J. W. (1965). Bayesian interpretation of standard inference statements. *Journal of the Royal Statistical Society*, Series B, 27: 169–203.

Rosenthal, R., and Rosnow, R. L. (1975). *The Volunteer Subject*. New York: Wiley.

Royall, R. (1968). An old approach to finite population sampling theory. *Journal of the American Statistical Association* 63: 1269–1279.

Rubin, D. B. (1976). Inference and missing data (with discussion and reply). *Biometrika* 63: 581–592.

Rubin, D. B. (1977). Formalizing subjective notions about the effect of nonrespondents in sample surveys. *Journal of the American Statistical Association* 72: 538–543.

Rubin, D. B. (1978a). Bayesian inference for causal effects: The role of randomization. *Annals of Statistics* 6: 34–58.

Rubin, D. B. (1978b). Multiple imputations in sample surveys—A phenomenological Bayesian approach to nonresponse (with discussion and reply). In *Imputation and Editing of Faulty or Missing Survey Data*, pp. 1–9. U.S. Social Security Administration and Bureau of the Census.

Rubin, D. B. (1978c). The phenomenological Bayesian perspective in sample surveys from finite populations: Foundations. In *Imputation and Editing of Faulty or Missing Survey Data*, pp. 10–18. U.S. Social Security Administration and Bureau of the Census.

CHAPTER 13

Weighting Adjustment for Unit Nonresponse

H. Lock Oh
Frederick J. Scheuren

1. INTRODUCTION

In this chapter we examine weighting methods commonly employed in adjusting for unit or total questionnaire nonresponse. The treatment focuses on both the bias and variance impacts of nonresponse. Attention, however, has been given only to the special case where just nonresponse and sampling errors are present. Part V of this volume deals with the general case in which contributions to the mean square error of the survey estimator also include other components, e.g., the response variance.

The principal goal of the chapter is to relate standard adjustment strategies for nonresponse, like poststratification, to the assumptions made about how the missing data arose. Ideas introduced by Rubin in the previous chapter will be the starting point in our development. Most of the material is a restatement of the results and observations of other practitioners. Citations to the literature usually take the place of proofs. Our focus will be on what might be called quasi-randomization models of the response probabilities. These models will motivate the weighting adjustments examined.

Basically, the "quasi-randomization" approach to weighting adjustments, as formulated here, is equivalent to the treatment of the response mechanism as another stage in the overall probability sample design. Put another way, given the essential survey conditions, each unit in the population is assumed to have a positive probability of being a respondent. The ingenuity and experience of the practitioner come into play essentially in the conjectures made about the

INCOMPLETE DATA
IN SAMPLE SURVEYS
Volume 2, Part IV

structure of the response mechanism and how to estimate the response probabilities given that structure. To oversimplify somewhat, the missing data problem is handled as if it were a sample design problem where some of the information about the selection probabilities is unknown. Generally explicit models are not stated for the underlying distribution of the variables to be measured—in contrast, for example, to methods considered in Part VI of this volume.

1.1. General Viewpoint

Before proceeding with the details, some general observations might be made here about the basic point of view taken:

(1) Emphasis has been placed on describing the better-known methods in a very elementary setting. Our primary reason for this is that it makes the subject more accessible to nonpractitioners; however, of almost equal force is the fact that the full implications of weighting as an adjustment technique for survey nonresponse are only now being given a rigorous general treatment (as, say, by Platek and Gray in Part V of this volume).

(2) A recurring theme of the presentation, especially in the examples, is that there is really no totally satisfactory substitute for complete or nearly complete response. The models employed in adjusting for missing data, no matter how cleverly structured, virtually never hold exactly in practice; hence, the more nonresponse present, the greater is the sensitivity of one's results to the mechanism assumed in carrying out the adjustments.

(3) Emphasis is placed on the fact that nonresponse always brings with it an increase in the mean square error. Even if one models the response mechanism properly, there is an additional component of the variance due directly to the nonresponse (because of the reduced sample size). There can also be a further variance increase depending on exactly how the adjustment is carried out—a point made explicitly in Section 5.

(4) Another recurring theme in the chapter is that, typically, in a multipurpose survey there is no single optimal nonresponse weighting adjustment. In reducing the bias for some statistics, it is possible, even if the response mechanism is modeled correctly, to increase significantly the variance for other statistics. (Of course, if the chosen model is incorrect, then, in attempting to reduce the bias of some statistics, it is possible to increase the bias of others.)

1.2. Some Limitations on Presentation

The standard nonresponse weighting adjustments described in this chapter have the advantages of simplicity and familiarity. Also, in applications where there is a high response rate, quasi-randomization methods often seem to yield estimators with small biases.

There are, of course, disadvantages in modeling the response mechanism as an additional stage of sampling. One of these is that some practitioners may be lulled into the belief that their results have the same robustness as probability sampling inferences in the complete data case—a misconception that could have particularly disastrous consequences if there is a high nonresponse rate. In any case, whether practitioners are "lulled" or not, in applied settings analyses of the sensitivity of inferences to alternative specifications of the response mechanism appear to be quite rare indeed. This is so despite the fact that thoughtful practitioners, when questioned about their assumptions, generally indicate that they believe them to be only approximately true at best. Most household surveys, for example, have a group of hard-core refusals for which the assumption that the response probabilities are positive would seem to be untenable. To the extent, of course, that the response probabilities are zero, the approach as formulated here will be less successful, even unsuccessful, in reducing bias. Zero response probabilities are only an extreme form of the problem. Generally, two kinds of nonrobustness need to be distinguished. One is our inability to model accurately the statistical dependence of the response probability on the observed characteristics of the population, such as those used to define weighting classes or poststrata. The second kind of model failure is our inability to get at the root causes of the nonresponse.

Generally, no matter how well the survey is designed, we cannot observe all the characteristics of the measurement process that determine the probability of a response; hence, the possibility of an undetectable (and uncorrectable) bias cannot be avoided. Nonetheless, despite their inherent limitations, the weighting adjustments described in this chapter may be of considerable interest because of their wide applicability.

1.3. Organization of Chapter

The chapter is divided up into five sections following the introduction. In Section 2 we explore two responding mechanisms that are often assumed by practitioners. Application issues arising in the use of poststratified and weighting class estimators are illustrated in Section 3. Raking ratio estimators are examined in Section 4. Integerized or duplication weight adjustments for nonresponse are taken up briefly in Section 5. Such methods, as we shall see, may also be considered a form of imputation—indistinguishable in many respects from certain of the "hot-deck" schemes described in the chapter by Ford in this part. The concluding section of the chapter consists of some recommendations to practitioners on application issues and suggestions on areas for future study. The comments, however, are not intended to provide a full agenda for the research that is needed. They simply draw out some of the main implications of the treatment given in the chapter to weighting adjustments for nonresponse.

Extensive simulation results are provided which illustrate the sensitivity of the estimators in the presence of model failure. Throughout the discussion we assume simple random sampling. This allows us to concentrate on essential issues.

2. PROBABILITY RESPONSE MECHANISMS IN SIMPLE RANDOM SAMPLING

To examine alternative weighting adjustments for nonresponse, we shall employ essentially the same notational conventions as in the chapter by Rubin in this part. Specifically, we assume that a probability sample of size n has been drawn from a population of size N. For each of the $i = 1, \ldots, N$ elementary units of this finite population, a vector of characteristics $\mathbf{Y}_i$ is to be recorded in the survey if the unit is selected for the sample. Our interest will center on the estimation of functions of the vector of population totals:

$$\mathbf{Y} = \sum_{1}^{N} \mathbf{Y}_i. \tag{1}$$

In the unit nonresponse problem, unlike that for item nonresponse, most of the main points can be made by treating $\mathbf{Y}_i$ as univariate; hence, this is the path followed initially.

Two sets of indicator random variables are required: one for the sampling mechanism and one for the response mechanism. Let the vector

$$\mathbf{D} = (D_1, \ldots, D_i, \ldots, D_N) \tag{2}$$

identify the sampled and unsampled units in the survey where

$$D_i = \begin{cases} 1 & \text{if the } i\text{th unit is selected} \\ 0 & \text{if the } i\text{th unit is not selected.} \end{cases} \tag{3}$$

Similarly, let the vector

$$\mathbf{R} = (R_1, \ldots, R_i, \ldots, R_N) \tag{4}$$

indicate whether the ith unit will respond ($R_i = 1$) if sampled for this survey or not ($R_i = 0$). For inferences to be made, we further have to specify the probabilities $\Pr(\mathbf{D}|\mathbf{Y})$ and $\Pr(\mathbf{R}|\mathbf{D}, \mathbf{Y})$ subject to the constraint that by design

$$\Pr(D_i = 1|\mathbf{Y}) > 0 \quad \text{for each } i \text{ and all possible values of the } \{\mathbf{Y}_i\}, \tag{5}$$

while by assumption

$$\Pr(R_i = 1|\mathbf{D}, \mathbf{Y}) > 0 \quad \text{for each } i \text{ and all possible}$$

$$\text{combinations of the } \{\mathbf{Y}_i\} \text{ and } \{D_i = 1\}. \tag{6}$$

In simple random sampling without replacement, the first constraint is obviously satisfied since the probability of any particular sample of size n from the population of size N is

$$\Pr(\mathbf{D}\,|\,\mathbf{Y}, n) = \Pr(\mathbf{D}\,|\,n) = \binom{N}{n}^{-1}, \tag{7}$$

where, for all units i and j in the population (suppressing the conditional notation),

$$\Pr(D_i = 1) = \frac{n}{N} \quad \text{and} \quad \Pr(D_i D_j = 1) = \left(\frac{n}{N}\right)\left(\frac{n-1}{N-1}\right), \quad i \neq j. \tag{8}$$

To satisfy the second constraint, we have postulated two alternative response mechanisms which motivate weighting adjustments that are commonly used in practice. For each such mechanism, the statistical properties of estimators of the population total will be examined.

2.1. Uniform Global Response Mechanism

Let us first assume that the response probabilities are all equal, positive, and independent. This yields an unconfounded probability responding mechanism as defined in the first chapter of this part. To say it another way, the response mechanism is an independent Bernoulli sampling process with common probability $\Phi > 0$ repeated for all n sampled units; thus, the probability of a particular sample containing exactly m responses is $\Phi^m (1 - \Phi)^{n-m}$. The probability of observing any one of the samples with m responses is the binomial expression $\Phi^m (1 - \Phi)^{n-m}$; hence, if one conditions on the number of responses m, then

$$\Pr(\mathbf{R}\,|\,\mathbf{D}, \mathbf{Y}, n, m) = \Pr(\mathbf{R}\,|\,n, m) = \binom{n}{m}^{-1}, \tag{9}$$

where, suppressing n, m of the conditional notation,

$$\Pr(R_i = 1\,|\,D_i = 1) = \frac{m}{n} \quad \text{and} \quad \Pr(R_i R_j = 1\,|\,D_i D_j = 1)$$

$$= \left(\frac{m}{n}\right)\left(\frac{m-1}{n-1}\right), \quad i \neq j. \tag{10}$$

In this case, the respondents are just a simple random subsample of size m drawn from the initial sample of size n.

An unbiased estimator of the population total **Y** is

$$\tilde{Y} = \frac{N}{m} \sum_{1}^{N} D_i R_i Y_i, \tag{11}$$

where $\sum_{1}^{N} D_i R_i Y_i$ is just the overall sample sum of the responding units. Unbiasedness follows since for $m \geq 1$

$$E(\tilde{Y}\,|\,n,m) = \left(\frac{N}{m}\right) \sum_{1}^{N} \left(\frac{n}{N}\right)\left(\frac{m}{n}\right) Y_i = \sum_{1}^{N} Y_i = N\bar{Y}. \tag{12}$$

Also, in keeping with the development in the previous chapter, the conditional variance of $\tilde{Y}$, given $m \geq 1$, is

$$\mathrm{Var}(\tilde{Y}\,|\,n,m) = N^2 \left(\frac{1}{n} - \frac{1}{N}\right) V + N^2 \left(\frac{1}{m} - \frac{1}{n}\right) V = N^2 \left(\frac{1}{m} - \frac{1}{N}\right) V, \tag{13}$$

where V is defined by

$$(N-1)V = \sum_{1}^{N} (Y_i - \bar{Y})^2, \tag{14}$$

with an unbiased estimator for V, under the model, being

$$(m-1)\tilde{V} = \sum_{i=1}^{N} D_i R_i Y_i^2 - \frac{1}{m}\left(\sum_{i=1}^{N} D_i R_i Y_i\right)^2. \tag{15}$$

The reason for writing expression (13) as we did is to call attention to the increase in the variance that results from the nonresponse. The first component, $N^2[(1/n) - (1/N)]V$, is the variance in a simple random sample of size n when there is no nonresponse; the second component, $N^2[(1/m) - (1/n)]V$, is directly attributable to the additional level of sampling introduced by the response mechanism.

2.2. Uniform Response Mechanisms within Subpopulations

Postulating a uniform global response mechanism makes the mathematics trivial but generally is not very realistic. Somewhat more realistic are two-phase or double-sampling mechanisms that assume the response probabilities are always positive and independent but may differ among subpopulations. (See Part III of this volume.)

To talk about such mechanisms we have to refine the notation to distinguish one subpopulation from another. For example, let Y_{hi} be a characteristic to be studied from the ith unit in the hth subpopulation with $i = 1, \ldots, N_h$ and $h = 1, \ldots, H$. The other quantities needed will be similarly subscripted.

Two basic estimation approaches are possible depending upon whether the sizes $\{N_h\}$ of the subpopulations are known:

(1) *Poststratification approach*—The poststratified estimator employs the subpopulations as strata employing the known $\{N_h\}$ and the number of responses $\{m_h\}$ in each of the H groups.

2. *Weighting-class approach*—The weighting-class estimator can be used when the $\{N_h\}$ are unknown. It is derived by conditioning on the initial sample sizes in each subgroup $\{n_h\}$ and the number of responses $\{m_h\}$ obtained. [In some cases, e.g., Schaible (1979), the weighting-class approach is also referred to as a form of poststratification. We, however, distinguish the two methods in our terminology.]

Both the poststratified and weighting-class estimators assume, of course, that the $m_h > 0$ for all $h = 1, \ldots, H$. Also, for both estimators, we are assuming that within each subpopulation, the response mechanism is an independent Bernoulli sampling process with common probability $\Phi_h > 0$ of a response for each of the n_h sampled units. Finally, the response mechanisms are postulated to be independent from one subpopulation to another. Hence, if one conditions on the number of units sampled $\mathbf{n} = (n_1, \ldots, n_H)$ and the number responding $\mathbf{m} = (m_1, \ldots, m_H)$, then, in a fashion parallel to expressions (7) and (9), we have

$$\Pr(\mathbf{D}|\mathbf{Y}, n) = \left\{ \prod_1^H \binom{N_h}{n_h} \right\}^{-1} \quad \text{and} \quad \Pr(\mathbf{R}|\mathbf{D}, \mathbf{Y}, \mathbf{n}, \mathbf{m}) = \left\{ \prod_1^H \binom{n_h}{m_h} \right\}^{-1}. \quad (16)$$

It follows that

$$\Pr(D_{hi} = 1|\mathbf{n}) = \frac{n_h}{N_h} \quad \text{and} \quad \Pr(R_{hi} = 1|D_{hi} = 1, \mathbf{n}, \mathbf{m}) = \frac{m_h}{n_h}. \quad (17)$$

The joint conditional probabilities within weighting classes or post-strata are also of the same form as in expressions (8) and (16), that is, for $h = h'$, $i \neq j$,

$$\Pr(D_{hi}D_{h'j} = 1|\mathbf{n}) = \left(\frac{n_h}{N_h} \right)\left(\frac{n_h - 1}{N_h - 1} \right),$$

$$\Pr(R_{hi}R_{h'j} = 1|D_{hi}D_{h'j} = 1, \mathbf{n}, \mathbf{m}) = \left(\frac{m_h}{n_h} \right)\left(\frac{m_h - 1}{n_h - 1} \right). \quad (18)$$

From stratum to stratum the conditional probabilities are independent, that is for $h \neq h'$,

$$\Pr(D_{hi}D_{h'j} = 1|\mathbf{n}) = \left(\frac{n_h}{N_h} \right)\left(\frac{n_{h'}}{N_{h'}} \right),$$

$$\Pr(R_{hi}R_{h'j} = 1|D_{hi}D_{h'j} = 1, \mathbf{n}, \mathbf{m}) = \left(\frac{m_h}{n_h} \right)\left(\frac{m_{h'}}{n_{h'}} \right). \quad (19)$$

2.3. Statistical Properties of Poststratified and Weighting-Class Estimators Given Uniform Response Mechanisms

We are now ready to consider the statistical properties of the poststratified estimator of the population total

$$\tilde{Y}_s = \sum_1^H \frac{N_h}{m_h} \sum_1^{N_h} D_{hi} R_{hi} Y_{hi} = \sum_1^H \frac{N_h}{m_h} \tilde{Y}_h \tag{20}$$

as well as the corresponding weighting class estimator

$$\tilde{Y}_c = \frac{N}{n} \sum_1^H \frac{n_h}{m_h} \sum_1^{N_h} D_{hi} R_{hi} Y_{hi} = \sum_1^H \frac{N}{n} \frac{n_h}{m_h} \tilde{Y}_h. \tag{21}$$

The sample or subpopulation totals $\tilde{Y}_h$ are being weighted by (N_h/m_h) for the poststratified estimator and $(N/n)(n_h/m_h)$ for the weighting-class estimator, since N_h is being estimated by $N(n_h/n)$.

2.3.1. Bias

The conditional expected values, given **n** and **m**, of $\tilde{Y}_s$ and $\tilde{Y}_c$ are

$$E(\tilde{Y}_s | \mathbf{n}, \mathbf{m}) = \sum_1^H N_h \bar{Y}_h = \mathbf{Y} \tag{22}$$

and

$$E(\tilde{Y}_c | \mathbf{n}, \mathbf{m}) = \frac{N}{n} \sum_1^H n_h \bar{Y}_h = \mathbf{Y} - \sum_1^H (\bar{Y}_h - \bar{Y})\left(N_h - \frac{N}{n} n_h\right). \tag{23}$$

The two estimators vary in their conditional expected values to the extent that the estimated strata sizes $\{(N/n)n_h\}$ vary from the true ones $\{N_h\}$. Since $E(n_h) = (n/N)N_h$ we see that $\tilde{Y}_c$, although conditionally biased, will be unbiased over repeated simple random samples.

Before completing our comparison between the expected values of $\tilde{Y}_s$ and $\tilde{Y}_c$ several important qualifications seem needed. First, in many settings where poststratification is employed, the subpopulation totals $\{N_h\}$ are not known exactly; instead, approximations, say, $\{N_h^*\}$, are employed, so that

$$E(\tilde{Y}_s^* | \mathbf{n}, \mathbf{m}) = \sum_1^H N_h^* \bar{Y}_h = \mathbf{Y} - \sum_1^H (\bar{Y}_h - \bar{Y})(N_h - N_h^*). \tag{24}$$

A second point to make is that sometimes because of coverage errors, such as an incomplete frame, $E(n_h) \neq (n/N)N_h$. Put another way, we can have two different types of response mechanisms: one which alters the $E(n_h)$ from what they would be under simple random sampling and the other which, given the $\{n_h\}$, generates the $\{m_h\}$ responses. If both these mechanisms can each separately be modeled as Bernoulli sampling processes with positive subgroup probabilities $\{\Phi_h^*\}$ and $\{\Phi_h\}$, respectively, then $\tilde{Y}_s$ would still be unbiased unconditionally, while $\tilde{Y}_c$ would *not* (unless the $\Phi_h^* = \Phi^*$ for all $h = 1, \ldots, H$).

The real Hobson's choice for practitioners, though, occurs when there are suspected differential coverage errors and the poststrata totals may be in error as well. Of course, when the (biased) estimator $\tilde{Y}_s^*$ is used, an attempt might be made to model the likely errors in the $\{N_h^*\}$ so that sensitivity analyses could be carried out. One possible approach would be to weight the sample several times with estimated subpopulation sizes drawn from alternative postulated error distributions of the $\{N_h^*\}$. This multiple weighting approach (Scheuren, 1980) is very similar at least in spirit to the multiple imputation techniques described in the chapter by Herzog and Rubin in this part.

2.3.2. Conditional Mean Square Errors

The conditional variance of $\tilde{Y}_s$ and the conditional mean square error of $\tilde{Y}_c$ can be shown, under simple random sampling, to be, respectively

$$\text{Var}(\tilde{Y}_s | \mathbf{n}, \mathbf{m}) = \sum_1^H (N_h)^2 \left(1 - \frac{m_h}{N_h}\right) \frac{V_h}{m_h} \tag{25}$$

and

$$\text{MSE}(\tilde{Y}_c | \mathbf{n}, \mathbf{m}) = \sum_1^H \left(\frac{Nn_h}{n}\right)^2 \left(1 - \frac{m_h}{N_h}\right) \frac{V_h}{m_h} + \left\{\sum_1^H (\bar{Y}_h - \bar{Y})\left(N_h - \frac{Nn_h}{n}\right)\right\}^2. \tag{26}$$

(These results follow directly from considerations such as those set forth in Holt and Smith, 1979.)

Conditional inferences readily can be constructed for the population total Y if the estimator $\tilde{Y}_s$ is being utilized. All we have to do is to substitute into expression (25) the (usual) estimates for $\{V_h\}$ given by

$$(m_h - 1)\tilde{V}_h = \sum_{i=1}^{N_h} D_{hi} R_{hi} Y_{hi}^2 - \frac{1}{m_h}\left(\sum_{i=1}^{N_h} D_{hi} R_{hi} Y_{hi}\right)^2 \tag{27}$$

subject to the requirement that the $m_h \geq 2$ for all $h = 1, \ldots. H$. Then, if $\tilde{Y}_s$ can be treated as approximately normally distributed, 95% confidence intervals

$$\tilde{Y}_s \pm 2 \sqrt{\sum_1^H (N_h)^2 \left(1 - \frac{m_h}{N_h}\right) \tilde{V}_h / m_h} \tag{28}$$

can be formed under our quasi-randomization model for the nonresponse just as in the chapter by Rubin in this part.

There are some obvious dangers in the uncritical use of confidence intervals like expression (28). Two deserve mention:

(1)   First, since the response probabilities Φ_h within strata are not under the direct control of the statistician, some of the m_h could get very small, with the consequence that the $\tilde{V}_h$ might be quite poor estimates.

(2)   Second, if a small number of the strata contribute most of the variance and if the number of responses in each of these strata are only small to moderate, the normality assumption may not be a safe one. (In this case the implicit appeal to the central limit theorem might not be justified.)

To make the assumption about a uniform response mechanism within subpopulations seem plausible, many practitioners employ a large number of poststrata. However, even if the response mechanism is perfectly modeled in this way, with the result that unbiasedness can be achieved, the inferences we want to make might still be seriously disturbed if the strata chosen were such that the $\{V_h\}$ were large when the corresponding $\{\Phi_h\}$ were small. Given a choice, it might be argued that it would be better to have a stable (i.e., small variance) estimator with a small bias than an unbiased but unstable and possibly non-normal estimator. (We shall return to this issue again in the next section.) The inference setting when using the weighting class estimator $\tilde{Y}_c$ is similar to that for $\tilde{Y}_s$. There is, though, the additional complication that the $\{N_h\}$ are unknown. We can readily estimate the conditional variance of $\tilde{Y}_c$ by

$$\mathrm{Var}(\tilde{Y}_c \,|\, \mathbf{n}, \mathbf{m}) = \left(\frac{N}{n}\right)^2 \sum_1^H n_h^2 \left(1 - \frac{nm_h}{n_h N}\right) \tilde{V}_h / m_h. \tag{29}$$

Without knowledge of the $\{N_h\}$ it is not possible to estimate the *actual* conditional bias for the sample at hand. The *average* squared conditional bias can, however, be estimated from the sample and might form a starting point for constructing approximate confidence intervals for $\tilde{Y}_c$. We have, for example, that the average squared bias of $(\tilde{Y}_c \,|\, \mathbf{n}, \mathbf{m})$ is

$$E\left(\sum_1^H (\overline{Y}_h - \overline{Y})\left(N_h - \frac{N}{n} n_h\right)\right)^2 = \frac{N}{n}\left(\frac{N-n}{N-1}\right)\sum_1^H N_h(\overline{Y}_h - \overline{Y})^2, \tag{30}$$

with an estimator of the average squared conditional bias being

$$\widetilde{\mathrm{Bias}}^2(\tilde{Y}_c \,|\, \mathbf{n}, \mathbf{m}) = \left(\frac{N}{n}\right)^2 \left(\frac{N-n}{N-1}\right)\sum_1^H n_h(\bar{y}_h - \bar{y})^2, \tag{31}$$

where $\bar{y} = (1/n)\sum_1^H n_h \bar{y}_h$ and the $\{\bar{y}_h\}$ are the sample means of the responses within each weighting class. Unfortunately, even if we assume that the $\{m_h\}$ are large enough so that $(\bar{y}_h - \bar{y})^2$ is a reasonable estimator of $(\bar{Y}_h - \bar{Y})^2$, expression (31) is still conditionally biased; in any case expression (29) is just an overall average not necessarily relevant as a measure of the squared bias for the sample at hand. It should be added that the difficulty we are alluding to here is a general one for conditional inference and does not have any new force when the complication of nonresponse is introduced.

To explore further the inference issues being raised, consider a nominal 95% confidence interval of the form

$$\tilde{Y}_c \pm 2\sqrt{\widehat{\mathrm{MSE}}(\tilde{Y}_c | \mathbf{n}, \mathbf{m})}, \tag{32}$$

where the mean square error of $\tilde{Y}_c$ is estimated by employing (29) and (31). If there is no nonresponse (so $m_h = n_h$ for all h) and if the $\{n_h\}$ are all such that $n_h/(n_h - 1) \doteq 1$, the statistic $\widehat{\mathrm{MSE}}(\tilde{Y}_c | \mathbf{n}, \mathbf{m})$ approximates the usual *unconditional* variance estimator in simple random sampling. Expression (32) is seen, therefore, to be approximately true if one considers all possible samples of size n; that is, about 95% of all the intervals (32) will cover the true population total Y. As has been pointed out by a number of practitioners, however, the usual variance estimator is unsatisfactory in a conditional framework. Holt and Smith (1979) provide an excellent example which demonstrates that when treated as a conditional statement, expressions such as (32) may lead to intervals which are far too wide in some cases and far too narrow in others.

2.3.3.   Unconditional Mean Square Errors

The form of the unconditional variances of $\tilde{Y}_s$ and $\tilde{Y}_c$ depend initially on the assumption of uniform response probabilities $\{\Phi_h\}$ within each subpopulation. (For the conditional results the $\{\Phi_h\}$ play only an indirect role through $E(m_h | n_h) = \Phi_h n_h$; that is, for small Φ_h the m_h also tend to be small with a consequent increase in the conditional variance.)

To obtain the unconditional variance of $\tilde{Y}_s$ we note that since $E(\tilde{Y}_s | \mathbf{n}, \mathbf{m}) = Y$, $\mathrm{Var}(\tilde{Y}_s)$ can be approximated reasonably well by

$$\mathrm{Var}(\tilde{Y}_s) = E(\mathrm{Var}(\tilde{Y}_s | \mathbf{n}, \mathbf{m})) = E\left(\sum_1^H N_h^2 \left(\frac{1}{m_h} - \frac{1}{N_h}\right) V_h\right)$$

$$\doteq \sum_1^H N_h^2 \left(1 - \frac{\bar{m}_h}{N_h}\right) V_h/\bar{m}_h + \sum_1^H N_h^2 \left(1 - \frac{\bar{m}_h}{n}\right) V_h/\bar{m}_h^2, \tag{33}$$

where $\bar{m}_h = n(N_h/N)\Phi_h$, and the $\bar{m}_h$ are not too small. This follows immediately by applying the argument given in Cochran (1977, pp. 134–135).

In order to derive the unconditional variance of $\tilde{Y}_c$ we can again appeal to standard results. Perhaps the most direct approach would be to note that

$$
\begin{aligned}
\mathrm{Var}(\tilde{Y}_c) = {} & E\left(\sum_1^H (\bar{Y}_h - \bar{Y})\left(N_h - \frac{Nn_h}{n}\right)\right)^2 \\
& + E\left(\sum_1^H \left(\frac{Nn_h}{n}\right)^2 \left(1 - \frac{m_h}{N_h}\right) V_h/m_h\right) \\
\doteq {} & \left(\frac{N}{n}\right)\left(\frac{N-n}{N-1}\right)\sum_1^H N_h(\bar{Y}_h - \bar{Y})^2 + \sum_1^H N_h^2\left(1 - \frac{\bar{m}_h}{N_h}\right) V_h/\bar{m}_h \\
& + \sum_1^H N_h^2\left(1 - \frac{\bar{m}_h}{\bar{n}}\right) V_h/\bar{m}_h^2,
\end{aligned}
\tag{34}
$$

where $\bar{n}_h = n(N_h/N)$ and $\bar{m}_h = n(N_h/N)\Phi_h$ as before.

In general we see that if the $\{m_h\}$ are large and the finite population correction factors can be ignored, then

$$
\mathrm{Var}(\tilde{Y}_c) \doteq \left(\frac{N}{n}\right)\sum_1^H N_h(\bar{Y}_h - \bar{Y})^2 + \mathrm{Var}(\tilde{Y}_s),
$$

which is the standard result when there is no nonresponse (Cochran, p. 100).

3. APPLICATIONS OF POSTSTRATIFIED AND WEIGHTING-CLASS ESTIMATORS IN SIMPLE RANDOM SAMPLING

There are a number of issues that need to be examined before employing a poststratified or weighting-class estimator. Some of these are

(1)   How should the subpopulations be chosen within which to make the adjustments?

(2)   How can the increased variance arising from the nonresponse be kept small?

(3)   How can the bias arising from the nonresponse be kept small even if the response mechanism is postulated in error?

(4)   How can complications in the variance estimation be reduced when employing poststrata or weighting-class adjustments?

(5)   How can reasonable trade-offs be made between bias reductions for some statistics and variance increases for others?

Perhaps some elementary remarks will make it possible to begin addressing these questions.

3.1. Elementary Remarks

3.1.1. Variance Considerations in Choosing Subpopulations

First, to fix ideas, assume that we have two subpopulations, with $\overline{Y}_1$ being the mean of the first and $\overline{Y}_2$ of the second. Now if $\overline{Y}_1 = \overline{Y}_2$, then there will be no bias if we employ the overall estimator

$$\tilde{Y} = \frac{N}{m} \sum_{h=1}^{2} \sum_{i=1}^{N_h} D_{hi} R_{hi} Y_{hi} \tag{35}$$

whether or not the response probabilities in the two subpopulations Φ_1 and Φ_2 are equal or not. In fact, if the variances V_1 and V_2 are equal for the two subpopulations, then when $\Phi_1 \neq \Phi_2$ the variance of a weighting-class or post-stratified estimator would be larger than that of the overall estimator. For example, if $N_1 = N_2$, $V_1 = V_2$ but $\Phi_1 = (1/10)\Phi_2$, then $\mathrm{Var}(\tilde{Y}_s)$ will be more than 2.5 times greater than $\mathrm{Var}(\tilde{Y})$.

A basic principle would seem to be that if the means of two subpopulations are likely to be quite different, then the nonresponse adjustment should be done separately for each group. On the other hand, if the means are suspected of being equal or nearly so, then a combined estimator may give a smaller mean square error.

3.1.2. Bounding Variance Increases

If the means of each subpopulation are different and if we have a uniform response mechanism within each group, then essentially the more classes employed, the smaller the nonresponse bias that will remain after the adjustment.

Usually, of course, the practitioner only has a very rough idea of what the means might be. However, if the sample is large, then many weighting classes may be used in the belief that greater bias reductions would result. To protect against a large increase in the variance, commonly rules are formulated to pool or collapse classes or strata where the number of responses m_h is small or the weighting-adjustment factors N_h/m_h or $(N/n)(n_h/m_h)$ are large (Hanson, 1978). Such rules, although reducing the degree to which bias may be eliminated, do have the effect of bounding the variance increase that the adjustment may create.

3.1.3. Achieving Bias Reductions

In general, it is not possible to guarantee a bias reduction by employing a great many poststrata (Thomsen, 1973, 1978). The reason for this is that, if the uniform response mechanisms postulated within the strata do not hold, then there will be a residual bias within each group. It is conceivable that the magnitude of these within-class biases could be such that eliminating the between-group bias, if it were of opposite sign from the within-group bias, could actually make matters worse. (For an illustration of this possibility in the continuous case, see Example 1.2.2 in the first chapter of Part V.)

In practice, however, if the strata are chosen so that the $\bar{Y}_h$ are expected to be quite different from stratum to stratum and the within-stratum variation is small, then a bias reduction should occur.

3.1.4.   Mean Square Error Calculation

Calculating the mean square error for the basic estimators $\tilde{Y}_s$ and $\tilde{Y}_c$ is quite routine, as we saw in the last section. For many applications, however, constraints are imposed on the weighting process which are intended to reduce the variance but which also can considerably complicate the variance estimation.

Generally, the final form of the poststratified or weighting-class estimator, in particular, the number and nature of the classes or strata, will depend on the actual $\{m_h\}$, $\{n_h\}$, and even $\{\bar{y}_h\}$ obtained in the sample at hand.

There seems to have been almost no consideration of the theoretical properties of modified poststratified or weighting-class estimators for non-response. What, for example, are the variance and bias of a procedure which requires that

$$m_h \geq K_1 \qquad \text{for all} \quad h = 1, \ldots, H,$$

$$\frac{n_h}{m_h} \leq K_2 \qquad \text{for all} \quad h = 1, \ldots, H \tag{36}$$

and when expression (36) is not satisfied pooling the classes based on the $\{\bar{y}_h\}$? Alternatively pooling could be used when m_h is small and a "spillover" procedure when n_h/m_h is large. In a spillover procedure the adjustment factor is set not to exceed, say, K_2 and if a larger adjustment is required this "spills over" and the adjustments of other cells are altered accordingly (Hanson, 1978).

In some settings restrictions like expression (36) pose no new difficulties. For example, if $\Phi_h = \Phi$ for all h, then the *conditional* mean square errors of $\tilde{Y}_s$ and $\tilde{Y}_c$ would be unaffected. In general though, developing an expression for the *unconditional* variance and mean square error is another matter altogether. The unconditional results are, of course, essential if one is designing such a procedure from a quasi-randomization perspective.

3.1.5.   Replicate Variance Estimators as a Partial Solution

One straightforward approach to variance estimation, given the constraint (36), is to subdivide the sample before data collection into independent subsamples or panels of identical design. The nonresponse adjustment could then be made separately within each panel. If there were G such subsamples, then the average

$$\tilde{Y}_{c.} = \frac{1}{G}\sum_{1}^{G}\tilde{Y}_{cg} \tag{37}$$

would have a variance that, by first principles, could be estimated as

$$\mathrm{Var}(\tilde{Y}_{c.}) \doteq \sum_{1}^{G}(\tilde{Y}_{cg} - \tilde{Y}_{c.})^2/G(G-1). \tag{38}$$

A difficulty with this strategy is that we would generally have to collapse over, or pool, more of the $h = 1, \ldots, H$ subpopulations for the subsamples than for the overall sample taken as a whole; hence, we could be sacrificing a possibly greater reduction in the nonresponse bias for the sake of estimating the variance. Other replicatelike methods, such as jackknifing (e.g., Mosteller and Tukey, 1968) or pseudoreplication (e.g., McCarthy, 1966), would reduce the amount of "collapsing" needed and so might be preferred. (See also Efron, 1979; Efron and Gong, 1983.)

If the nonresponse is at all substantial, or if the number of panels employed is large, then the trade-off between bias reduction and variance estimation may be such that we would want to calculate not only the average weighting-class adjustment $\tilde{Y}_{c.}$ but also the overall estimator $\tilde{Y}_{c}$ obtained by first combining together all G panels. $\mathrm{Var}(\tilde{Y}_{c.})$ may or may not prove to be a satisfactory estimator of $\mathrm{Var}(\tilde{Y}_{c})$, a point made in the general case in the references cited earlier.

3.1.6. Bias–Variance Trade-Offs

In a multipurpose survey where a vector of characteristics Y_i is being obtained, it is quite possible that the nonresponse will affect different components differently. For some, the only effect of the nonresponse would be to reduce the sample size; that is, there might be no bias impact whatever. For other components, there would be a bias, but the nonresponse adjustment might essentially eliminate it. For the remainder of the components, the adjustment might leave significant residual biases or conceivably could even increase them.

Elaborate poststratification or weighting-class schemes are clearly unnecessary for variables not biased by the nonresponse; in fact, if the subpopulations are chosen so that the $\{m_h\}$ are small or the ratios n_h/m_h vary greatly, then the adjustment process could have important adverse consequences on the mean square error of such variables.

The fundamental problem with regard to bias reduction is to choose the subpopulation so that the assumption of a uniform response probability within the group is tenable. A seemingly robust approach is to choose the subgroups such that for the variable(s) to be analyzed, the within-group variation for nonrespondents is small (and the between-group mean differences are large); then, even if the response mechanism is postulated incorrectly, the bias impact will be small. Obviously, though, with a multipurpose survey the subpopulations chosen to be robust for one set of variables might be "frail" for others. A further difficulty with this prescription is that it is only for the respondents that within-group variability can be observed.

These elementary considerations suggest that practitioners employ more than one set of nonresponse weighting adjustments, with the actual number of alternatives being a function of the resources available, the amount of nonresponse, the degree of uncertainty about the response mechanism, and the extent to which different purposes are to be served by the same data set. It is further recommended that, as is consistent with much existing practice, when employing these alternative adjustments, steps be taken to reduce the adverse variance impacts that can occur if the subpopulations chosen have small m_h or large n_h/m_h.

3.2. Illustration of Alternative Nonresponse Adjustments

A concrete illustration of the remarks in this section may be worthwhile. Suppose we are sampling from a finite population of $N = 12,000$ individual units which can be divided into six equal subpopulations characterized by either differing mean vectors $\{\overline{Y}_h\}$ or differing response probabilities $\{\Phi_h\}$. The particular values these constants take on for our present purposes are shown in Table 1.

TABLE 1

Constants Established for Illustrative Simulation Study with Samples of Size $n = 120$

Simulation constants	Designated subpopulations					
	I	II	III	IV	V	VI
	Part I—population values					
N_h	2000	2000	2000	2000	2000	2000
$\overline{Y}_h$	$\left\{\begin{array}{l}100\\200\\100\end{array}\right.$	$\begin{array}{l}100\\50\\200\end{array}$	$\begin{array}{l}100\\50\\50\end{array}$	$\begin{array}{l}100\\100\\200\end{array}$	$\begin{array}{l}100\\100\\200\end{array}$	$\begin{array}{l}100\\200\\50\end{array}$
$\bar{n}_h$	20	20	20	20	20	20
	Part II—high-response model					
Φ_h	.8	.8	1.0	1.0	.9	.9
$\bar{m}_h$	16	16	20	20	18	18
	Part III—low-response model					
Φ_h	.2	.2	1.0	1.0	.5	.5
$\bar{m}_h$	4	4	20	20	10	10

To conduct the simulation here, we selected at random 12,000 vectors S with five independent uniform $U(0, 1)$ components each. The vectors were grouped into 1000 samples of $n = 120$. The individual components of $S = (D, R, \mathbf{U})$, where $\mathbf{U} = (U_1, U_2, U_3)$, were then used as follows:

(a)   The component D was used to assign the unit to a subpopulation, that is, $.00000 \leq D \leq .16666$ (first subpopulation), $.16667 \leq D \leq .33333$ (second subpopulation), and so forth.

(b)   The component R was used to determine whether the unit was a respondent. For example, for the first two subpopulations and the low response model, if $.00000 \leq \mathbf{R} \leq .19999$, the case was a response; otherwise it was treated as a nonresponse.

(c)   The elements of $\mathbf{U}$ were converted from uniform random variables into exponential ones with the means $\bar{Y}_h$ shown in Table 1 inserted for θ in the (probability integral) transformation $U = 1 - \exp\{-Y/\theta\}$.

From Table 1 it can be observed that the first component of $\mathbf{U}$ when transformed will always have the same mean in each subpopulation; for the second and third components of $\mathbf{U}$ the transformed variables $\tilde{\mathbf{Y}}$ will have means which differ in expected value depending on the subpopulation of which the unit is a member.

3.2.1.   Estimators Compared

For all of the 1000 samples of $n = 120$ that were selected seven basic estimators have been compared for each of the two response probability models. First, the simple overall inflation estimator $\tilde{Y}$ was calculated from expression (35). Three poststratification estimators $\tilde{Y}_s$ were constructed as well. These were based on three different groupings of the subpopulations into three strata:

Grouping A—subpopulations (I, VI), (II, III), (IV, V)
Grouping B—subpopulations (I, IV), (II, V), (III, VI)
Grouping C—subpopulations (I, II), (III, IV), (V, VI)

Corresponding to the three poststratified estimators $\tilde{Y}_s$, we also calculated three weighting-class estimators $\tilde{Y}_c$ which employed the same groupings. For the first component of $\tilde{Y}$, all the estimators, grouped and ungrouped, are (unconditional) unbiased; hence, in this case our interest focuses on the variance impact of the alternative weighting adjustments. For the second component $\tilde{Y}_s$ and $\tilde{Y}_c$ are unbiased only for groupings A and C. For the third component unbiasedness is achieved only with grouping C. Since the weighting adjustments are being made simultaneously to all components it is only for grouping C that $\tilde{Y}_c$ and $\tilde{Y}_s$ are completely (unconditionally) unbiased; hence if we were interested in some function relating one component of $\mathbf{Y}$ with another, say, a correlation coefficient, then in general a grouping C adjustment would be needed to achieve even approximate asymptotic unbiasedness.

3.2.2. High- and Low-Response Models

A few brief comments may be in order comparing the bias and variance of the high- and low-response models. Parts I and II of Table 2 will be the basis of these:

1. *Bias*—Estimator for estimator, in general, the high-response model ($\Phi. \doteq .9$) yields values that are closer to the true population totals for each

TABLE 2

Alternative One-Way Poststratification and Weighting-Class Estimators:
High- and Low-Response Models Compared[a]

	First component		Second component		Third component	
Type of estimator	*Simulation* average	*Simulation* $\sqrt{variance}$	*Simulation* average	*Simulation* $\sqrt{variance}$	*Simulation* average	*Simulation* $\sqrt{variance}$
Part I—high-response model						
Overall estimator	1198.4	117.6	1381.6	162.3	1587.8	183.9
Poststratified						
Grouping A	1197.9	118.5	1407.0	154.0	1560.0	173.1
Grouping B	1198.0	118.5	1373.2	159.3	1619.9	174.7
Grouping C	1198.6	119.5	1402.2	166.1	1599.6	186.7
Weighting class						
Grouping A	1198.7	117.8	1403.9	167.2	1560.3	179.2
Grouping B	1198.4	117.6	1372.4	159.8	1620.2	187.8
Grouping C	1198.7	118.0	1403.0	167.9	1598.8	185.8
Part II—low-response model: unconstrained (no collapsing of classes)						
Overall estimator	1196.8	144.3	1245.0	184.5	1538.7	231.7
Poststratified						
Grouping A	1196.1	153.6	1409.1	233.0	1369.9	189.3
Grouping B	1194.7	153.9	1218.8	177.7	1734.0	268.1
Grouping C	1194.5	182.1	1400.8	270.5	1608.5	297.4
Weighting class						
Grouping A	1197.5	153.1	1405.7	239.8	1369.6	197.2
Grouping B	1195.2	152.9	1218.2	175.8	1734.2	277.2
Grouping C	1195.3	181.7	1401.5	271.5	1609.3	301.1
Part III—low-response model: constrained (collapsing where $m_h < 10$ or $n_h/m_h > 4$)						
Poststratified						
Grouping A	1197.3	151.6	1386.6	242.0	1370.5	188.9
Grouping B	1194.7	150.0	1223.3	177.9	1704.3	276.5
Grouping C	1195.0	151.2	1299.8	205.7	1552.1	241.5
Weighting class						
Grouping A	1198.0	151.6	1387.0	247.7	1370.2	197.1
Grouping B	1195.2	149.7	1221.8	176.4	1707.5	284.8
Grouping C	1195.9	150.8	1301.4	209.3	1551.1	242.7

[a] Numbers in thousands; estimates based on 1000 samples of size 120 as described in the text. For the constrained adjustment if pooling was necessary, the first subpopulation in any grouping, if it did not satisfy the restrictions, was combined with the second, the second with the third, and the third with the first. The subpopulations for each grouping are shown in Table 1 and in the text. Each row of the table is for a different weight adjustment carried out simultaneously for all components. The simulation variances are estimates of the unconditional variances of each approach.

component than occurs for the low-response model. Perhaps more important still is the fact that for the high-response model there is far less sensitivity to the estimator chosen than is the case with the low-response model. (The true overall population totals, by the way, are 1,200,000, 1,400,000, and 1,600,000 for the first, second, and third, components, respectively.)

2. *Variance*—For the low-response model ($\Phi. = .6$), the average (actual) standard errors are much larger (by at least 20%) than those for the high-response model. Furthermore, for the low-response model the standard errors are extremely sensitive to which estimator is being employed.

In summary, the high-response model exhibits smaller biases, has smaller standard errors, and is relatively insensitive to which estimator we employ; clearly in this example, and probably in general, the requirement of a robust adjustment for nonresponse would seem to necessitate fairly high response rates. Without good response our estimators depend far too heavily on specific knowledge of the underlying mechanism—information we rarely have in practice.

3.2.3.   Constrained and Unconstrained Estimators

In order to illustrate the trade-offs when collapsing, or pooling, classes to increase the $\{m_h\}$ or to reduce the $\{n_h/m_h\}$, we applied the weighting-class and poststratified estimators both without any constraints and after requiring that the data be pooled if for any group $m_h < 10$ or $n_h/m_h > 4$. For the high-response model, both the constrained and unconstrained estimates were the same, so only one set of figures is shown. Standard cutoffs for pooling, such as $m_h < 20$ or $n_h/m_h > 2$, which have been used in the Current Population Survey (e.g., U.S. Bureau of the Census, 1963; Hanson, 1978), were not employed chiefly because to be realistic the simulations would have had to be conducted on a much larger scale.

Constrained and unconstrained adjustments can be compared for the low-probability model by examining Parts II and III of Table 2. Our discussion will be made component-by-component and will concentrate on the overall and poststratified estimators $\tilde{Y}$ and $\tilde{Y}_s$, since $\tilde{Y}_s$ and $\tilde{Y}_c$ behave in such a similar manner in this particular example:

(1) *First component*—As mentioned, the estimators will be unbiased for the first component. Since the mean is the same in each subpopulation, the only impact the grouping has is on the standard error. For groupings where the number of responses in each group is almost never small (groupings A and B), the standard error increase is modest (between 2% and 11%) over the optimal ungrouped estimator. In grouping C, where small cells can occur with high probability, the standard error increase is sizable, almost one-third greater than that for the ungrouped estimator. In the constrained case, the pooling of responses across subpopulations generally reduces the standard error for all

groupings, with the most dramatic change occurring for Grouping C—in fact, a large enough change to bring it into rough alignment with the other approaches.

(2) *Second component*—For the second component, the unconstrained estimators based on groupings A and C are unbiased. (Grouping B is badly biased, by almost 200,000.) In terms of standard errors, we again pay a high price with the estimator from grouping C, which has an unconditional standard error that is one-sixth larger than the grouping A estimator and over 50% larger than the (biased) ungrouped estimator. For the constrained estimator, a substantial standard error reduction is obtained (of about 25% for grouping C). The bias increase, however, still more than offsets the reduced variance.

(3) *Third component*—For the third component, the only unbiased estimators are those based on grouping C (in the unconstrained case). Again, there is a sizable variance "price" to pay, however. This time, though, when the constrained estimator for the third grouping is used, the reduction in the standard error roughly equals the bias increase.

The comparisons between constrained and unconstrained estimators in this illustration show dramatic differences between them; the constrained estimators tend to have much small variances and correspondingly larger biases. In good practice, however, usually pooling or collapsing has a much more modest effect. For instance, the bias implications can be quite insignificant (Bailar, Bailey, and Corby, 1978). The variance reduction potential of pooling is generally of some importance if only as a "fail-safe" to prevent anomalous weights from occurring. An example from the Current Population Survey would be the revised Census Bureau weighting procedures employed for the March Supplement weighting (see Oh and Scheuren, 1978a, for a discussion; see also Fuller, 1966, for some theoretical results on the effects of pooling).

4. RAKING RATIO ADJUSTMENTS
FOR NONRESPONSE

Raking ratio estimation was first proposed by Deming and Stephan as a way of assuring consistency between complete count and sample data from the 1940 U.S. Census of Population (Deming and Stephan, 1940). Since then their procedure has been used for a wide variety of problems (Fienberg, 1970; Purcell and Kish, 1980), including that of adjusting for nonresponse (e.g., Chapman, 1976).

In this section we briefly describe the basic technique and mention some of the common variants. The focus will, of course, be on the application of raking to nonresponse. For illustrative purposes, the example in Section 3 is also continued.

4.1. General Raking Technique

"Raking," or raking ratio estimation, is an iterative procedure for scaling sample data to known (outside) marginal totals.[1] One way to specify the raking algorithm is to set up a series of condition (or constraint) equations. Consider, for example, a two-way table of weighted counts $\{(N/n)n_{hk}\}$ where $h = 1, \ldots, H$ and $k = 1, \ldots, K$. Assume we know the $\{N_{h.}\}$ and column $\{N_{.k}\}$ population marginal totals. Suppose further that we wish to obtain adjusted counts $(N/n)\tilde{n}_k$ such that

$$\sum_{1}^{K} \frac{N}{n} \tilde{n}_{hk} = N_{h.} \tag{39}$$

and

$$\sum_{1}^{H} \frac{N}{n} \tilde{n}_{hk} = N_{.k}. \tag{40}$$

To derive the $\{\tilde{n}_{hk}\}$ so that expressions (39) and (40) both hold, the raking algorithm proceeds by proportionately scaling the cell values $\{n_{hk}\}$ so that each of the equations is satisfied in turn. Each step begins with the results of the previous step, the process terminating when all the equations are simultaneously satisfied to the closeness desired.

Specifically, in the present case, one could begin with a proportionate ratio adjustment by rows

$$\frac{N}{n} n_{hk}^{(1)} = \left(\frac{N_{h.}}{n_{h.}}\right) n_{hk}^{(1)} = a_h^{(1)} n_{hk} \tag{41}$$

followed by a column adjustment

$$\frac{N}{n} n_{hk}^{(2)} = \left(\frac{N_{.k}}{n_{.k}^{(1)}}\right) n_{hk}^{(1)} = b_k^{(1)} n_{hk}^{(1)}$$

$$= a_h^{(1)} b_k^{(1)} n_{hk} = W_{hk}^{(1)} n_{hk}, \tag{42}$$

where the $\{a_h^{(1)}\}$ and $\{b_k^{(1)}\}$ are the row and column adjustment factors and the $\{W_{hk}^{(1)}\}$ are the combined factors or weights.

These two successive ratio adjustments constitute a cycle that is then repeated in whole or in part until the individual cell entries cease to change appreciably.

---

[1] The term "raking" for this procedure seems to have arisen among practitioners at the U.S. Census Bureau (Rosenblatt, 1970). It appears to derive from the analog between the use of an ordinary garden rake and the successive steps in the iterative proportional fitting method. (To set this analogy requires a good bit of experience both in gardening and in doing the iterations by hand— something that the Census staff must have had when they established the usage.)

By an application of the theory of minimum discrimination information (Kullback, 1968), it can be shown (Ireland and Kullback, 1968) that if the $\{n_{hk}\}$ arise in a simple random selection from a population with domain totals $\{N_{hk}\}$, then for large samples

$$\left(\frac{N}{n}\right) E(\tilde{n}_{hk}) \doteq N_{hk},$$ (43)

so that the $\{\tilde{n}_{hk}\}$ are asymptotically unbiased, while

$$\mathrm{Var}(\tilde{n}_{hk}) \leq \mathrm{Var}(n_{hk}).$$ (44)

In fact, under regularity conditions, the $\{\tilde{n}_{hk}\}$ are best asymptotically normal (BAN) estimators. Heuristically the reason why the $\{\tilde{n}_{lk}\}$ are better estimators than $\{n_{hk}\}$ is that they make use of more information—namely, the (preserved) known marginal totals.

4.2. Raking Nonresponse Adjustment

Our discussion of raking as a nonresponse adjustment technique requires the following stipulations. Suppose, first, that we have L subpopulations ($L = HK$) with the number of respondents in each subpopulation being given by $\{m_{hk}\}$, where $h = 1, \ldots, H$ and $k = 1, \ldots, K$. Further, we postulate that

(1)   Within each subgroup, the responses are generated by an independent Bernoulli sampling process with common probability $\Phi_{hk} > 0$.

(2)   The response mechanisms are independent from one subpopulation to another.

(3)   The $\{\Phi_{hk}\}$ have a structure across subgroups such that

$$ln(\Phi_{hk}/(1 - \Phi_{hk})) = \alpha_h + \alpha_k$$

where the logarithm of response probabilities in $\Phi_{hk}/(1 - \Phi_{hk})$ depends on constants $\{\alpha_h\}$ and $\{\alpha_k\}$, or, in words, that the response probabilities are determined solely by the row or column a unit falls in and do not depend also on the particular cell. Notice that the first two of these conditions are the same as those we postulated for the standard poststratification or weighting-class adjustments of Section 2. The third condition is new and imposes a restriction that we did not require earlier. On the other hand, though, we are *not* assuming here, as we did before, that all the $m_{hk} > 0$. All that is needed is that the pattern of zeros among the $\{m_{hk}\}$ be such that the algorithm converges (for example, the $\{m_{hk}\}$ could not be all zero for a particular h or k). Now consider the raking estimator $\tilde{Y}_r$, where

$$\tilde{Y}_r = \sum_1^L \sum_1^K \tilde{N}_{hk} \bar{y}_{hk}^*$$ (45)

with

$$\tilde{N}_{hk} = \tilde{a}_h \cdot \tilde{b}_k m_{hk}, \tag{46}$$

where the $\{\tilde{a}_h\}$ and $\{\tilde{b}_k\}$ are the convergent positive adjustment factors developed from steps similar to (41) and (42).

The $\{\bar{y}_{hk}^*\}$ are the *sample* means for respondents in all the subgroups where $m_{hk} > 0$. We shall let $\bar{y}_{hk}^*$ be the subgroup *population* mean whenever $m_{hk} = 0$. (This does not change the value of expression (45) but does make it simple to show that $E(\tilde{N}_{hk}\bar{y}_{hk}^* | \tilde{N}_{hk}) = \tilde{N}_{hk}\bar{Y}_{hk}$, a quantity needed in deriving the bias of $\tilde{Y}_r$.) The (one-way) poststratified and weighting-class adjustments of the last section both have raking analogues. If the $\{N_{hk}\}$ satisfy

$$\sum_1^K \tilde{N}_{hk} = N_{h.} \quad \text{and} \quad \sum_1^H \tilde{N}_{hk} = N_{.k}, \tag{47a}$$

then $\tilde{Y}_r$ is a poststratified raking ratio estimator; if the $\{N_{hk}\}$ are such that

$$\sum_1^K \tilde{N}_{hk} = \frac{N}{n} n_{h.} \quad \text{and} \quad \sum_1^H \tilde{N}_{hk} = \frac{N}{n} n_{.k}, \tag{47b}$$

then $\tilde{Y}_r$ is a weighting-class raking ratio estimator.

4.2.1.   Bias

The conditional expected value of $\tilde{Y}_r$, given $\mathbf{n} = (n_{11}, \ldots, n_{HK})$ and $\mathbf{m} = (m_{11}, \ldots, m_{HK})$ fixed, is

$$E(\tilde{Y}_r | \mathbf{n}, \mathbf{m}) = \sum_1^H \sum_1^K \tilde{N}_{hk}\bar{Y}_{hk} = Y - \sum_1^H \sum_1^K (\bar{Y}_{hk} - \bar{Y})(N_{hk} - \tilde{N}_{hk}). \tag{48}$$

In general $\tilde{Y}_r$ is seen to be conditionally biased, with the importance of this bias depending on the structure of the population and the form of raking used. We can rewrite the $\bar{Y}_{hk}$, following the usual analysis of variance conventions (e.g., Scheffé, 1959, pp. 106–119), as

$$(\bar{Y}_{hk} - \bar{Y}) = (\bar{Y}_{h.} - \bar{Y}) + (\bar{Y}_{.k} - \bar{Y}) + (\bar{Y}_{hk} - \bar{Y}_{h.} - \bar{Y}_{.k} + \bar{Y}); \tag{49}$$

hence, the conditional bias is expressible as

$$\text{Bias}(\tilde{Y}_r | \mathbf{n}, \mathbf{m}) = \sum_1^H (\bar{Y}_{h.} - \bar{Y})(N_{h.} - \tilde{N}_{h.}) + \sum_1^K (\bar{Y}_{.k} - \bar{Y})(N_{.k} - \tilde{N}_{.k})$$
$$+ \sum_1^H \sum_1^K (\bar{Y}_{hk} - \bar{Y}_{h.} - \bar{Y}_{.k} + \bar{Y})(N_{hk} - \tilde{N}_{hk}). \tag{50}$$

Since $E\tilde{N}_{hk} = N_{hk}$, $\text{Bias}(\tilde{Y}_r | \mathbf{n}, \mathbf{m})$ is approximately zero unconditionally for large samples. It is the conditional behavior, however, of the estimator $\tilde{Y}_r$ that makes it an attractive adjustment for nonresponse in some settings.

For the poststratified raking estimator, the first two terms of the bias are zero because of the constraint equations (47a). With the weighting-class raking estimator each of the first two terms of the bias, behaves like the conditional bias of a weighting-class estimator based only on the row or column totals.

The third term of the conditional bias will generally not be zero for either form of raking unless the $\{Y_{hk}\}$ are such that there is no interaction. Generally, if the interaction is a minor part of the decomposition of $\bar{Y}_{hk}$, the raking adjustment will have good variance properties and small biases even in moderate sized samples.

4.2.2. Conditional Variance

The conditional variance of $\tilde{Y}_r$ can be written as

$$\text{Var}(\tilde{Y}_r | \mathbf{n}, \mathbf{m}) = \sum_1^H \sum_1^K (\tilde{N}_{hk})^2 \left(1 - \frac{m_{hk}^*}{N_{hk}}\right) \frac{V_{hk}}{m_{hk}^*}$$

$$= \sum_1^H \sum_1^K (\tilde{a}_h^2 \tilde{b}_k^2 m_{hk}) \left(1 - \frac{m_{hk}}{N_{hk}}\right) V_{hk}. \qquad (51)$$

This follows in a manner similar to the derivation of (24), where

$$m_{hk}^* = \begin{cases} m_{hk} & \text{for} \quad m_{hk} > 0 \\ \bar{m}_{hk} & \text{for} \quad m_{hk} = 0, \end{cases} \qquad (52)$$

with $\bar{m}_{hk} = (n/N)(\Phi_{hk})(N_{hk})$. (If $N_{hk} = 0$ or 1 we also define $V_{hk} = 0$ and adopt the convention that $0/0 = 0$.)

Since the $\{m_{hk}\}$ do not appear in the denominator of the conditional variance of $\tilde{Y}_r$ one can see why, on intuitive grounds at least, the $\tilde{Y}_r$ might be more stable for small $\{m_{hk}\}$ than, say, the estimator

$$\tilde{Y}_s = \sum_1^H \sum_1^K N_{hk} \bar{y}_{hk}, \qquad (53)$$

where, as we have seen, for $\{N_{hk}\}$ known,

$$V(\tilde{Y}_s | \mathbf{n}, \mathbf{m}) = \sum_1^H \sum_1^K N_{hk}^2 \left(1 - \frac{m_{hk}}{N_{hk}}\right) \frac{V_{hk}}{m_{hk}}. \qquad (54)$$

Of course, it must be added that it is possible to envision cases where the raking estimator could be inferior to that given by expression (53). Suppose, for example, that the variance V_{hk} was quite large in a particular subpopulation, relative to the remaining population. If N_{hk} was also large for this cell so that the cell dominated the overall variance, then essentially whenever $\tilde{N}_{hk} > N_{hk}$ we would have $V(\tilde{Y}_r | \mathbf{n}, \mathbf{m}) > V(\tilde{Y}_s | \mathbf{n}, \mathbf{m})$.

In cases where a few very large cells dominate the cross-classification being raked an obvious compromise (Leszcz, Oh, and Scheuren, 1983) is to employ a mixed approach as follows: for large subpopulations the estimator $N_{hk}\bar{y}_{hk}$ might be utilized. The remaining table could then be raked to marginal totals constructed from

$$N^*_{h.} = \sum_1^K N^*_{hk} \quad \text{and} \quad N^*_{.k} = \sum_1^H N^*_{hk},$$

where $N^*_{hk} = N_{hk}$ if the cell has not been separately estimated and equals zero otherwise.

4.2.3. Mean Square Error

There are, of course, many situations where $\tilde{Y}_s$, as given by expression (53), might be preferred in a mean square error sense over $\tilde{Y}_r$ even when $V(\tilde{Y}_s|\mathbf{n}, \mathbf{m}) > V(\tilde{Y}_r|\mathbf{n}, \mathbf{m})$. For example, suppose that m_{hk} is nonzero whenever N_{hk} is nonzero, then $\tilde{Y}_s$ is conditionally unbiased, while $\tilde{Y}_r$ in general is not. Furthermore, $\tilde{Y}_s$ (unlike $\tilde{Y}_r$) does not depend for its unbiasedness on the assumption that $\Phi_{hk} = \Phi_h\Phi_k$, i.e., assumption (3).

When raking is an option, the $\{N_{hk}\}$ are often unknown. Usually the practitioner has to choose between raking and one-way poststratification or raking and a (two-way) weighting-class estimator. Combined strategies are also possible and in fact are common in practice. For example, the initial non-response adjustment might be a weighting-class estimator using, say, geographic information, where collapsing has been done to reduce the variance impact of small cells. This could then be followed up by poststratified raking estimation using overall known totals, say, age and sex (Oh and Scheuren, 1973).

It is very hard to generalize about whether one estimation procedure will be better than another. Examining the average mean square error

$$\text{MSE}(\tilde{Y}_r) = E\left(\sum_1^H \sum_1^K \tilde{a}_h^2 \tilde{b}_k^2 m_{hk}\left(1 - \frac{m_{hk}}{N_{hk}}\right)\right)V_{hk}$$
$$+ E\left(\sum_1^H \sum_1^K (\bar{y}_{hk} - \bar{Y})(N_{hk} - \tilde{N}_{hk})\right)^2, \tag{55}$$

while useful, does not lead directly to suggestions about the best attack on the estimation problem. There simply are too many quantities to speculate about. Basically, though, the same kind of bias–variance trade-offs exist in the raking problem as in one-way poststratification or weighting-class applications. We need to choose dimensions that make the assumption of a uniform within-cell (or within-subpopulation) response probability tenable. Beyond that, as a device to achieve robustness, we would like to employ classification variables that are related to the statistics of primary interest to the investigators.

Raking has an important advantage over one-way poststratification and weighting-class schemes in that it allows for the simultaneous control of more than one variable without necessarily directly controlling groups with small sizes. We have talked about raking in this section as if it were only possible to deal with just two dimensions at a time. In fact, there is theoretically no limit to the number of dimensions that could be handled. (As a practical matter, though, a limit has to be imposed on the number of dimensions controlled if only to assure convergence of the algorithm. See Oh and Scheuren, 1978b.)

Raking has some important disadvantages which need to be considered before it is used:

(1) First, if the dimensions to be raked are badly chosen, the raking algorithm will not converge or will converge only very slowly. As yet there does not seem to exist any *easily verifiable* set of necessary and sufficient conditions which will assure convergence. The convergence proofs which do exist make strong assumptions about the cell counts—for example, say, that all the cells $\{m_{hk}\}$ are nonzero (Ireland and Kullback, 1968) or that particular combinations are present (Bishop and Fienberg, 1969). Usually, therefore, in many practical problems the best (albeit expensive) method of checking convergence is simply to attempt to carry out the raking adjustments. (The main things to guard against seem to be imposing too many constraints on the sample, imposing constraints that are themselves contradictory, or controlling, either explicitly or implicitly, groups with very small expected sample sizes.) An example of one rule of thumb that appears to have worked well in practice (Oh and Scheuren, 1978a) is not to rake a weighted survey total unless its effective sample size (e.g., $m_{h.}$ or $m_{.k}$ in this case) is greater than, say, 20 or 25 times the number of dimensions being constrained.

(2) Second, because of the complexity of the raking estimator, calculating the approximate mean square error can be extremely difficult. Variance estimators for the $\{\tilde{N}_{hk}\}$ are available, employing Taylor series methods, if our assumptions about the response mechanism are satisfied (e.g., Causey 1972, 1973). Direct estimation of the mean square error of $\tilde{Y}_r$ can, however, be another matter. What do we do, for example, to estimate V_{hk} for a cell where $m_{hk} = 1$? Replication methods could, of course, be utilized but might lead to only very rough estimates of the $MSE(\tilde{Y}_r)$ if there are many small cells. (As an aside jackknifing or pseudoreplicate raking MSE estimators might be preferred since they would have better convergence properties than an MSE estimator obtained by separately raking independent subsamples.)

(3) One final general point. The complexity of raking adjustments for nonresponse may lead to difficulties in practice until considerable experience has been gained. Put another way, raking is more sophisticated and less familiar than ordinary one-way poststratification or weighting-class estimation. For its full power to be achieved the practitioner must consider the application carefully. Cost factors, in particular, are a concern, especially if highly stable estimates of the variance or mean square error will be required.

4.3. Illustration of Raking Application

To complete this section we shall reexamine the numerical simulation described earlier in the chapter. This will allow us to illustrate concretely for a particular population some of the statistical properties of raking as a technique for adjusting nonresponse. Two variants of raking will be considered:

(1) Convergent raking ratio estimation (the procedure we have been discussing so far)

(2) Limited raking ratio estimation (where we cycle through the constraint equations only a few times, not to convergence)

Both variants are being included since several U.S. and Canadian census studies have shown that good results can be achieved when raking from one to four cycles (e.g., U.S. Bureau of the Census, 1974; Brackstone and Rao, 1978). Several comments might be made about the numerical results shown in Table 3.

(1) *Raked versus unraked estimators*—The one-way poststratification and weighting class estimators displayed in Table 2 compare favorably with the raking estimators of Table 3. Gains for the raking adjustments in bias reduction are generally small, if present at all, due to the weak relation which exists between the dimension added in the raking and the statistics being estimated. Intuitively, it might seem plausible that raking should not make us worse off in such situations; however, this is not the case. For example, in Oh and Scheuren (1978b), even without the complication of nonresponse, there tend to be small increases (depending on sample size) in the standard error when raking is applied in a context where the expected cell means are not related to one another. [The Oh-Scheuren paper further shows that, when there are (nonresponse) biases to "correct," the adverse variance impact of raking relative to, say, one-way poststratification can be quite sizable if the categories used in raking the $\{n_{hk}\}$ have little or no explanatory power in terms of the $\{\overline{Y}_{hk}\}$.]

(2) *High- versus low-response models*—Again the high-response model demonstrates its insensitivity to the adjustment technique. Only extremely minor changes are made in either the overall averages or the standard errors. For the low-response models larger differences among estimation techniques occurred, as one would expect.

(3) *Limited versus convergent raking*—There is basic agreement on the overall means and standard errors for the limited and convergent raking adjustments. Perhaps because of the restricted character of the illustration, there does not seem to be much evidence of what has been observed in some applications, namely greater bias reduction for convergent raking adjustments but at the price of some increase in the variance (Scheuren, 1980).

(4) *Raking versus pooling*—Unquestionably in this illustration, raking does not compare favorably to pooling as a way of controlling the standard error. For grouping C, the only one for which the raking adjustment should yield unbiased

TABLE 3

Alterative Raking Poststratification and Weighting Class Estimators:
High- and Low-Response Models Compared[a]

Type of raking estimator	First component		Second component		Third component	
	Simulation average	Simulation $\sqrt{variance}$	Simulation average	Simulation $\sqrt{variance}$	Simulation average	Simulation $\sqrt{variance}$
Part I—high-response model: raked only one cycle						
Poststratified						
Grouping A	1198.1	119.0	1406.4	155.2	1575.7	171.5
Grouping B	1197.7	119.3	1365.5	157.6	1613.2	173.9
Grouping C	1198.0	120.1	1402.7	166.7	1599.6	186.1
Weighting class						
Grouping A	1198.6	117.8	1403.8	167.2	1574.9	180.0
Grouping B	1198.6	117.8	1365.4	159.2	1613.2	186.5
Grouping C	1198.7	118.1	1403.2	168.3	1598.7	185.7
Part II—high-response model: raked to convergence						
Poststratified						
Grouping A	1198.2	118.9	1406.4	155.3	1576.8	171.5
Grouping B	1197.8	119.2	1364.9	157.9	1612.5	173.8
Grouping C	1198.0	120.2	1402.7	166.9	1599.7	186.2
Weighting class						
Grouping A	1198.6	117.8	1403.8	167.2	1575.9	180.0
Grouping B	1198.6	117.8	1364.8	159.4	1612.7	186.6
Grouping C	1198.7	118.1	1403.2	168.3	1598.6	185.8
Part III—low-response model: raked only one cycle						
Poststratified						
Grouping A	1195.5	156.0	1407.5	237.0	1420.6	203.7
Grouping B	1193.8	156.8	1179.3	172.6	1714.3	268.7
Grouping C	1194.8	184.8	1400.6	271.6	1608.6	299.3
Weighting class						
Grouping A	1196.8	155.7	1404.5	242.9	1421.5	208.3
Grouping B	1194.9	156.0	1182.2	172.5	1714.5	277.0
Grouping C	1195.7	183.2	1402.0	272.6	1608.8	302.4
Part IV—Low-response model: raked to convergence						
Poststratified						
Grouping A	1195.4	161.7	1405.5	243.6	1465.0	216.8
Grouping B	1193.9	162.3	1156.8	178.4	1694.8	273.6
Grouping C	1194.9	185.6	1400.5	273.9	1607.9	298.7
Weighting class						
Grouping A	1196.6	162.6	1402.8	250.3	1467.4	225.1
Grouping B	1195.0	162.3	1161.0	179.2	1695.3	283.3
Grouping C	1195.7	183.8	1402.0	275.0	1607.4	300.7

[a] Numbers in thousands; estimates based on 1000 samples of size 120 as described in the text. To carry out the raking adjustments the six subpopulation samples of respondents were arrayed into three 2 × 3 tables where the columns were the groupings described in the text. The pairs of subpopulations were ordered numerically (from I to VI) within each category. The first row always contained the smallest numbered subpopulation in every category.

results, standard errors were about the same for the low-response model between the unconstrained and raking adjustments.

The present illustration quite successfully demonstrates what happens in an inappropriate use of raking. What we are seeing in this raking illustration is what has been called elsewhere a case of "over-adjustment" (Frankel, 1969). Take grouping C, for instance. We know by construction that a single one-way poststratification or weighting-class adjustment is enough to achieve unbiasedness. The only legitimate reason for considering a second dimension in which to carry out the adjustment would be if there was a strong dependence between it and the statistics of interest.

We debated whether to construct another simulation to show some of the properties of raking in settings where it could realistically be of value. This was not done, however, because the main strengths of raking are already well illustrated elsewhere. For example, in the paper by Oh and Scheuren (1978b) referred to earlier, raking is carried out in a context where the simple (one-way poststratified) ratio estimator has a residual bias and where the added dimensions not only make it possible to reduce this bias but also to reduce the variance as well. Now the raking estimator can (and does) outperform its one-way analog with respect to both bias and variance.

5. SUBSAMPLE WEIGHTING FOR NONRESPONSE

All the adjusted estimators described so far in this chapter can be expressed in the form of a weighted sample sum

$$\tilde{Y}_w = \sum_1^m W_i Y_i, \tag{56}$$

where the $\{y_i\}$ are the values $\{Y_i\}$ obtained for the m respondents in the sample and the weights $\{W_i\}$ are chosen such that, for a particular response mechanism, $\{\tilde{Y}_w\}$ will be at least an approximately unbiased estimator of the population total Y. Conditional on $\mathbf{n}$ and $\mathbf{m}$, the $\{W_i\}$,

$$W_i = W_i(\mathbf{n}, \mathbf{m}),$$

are fixed. In this section an additional level of sampling will be introduced so that the weights may vary. Two subsampling schemes are considered briefly. These are

(1) *Duplication weighting*—A simple random sample of size $n - m$ is drawn from the m respondents and these additional cases are used in place of the $n - m$ nonrespondents. The original estimation procedure is then carried out as if there had been complete response.

(2) *Integerization weighting*—The adjusted weights $\{W_i\}$ are corrected to integers by a two-step process. First, we write $W_i = I_i + \theta_i$, where I_i is the largest integer less than or equal to W_i and $0 \le \theta_i < 1$ is the difference between W_i and I_i. The second step is to replace each θ_i by an indicator random variable, B_i, such that $\Pr(B_i = 1) = \theta_i$. This will mean that our final weight for the ith respondent will be either I_i or $I_i + 1$.

There is also some discussion of subsample weighting adjustments in general. Illustrations are again provided to make concrete comparisons among alternative approaches.

We are including subsample weighting schemes in this chapter for several reasons. First such methods are among the earliest weighting adjustments for nonresponse (Hansen, Hurwitz and Madow, 1953a); hence they have historical interest. Perhaps of even more importance, they are related to many of the so-called hot-deck imputation techniques discussed in Chapter 14. Our final reason for dealing with them here is that they offer another practical strategy that, like poststratification, when properly employed may reduce the non-response bias.

5.1. Duplication Weight Adjustments for Nonresponse

If we have an unconfounded probability mechanism, then

$$\tilde{Y}_w = \frac{N}{n} \sum_1^m \frac{n}{m} y_i = \frac{N}{m} \sum_1^m y_i \tag{57}$$

will be an unbiased estimator of Y. The duplication estimator in this setting could be

$$\tilde{Y}_D = \frac{N}{n} \left[\sum_1^m y_i + \sum_1^{n-m} y_i^* \right], \tag{58}$$

where the $\{y_i^*\}$ are a simple random subsample (SRS) of size $n - m$ taken without replacement from the m respondents. For example, suppose $N = 6000$, $n = 30$, and $m = 20$; then $n - m = 10$; half the respondents would have the weight $W_i = (6000/30)$, while the remainder had a weight twice as large. (There are of course $\binom{20}{10}$ possible ways in which these weights could be assigned to the respondents.)

We have implicitly assumed, so far, that the number of respondents equals or exceeds the number of nonrespondents. If this is not the case, i.e., if $n - m > m$, then we cannot do the subsampling without replacement. One approach when $n - m > m$, which we prefer, is to use each respondent the minimum number of times by cycling through the respondents completely until the $n - m$ cases have been drawn. For instance, suppose $n - m = km + m^*$, where k is an integer and $m^* < m$, then we would choose $m - m^*$ of the respondents exactly k times and the remaining m^* respondents $k + 1$ times. This technique would yield an estimator with a smaller variance than, say, drawing the subsample of $n - m$ cases from the respondents by employing a with-replacement SRS design.

5.1.1. Variance Properties

It can be shown that the conditional variance of the estimator $\tilde{Y}_w$ is always less than or equal to that of the duplication estimator $\tilde{Y}_D$. (The proof is similar to that to be given for $\tilde{Y}_I$.) For the case of simple random sampling (Hansen, Hurwitz and Madow, 1953b) the relative loss of efficiency is

$$\frac{\text{Var}(\tilde{Y}_D) - \text{Var}(\tilde{Y}_w)}{\text{Var}(\tilde{Y}_w)} \doteq \frac{x - x^2}{(1 + x)^2}, \tag{59}$$

where $x = (n - m)/m$ is assumed to be such that $0 < x < 1$ and N is large relative to m. (The maximum loss occurs when $x = 1/3$ for a drop in efficiency of 12.5%.) When $n - m > m$, if the duplication is carried out with the minimum amount of respondent reuse as described then the loss in efficiency is the same as that of the integerized estimator with k substituted for I in expression (66).

An obvious question is why use an estimate which always has a larger variance than its natural competitor? Simplicity is the basic answer. In particular, in some (primitive?) computer environments or with some computer packages, a self-weighting sample is required. A duplication estimator will retain this property of a simple random sample (or of any other self-weighting design) no matter how many weighting classes are used (so long as there is at least one respondent in each class for which there are nonrespondents).

A serious disadvantage of the duplication estimator is that some practitioners treat the reconstituted sample as if there were n respondents rather than m. Variance estimators can then be badly biased with the consequence that confidence intervals may be far too short. This abuse has been a common one in hot-deck applications (e.g., Ford, 1976; Scheuren, 1976b), a point dwelt on at length in the next chapter.

5.2. Integer Weight Adjustment for Nonresponse

Integer weighting, like duplication weighting, attempts to simplify the weights by an additional randomization step (Murthy and Sethi, 1961). One way to motivate integer weighting for nonresponse is to note, as we have already, that

$$\tilde{Y}_w = \sum_1^m W_i Y_i = \sum_1^m (I_i + \theta_i) Y_i, \tag{60}$$

where I_i is the largest integer less than or equal to W_i and $0 < \theta_i < 1$ is the difference between W_i and I_i. An integer weight adjustment can then be defined by replacing the $\{\theta_i\}$ by indicator random variables $\{B_i\}$, where

$$\Pr(B_i = 1 \mid D_i R_i = 1, \mathbf{n}, \mathbf{m}) = \theta_i, \qquad i = 1, \ldots, m. \tag{61}$$

5.2.1. Bias

The integer weighting estimator

$$\tilde{Y}_I = \sum_1^m (I_i + B_i) y_i \tag{62}$$

has the same expected value as the original estimator; hence, if the original estimator was unbiased, $\tilde{Y}_I$ is as well.

5.2.2. Variance

To evaluate the variance of $\tilde{Y}_I$, we need to specify the exact nature of the nonresponse adjustment which leads to the choice of the $\{W_i\}$. We further must decide how the extra sampling is to be carried out—in particular, the joint probabilities

$$\Pr(B_i B_j = 1 \mid D_i D_j = 1, \mathbf{n}, \mathbf{m}) = \theta_{ij} \tag{63}$$

must be determined.

However the $\{\theta_{ij}\}$ are determined, the new estimator $\tilde{Y}_I$ has a larger variance than $\tilde{Y}_w$. This follows immediately from

$$\begin{aligned}
\text{Var}(\tilde{Y}_I) &= E[\text{Var}(\tilde{Y}_I \mid \mathbf{W})] + \text{Var}[E(\tilde{Y}_I \mid \mathbf{W})] \\
&= E[\text{Var}(\tilde{Y}_I \mid \mathbf{W})] + \text{Var}(\tilde{Y}_w) \geq \text{Var}(\tilde{Y}_w),
\end{aligned} \tag{64}$$

where $\mathbf{W}$ is the vector of weights $(W_1, \ldots, W_i, \ldots, W_m)$.

The integerized estimator, like the duplication estimator, tends to increase the variance although, as we will see, this effect may be quite small. One advantage that integer weights provide is that they assure consistency in weighted counts within (and among) multiple cross-tabulations and thus allow one to avoid the otherwise ubiquitous note "Details may not add to totals due to rounding."

5.2.3. Integerization Example

No attempt will be made to discuss further the general nature of the variance of $\tilde{Y}_I$. Instead, we shall look at the special case when the integerization subsample is a simple random one drawn without replacement.

In the context of the adjustments explicated in the earlier sections, we have that within a particular weighting class (poststratum or raking cell) the $\{\theta_i\}$ are all equal, say, to θ. To carry out the sampling one straightforward strategy, therefore, would be to determine the largest integer, denoted m', less than or equal to $m\theta$, where m is the number of respondents in the weighting class. A random number U is now drawn. If $0 \leq U \leq m\theta - m'$, then a simple random subsample of $m' + 1$ respondents will be taken; otherwise, only m' will be selected.

Letting $m^* = m' + 1$ or m', we can write the integer estimator for a particular class under this scheme as

$$\tilde{Y}_I = \sum_1^m (I)y_i + \sum_1^{m^*} (I + 1)y_j. \tag{65}$$

It can be shown by an extension of the duplication estimator results in Hansen et al., (1953b), that the relative loss in efficiency of $\tilde{Y}_I$ over $\tilde{Y}_w$ in this case is

$$\frac{\mathrm{Var}(\tilde{Y}_I) - \mathrm{Var}(\tilde{Y}_w)}{\mathrm{Var}(\tilde{Y}_w)} \doteq \frac{x - x^2}{(I + x)^2}, \tag{66}$$

where $x = m^*/m$, N is large relative to m, and the impact on the variance of the randomization to determine m^* is ignored.

The maximum loss occurs when $x = I/(2I + 1)$. For $I = 1$ this is the duplication estimator result of $x = 1/3$ with $x \to 1/2$ as I gets large. The drop in efficiency due to integerization is greatest for the case when $I = 1$ and declines rapidly thereafter, as Table 4 indicates. (For $I = 2$ for instance the loss drops from 12.5% to only about 4% at the maximum.)

TABLE 4

Relative Loss in Efficiency due to Integer Weighting
under the Assumption of Simple Random Sampling[a]

Integer value [I]	Subsampling rate m^*/m (%)									
	10	20	30	40	50	60	70	80	90	$I/(1 + 2I)$
1	7.4380	11.1111	12.4260	12.2449	11.1111	9.3750	7.2664	4.9383	2.4931	12.5000
2	2.0408	3.3058	3.9698	4.1667	4.0000	3.5503	2.8807	2.0408	1.0702	4.1667
3	.9365	1.5625	1.9284	2.0761	2.0408	1.8519	1.5340	1.1080	.5917	2.0833
4	.5354	.9070	1.1357	1.2397	1.2346	1.1342	.9507	.6944	.3748	1.2500
5	.3460	.5917	.7476	.8230	.8264	.7653	.6464	.4756	.2585	.8333
6	.2419	.4162	.5291	.5859	.5917	.5510	.4678	.3460	.1890	.5952
7	.1785	.3086	.3941	.4383	.4444	.4155	.3542	.2630	.1442	.4464
8	.1372	.2380	.3048	.3401	.3460	.3245	.2774	.2066	.1136	.3472
9	.1087	.1890	.2428	.2716	.2770	.2604	.2232	.1666	.0918	.2778
10	.0882	.1538	.1979	.2219	.2268	.2136	.1834	.1372	.0758	.2273
20	.0223	.0392	.0510	.0577	.0595	.0566	.0490	.0370	.0206	.0595
30	.0099	.0175	.0229	.0260	.0269	.0256	.0223	.0169	.0094	.0269
40	.0056	.0099	.0129	.0147	.0152	.0146	.0127	.0096	.0054	.0152
50	.0036	.0063	.0083	.0094	.0090	.0094	.0082	.0062	.0035	.0098

[a] See text for definition of approximate relative efficiency.

5.2.4. Illustration

To complete this discussion we return to the numerical simulation described earlier. In particular, we compare the standard weighting-class estimator $\tilde{Y}_c$ with the duplication and integerization estimators $\tilde{Y}_D$ and $\tilde{Y}_I$, respectively. The calculations have been carried out on an overall basis and for the same three groupings as before. Table 5 shows the results obtained for 1000 samples of size $n = 120$; it offers no real surprises. The duplication and integerization estimators have simulation averages which, if one holds the grouping constant, are virtually indistinguishable from each other or from $\tilde{Y}_c$. It is only in the standard errors that any consistent differences emerge. Here, as expected, the standard error of $\tilde{Y}_D$ always exceeds that of $\tilde{Y}_c$, although not by very much. The duplication estimator of the first component, for example, has a standard error about 3.1% greater than the standard error of $\tilde{Y}_c$ in the high-response model. With the low-response model the increase averages somewhat less in percentage terms (roughly 2%).

The standard errors of $\tilde{Y}_I$ and $\tilde{Y}_c$ behave as expected for each grouping, i.e., $\sqrt{\text{Var}(\tilde{Y}_I)} \geq \sqrt{\text{Var}(\tilde{Y}_c)}$. Also, as suggested by Table 4, the standard errors are virtually undistinguishable numerically, since I is so large (on the order of 100).

5.3. Additional Comments

Subsample weighting adjustments afford us an opportunity to change the character of our estimates so that they possess certain desirable properties. This has been the rationale employed to motivate the duplication and integerization techniques. Subsampling also allows us to incorporate information or conjectures about the nonrespondents that might otherwise be unused. For example, we may hypothesize that overall (or within-weighting classes) we have an unconfounded response mechanism but wish to examine the sensitivity of our results to the possibility that in actual fact the response probabilities were proportional to some characteristic x_i, where the $\{x_i\}$ are positive quantities known for all respondents $i = 1, \ldots, m$. A ratio estimation procedure could be employed to handle this situation but subsampling with probabilities inversely proportional to the $\{x_i\}$ may also warrant consideration.

Assume that $\Pr(R_i = 1 \mid D_i = 1) = \psi x_i$ with $\psi > 0$; then in simple random sampling the estimator

$$\tilde{Y}_x = N \left(\sum_1^m \frac{1}{x_i} y_i \right) \left(\sum_1^m \frac{1}{x_i} \right)^{-1} = \frac{N}{m} \sum_1^m x_i^* y_i \tag{67}$$

will be approximately unbiased. Now suppose we draw a systematic subsample $\{y_i^*\}$ of size m from the respondents with probability proportional to the $[x_i^*]$; then it follows that the conditional expected value of the subsample estimator $\tilde{Y}_x = (N/m) \sum y_i^*$, given the respondents, would be equal to $\tilde{Y}_x$. The variance

TABLE 5

Duplication and Integerization Weighting Adjustments Compared to the
Standard Weighting-Class Estimator[a]

Type of estimator	First component Simulation average	First component Simulation $\sqrt{variance}$	Second component Simulation average	Second component Simulation $\sqrt{variance}$	Third component Simulation average	Third component Simulation $\sqrt{variance}$
			Part I—high-response model			
Standard						
Overall	1197.4	115.4	1372.8	165.9	1591.2	194.5
Grouping A	1197.3	115.4	1394.5	170.1	1564.5	190.2
Grouping B	1197.2	115.5	1362.9	163.6	1624.5	198.0
Grouping C	1197.3	116.2	1394.3	171.0	1602.4	194.4
Duplication						
Overall	1198.1	118.3	1371.9	171.5	1592.1	202.2
Grouping A	1198.6	118.9	1394.6	174.1	1566.5	196.2
Grouping B	1196.9	120.3	1362.9	170.6	1623.0	208.6
Grouping C	1198.4	119.3	1394.6	180.4	1602.9	204.6
Integerization						
Overall	1197.5	115.5	1372.8	165.9	1591.2	194.5
Grouping A	1197.3	115.5	1394.5	170.1	1564.5	190.2
Grouping B	1197.2	115.5	1363.0	163.6	1624.5	198.0
Grouping C	1197.3	116.2	1394.3	171.0	1602.4	194.4
			Part II—low-response model			
Standard						
Overall	1199.8	145.7	1233.6	184.1	1527.8	246.4
Grouping A	1200.1	155.6	1391.9	240.2	1357.0	205.2
Grouping B	1200.4	154.3	1204.2	176.1	1715.7	281.8
Grouping C	1201.1	181.5	1384.3	264.8	1579.3	287.2
Duplication						
Overall	1200.0	148.7	1234.5	189.9	1527.6	251.7
Grouping A	1198.6	159.4	1388.7	241.7	1357.0	215.1
Grouping B	1200.9	157.3	1203.0	179.9	1717.3	287.8
Grouping C	1200.6	182.1	1383.0	267.0	1579.3	290.2
Integerization						
Overall	1199.8	145.7	1233.6	184.1	1527.7	246.4
Grouping A	1200.1	155.6	1391.9	240.2	1357.0	205.3
Grouping B	1200.4	154.3	1204.2	176.1	1715.7	281.8
Grouping C	1201.1	181.5	1384.3	264.8	1597.3	287.2

[a] Numbers in thousands; estimates based on 1000 samples of size 120, as described in the text. This stimulation was conducted independently of those detailed in Sections 3 and 4; hence, the weighting class estimates differ slightly.

of $\tilde{\tilde{Y}}_x$ will, of course, exceed that of $\tilde{Y}_x$ for the same reasons that we saw earlier when comparing $\tilde{Y}_1$ and $\tilde{Y}_c$. The estimator $\tilde{\tilde{Y}}_x$, though, has an especially attractive feature common to all the subsampling methods we have been discussing: By repeated independent drawings we can readily estimate the variance component due to the nonresponse, conditional on the respondents actually obtained and the estimator chosen (see the chapter by Herzog and Rubin in this part).

Two methods of reducing the variance of $\tilde{\tilde{Y}}_x$ might be mentioned:

(1)   The variance of $\tilde{\tilde{Y}}_x$(or indeed $\tilde{Y}_x$) could be very large if one or more of the x_i happened to be close to zero. As a protection against this possibility it might be better to construct a new estimator

$$\tilde{Y}_z = \left\{ \sum_1^m \frac{1}{z_i} y_i \right\} \left\{ \sum_1^m \frac{1}{z_i} \right\}^{-1} = \frac{N}{m} \sum_1^m z_i^* y_i, \qquad (68)$$

where $z_i = \max[x_i, k^{-1}]$ with k being set equal to, say, $2n/m$. The estimator $\tilde{Y}_z$ will be biased if $\Pr[x_i < k^{-1}] > 0$ (unless the x_i and y_i are uncorrelated, in which case $\tilde{Y}_z$ would again be asymptotically unbiased in the same way that $\tilde{Y}_x$ is).

(2)   The variance of $\tilde{\tilde{Y}}_x$ or $\tilde{Y}_z$ can also be reduced by averaging our estimates over repeated subsamples. (It almost goes without saying that *only* the component of $\text{Var}(\tilde{Y}_x)$ or $\text{Var}(\tilde{Y}_z)$ introduced by the subsampling can be reduced in this way.)

Perhaps it is worth noting in passing that imposing a lower limit on the x_i is very similar to the idea discussed earlier of collapsing or pooling when the weighting factors $\{n_h/m_h\}$ become too large. We again, though, may pay a price in bias to get an estimator with a smaller variance.

5.3.1.   Distinction between Imputation and Weighting

For techniques like raking or (one-way) poststratification, the distinction between imputation and weighting is easy to grasp. With subsample weighting adjustments, however, the differences became much smaller and, indeed, for some statistics disappear altogether, provided we properly treat imputed information as imputed (and not reported) in calculating estimated variances.

Consider, for example, a setting in which we have $h = 1, \ldots, H$ weighting classes with $\{m_h\}$ respondents and $\{n_h - m_h\}$ nonrespondents. If a duplication weighting adjustment were made in each class separately we would be selecting $n_h - m_h$ respondents at random from the m_h in the class. If $n_h - m_h < m_h$, then $n_h - m_h$ respondents will appear twice in the enlarged respondent sample, i.e., have their weight doubled, while the rest of the respondents have weights which remain unchanged. In an imputation context, all other things being equal, we would *match* $n_h - m_h$ respondents at random to the $n_h - m_h$ nonrespondents in the class. The estimator based on the enlarged samples of the form

$$\left\{ \sum_1^{m_h} y_{hi} + \sum_1^{n_h - m_h} y_{hi*} \right\} \qquad (69)$$

obviously would be identical in these two cases for all characteristics Y_{hi} obtained *only* from the respondents.

Where then does the distinction lie? To answer this question consider three types of variables $(\mathbf{X}, \mathbf{Y}, \mathbf{Z})$, where the $\{X_i\}$ are being used in the nonresponse adjustment (to define the weighting classes, say), while the $\mathbf{Z}$ are not involved. As before the $\mathbf{Y}$ are assumed to be known only for the respondents. In this setting, there is no difference between duplication weighting and (hot-deck) imputation for statistics involving the $\mathbf{X}$, $\mathbf{Y}$, or relations between them. For statistics involving $\mathbf{Z}$ or relations between $\mathbf{Z}$ and $\mathbf{X}$, the variance of the duplication estimator would tend to be larger than for the imputation estimator, since it is being based on a smaller sample. Finally, if the (common) model for the response mechanism is valid, duplication estimators of the relations between $\mathbf{Y}$ and $\mathbf{Z}$ would have their (asymptotic) expected values unaltered by the nonresponse. In general though, imputation estimators of relations between $\mathbf{Y}$ and $\mathbf{Z}$ would have their expected values altered unless $\mathbf{Y}$ and $\mathbf{Z}$ were conditionally independent given $\mathbf{X}$. [Sims (1974) discusses a related problem.]

The decision whether to employ imputation or weighting procedures depends greatly on the particular estimation setting that has to be faced. Usually, for example, in the unit nonresponse or total noninterview case weighting would be the natural method to choose, since typically very little may be known about the individual respondents—perhaps so little that virtually all of it could be used in the nonresponse adjustment. For the item nonresponse problem, imputation may be the natural choice, since we may know far more about the nonrespondents than we could conveniently employ in any single weighting adjustment. Indeed multiple imputation might be the best option of all in the item nonresponse case—a point made at length in the past chapter of this part.

6. RECOMMENDATIONS FOR FUTURE STUDY

In this chapter we have described many of the common weighting adjustments for nonresponse: notably poststratification and weighting-class techniques, raking and other general ratio methods, and duplication and integerization procedures. The primary focus of the discussion has been on the implications of these nonresponse adjustments in simple random sampling.

An attempt has been made to highlight the extent to which the unit nonresponse problem is handled by employing tools and insights developed in probability sampling. While such "quasi-randomization" models generally reflect much of current practice, there is no question that a broader set of models is needed. The work by Särndal and Hui (1980), for example, illustrates adaptations that could be fruitful in employing regression estimators. Certainly desirable would be explicitly incorporating the general Bayesian notions set forth by Rubin earlier in this volume (see also Smouse, 1979).

Perhaps two of the most serious gaps in the theory of current practice that need addressing are

(1)   How to handle lack of validity of the assumption that the $\{\Phi_i\}$ are positive for all i. (Perhaps the only solution here is to directly model the y, something beyond the scope of this chapter.)

(2)   How to realistically model the dependence which may exist between the probability of a response and the quantities to be observed.

In any case, there is definitely a need to develop methods that will improve our ability to examine the sensitivity of survey results to alternative "conjectures" about the response mechanism (see Drew and Fuller, 1980; Greenlees, Reece, and Zieschang, 1982).

Several other recommendations about application issues have already been made at various points in this chapter. Perhaps some of them bear repeating:

(1)   All too often weighting adjustments for nonresponse are chosen for their convenience rather than their appropriateness (Bailar, Bailey, and Corby, 1978). Part of the reason for this is that, despite protestations to the contrary, we may be grossly underestimating the seriousness of the nonresponse bias in surveys. It is essential that at the design stage plans be made for the nonresponse adjustment, including plans to collect good predictor variables (if possible) for use in the adjustment process.

(2)   Inadequate attention is being given to validation studies which measure the nonresponse bias and, until recently, to improving our techniques for handling nonresponse or for thinking through the analysis implications of the residual errors which remain in the survey data even after adjustment. (The need for validation studies has special force in large-scale surveys, where the biases due to response and nonresponse errors tend to dominate the mean square error.)

(3)   Practitioners should explicitly state the response mechanism assumed by the adjustment procedure they employ. Evidence, if available, should be cited on why such a mechanism may be plausible.

(4)   The impact of alternative estimators should be examined so that questions of sensitivity to alternative assumptions can be brought out concretely.

(5)   It is desirable that practitioners provide sets of survey weights rather than a single estimator (see Scheuren, 1980, for an illustration). This may be especially important for secondary users whose analysis goals were not incorporated in developing the adjustments.

(6)   The value of replication cannot be stressed too much as a way of introducing robustness into the variance estimation. Replication also seems an essential aid in interpreting differences introduced in our results by alternative estimators.

(7)   Since response models almost never hold exactly, the only truly robust approach to the problem of bias is to keep nonresponse to a minimum. There is no adequate substitute for complete response as the simulations in this chapter concretely illustrate.

Weighting adjustments for nonresponse are also discussed in Part V of this volume. A total survey error approach is taken there in order that the important tradeoffs that exist between response and nonresponse errors can be realistically addressed.

REFERENCES

Bailar, B. A., Bailey, L., and Corby, C. (1978). A comparison of some adjustment and weighting procedures for survey data. *Survey Sampling and Measurement*, 175–198.

Bishop, Y. M., and Fienberg, S. E. (1979). Incomplete two-dimensional contingency tables. *Biometrics* 25: 383–400.

Brackstone, G. J., and Rao, J. N. K. (1978). An Investigation of Raking Ratio Estimators. Unpublished Statistics Canada Working Paper.

Causey, B. D. (1972). Sensitivity of raked contingency table totals to changes in problem conditions. *Ann. Math. Stat.* 43: 656–658.

Causey, B. D. (1973). Variance of Raked-Table Entries. *U.S. Census Bureau Memorandum* (unpublished).

Chapman, D. W. (1976). A survey of nonresponse imputation procedures. *Proceedings of the American Statistical Association, Social Statistics Section*, pp. 245–251.

Cochran, W. G. (1977). *Sampling Techniques*. New York: Wiley.

Deming, W. E., and Stephan, F. F. (1940). On a least square adjustment of a sampled frequency table when the expected marginal totals are known. *Annals of Mathematical Statistics* 11: 427–444.

Raj, Des (1968). *Sampling Theory*. New York: McGraw-Hill.

Drew, J. H., and Fuller, W. A. (1980). Modeling Nonresponse in Surveys with Callbacks. *Proceedings of the Section on Research Methods*. American Statistical Association, pp. 639–642.

Efron, B. (1979). Bootstrap methods: Another look at the jackknife. *Annals of Mathematical Statistics* 7: 1–26.

Efron, B., and Gong, G. (1979). A leisurely look at the bootstrap, the jackknife, and cross-validation. *The American Statistician* 37: 36–48.

Fienberg, S. E. (1970). An iterative procedure for estimation in contingency tables. *Annals of Mathematical Statistics* 41: 907–917.

Ford, B. L. (1976). Missing data procedures: A comparative study. *Proceedings of the Social Statistics Section*, American Statistical Association, pp. 324–329.

Frankel, L. R. (1969). Are survey data being over-adjusted. *Current Controversies in Marketing Research*. Markham.

Fuller, W. A. (1966). Estimation employing post-strata. *Journal of the American Statistical Association* 61: 1172–1183.

Greenlees, J. S., Reece, W. S., and Zieschang, K. D. (1982). Imputation of missing values when the probability of response depends upon the variable being imputed. *Journal of the American Statistical Association* 77: 251–261.

Hansen, M. H., Hurwitz, W. N., and Madow, W. G. (1953a). *Sample Survey Methods and Theory* (Vol. 1) p. 569. New York: Wiley.

Hansen, M. H., Hurwitz, W. N., and Madow, W. G. (1953b). *Sample Survey Methods and Theory* (Vol. 2) pp. 139–141. New York: Wiley.

Hanson, R. (1978). The current population survey: Design and methodology, pp. 55–59. *Technical Paper No. 40*, U.S. Bureau of the Census.

Hartley, H. O. (1946). Discussion of paper by F. Yates. *Journal of the Royal Statistical Society* 109: 37.

Holt, D., and Smith, T. M. F. (1979). Post-Stratification. *Journal of the Royal Statistical Society*, series A, 142: (1): 33–46.

Ireland, C. T., and Kullback, S. (1968). Contingency tables with given marginals. *Biometrika* 55: 179–188.

Kish, L., and Frankel, M. (1970). Balanced Repeated Replications for Standard Errors. *Journal of the American Statistical Association* 65: 1071–1094.

Kish, L., and Frankel, M. R. (1974). Inference from complex samples (with discussion). *Journal of the Royal Statistical Society*, Series B, 36: 1–37.

Kullback, S. (1968). *Information Theory and Statistics*. New York: Dover.

Leszcz, M. K., Oh, H. L., and Scheuren, F. J. (1983). Modified raking estimation in the corporate statistics of income program, *Proceedings of the Section on Survey Research Methods*, American Statistical Association (in preparation).

McCarthy, P. J. (1966). Replication: An approach to the analysis of data from complex surveys. *Vital and Health Statistics*. PHS Pub. No. 1000-Series 2, No. 14. Public Health Service.

Mosteller, F., and Tukey, J. W. (1968). Data analysis, including statistics. *The Handbook of Social Psychology* (Vol. 2), pp. 80–203.

Murthy, M. N., and Sethi, V. K. (1961). Randomized rounded-off multiples in sampling theory. *Journal of the American Statistical Association* 56: 328–334.

Oh, H. L., and Scheuren, F. J. (1973). Household comparison sample weights: Wave 2, 3, 4 and able test cases. *Longitudinal Manpower Evaluation Studies*. U.S. Office of Economic Opportunity.

Oh, H. L., and Scheuren, F. J. (1978a). Multivariate raking ratio estimation in the 1973 exact match study. *Proceedings of the Section on Survey Research Methods*, American Statistical Association, pp. 716–722.

Oh, H. L., and Scheuren, F. J. (1978b). Some unresolved application issues in raking ratio estimation. *Proceedings of the Section on Survey Research Methods*, American Statistical Association, pp. 723–728.

Purcell, N. J., and Kish, L. (1980). Post censal estimates for local areas (or domains). *International Statistical Review* 48: 3–18.

Rosenblatt, H. M. (1970). Notes on a study of proposed ratio estimators for the 1970 census. Unpublished U.S. Census Bureau working paper.

Särndal, C. E., and Hui, T. (1980). Estimation for nonresponse situations: To what extent must we rely on models? Presented at the May 1980 Ottawa Sampling Symposium.

Schaible, W. L. (1979). Estimation of finite population totals from incomplete data: Prediction approach. Presented at the Symposium on Incomplete Data sponsored by the Panel on Incomplete Data. Committee on National Statistics, National Research Council, August, 1979.

Scheffé, H. (1959). *The Analysis of Variance*, pp. 106–119. New York: Wiley.

Scheuren, F. J. (1976b). Preliminary notes on the partially missing data problem—some (very) elementary considerations. Delivered at the April 1976 meeting of the Social Security Administration's Statistical Methodology Group.

Scheuren, F. J. (1980). Methods of estimation for the 1973 exact match study. In *Studies from Inter-agency Data Linkages, Report No. 10*, Social Security Administration.

Sims, C. A. (1974). Comments on statistical matching. *Annals of Economic and Social Measurement*, 3: 395–397. *1978 Compendium of Tax Research*, pp. 172–177. Office of Tax Analysis, Treasury Department.

Smouse, E. P. (1979). Estimating a finite population total when there is nonresponse. Presented at the 1979 Annual Meeting of the American Statistical Association.

Thomsen, I. (1973). A note on the efficiency of weighting subclass means to reduce the effects of nonresponse when analyzing survey data. *Statistisk Tidskrift* 11: 278–285.

Thomsen, I. (1978). A second note on the efficiency of weighting subclass means to reduce the effects of non-response when analyzing survey data. *Statistisk Tidskrift* 16: 191–196.

U.S. Bureau of the Census (1963). The current population survey: A report on methodology. *Technical Paper No. 7*, pp. 53.

U.S. Bureau of the Census (1974). *Procedural History*. Sampling and Estimation, PHC(R)-1E.

FURTHER READING

Bankier, M. D. (1978). An estimate of the efficiency of raking ratio estimators under simple random sampling. *Surv. Methodol.* 4: 115–124.

Banks, M. J. (1977). An indication of the effect of noninterview adjustment and post-stratification on estimates from a sample survey. *Proceedings of the Social Statistics Section*, American Statistical Association, pp. 291–295.

Basu, D. (1979). A discussion of survey theory. Presented at the Symposium on Incomplete Data sponsored by the Panel on Incomplete Data, Committee on National Statistics, National Research Council, August 1979.

Brewer, K. R. (1979). Discussion of Cassel–Särndal–Wretman paper, some uses of statistical models in connection with the nonresponse problem. Presented at the Symposium on Incomplete Data sponsored by the Panel on Incomplete Data. Committee on National Statistics, National Research Council, August 1979.

Cassel, C. M., Särndal, C. E., and Wretman, J. H. (1979). Some uses of statistical models in connection with the nonresponse problem. Presented at the Symposium on Incomplete Data sponsored by the Panel on Incomplete Data. Committee on National Statistics, National Research Council, August 1979.)

Colledge, M. J., Johnson, J. H., Paré, R., and Sande, I. G. (1979). Large scale imputation of survey data. *Surv. Methodol.* 4: 203–224. Also available in a preliminary form in the 1978 *Proceedings of the American Statistical Association, Section on Survey Research Methods*, pp. 431–436.

Hartley, H. O. (1946). Discussion of paper by F. Yates. *Journal of the Royal Statistical Society* 109: 37.

Kish, L., and Frankel, M. (1970). Balanced Repeated Replications for Standard Errors. *Journal of the American Statistical Association* 65: 1071–1094.

Nargundkar, M. S., and Joshi, G. B. (1975). Nonresponse in sample surveys. Contributed papers. 40th Session of the International Statistical Institute, pp. 626–628.

Politz, A. N., and Simmons, W. R. (1949–1950). An attempt to get the "not-at-homes" into the sample without callbacks. *JASA*, 44: 9–31: *Journal of the American Statistical Association* 45: 136–137.

Särndal, C. E. (1979). Rejoinder to discussion comments on, some use of statistical models in connection with the nonresponse problem. Presented at the Symposium on Incomplete Data sponsored by the Panel on Incomplete Data. Committee on National Statistics, National Research Council, August, 1979.

Scheuren, F. J. (1972). Wave 1 enrollee and comparison samples. Longitudinal Manpower Evaluation Studies. U.S. Office of Economic Opportunity.

Simmons, W. R. (1954). A Plan to account for, "not-at-homes" by combining weighting and callbacks. *Journal of Marketing* 11: 42–53.

Thomsen, I., and Siring, E. (1979). On the causes and effects of nonresponse: Norwegian experiences. Presented at the Symposium on Incomplete Data sponsored by the Panel on Incomplete Data, Committee on National Statistics. National Research Council, August 1979.

Tupek, A. R., and Richardson, W. J. (1978). Use of ratio estimates to compensate for nonresponse bias in certain economic surveys. *Proceedings of the Section on Survey Research Methods*, American Statistical Association, pp. 197–202.

CHAPTER **14**

An Overview of Hot-Deck Procedures

Barry L. Ford

The goal of this chapter is to introduce the reader to hot-deck procedures and the issues that arise from their use. Section 1 provides a background to the subject and discusses three reasons for using hot-deck procedures. Section 2 discusses the impact of hot-deck procedures on the variances of estimators for some simple situations and the estimation of these variances. After describing several other considerations besides variances, I then present three case studies which illustrate the application of hot-deck procedures to surveys. The last section of the chapter summarizes five empirical studies which compare hot-deck procedures to other procedures which adjust for missing data.

1. BACKGROUND

Hot-deck procedures are common methods of adjusting data sets for missing values. Because hot-deck procedures originated in survey practice with little theory to direct their development, the statistical literature provides few definitions or results about these procedures. Widespread practice in the absence of well-developed theory clouds the subject with ambiguities and inconsistencies. For example, there is no general agreement on the exact definition of a hot-deck procedure. This chapter reflects the present state of development not only by pointing to the lack of well-developed theory but also by using, for the sake of discussion, definitions and principles which are still being debated.

Current survey practice uses many variations of hot-deck procedures. Some of these variations do not exactly fit the definition of hot-deck procedures but merge into a more general class of procedures of which hot-deck procedures are

185

only a subset. This general class is the set of imputation procedures. An imputation procedure is defined as a procedure that imputes a value for each missing value—exactly how the imputed value is calculated is not important to the definition.

In general, a hot-deck procedure is a duplication process—when a value is missing from a sample, a reported value is duplicated to represent this missing value. Thus, the terms "imputation procedure" and "hot-deck procedure" are not interchangeable. For instance, a procedure which imputes the average of all reported values for each missing value is an imputation procedure but it is not a hot-deck procedure. The adjective "hot" refers to imputing with values from the current sample. In contrast, a "cold"-deck procedure refers to using information from data other than the current sample. For example, values or relations from previous surveys may be used to impute values for missing values.

The primary reason for using a hot-deck procedure is to attempt the reduction of nonresponse bias. To reduce this bias, a hot-deck procedure usually has some *classification process* associated with it. All of the sample units are classified into disjoint groups so that the units are as homogeneous as possible within each group. For each missing value, a reported value is imputed which is in the same classification group. Thus, the assumption is made that *within each classification group* the nonrespondents follow the same distribution as the respondents.

This assumption places a heavy burden on the classification variables. These variables must correlate well with the reported values (a relation the statistician can assess after data collection) and also correlate well with the missing values (a relation at which the statistician can often only guess). The application of a hot-deck procedure in which the classification variables are not well correlated with the missing values is likely to cause misleading results.

The classification process is usually a poststratification, but the population sizes may be known or unknown depending on the variables used to classify the units. For example, although someone may refuse to cooperate on a survey using personal interviews, the interviewers can observe general, qualitative traits about the person, such as race, sex, or age range. Variables observed by the interviewers, geographic variables, and variables from partially completed questionnaires are examples of information that can be used as classification variables. If one uses characteristics like race, age, and sex as classification variables, institutions such as the Bureau of the Census can furnish population sizes. However, for more unusual types of variables, the population sizes may not be known. For example, a variable indicating the market value of a residence probably has an unknown population size.

When the "auxiliary" variables employed by a hot-deck procedure to impute values are categorical variables, they are called classification variables. However, these "auxiliary" variables may be quantitative. For example, a hot-deck procedure may use a quantitative variable which was reported on a partially completed questionnaire as auxiliary information to impute for the missing values on the questionnaire.

When the auxiliary variables are quantitative, the reported value duplicated for a missing value can be from the unit which has auxiliary values "closest" to the auxiliary values of the missing value. Thus, the duplication process may involve the minimization of a distance function. The distance function can be the Euclidean distance or a more complicated function. For example, the distance function may take into a account the correlations between each of the auxiliary variables and the primary variables. The Canadian Census of Construction provides an example of the use of a distance function in a hot-deck procedure in Section 5. This chapter uses the convention that a classification process implies qualitative auxiliary variables, and a distance function implies quantitative or mixed auxiliary variables.

A sequential hot-deck procedure is one in which the sample is put in some type of order within each classification group, and for each missing value the previous reported value is duplicated. For example, the ordering might be based on a geographic variable. The result of a geographic ordering is that the reported value duplicated for a missing value is from a unit which is geographically close to the unit with the missing value. Sequential procedures require an initial value which can be imputed for the first value in the data set if it is missing. Cold deck values are often used as initial values.

For most of the hot-deck procedures currently used, survey statisticians have developed little theory and published few articles in the statistical journals. Many hot-deck procedures employed in current surveys rely on a "common-sense" development rather than a rigorous theoretical development. The class of hot-deck procedures, like cluster analysis, is a good example of the divergence of statistical theory and statistical practice. This separation of theory and application has left many aspects of hot-deck procedures relatively unexplored. Thus, the effectiveness of these procedures is often unknown.

2.   REASONS FOR USING HOT-DECK PROCEDURES

This section discusses three general statistical characteristics which are major arguments for the use of hot-deck procedures: reduction of the non-response bias, production of a clean data set, and preservation of the distribution of the population as represented by a sample. The first characteristic is included in the third, but it is important enough to deserve separate attention.

2.1.   Reduction of Nonresponse Bias

The most obvious aim of a hot-deck procedure is to reduce the nonresponse bias of estimators without imposing a highly specific model. Through the use of classification groups a survey statistician hopes to impute values which will cause the data set to reflect more accurately the target population. Given that the classification variables are closely associated with missing values, then as the classification groups become smaller and more homogeneous, the nonresponse bias should be reduced. Some simple formulas may make this intuitive notion clearer.

Suppose one has a simple random sample of size n, out of which m units respond. Also, assume B is the nonresponse bias associated with using only the m reported values to form the estimate $\bar{x}$ of μ, the population mean. Thus,

$$B = E(\bar{x}) - \mu, \qquad \text{where} \quad \bar{x} = \sum_{i=1}^{m} x_i/m. \tag{1}$$

Suppose one uses a hot-deck procedure which classifies each of the n sample units among H groups and within each group randomly selects a reported value to replace each missing value. Also, suppose p_h $(h = 1, 2, \ldots, H)$ is the proportion of the sample units that fall into group h, and $\bar{x}_h$ is the average of the reported values in group h. Let $\bar{x}_{\text{HD}}$ represent this hot-deck estimator; then the nonresponse bias B_{HD} of this estimator is $B_{\text{HD}} = E(\bar{x}_{\text{HD}}) - \mu$.

In evaluating $E(\bar{x}_{\text{HD}})$, two expectations are involved—one is the expected value over many selected samples, and the other is the expected value over all possible imputations *given the selected sample* (p_h and $\bar{x}_h$ are fixed). Thus,

$$E(\bar{x}_{\text{HD}}) = E\big[E\{\bar{x}_{\text{HD}}|\text{sample}\}\big] = E\Big[\sum_{h=1}^{H} p_h\bar{x}_h\Big] = \sum_{h=1}^{H} E[p_h\bar{x}_h]. \tag{2}$$

Although $\bar{x}_h$ and p_h are not independent, they are uncorrelated provided there is at least one respondent in each classification group. Let $p_h^* = E(p_h)$. Then

$$E[\bar{x}_{\text{HD}}] = \sum_{h=1}^{H} E(p_h)E(\bar{x}_h) = \sum_{h=1}^{H} p_h^* E(\bar{x}_h). \tag{3}$$

One can then obtain

$$B_{\text{HD}} = \sum_{h=1}^{H} p_h^* E(\bar{x}_h) - \mu = \sum_{h=1}^{H} p_h^* E(\bar{x}_h - \mu_h) = \sum_{h=1}^{H} p_h^* B_h. \tag{4}$$

Here μ_h and B_h are implicitly defined. Equation (4) shows that the bias from using the hot-deck procedure is expressed in terms of the biases of the reported means in each classification group. As the classification groups become more homogeneous, the size of the B_h shrinks, and B_{HD} also shrinks. Therefore, the most important principle in the construction of any hot-deck procedure is to form classification groups which are as homogeneous as possible with regard to reported and missing values. Bailar and Bailar (1979) discuss the bias of the hot-deck procedures more extensively.

2.2. Production of a Clean Data Set

Imputation procedures in general have a property that is important to the discussion of hot-deck procedures. This property is the production of a "clean" data set, i.e., a data set which appears complete and consistent. "Cleanness" can be a misleading trait when the user treats the clean data set as if there were no missing values originally. For example, using a clean data set as if it were originally complete leads to incorrect estimates of standard errors. The survey statistician accepts the possibility of such abuses because data users need a clean data set in order to perform many standard types of statistical analysis, such as regression analysis, without omitting the missing values.

When the data collector and data analyst are different individuals, a clean data set is usually a responsibility of the data collector for the following reasons:

(1)   The data collector has firsthand knowledge of the data. This knowledge is his greatest asset when adjusting for missing values.

(2)   Data collectors must usually make estimates from the data set. For complex output tables from a complex survey design, a clean data set keeps the estimation phase as short and simple as possible.

(3)   Most data analysits do not want the responsibility of adjusting for missing data. Their interests pertain to mainstream statistics which emphasize estimation and analysis *given the ability to obtain an entire data set.*

(4)   A clean data set allows all future analyses to have a common starting point without each analyst imputing his own values.

If an analyst wishes to study only the reported data, missing items for which a hot-deck procedure has imputed values can be "flagged" by the survey statistician. The flagging concept is important because, among other things, it also allows for the data analyst to "second guess" the survey statistician and apply whatever missing data procedure he wishes. The 1970 Public Use Samples of Basis Records from the Census of Population and Housing is an example of a data set which flagged the imputations from a hot-deck procedure.

The disadvantage of producing a clean data set and not flagging the imputed data is that the user cannot assess the impact of nonresponse on his analysis. Admittedly, many users simply wish to ignore the nonresponse problem, and clean data sets allow them to do that. However, a user should have the option to assess this impact, especially if the nonresponse rate is high.

If imputed values are flagged, the assessment of the effect of imputations on an analysis can still be difficult. A suggestion by Rubin (see Chapter 15) to overcome this problem is to make multiple imputations for each missing item. Herzog (1980) gives an application of the multiple imputation strategy to survey data.

2.3. Distribution of Values

Fellegi and Holt (1976) mentions that one of the primary principles that govern the construction of hot-deck procedures is to reduce the bias while preserving joint and marginal distributions. For example, if for a given variable, one were to substitute the mean of the sample for each missing value, then the distribution of sample values is obviously an incorrect representation of the population values. One has distorted the shape of the sample distribution by adding a large proportion of values equal to the mean of the sample. If one chooses a reported value at random to replace a missing value, one greatly reduces this distortion in the distribution of the sample values. Of course, one is still assuming that the distribution of the imputed values is the same as the distribution of the reported values, but that assumption is more realistic than assuming that all of the missing data have the same value.

Most hot-deck procedures do try to preserve distributional properties within each classification group. Although such an objective appears to be a minimum goal for a hot-deck procedure, it is extraordinarily difficult not to disturb some aspect of the marginal and joint distributions. One way to discuss this difficulty is to look at what might be called the internal and external consistency of the imputed data:

1. *Internal consistency* pertains to relations among the variables *for a given sample unit* and is the reason for the edits in most survey procedures. On each record both the imputed and reported values must obey a series of inequalities and logical consistencies. For example, the sum of variables x and y must be less than z. When a value fails an edit, it is changed. The relation between editing and imputing is discussed at length by Fellegi and Holt (1976) and Hill (1978). An example of a problem in internal consistency occurs when a data vector has multiple missing items and imputations are made from different responding units. The correlation structure may be adversely affected in this instance.

(2) *External consistency* pertains to relations among the sample units *for a given variable*. External consistency refers to the distributional properties of each variable. A previous example of distortion in a distribution by imputation of the sample mean is a problem in external consistency. (Imputation of the sample mean also affects internal consistency because of the effect on the correlation structure.)

3.   THE IMPACT OF HOT-DECK PROCEDURES ON THE VARIANCE OF ESTIMATORS

This section is divided into two parts. The first part discusses and compares the variances of hot-deck estimators. The second part is a short discussion of the estimation of variances, including the principle of replication. Both parts are limited to simple situations, as is the case with most of the literature in the field. Thus, this section illustrates some basic effects of hot-deck procedures but does not provide variance formulas for the more sophisticated hot-deck procedures found in actual applications.

3.1. Some Variances of Hot-Deck Estimators

Suppose only m units ($m > 0$) in a sample of size n do respond. Let $\bar{x}_R$ be the estimator which uses the m responding units and omits any missing values. Let $\bar{x}_M$ be the estimator which imputes the mean of the responding units for each of the nonresponding units. With a simple random sample these two estimators produce identical estimates and are unbiased estimators of μ_R, the mean of the *respondent* population. For these two estimators to be unbiased estimators of μ, the mean of the total population, one must assume that $\mu_R = \mu$. Such an assumption is true if the probability of nonresponse is not related to the survey variables. However, for many survey applications, this assumption is not likely to be true because the nonrespondents tend to have characteristics which are different from the respondents.

For simple random samples (with V denoting the population variance)

$$\mathrm{Var}[\bar{x}_R] = \mathrm{Var}[\bar{x}_M] = \frac{V}{m} = \frac{V}{n}\left[1 + \frac{n - m}{m}\right]. \tag{5}$$

Suppose one uses a hot-deck procedure which randomly duplicates a responding unit without replacement for each missing unit, and suppose $m \geq n/2$. Of the m responding units, there will be $m - (n - m) = 2m - n$ unduplicated units labeled $x_1, x_2, \ldots, x_{2m-n}$ and $n - m$ duplicated units labeled $x_{2m-n+1}, x_{2m-n+2}, \ldots, x_m$. This hot-deck estimator

$$\bar{x}_H = \frac{\sum_{i=1}^{2m-n} x_i + 2\sum_{i=2m-n+1}^{m} x_i}{n} \tag{6}$$

is an unbiased estimator of μ_R, and its variance without a finite population correction factor is given by Hansen, Hurwitz, and Madow (1953):

$$\mathrm{Var}[\bar{x}_H] = \frac{V}{n}\left[1 + \frac{2(n - m)}{n}\right]. \tag{7}$$

If $m \geq n/2$ and the responding units are duplicated without replacement, Eq. (7) is greater than or equal to (5). If $m/n < 1/2$, the hot-deck procedure must duplicate with replacement, and one obtains

$$\mathrm{Var}[\bar{x}_H] = \frac{V}{n}\left[1 + \left\{\frac{n - m}{m}\right\}\left\{\frac{n + m - 1}{n}\right\}\right]. \tag{8}$$

The variance in (8) is also greater than or equal to (5) because $(n + m - 1)/n \geq 1$ (in other words $m > 0$). If $m = 0$, there is no reported value to duplicate and the hot-deck estimator does not exist. Also, for $m > 0$, (8) is greater than or equal to (7). Thus, the hot-deck procedure yields a larger variance than a procedure imputing the means of the responding units or a procedure ignoring the missing values, but the hot-deck variance is less if one uses a hot-deck procedure which duplicates reported values without replacement.

For sequential hot-deck procedures, the variance formulas are slightly different. If the order of the units in the file is random, Bailar, Bailey, and Corby (1978) show that the estimator $\bar{x}_S$ is unbiased for a sequential hot deck-procedure which they investigate. They also show that its variance is given by

$$\text{Var}[\bar{x}_S] = \frac{V}{n}\left[1 + \left\{\frac{2(n - m)}{n}\right\}\left\{\frac{(mn + n - 1)}{(m + 1)(m + 2)}\right\}\right]. \tag{9}$$

The authors show that (9) is larger than (5) if $m > 0$.

In the sequential procedure an arbitrary initial value is used for imputation. For theoretical purposes Bailar, Bailey, and Corby assume this initial value is selected from the population independently of the other responses in the sample. This assumption leads to Eq. (9), which does not equal Eq. (8), although the procedures are similar. This similarity arises because the procedure corresponding to Eq. (9) is basically imputing with replacement—a reported value may be imputed several times if the random ordering places several missing values together.

For large n, $\text{Var}[\bar{x}_S]$ can be approximated by

$$\text{Var}[\bar{x}_S] \doteq \frac{V}{n}\left[1 + \frac{2(n - m)}{m}\right]. \tag{10}$$

Approximation (10) is greater than or equal to Eq. (7). Thus, this approximation implies that for large samples the variance for a sequential hot-deck procedure is larger than the variance of a hot-deck procedure which duplicates randomly without replacement.

When the data file is not randomly ordered but is ordered so that there are serial correlations—the duplication of a previous, reported value does not result in an uncorrelated structure—variances can be computed with some additional assumptions. Assuming that the serial correlation structure has the form

$$\text{Cov}(x_i, x_j) = \sigma^2 \delta^{|i - j|}, \qquad i, j, = 1, \ldots, n, \tag{11}$$

and the initial value is selected independently of the other reported values in the current sample, Bailar and Bailar (1978) derive the variance as

$$\text{Var}[\bar{x}_{\text{SC}}] = \frac{V}{n^2}\left[n + 2\frac{(n-m)(nm+n-m)}{(m+1)(m+2)}\right.$$

$$+ 2\left\{\frac{(n+1)(m)}{m+1}\frac{\delta - \delta^n}{1-\delta}\frac{\delta}{(1-\delta)^2}[1 - n\delta^{n-1} + (n-1)\delta^n]\right.$$

$$+ \frac{\delta^{m+1}}{\binom{n}{n-m}(1-\delta)^{m+1}}\sum_{i=m+2}^{n}\binom{n}{i}(1-\delta)^i\delta^{n-1}$$

$$\left.\left.- \frac{m}{\binom{n}{n-m}}\sum_{i=1}^{n}\binom{n+1-i}{m+1}\delta^i\right\}\right], \tag{12}$$

which for large n can be approximated by

$$\text{Var}\,\bar{x}_{\text{SC}} \doteq \frac{V}{n}\left[1 + \frac{2(n-m)}{m} + 2\left\{\frac{\delta}{1-\delta} - \frac{(n-m)}{n}\frac{2\delta}{2-\delta}\right\}\right]. \tag{13}$$

The variances (12) and (13) are not monotonic in δ, although high values of δ are effective in the reduction of nonresponse bias.

Variance derivations for hot-deck procedures which use a classification process are rare in the literature. However, using a prediction theory approach, Schaible (1979) does present a variance derivation for this type of hot-deck procedure. For a sample of size n, Schaible defines the hot-deck estimator as

$$\bar{x}_{\text{P}} = \sum_{h=1}^{H}\left[\sum_{i=1}^{m_h} x_{hi} + \sum_{i=1}^{m_h} I_{hi}x_{hi}\right]/n, \tag{14}$$

where H is the number of classification groups; n_h is the number of selected units in group h; m_h is the number of selected units in group h which have reported values; I_{hi} is the number of times unit i in group h is duplicated to represent a missing value; the reported values in group h are denoted by $x_{h1}, x_{h2}, \ldots,$ x_{h,m_h}; $n = \sum_{h=1}^{H} n_h$; and $m = \sum_{h=1}^{H} m_h$.

If a population is composed of N units, then under a prediction model the quantities $x_1, x_2, \ldots, x_N$ (whose mean $\bar{x}_* = \sum_{i=1}^{N} x_i/N$, is to be estimated) are assumed to represent a realization of the independent random variables $X_1, X_2, \ldots, X_N$, where each X_i is of the form

$$X_i = \beta_0 + \sum_{j=1}^{r} \beta_j z_{ij} + \varepsilon_i, \tag{15}$$

and where the z_{ij} $(j = 1, 2, \ldots, r)$ represent auxiliary information known about the ith unit; β_j $(j = 1, 2, \ldots, r)$ is an unknown regression coefficient relating z_{ij} to x_i; and ε_i is an error term with mean zero and variance V_ε. It will be assumed that whether or not an x is missing is independent of ε_i if one conditions on the z_{ij}.

The error variance of $\bar{x}_P$ is defined as $\mathrm{Var}[\bar{x}_P - \bar{x}_*]$. Schaible shows that this variance for a finite population equals

$$\mathrm{Var}[\bar{x}_P - \bar{x}_*] = \frac{[1 - (n/N)]\, V_\varepsilon}{n} + \frac{[1 - (m/n)]\, V_\varepsilon}{m} + \frac{[1 - (m/n)]\, V_\varepsilon}{m}$$

$$\times \left[\frac{\{[m/(n-m)]\sum_{h=1}^{H}\sum_{i=1}^{m_h} I_{hi}^2\} - (n-m)}{n} \right]. \qquad (16)$$

The first term in (16) represents the variance due to sampling, the second term represents the increase in variance due to missing values, and the third term represents the increase in variance due to the random duplication of the hot-deck procedure.

Under the prediction theory approach, the reported value duplicated for a missing value should have its z_{ij} values as close as possible to the z_{ij} values of the missing value—for example, one might minimize $(\sum \beta_j z'_{ij} - \sum \beta_j z_{ij})^2$, where the prime indicates auxiliary values associated with a missing x_i. This requirement minimizes the nonresponse bias of $\bar{x}_P$ and is related to the idea of minimizing a distance function discussed in Section 1. If the z_{ij} values of each missing value match exactly the z_{ij} values of the reported value which is imputed for it, then the prediction theory approach implies that $\bar{x}_P$ is unbiased.

3.2. Estimation of Variances

A reasonable estimator of $\mathrm{Var}[\bar{x}_R] = \mathrm{Var}[\bar{x}_M]$ is $\hat{V}/m$, where $\hat{V}$ is calculated using only the reported values, that is,

$$\hat{V} = \sum_{i=1}^{m} (\bar{x}_i - \bar{x}_R)^2/(m-1). \qquad (17)$$

When a hot-deck procedure is used to impute values, some practitioners will often use *all* the sample values, including imputed values, and estimate the variance as if the sample was of size n with no missing values. In other words, they ignore the fact that a hot-deck procedure was applied. These variance estimates are only estimating V/n in expression (7), for instance, and, thus, are underestimating the variance in (7) by $[2(n-m)/n]\,100\%$.

If classification groups and a prediction theory approach are used, the variance of a hot-deck estimator is given by Eq. (16). To estimate $\mathrm{Var}[\bar{x}_P - \bar{x}_*]$ one must estimate V_ε, for which a typical estimator is

$$\hat{V}_\varepsilon = \sum_{i=1}^{m} (x_i - \sum_{j=1}^{r} \hat{\beta}_j z_{ij})^2/(m-1), \qquad (18)$$

where $\hat{\beta}_j$ is the standard estimator of a linear regression coefficient.

Neither Bailar and Bailar (1978) nor Bailar, Bailey, and Corby (1978), who discuss the variance of sequential hot-deck procedures, suggest an estimator for

$V[\bar{x}_s]$. One possible strategy is to use only the reported data to estimate V; however, this will be a rather awkward solution when the survey is complex, for example, multistage. Alternatively, one could use replication as discussed in Kish and Frankel (1970) and McCarthy (1969).

Replication is an established method of estimating variances when direct formulas are extremely complicated and difficult to derive. Although replication does not allow the statistician to estimate the component of the standard error due to imputation, replication does give an unbiased estimate of overall error which *includes* the error component due to imputation or to any other modeling of the missing data. An unbiased, overall measure of standard error is usually all that is needed by most surveys in an operational (as opposed to research) context.

There are two problems in using replicates to estimate the standard error of a hot-deck estimator:

(1)   Unstable estimates of standard errors: replication may require many replicates in order to stabilize the estimates of standard error.

(2)   Imputations from a hot-deck procedure must be made independently among the replicates; in other words, no information from one replicate should affect the imputation in another replicate and, thus, the result may be a less accurate imputation for each missing value.

A possible strategy is to use the hot-deck procedure once on the entire data set to make estimates of means (or totals) and then use the hot-deck procedure independently on each replicate to make standard error estimates. This strategy incurs an additional cost that a direct estimate of variance would not entail.

4.   SOME OTHER CONSIDERATIONS

A statistician should consider more than just variance arguments when implementing a hot-deck procedure. If the data set is large, data processing is an important factor. Also, randomization versus nonrandomization arguments affect the decision whether to use a sequential hot-deck procedure. A third consideration is the problem of imputing the same reported value several times. Each of these three considerations can have an impact on the structure of a hot-deck procedure.

4.1.   Data Processing

Data processing of large data sets has tended *in the past* to favor sequential hot-deck procedures. Generally, computer costs and programming complexity are minimized by the "one record at a time principle"—the computer reads a data record, processes that record, reads a second record into the computer space occupied by the first record, processes the second record, etc. Thus, the computer "forgets" the first record before it processes the second. This principle is usually followed during the computer summarization of means, totals, standard errors, and other common statistics from even the most complex sample designs.

To adhere to this principle, many hot-deck procedures impute for a missing value the reported value in the classification group which was *last read by the computer*. Thus, the imputation only requires the computer to remember one additional value—the hot-deck value—for each variable. The effect of this "one record at a time principle" is still a major factor in the summarization of large-scale surveys. However, advances in data processing and innovative programming are overcoming this constraint, as can be seen in the discussion of the March CPS Supplement in Section 5.

4.2. Randomization versus Nonrandomization

The principle of randomly duplicating the units within each classification group is appealing because it puts a known probability mechanism into the duplication process. Even if one must operate under the precept of only keeping one hot-deck value in the computer at a time, a random ordering within each classification group can be used. Objections to randomization are made by statisticians who feel that a nonrandom ordering, for instance, a geographic ordering, is more meaningful for some data sets. Historically, the ability to use a nonrandom ordering was an argument for the superiority of hot-deck procedures over other missing data procedures, as noted in Nordbotten (1963).

Suppose the records in the data set are in a geographic order. If there is a tendency for records which are geographically close to be similar in value, then duplicating the last reported value is better than duplicating a random one. Of course, a belief in a geographic relation should not be assumed, but demonstrated by computing serial correlations which measure the strength of the relation. If a nonrandom ordering of the data set is important, an alternative procedure is to use the ordering variables as classification variables and apply random duplication.

4.3. Multiple Duplication of the Same Reported Value

One possible danger in using a hot-deck procedure is the duplication of the same reported value many times. This danger is more likely to occur when using classification groups which so accurately divide the sample that some groups have many missing values and few reported values or when using sequential duplication where the ordering causes the missing values to cluster together. As

Scheuren (1976) points out, classification variables and ordering variables need to be correlated with survey variables but not *too* correlated with nonresponse. For example, if an exact correlation with nonresponse exists, then classification cells will only have missing values and no reported values to duplicate. If the correlation with nonresponse is high, only a few reported values are in a cell and may be duplicated many times.

The Bureau of the Census investigated whether this situation was a problem for the Current Population Survey in the article by Bailar, Bailey, and Corby (1978). The monthly sample size was large enough (approximately 47,000 households in 1975) so that multiple duplication of the same values probably had a very small effect on the national estimates. However, small-area estimates might have been affected. Also, the cells of contingency tables could have been affected, especially if the cells only applied to a small part of the sample or if the partitioning variables of the tables were highly correlated with nonresponse.

By avoiding all sequential procedures and using procedures which impute randomly *without* replacement, the survey statistician helps minimize the amount of multiple duplication. This criticism of sequential procedures does not relate to ordering the data set nonrandomly but does relate to *always* imputing the previous reported value. If a distance measure is used to select a reported value, the amount of multiple duplication is minimized by defining this measure to be a function of how often a reported value has already been selected. Use of this approach by the Canadian Census of Construction is discussed in Section 5.

5. THREE EXAMPLES OF HOT-DECK APPLICATIONS

5.1. Current Population Survey

Bailar, Bailey, and Corby (1978) describe the basic hot-deck procedure for the Current Population Survey (CPS). The Bureau of the Census uses the CPS to provide "monthly estimates of employment, unemployment, and other general labor force characteristics of the nation." The CPS is a major, national survey which is repeated from month to month. The sample design is a stratified, multistage, cluster sample design in which each primary sampling unit is a county or group of counties. The monthly sample size of the CPS at the time of the Bailar, Bailey, and Corby study was approximately 47,000 households.

The Bureau of the Census applies a weighting procedure for noninterview adjustments and a hot-deck procedure for item nonresponse. The CPS hot-deck procedure divides the sample into 20 cells in order to duplicate values for labor force items which are missing. These cells are formed by cross-classifying two sex groups, two racial groups, and five age groups. Thus, the hot-deck procedure assumes that these three classification variables are highly correlated with the labor force items and are always present.

The CPS hot-deck procedure is a sequential procedure in which the ordering is roughly geographic. As the computer processes the sample, the hot-deck values are continually updated to reflect the most recently processed sample cases. When a labor force item is missing, the hot-deck value—a value obtained from the most recently processed record which does not have any missing items—is imputed for the missing item. Because the first record in a sex–race–age cell may have missing values, cold-deck values are stored in the computer before processing the sample. Cold-deck values are based upon the data of the previous CPS surveys.

Before processing, the Bureau of the Census has a raw data set with gaps caused by missing items. After processing, the Bureau of the Census has a clean data set from which to prepare estimates. Standard errors for these estimates do *not* account for the fact that the bureau has imputed data.

5.2. The March Income Supplement to the CPS

In a 1978 paper, Coder (1978) gives a description of the new hot-deck procedure developed for the income supplement to the March CPS. This hot-deck procedure not only offers a contrast to the older procedure described by Bailar *et al.* (1978), but also shows how recent improvements in data processing allow greater freedom in the construction of hot-deck procedures.

The supplement to the March CPS "yields estimates of income and poverty at national and regional levels on an annual basis." Because of the sensitivity of income questions, the supplement has item nonresponse which is quite a significant problem. The imputation system to adjust for the item nonresponse is a hot-deck procedure which uses a matrix of enormous size, a larger size than can be held in computer memory. Through a complex system of sorting and matching, the procedure can search through the *entire* data file to locate a "similar" respondent for each unit which has a missing item. If a unit has several missing items, all imputations are from one "similar" respondent. This method helps preserve the correlation structure of the data.

This hot-deck procedure also uses a large number of socioeconomic variables to find a match for each unit with missing items. The number and detail of these variables result in a high probability that some units with missing items will have no match in the entire data set. To avoid this problem, the hot-deck procedure is designed so that a match can be made at a less exact level. If several respondents match with a unit and these matches are all at the same level of exactness, a respondent is chosen randomly from the respondents which have not had any values imputed to other units. In cases where the number of respondents is less than the number of units with item nonresponse, respondents may be used more than once for imputation.

To evaluate the new procedure, Coder (1978) conducted a simulation experiment which indicated less bias as compared to the old procedure. Although there was only a small impact on median family income, there was a significant impact on the accuracy of imputation for individuals and certain subpopulations. A more complete evaluation is given in Welniak and Coder (1980).

Coder also indicates some unresolved problems. One problem is the determination of the optimal set of classification variables and the level of detail on each variable. The set which is optimal for one subpopulation may not be optimal for another subpopulation. For example, educational level has a different importance for different occupations and different age groups. Other problems include the possibility of duplicating the values of outliers and duplicating respondent values several times. In a discussion of the Coder article, Scheuren (1978) also mentions the problems of (1) understating the standard errors because of calculations that assume no missing data, (2) overuse of hot-deck procedures—imputing when most income variables are missing instead of considering weighting procedures such as raking, and (3) further validation of the hot-deck procedure devised by Coder and his associates by using actual CPS nonrespondents for whom data have been obtained from other sources. Further work on these problems is in progress.

5.3. Canadian Census of Construction

Colledge, Johnson, Paré, and Sande (1978) describe the imputation used on the Census of Construction (COC) in Canada. The COC is a survey by Statistics Canada of a population composed of 80,000 Canadian businesses whose primary activity is construction. Although large businesses are completely enumerated, small businesses are sampled. The hot-deck procedure adopted by Statistics Canada for the COC in 1975 is a good contrast to the one used by the Bureau of the Census and illustrates the basic approach of Statistics Canada to devising hot-deck procedures for many of its surveys.

In order to impute values, the data file of the COC was stratified by province, by a standard industrial classification, and by an indicator variable representing whether salaries and wages were paid. Within each of these cells the units were ordered by a measure of gross business income (GBI). Suppose a unit in a classification cell has a missing value; then it is a "candidate" unit. Then among the units which are in that cell and have no missing values, 10 possible "donor" units are selected. These 10 units are the 5 units with a GBI closest to but less than the GBI of the "candidate" unit and the 5 units with a GBI closest to but greater than the GBI of the "candidate" unit. From the 10 possible "donor" units, 1 "donor" unit is selected which minimizes a distance function. Although modified in various ways, essentially this distance function is the metric

$$\mathrm{DIST}(C, D) = |\log T_\mathrm{C} - \log T_\mathrm{D}|, \tag{19}$$

where T is the total expenses of the business, and C represents a "candidate" record and D represents a "donor" record. Then any missing values on the candidate record are imputed by duplicating the corresponding values on the donor record. Any i. .onsistencies between the imputed values and other values on the candidate record are corrected by a computerized edit program. The distance function can be changed to increase with the number of times a donor record has been used.

Unlike the CPS, the calculation of variance estimates for the COC avoided the assumption of no imputation to the data set. Because the imputed values were often prorated based on auxiliary variables, it seemed reasonable to investigate the variances of the hot-deck estimator in comparison to a ratio estimator. Statistics Canada did a simulation study and found that the variances when imputing with this system were fairly close to the variances when using a ratio estimator in a double sampling scheme with T as the auxiliary variable. Therefore, Statistics Canada used the estimated variance from this ratio estimator to estimate approximately the variance of the hot-deck estimator.

One should note that both the COC and the CPS use a great deal of auxiliary information. For example, the COC uses the province, the standard industrial classification, the salaries and wages indicator, the gross business income, and the total business expenses as auxiliary variables. For units with a missing item, auxiliary variables may not be a problem because there are reported variables which can be used. For units with total nonresponse other surveys may find good auxiliary variables hard to obtain. The result may be a much simpler procedure than the CPS or COC.

6.   RESULTS FROM EMPIRICAL COMPARATIVE STUDIES

6.1.   Comparisons by Ford

This section discusses five recent studies which describe empirical investigations comparing hot-deck procedures to alternative missing data procedures. Alternatives include weighting procedures, regression procedures, raking procedures, and procedures which simply use the reported data set as though it were the entire, selected sample. Other chapters in this volume as well as Chapman (1976) give descriptions of these procedures.

Three of the comparative studies are simulation experiments in which a researcher deletes values from a complete data set in order to simulate which values are missing. Then the researcher applies the missing data procedures he wishes to compare. These types of experiments, although artificial, do allow comparisons of the estimates from the procedures to a "true" estimate. Also, the experiments allow comparisons over a wide range of conditions—different response rates, different methods of designating missing items, etc. However, in most situations a simulation study should also be coupled with a study which applies the procedures to the actual survey environment.

One of the earlier examples of a simulation study was given in a paper by Ford (1976). The purpose of this project was to compare several variations of hot-deck procedures with ratio and regression procedures. The simulations occurred under two conditions. The first condition was the level of the non-response rate, which was either 5, 10, or 20%. The second condition involved the probability of "missingness," the probability that a sample unit would be designated as missing during simulations. This probability was either (1) the same for all units, (2) slightly larger for units whose values were larger, or (3) much larger for units whose values were larger. These two conditions led to testing at 9 levels, 3 nonresponse levels × 3 probability levels. The relative bias in the mean of the reported data ranged from 0 to −15% over the 9 levels.

The data set of the Ford study was from a stratified survey by the U.S. Department of Agriculture. Each sample unit was a name from a list of farm operators. There was only one auxiliary variable available, a quantitative variable which had been used initially to stratify the population. The operational procedure of the survey at that time was to ignore completely those units with total nonresponse. For a specific survey variable, six missing data procedures were tested as alternatives to the operational procedure: (1) a double-sampling ratio procedure, (2) a double-sampling regression procedure, (3) a hot-deck procedure which randomly duplicated a unit from the classification group, (4) a hot-deck procedure which duplicated the value of the unit minimizing the Euclidean distance between the survey variable and the auxiliary variable, (5) a hot-deck procedure which imputed the average value of two units (one on each side of the unit with the missing value) minimizing the Euclidean distance between the survey variable and the auxiliary variable, and (6) a hot-deck procedure which imputed the average value of the classification group.

The results of the study showed no significant difference in the estimated means from these procedures. This result could have been expected because within each stratum the auxiliary variable was so poorly correlated with the survey variable. Therefore, little reduction in bias resulted from *any* of the six procedures. In order to assess the effect of the correlation on the missing data procedures, another study by Ford (1978) created two variables to be highly correlated with the auxiliary variable. Table 1 shows the results when three missing data procedures were applied to the original variable A, and to the two created variables B and C. A correlation of at least .67 between the auxiliary and survey variables was needed within each stratum for any of the missing data procedures to be effective. For all three variables, the hot-deck and ratio procedures yielded about the same gains in the reduction of bias. The Ford study also noted that the standard error estimates from a hot-deck procedure were too low; they were even lower than the standard error estimates from the *complete* data set. The recommendation of this study was to adopt a new missing

TABLE 1

Results from Ford Study (1978) Showing Estimates from Four Missing Data
Procedures Divided by the Estimate from the Complete Data Set

	Variable A (correlation with auxiliary variable equals .30)	Variable B (correlation with auxiliary variable equals .67)	Variable C (correlation with auxiliary variable equals .87)
Complete data set	1.00	1.00	1.00
Omission of missing data from sample	.88	.88	.88
Hot deck	.89	.92	.95
Ratio adjustment	.89	.91	.95

data procedure *only* if a new source of auxiliary information could be found
which was highly correlated with the survey variable.

6.2. Comparisons by Cox and Folsom

In contrast to Ford's simulation experiment, a study by Cox and Folsom
(1978) and updated in Cox (1980) compared procedures under actual survey
conditions. Using data from the National Longitudinal Survey of the High
School Class of 1972, the Cox and Folsom study obtained the true responses to
most of the missing or inconsistent values by using a telephone follow-up. A
hot-deck procedure and a weighting-class procedure were used for the
pretelephone data and then compared to the complete data set.

The Cox and Folsom study differed from the Ford study in several other
aspects. First, the testing was more concerned with the problem of item nonresponse than the problem of total nonresponse. Second, there were five
auxiliary variables to form classification groups—race, sex, high school grades,
high school curriculum, and parents' education. Within each classification
group the data file was sorted according to stratum and school. Third, the
procedures were slightly different. The hot-deck procedure was sequential, and
the weighting class procedure simply imputed the mean response in a weighting
class for each missing value. Fourth, balanced repeated replications were used
to make unbiased estimates of variance.

Cox and Folsom found little difference in the estimates from the procedures
because of the extremely high response rates on most items. When there was a
slight gain in bias reduction, such as for the hot-deck procedure, the mean
square errors did not improve because of an offsetting increase in variance.
Thus, the mean square errors were not greatly affected.

Table 2 shows this result by displaying the absolute bias and the square root

TABLE 2

A Comparison of the Performance of Three Missing Data Procedures[a]

	|Relative bias| (%)	Relative square root of the mean square error (%)
Omission of missing data	2.2	4.6
Hot deck	1.9	4.5
Weighting class	3.1	5.1

[a] From Cox and Folsom (1978).

of the mean square error (in percentages) when estimates from 51 discrete variables were averaged. Cox and Folsom concluded that for the National Longitudinal Survey the imputation procedures did not improve the estimation of means and proportions over using no imputation. However, they did think that imputation might be useful if any analysis of the data set was planned for the future.

6.3. Comparisons by Ernst

An article by Ernst (1978) also compared a hot-deck procedure to a weighting-class procedure. The hot-deck procedure he studied was an earlier version of the one now used by the Bureau of the Census for the March income supplement to the Current Population Survey (see Section 5). The weighting-class procedure he studied was one in which the weights of all responding units in a classification group were increased to account for the missing units in the group.

To design the weighting-class procedure, Ernst used a computer program to determine the classification variables and cells which would minimize the standard errors of the estimates. However, Ernst discovered that the variables which minimized the standard errors were not the variables which minimized the bias. Variables that minimized the bias tended to form cells within which there was a large variation among the reported values and a high nonresponse rate—a combination resulting in large contributions to the standard errors. This type of relation may also have been a reason for the result in the Cox and Folsom study, which found that a decrease in the bias of an estimator was often offset by an increase in the standard error. Because the Ernst study was associated with the CPS, which is a large-scale survey, Ernst regarded reduction of the bias to be the more important criterion for forming classification groups than reduction of the standard error.

Ernst found that the weighting scheme he eventually created used many more classification cells than the hot-deck procedure used for the CPS in 1973. He also found that the weighting-class procedure yielded estimates with a smaller bias than the hot-deck procedure. This result, however, indicates the superiority of using more cells and not that the weighting-class procedure is better in general than the hot-deck procedure.

6.4. Comparisons by Paré

A 1978 paper by Paré (1978) described a simulation study for a Canadian business survey. This study compared a hot-deck procedure, a ratio procedure, and a procedure which ignored any missing values and assumed that the reported values were the entire sample. The hot-deck procedure was similar to the one discussed in Section 5 for the Canadian Census of Construction. This procedure sorted the units according to gross income, designated as "donor" units the 5 reported units in front of a missing unit and the 5 reported units behind the unit, selected from the 10 "donor" units that unit which minimized a distance measure based on expenses, and imputed the values from the selected unit to the missing values. Imputed values were then prorated based on auxiliary variables to accommodate the edit system. The ratio procedure was a double-sampling technique which only employed expenses as an auxiliary variable.

Paré structured his study in much the same way that Ford did. Given a sample size of 1000, three levels of response rates were used—10, 20, and 50%. There were three ways of choosing missing units: (1) equal selection probabilities, (2) selecting 75% of the missing units with a higher gross income than the median and 25% lower, and (3) selecting 25% higher than the median and 75% lower. Twenty-five simulations were run under each of the nine conditions—3 nonresponse levels × 3 levels of nonresponse selection. The results

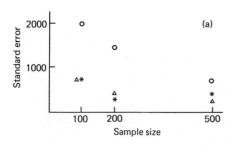

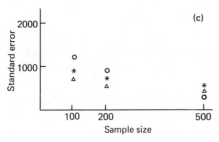

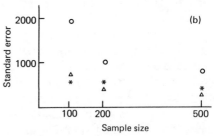

Fig. 1. *Results from Paré (1978) study comparing the standard errors of the estimates for three missing data procedures. Key: ○, omission of missing values; ∗, hot-deck procedure; △, ratio procedure. (a) Condition 1: random deletion of missing values; (b) Condition 2: deletion of 75% of missing values above the median and 25% below; (c) Condition 3: deletion of 25% of missing values above the median and 75% below.*

showed that the hot-deck procedure gave much better protection against non-response bias than the other two procedures.

Figure 1 displays the standard errors (calculated by using replication) that resulted for one variable in Paré's study. The relations in the graphs are typical of all three variables studied by Paré. The standard errors for the hot-deck procedure and the ratio procedure are very close. This result supports the survey methodology used in the Canadian Census of Construction (discussed in Section 5) in which the standard errors of hot deck estimates were estimated by using the standard errors of ratio estimates. Figure 1 also shows the puzzling result that the procedure which omits the missing values tends to yield larger standard errors than the hot-deck and ratio procedures. This result is typical of results from simulated and theoretical work on other hot-deck procedures.

6.5. Comparisons by Schieber

A simulation study by Schieber (1978) compared three methods of imputing data on the Survey of the Low-Income Aged and Disabled. The three methods were (1) a sequential hot-deck procedure, (2) an administrative record match, and (3) a two-stage procedure in which the first stage was a multivariate LOGIT analysis to designate which units were Social Security recipients and the second stage was a regression procedure to determine the level of the Social Security benefits. During the study the third method was modified so that a hot-deck procedure was used to add error residuals to the level assigned by the regression equation. This modification, as suggested by Scheuren (1976), protected against the possibility that there was some part of the response surface which was fit quite badly.

In the Schieber study the administrative record match was the most effective overall procedure because the administrative data were very accurate. In many other surveys, however, the administrative data are not as good. For the hot-deck and the two-stage procedures, there were no clear benefits in choosing one procedure over the other.

6.6. Concluding Comments

Because each of these empirical studies is confined to the investigation of one particular survey, broad generalizations of their results are difficult to make. These studies do, however, support the theoretical conclusion that the standard errors of hot-deck estimators are underestimated by computations which assume that the data set was originally complete. They also indicate that there *may* not be much improvement in the mean square error of a hot-deck estimator in comparison to an estimator which omits the missing values unless there is auxiliary information which is highly correlated with the survey data.

They do *not* consistently show that one missing data procedure is better than another.

These empirical studies should encourage other survey organizations to carry out experiments which detect the effects of missing data and missing data procedures in their own surveys. The objective of such studies should be not only to find procedures yielding low mean square errors of estimates but also to ensure that the multivariate structure of the data set after imputation is representative of the population.

REFERENCES

Bailar, Barbara A., and Bailar, John C. III (1978). Comparison of two procedures for imputing missing survey values. *American Statistical Association Proceedings of the Section on Survey Research Methods*, pp. 462–467.

Bailar, Barbara A., and Bailar, John C. III (1979). Comparison of the biases of the "Hot Deck" imputation procedure with an "Equal-Weights" imputation procedure. *National Academy of Science, Proceedings of the Symposium on Incomplete Data.*

Bailar, Barbara A., Bailey, Leroy, and Corby, Carol (1978). A comparison of some adjustment and weighting procedures for survey data. In N. Krishnam Namboodiri (ed.), *Survey Sampling and Measurement*, pp. 175–198. New York: Academic Press.

Chapman, David W. (1976). A survey of nonresponse imputation procedures. *American Statistical Association, Proceedings of the Social Statistics Section*, pp. 245–251.

Colledge, M. J., Johnson, J. H., Paré, R., and Sande, I. G. (1978). Large scale imputation of survey data. *American Statistical Association, Proceedings of the Section on Survey Research Methods*, pp. 431–435.

Coder, John (1978). Income data collection and processing for the March income supplement to the current population survey. *Proceedings of the Data Processing Workshop: Survey of Income and Program Participation.* U.S. Department of Health, Education and Welfare, Washington, D.C.

Cox, Brenda G. (1980). A weighted sequential hot-deck imputation procedure. *American Statistical Association, Proceedings of the Section on Survey Research Methods*, pp. 721–726.

Cox, Brenda G., and Folsom, Ralph E. (1978). An empirical investigation of alternative item nonresponse adjustments. *American Statistical Association, Proceedings of the Section on Survey Research Methods*, pp. 219–221.

Ernst, Lawrence R. (1978). Weighting to adjust for partial nonresponse. *American Statistical Association, Proceedings of the Social Statistics Section*, pp. 468–473.

Fellegi, I. P., and Holt, D. (1976). A systematic approach to automatic edit and imputation. *Journal of the American Statistical Association* 71:17–35.

Ford, Barry L. (1976). Missing data procedures: A comparative study (Part 2). *American Statistical Association, Proceedings of the Social Statistics Section*, pp. 524–529.

Ford, Barry L. (1978). Missing data procedures: A comparative study (Part 2). Statistical Reporting Services, U.S. Department of Agriculture, Washington, D.C.

Hansen, Morris H., Hurwitz, William N., and Madow, William G. (1953). *Sample Survey Methods and Theory* (Vol. 2), pp. 129–141. New York: Wiley.

Herzog, Thomas N. (1980). Multiple imputation of individual social security benefit amounts. *American Statistical Association, Proceedings of the Section on Survey Research Methods.*

Hill, Christopher J. (1978). A report on the application of a systematic method of automatic edit and imputation to the 1976 Canadian census. *American Statistical Association, Proceedings of the Section on Survey Research Methods*, pp. 474–479.

Kish, Leslie, and Frankel, Martin R. (1970). Balanced repeated replications for standard errors. *Journal of the American Statistical Association* 65:1071–1094.

McCarthy, P. J. (1969). Pseudo-replication: Half samples. *Journal of the International Statistics Institute* 37:239–264.

Nordbotten, Svein (1963). Automatic editing of individual statistical observations. *Conference on European Statisticians, Statistical Studies* No. 2, United Nations.

Paré, R. M. (1978). Evaluation of 1975 methodology: Simulation study of the imputation system developed by BSMD. Business Survey Methods Division, Statistics Canada.

Schaible, Wesley L. (1979). Estimation of finite population totals from incomplete sample data: Prediction approach. *National Academy of Sciences, Proceedings of the Symposium of Incomplete Data*.

Scheuren, Frederick J. (1978). Discussion of the paper entitled, Income data collection and processing for the March income supplement to the current population survey, by John Coder. *Proceedings of the Data Processing Workshop: Survey of Income and Program Participation*. U.S. Department of Health, Education and Welfare, Washington, D.C.

Scheuren, Frederick J. (1976). *Preliminary Notes on the Partially Missing Data Problem—Some Very Elementary Consideration*. Methodology Group, Social Security Administration, Washington, D.C.

Schieber, Sylvester J. (1978). A comparison of three alternative techniques for allocating unreported social security income on the survey of low-income aged and disabled. *American Statistical Association, Proceedings of the Section on Survey Research Methods*, pp. 212–218.

Welniak, Edward J., and Coder, John F. (1980). A measure of the bias in the March CPS earnings imputation system and results of a sample bias adjustment procedure. *American Statistical Association, Proceedings of the Section on Survey Research Methods*, pp. 421–425.

CHAPTER 15

Using Multiple Imputations
to Handle Nonresponse in Sample Surveys

Thomas N. Herzog
Donald B. Rubin

This chapter discusses the use of multiple imputations for handling nonresponse in sample surveys. Section 1 presents the practical motivation for wanting to handle nonresponse by using imputations and the theoretical underpinnings for the use of multiple imputations. Imputing for missing values allows the use of standard complete-data methods of analysis. Multiple imputations within one model for nonresponse generate appropriate inferences under that model using only standard complete-data methods of analysis. Multiple imputations that represent several models for nonresponse display sensitivity of inference to models for nonresponse. The material in this chapter differs from that in the preceding two chapters in that, in contrast to weighting and hot-deck methods, multiple imputation is not currently a standard technique. However, it appears to have substantial promise.

Section 2 studies the use of imputations in the "deceptively" simple case of a simple random sample with random nonresponse. First we consider the behavior of imputing the best prediction and of randomly imputing from the distribution of possible predictions. Then we consider the improvements that result when multiple random imputations are used and show that a minor adjustment to the simple multiple imputation scheme leads to the theoretically correct inference. This section also shows that a major benefit of multiple imputations under one model will often accrue with only two imputations for each missing value. These results are relevant to the practical implementation of hot-deck imputation procedures, suggesting that two imputations for each missing value may sometimes be adequate for each hot-deck model. Exhibiting

INCOMPLETE DATA
IN SAMPLE SURVEYS
Volume 2, Part IV

sensitivity of inference to different models for nonresponse requires imputations under each model.

Section 3 presents some possible extensions to the techniques presented earlier. Issues discussed are adjusting for small samples, incorporating non-response bias and dealing with multivariate and nonnormal data. In general, using only complete-data methods of data analysis, the technique of multiple imputations can (a) generate appropriate inferences under each of the nonre-sponse models used for imputation and (b) display sensitivity of inference to different nonresponse models. The material in Sections 1–3 has previously been presented in Rubin (1979).

Section 4 describes a two-stage model-based, multiple imputation protocol that has been used to predict the Social Security benefit amounts of a number of individuals surveyed by the Census Bureau during the March 1973 Current Population Survey (CPS). The results of this multiple imputation protocol are compared in Section 5 with the results of a two-imputation version of the Census Bureau's 1973 hot-deck procedure. In addition, the results of the imputations are compared to administrative data from the CPS–SSA–IRS Exact Match File (Aziz, Kilss, and Scheuren, 1978) which combines March 1973 CPS data with SSA (Social Security Administration) and IRS (Internal Revenue Service) data. Much of the material in Sections 4 and 5 has previously been presented in Herzog (1980) and Herzog and Lancaster (1980).

1. IMPUTING FOR MISSING VALUES

Imputation, that is, filling in for missing values, is a very common practical technique for handling nonresponse in sample surveys. The obvious advantage of imputation is that once the values have been filled in, standard data analysis methods may be used. In contrast, many theoretical approaches to nonresponse require new and often quite involved computer programs in order to handle the nonresponse problem. From a practitioner's point of view, it may not be clear that the extra expense and effort required to write these special programs is really worthwhile, say, relative to field efforts to reduce nonresponse or to increase the sample size. The practical question is whether the answers under these theoretical models are really that much better than (or even as good as) the answers that can be found from straightforward imputation procedures.

It is easy to be sympathetic towards the imputation position because much practice and experience has verified many standard data analysis techniques as being appropriate in the absence of nonresponse. Minimally, general acceptance of conclusions may be lost if we give up these standard analysis methods. Consequently, there is substantial practical advantage if imputation methods can be made theoretically sound. However, the technique of single imputations is not generally satisfactory because it ignores the fact that the missing values are not known. Multiple imputations (Rubin, 1978) allow us to use standard data analysis techniques and yet appropriately adjust for the nonresponse even in complicated problems.

1.1. Multiple Imputations and Analysis Using Standard Complete-Data Statistics

In order to see how multiple imputations allow the use of complete-data methods for data analysis, consider the following general case. Let Q be the function of population values to be estimated, and let S be an estimator of Q based on complete data from a sample survey (both S and Q can be vectors). For example, Q could be the population mean and S could be the sample mean in a simple random sample. Suppose, as is nearly always the case in practice that the inference for S follows from the statement that

$Q - S$ is approximately normally distributed with mean zero and variance

$$U = \tilde{\mathrm{Var}}(Q - S) = estimated\ variance\ of\ Q - S,$$

where S and U are the known values of the complete-data statistics and Q is unknown.

In the presence of nonresponse, S and U are generally not known (at least some components of S and U are not known). Suppose that according to some general rule (i.e., some model for the nonresponse) we impute for the missing values in the sample. Let S_* and U_* be the values of S and U calculated from the imputed data set. Then the usual inference for Q based on the imputed data set will be

$Q - S_*$ is approximately normally distributed with mean zero and variance U_*.

Now suppose that we have performed multiple imputations using the same rule as used to impute once. When the simple imputation rule is a random draw of values under a model for nonresponse, each set of imputed values is an independent random draw of values under the model. Let S_{*i}, U_{*i} be the values of S and U calculated on the ith imputed data set, $i = 1, \ldots, I$, where $I = $ the number of imputations. The variation in the S_{*i} and U_{*i} indicates the variety of inferences that might have been drawn if the nonrespondents had responded according to the assumed rule. For scalar Q, a plot of S_{*i} versus $\sqrt{U_{*i}}$ is an obvious display of the variety of inferences under the assumed model for nonresponse.

In many cases, it will be desirable to produce one summary inference for Q under the model for nonresponse. The I inferences can be combined to form the following (compromise) inference for Q:

$Q - \bar{S}_*$ is approximately normally distributed with mean

zero and variance $\overline{U}_* + W,$

where $\bar{S}_* = \sum_1^I S_{*i}/I$ = the average S_{*i}, $\bar{U}_* = \sum_1^I U_{*i}/I$ = the average U_{*i}, and $W = \sum_1^I (S_{*i} - \bar{S}_*)'(S_{*i} - \bar{S}_*)/(I - 1)$ = the estimated variance of the S_{*i} under the imputation rule (the prime indicates transpose).

The resultant estimate of Q, that is, $\bar{S}_*$, is the average of the estimates from the I imputed data sets. The resultant variance of estimation is the sum of (a) average variance of estimation given one set of imputed values, that is, $\bar{U}_*$, and (b) the variance of the estimates across the multiple imputations, that is, W.

Ideally, in practice, at least two imputations should be made under each of several different imputation models, with inferences being calculated separately for each imputation model. This procedure, which allows the assessment of sensitivity to different models for nonresponse, is an important component of any satisfactory treatment of nonresponse.

In order to implement a multiple imputation scheme in practice, all that is needed is a data analysis system that can handle, in addition to the full data set, an auxiliary data set of size $m \times I_+$, where m = number of missing values and I_+ = total number of imputations across all models. This multiple imputation scheme is not only often practically feasible but is also theoretically sound, as is now discussed.

1.2. Theory Underlying Multiple Imputations

The theory underlying the multiple imputation approach was first presented in Rubin (1977) in a special case where the distribution of the estimator S_* across imputations could be worked out analytically. The idea is to estimate the distribution of the complete-data statistic S in the presence of nonresponse.

Following the notation in Chapter 12, let Y be the vector of (unknown) values in the population about which we wish to make inferences; let X be the vector of covariate values which is fully observed; let D be the indicator variable for sampled values of Y, with R the indicator variable for response on Y; finally let $M = D \cdot R$ indicate observed and missing values in Y. Given (a) the observed values, (b) a model for nonresponse $\Pr(R \mid Y, X)$, and (c) a model for the population data $\Pr(Y \mid X)$, the complete-data statistic has a distribution, that is, a Bayesian posterior distribution. Random draw multiple imputations under the models $\Pr(R \mid Y, X)$ and $Pr(Y \mid X)$ simulate the posterior distribution of the complete-data statistic under those models.

In practice, an informal model (e.g., the hot deck) may be used for imputation, and then random draw multiple imputations under this model only approximate the posterior distribution of the complete-data statistic under a formal model. Section 3 presents the use of both a formal model and an informal model for imputation in the CPS. When the imputations are made under several models, the variation in values of the complete-data statistic reveals sensitivity of the complete-data inference to models of nonresponse.

When the multiple imputations are randomly drawn under a model

$\Pr(Y|X) \Pr(R|Y, X)$, the compromise inference for Q tends toward

$$(E_*(S) - Q) \sim N(0, V_*(S) + E_*(\tilde{V}\text{ar}(Q - S))), \tag{1}$$

where E_* and V_* refer to the mean and variance of S and $\tilde{V}\text{ar}(Q - S)$ over the posterior distribution of the complete data statistics, e.g., $E_*(S) = \int S \Pr(Y_U|Y_K, X, D, M) \, dY_U$, where Y_U are unobserved (unknown) Y values and Y_K are observed (known) Y values.

The compromise inference will give the correct Bayesian posterior mean and variance if the model $P(Y|X)$ used to generate the complete data statistics for the complete-data inference is consistent with the models $\Pr(Y|X)$ and $\Pr(R|Y, X)$ used to generate the posterior distribution of the complete-data statistics when faced with nonresponse. Often with confounded responding mechanisms, it will be computationally desirable to violate this condition by using convenient models to generate a posterior distribution for the complete-data statistic which will not perfectly agree with the model used to generate the complete-data statistics. For example, if $\Pr(Y)$ is the independently identically distributed normal model leading to $S = \bar{y}$, the sample mean, and $\Pr(Y|R)$ specifies one i.i.d. normal model when $R_i = 1$ and another i.i.d. normal model when $R_i = 0$, then the $\Pr(Y)$ and $\Pr(Y|R)$ models are inconsistent unless the $R_i = 0$ and $R_i = 1$ normal models are identical, i.e., unless $\Pr(Y|R) = \Pr(Y)$. As a consequence, in this example with $\Pr(Y|R) \neq \Pr(Y)$, the compromise inference will only approximate the correct Bayesian inference. Results in Rubin (1980) show that under quite general conditions this approximation should be satisfactory.

The compromise inference can also have approximately the correct coverage probability over its randomization distribution, and thus may be considered to be a valid randomization inference. The actual coverage probability of the compromise inference will depend on functions of the values of Y_i for nonrespondents. If these values of Y_i are distributed in a manner consistent with the Bayesian model for them generated by $\Pr(R|Y)$ and $\Pr(Y)$, then the coverage probability of the compromise inference will be approximately correct. The root of this claim is the fundamental similarity of sound Bayesian and sound frequentist inferences.

2. MULTIPLE IMPUTATION IN SIMPLE RANDOM SAMPLES

Suppose that we wish to estimate $\bar{Y}$, the mean of a variable Y in a finite population of size N, where the values of Y are $Y_1, \ldots, Y_N$. Suppose further for simplicity that the distribution of the values of Y is approximately normal. Let $y_1, \ldots, y_n$ be a simple random sample of size n from the population $Y_1, \ldots, Y_N$, and let $\bar{y}$ and $\hat{V}$ be the sample mean and variance of $y_1, \ldots, y_n$; $(\bar{y}, \hat{V})$ is the standard complete-data statistic in this case. If all of the $y_1, \ldots, y_n$ were observed, the standard randomization and Bayesian inferences with complete data would be that

$$\bar{y} \pm 2 \sqrt{\frac{N-n}{nN}} \, \hat{V} \qquad (2)$$

covers $\bar{Y}$ with 95% probability.

Suppose now that because of nonresponse only $m < n$ values of y_i are observed, and let $\bar{y}_1$ and $\hat{V}_1$ be the sample mean and variance of the m respondents' Y values. Further, consider the case with an obvious right answer. That is, suppose a probability responding mechanism so that nonresponse is just like another level of simple random sampling. As discussed in the chapter by Rubin (Chapter 12), in this case both randomization and Bayesian inferences for $\bar{Y}$ are that

$$\bar{y}_1 \pm 2 \sqrt{\frac{N-m}{mN}} \, \hat{V}_1 \qquad (3)$$

covers $\bar{Y}$ with 95% probability.

For simplicity, we shall let n, m and N/n be large so that we can avoid cluttering expressions with the ratio of n to $n - 1$ and corrections of that sort. Consequently, we shall consider the "right answer" for the basic case to be that

$$\bar{y}_1 \pm 2 \sqrt{\hat{V}_1/m} \qquad (4)$$

covers $\bar{Y}$ with 95% probability. If a general imputation method does not produce this answer in this basic case, we should doubt the appropriateness of the method in more complicated cases because the method is deficient in some respect. In contrast, if a general method produces this answer in the basic case, it has the potential to be appropriate in more complicated problems.

2.1. Single Imputation Methods

There are two general methods for single imputations that will be considered here. The first is to impute the best prediction for each missing value and the second is to impute by randomly drawing *with replacement* from the respondents' values. There are of course other and more complicated methods of performing imputations (e.g., in such a way as to obtain a particular value of the statistics $\bar{y}$ and $\hat{V}$), but these methods may not generalize very well to more complicated problems, whereas both the "insert best prediction" and "randomly draw from distribution of possible predictions" methods do generalize to complicated cases. In particular, randomly drawing *without replacement* may be quite ambiguous in multivariate situations, especially if we wish to think of the multiple impulations as simulating the posterior distribution of missing values. Of course, in many cases it may be more efficient to use other methods of imputation than those covered here; our exclusion of other methods does not necessarily mean we disapprove of their use.

Let $\bar{y}_0$ be the mean of the $n - m$ imputed values and $\overline{y_0^2}$ be the mean of the squared imputed values. The inference for $\bar{Y}$ based on the imputed data set will be that

$$\bar{y}_* \pm 2\sqrt{\hat{V}_*/n} \tag{5}$$

covers $\bar{Y}$ with 95% probability, where $\bar{y}_*$ is the mean and $\hat{V}_*$ the estimated variance of the n values, observed and imputed. These can be expressed as

$$\bar{y}_* = \frac{m}{n}\bar{y}_1 + \frac{n - m}{n}\bar{y}_0 \tag{6}$$

and

$$\hat{V}_* = ((m - 1)\hat{V}_1 + m\bar{y}_1^2 + (n - m)\overline{y_0^2} - n\bar{y}_*^2)/(n - 1)$$

$$\doteq \frac{m}{n}[\bar{y}_1^2 + \hat{V}_1] + \left(1 - \frac{m}{n}\right)\overline{y_0^2} - \bar{y}_*^2. \tag{7}$$

Consider now imputing the best prediction for each observation. Because the sample is simple random and the data are approximately normally distributed, the best prediction for each observation is $\bar{y}_1$, the mean of the m observed values of Y. Hence, $\bar{y}_0 = \bar{y}_1$ and thus the resultant complete-data sample mean based on observed and imputed values $\bar{y}_*$ also equals $\bar{y}_1$. Furthermore, the complete-data variance $\hat{V}_*$, equals $(m/n)\hat{V}_1$; i.e., the total sum of squares about $\bar{y}_*$ for the n observations is the same as the total sum of squares about $\bar{y}_1$ for the m real observations because $\bar{y}_* = \bar{y}_1$ and all imputed values equal $\bar{y}_1$. Consequently, the resultant inference for $\bar{Y}$ is that

$$\bar{y}_1 \pm 2\left(\frac{m}{n}\right)\sqrt{\hat{V}_1/m} \tag{8}$$

covers $\bar{Y}$ with 95% probability.

Notice first that the center of this interval is correct, that is, expression (8) is centered at $\bar{y}_1$ just as the correct interval (4). However, also notice that the width of the interval is too short by a factor of m/n. In general, it is intuitively clear that imputing the best prediction for each missing value will underestimate variability. (Furthermore, in general, imputing the best values will not necessarily lead to the correct center of the interval unless the complete-data statistic is a linear function of the missing values. For example, consider regression coefficients calculated with missing independent variables; the correct center for the confidence interval will not be obtained by filling in the best prediction for each value of the missing independent variable.)

The second method for performing single imputations considered here is to randomly draw (with replacement) from respondents. The objective of the random draw is to preserve the variability of the observations; for example, the hot deck is often implemented using a random draw. Now the center of the interval (5) is given by (6), which is a random variable over the imputations because $\bar{y}_0$ can vary from imputation to imputation. Similarly, the complete-data sample variance given by (7) is a random variable. Let $E_*(\cdot)$ and $V_*(\cdot)$ be the expectation and variance over repeated imputations, but conditional on the observed design indicator D, the observed missing data indicator M, and Y; a more precise but cumbersome notation is $E_*(\cdot|D, M, Y)$ and $V_*(\cdot|D, M, Y)$. Then conditional on D, M and Y and assuming the random draw imputation procedure,

$$E_*(\bar{y}_0) = \bar{y}_1, \qquad V_*(\bar{y}_0) = \hat{V}_1/(n - m), \qquad \text{and} \qquad E_*(\overline{y_0^2}) = \bar{y}_1^2 + \hat{V}_1. \quad (9)$$

Consequently, from Eqs. (6) and (7) we have that

$$E_*(\bar{y}_*) = \bar{y}_1, \qquad V_*(\bar{y}_*) = \frac{n - m}{n^2}\hat{V}_1, \qquad \text{and} \qquad E_*(\hat{V}_*) \doteq \hat{V}_1. \quad (10)$$

Comparing inference (5) for this single random imputation with both the correct inference (4) and the inference (8) resulting from imputing $\bar{y}_1$ for each missing value reveals several important facts.

First, the center of the interval $\bar{y}_*$ is not equal to the correct center $\bar{y}_1$, although we see from Eq. (10) that the expected value of the center over repeated imputations is $\bar{y}_1$. The variance of $\bar{y}_*$ about $\bar{y}_1$ leads to the second fact, which is that the randomization in the imputation process reduces the efficiency of $\bar{y}_*$ as an estimate of the population mean $\bar{Y}$. Explicitly, let $E(\cdot|Y)$ and $\text{Var}(\cdot|Y)$ represent the expectation and variance over repeated simple random samples of size n with m randomly drawn respondents, and let $\text{Var}_*(\cdot|Y)$ represent the variance over repeated random samples of size n, with m randomly drawn respondents and $n - m$ randomly drawn imputed values filled in for the nonrespondents. Then

$$\text{Var}_*(\bar{y}_*|Y) = E[V_*(\bar{y}_*|Y)] + \text{Var}[E_*(\bar{y}_*)|Y] \quad (11)$$

and from Eq. (10)

$$\text{Var}_*(\bar{y}_*|Y) = E\left(\frac{n - m}{n^2}\hat{V}_1|Y\right) + \text{Var}(\bar{y}_1|Y). \quad (12)$$

Hence, the variance of $\bar{y}_*$ is greater than the variance of $\bar{y}_1$ by the amount $E[((n - m)/n^2)\hat{V}_1|Y]$, which approximately equals $[(n - m)\sum_1^N(Y_i - \bar{Y})^2]/[n^2(N - 1)]$. Because $\text{Var}(\bar{y}_1|Y) = [\sum_1^N(Y_i - \bar{Y})^2]/[m(N - 1)]$, if we define the relative efficiency of $\bar{y}_*$ based on one set of random imputations to be the standard error of $\bar{y}_1$ divided by the standard error of $\bar{y}_*$ we have

$$\text{R.E.}_{\cdot 1} = \left[1 + \frac{m}{n}\left(1 - \frac{m}{n}\right)\right]^{-1/2}, \quad (13)$$

where the subscript 1 on R.E.$_1$ indicates one imputation for each missing value. It is easy to see that R.E.$_1$ is minimized when $m/n = 0.5$, so that R.E.$_1 \geq 89.4\%$. Thus, in this case, the loss in efficiency (in units of standard deviations) cannot be greater than about 10% when using single random imputations rather than best-value imputations. The difference between this result and those cited in the chapter by Oh and Scheuren and the chapter by Ford on duplication estimators and appearing in Hansen, Hurwitz, and Madow, 1953) occurs because here (a) the sampling is with replacement and (b) standard errors are being compared rather than variances.

This small sacrifice in efficiency using single random imputations rather than using single best-prediction imputations might be acceptable if the width of the resulting confidence interval (5) were nearly correct. However, the width of the interval (5) is still too short in expectation. Even though the expectation of the complete-data variance $\hat{V}_*$ is approximately equal to $\hat{V}_1$, the width of the interval will be too short in expection by a factor $(m/n)^{1/2}$ because we are acting as if the real sample size were n when in fact it is only m.

2.2. Multiple Imputation Methods

The decreased efficiency and underestimation of variability just discussed can be alleviated to some extent by using multiple imputations, that is, by imputing several times for each nonrespondent, each imputation being a random draw (with replacement) from the set of respondent y_i. Suppose, for example, we impute I times for each of the $n - m$ missing values to form I complete-data sets, and from these I imputed data sets calculate I complete-data statistics. Let the resultant sample means be $\bar{y}_{*1}, \ldots, \bar{y}_{*I}$ and the sample variances be $\hat{V}_{*1}, \ldots, \hat{V}_{*I}$. The $\bar{y}_{*i}$ and $\hat{V}_{*i}$ are given by equations analogous to Eq. (6) and (7) with $\bar{y}_{0i}$ and $\overline{y_{0i}^2}$ replacing $\bar{y}_0$ and $\overline{y_0^2}$.

With I imputations from the same model, the 95% interval for $\bar{Y}$ will be

$$\bar{y}_* \pm 2(W + \bar{V}_*/n)^{1/2}, \tag{14}$$

where $\bar{y}_*$, $\bar{V}_*$, and W are defined by employing the multiple imputation inference given in Section 1. More precisely, the center of the interval is the average of the I centers,

$$\bar{y}_* = \sum_1^I \bar{y}_{*i}/I, \tag{15}$$

and the variance defining the width of the 95% interval is the average variance within the imputations plus the variance across imputations of the I centers; the average variance within the imputations is

$$\bar{V}_*/n = \frac{1}{I}\sum_1^I \frac{\hat{V}_{*i}}{n}, \tag{16}$$

and the variance across imputations of the centers is

$$W = \sum_{1}^{I} (\bar{y}_{*i} - \bar{y}_{*})^2/(I - 1). \tag{17}$$

Since for each i, the expectation of $\bar{y}_{*i}$ is $\bar{y}_1$, from Eq. (15) we have that the resultant interval (14) has the correct center in expectation, that is,

$$E_*(\bar{y}_*) = \bar{y}_1. \tag{18}$$

Also, since the $\bar{y}_{*i}$ are independent across the I imputations (given fixed $\bar{y}_1$ and $\hat{V}_1$), the variance of the center $\bar{y}_*$ across repeated multiple imputations (conditional on D, M, and Y) is given by the variance of each $\bar{y}_{*i}$ divided by I; from Eq. (10),

$$V_*(\bar{y}_*) = \frac{n - m}{n^2} \hat{V}_1/I. \tag{19}$$

Consequently, there is a reduced real variance of estimation of $\bar{Y}$ (over repeated sampling and imputation procedures) using multiple random imputations rather than a single random imputation because the center of a multiple imputation interval has less variability than the center of a single imputation interval. Across repeated samples of size n with m respondents and across repeated imputations, the variance of $\bar{y}_*$ is

$$\text{Var}_*(\bar{y}_*|Y) = E\left(\frac{n - m}{n^2} \hat{V}_1/I \,\middle|\, Y\right) + \text{Var}(\bar{y}_1|Y). \tag{20}$$

Since $E(\hat{V}_1|Y) = n_1 V(\bar{y}_1|Y)$, the relative efficiency of $\bar{y}_*$ (relative to $\bar{y}_1$) is

$$\text{R.E.}_I = \left[1 + \frac{m}{n}\left(1 - \frac{m}{n}\right)\middle/ I\right]^{-1/2}. \tag{21}$$

The increased efficiency resulting from using multiple imputations is usually not very important because as we have seen following Eq. (13), single imputations are at least 90% efficient. The underestimation of the width of the 95% interval for $\bar{Y}$ when using single imputations is a more serious problem.

The width of the 95% interval using simple multiple imputations is closer to the correct answer but is still too short; from Eqs. (14), (15), and (16), the expected value of the interval width is given by

$$E_*(\bar{V}_*/n + W) = \frac{\hat{V}_1}{n} + E_*(W). \tag{22}$$

Since W is an unbiased estimate of the variance of the $\bar{y}_{*i}$ across imputations, from Eq. (10), $E_*(W) = \text{Var}_*(\bar{y}_{*i}) = (n - m)\hat{V}_1/n^2$. Consequently, the width of the interval is typically too short by a factor given by

$$\left[E_*(\bar{V}_*/n + W)/(\hat{V}_1/m)\right]^{1/2} = \left[\frac{m}{n}\left(2 - \frac{m}{n}\right)\right]^{1/2}. \tag{23}$$

TABLE 1

Interval Width Based on Imputed Values Too Short by the Following Factors
(Correct = 1.00)

	Proportion of sample observed								
	.1	.2	.3	.4	.5	.6	.7	.8	.9
Impute $\bar{y}_1$	.10	.20	.30	.40	.50	.60	.70	.80	.90
Impute randomly	.32	.45	.55	.63	.71	.77	.84	.89	.95
Mult. Imp. ($I \geq 2$) (simple)	.44	.60	.71	.80	.87	.92	.95	.98	.99
Mult. Imp. ($I \geq 2$) (adj.)	1.00	1.00	1.00	1.00	1.00	1.00	1.00	1.00	1.00

Thus, we see that multiple random imputations do result in improvements over single random imputations in that (1) they have reduced the real variance of estimation and (2) they have adjusted partially for the underestimation of variability that follows from performing a single imputation. Table 1 shows the effect of the estimated width of the interval and Table 2 shows the effect on the relative efficiency of estimation. Table 1 also shows the results for "adjusted multiple imputations," which we now discuss.

2.3. Multiple Imputations with the Correct Variance

At first it may appear rather surprising that variability is underestimated when the imputations are randomly drawn from respondents. A useful way of understanding the deficiency of the simple multiple imputations is to consider the problem from a Bayesian point of view.

TABLE 2

Relative Efficiency of $\bar{y}_*$; Multiple Imputation (Simple)

Number of multiple imputations I	Proportion of sample observed								
	.1	.2	.3	.4	.5	.6	.7	.8	.9
1	.96	.93	.91	.90	.89	.90	.91	.93	.96
2	.98	.96	.95	.95	.94	.95	.95	.96	.98
3	.99	.97	.97	.96	.96	.96	.97	.97	.99
4	.99	.98	.98	.97	.97	.97	.98	.98	.99
5	.99	.98	.98	.98	.98	.98	.98	.98	.99
8	.99	.99	.99	.99	.99	.99	.99	.99	.99
10	1.00	.99	.99	.99	.99	.99	.99	.99	1.00
15	1.00	1.00	.99	.99	.99	.99	.99	1.00	1.00
20	1.00	1.00	1.00	.99	.99	.99	1.00	1.00	1.00

From the Bayesian perspective, $(\bar{y}, \hat{V})$ has a posterior distribution given observed values and model specifications. As mentioned earlier, the objective of the multiple imputations is to simulate this posterior distribution. This simulation is easily done in a two-step process: first draw the parameters of the model from their posterior distribution and then draw the missing values from their distribution conditionally given the drawn values of the parameters. Assuming that the Y_i are drawn from a normal distribution with mean μ and variance σ^2, μ and σ^2 have relatively simple posterior distributions. For relatively diffuse priors and random nonresponse, the posterior distribution of μ given σ is normal with mean $\bar{y}_1$ and variance σ^2/m, and the posterior distribution of σ^2 is $(m-1)$ $\hat{V}_1^2$ times an inverted χ^2 on $m-1$ degrees of freedom; the posterior distribution of the missing values given (μ, σ) is i.i.d. $N(\mu, \sigma^2)$. Thus in order to simulate the posterior distribution of the missing values and thence $\bar{y}$ and $\hat{V}$, we *first* must draw μ and σ^2 from their posterior distribution; having drawn μ and σ^2 from their posterior distribution, we can then draw values to impute and thereby calculate a simulated value for $(\bar{y}, \hat{V})$.

The simple multiple imputation method of the previous section essentially omits the step of drawing the parameters μ and σ^2 from their posterior distribution, and instead acts as if the respondents' distribution of values was exactly the same as the population distribution of values. Because we do not know precisely what the values are, when we act as if we have this knowledge, we underestimate variability. In other words, even if the respondents and nonrespondents are identical stochastically, $\bar{y}_1$ and $\hat{V}_1$ are not the exactly appropriate mean and variance for the nonrespondents in the sample. Under our model with random nonresponse, the respondents and nonrespondents share the same parameters (μ, σ), but the sample mean and sample variance are not necessarily the same for respondents and nonrespondents, and our imputations should reflect this extra variability.

Let us follow the Bayesian ideas just described to perform adjusted multiple imputations. For simplicity, assume m is large; small m is considered briefly in Section 3. Before performing the ith set of imputations, suppose that we draw a bias b_i from $N(0, \hat{V}_1/m)$ which is the posterior distribution of $\mu - \bar{y}_1$ assuming a large number of respondents. A new value of b_i will be drawn for each of the I sets of imputations. For the ith set of imputations, as before draw $n - m$ values from the m respondents' values (with replacement) but add b_i to each of the $n - m$ drawn values before imputing. The resultant value of the sample mean may be written following Eq. (6) as

$$\bar{y}_{+i} = \frac{m}{n}\bar{y}_1 + \frac{n-m}{n}[\bar{y}_{0i} + b_i], \tag{24}$$

where $\bar{y}_{0i}$ is the mean of the $n - m$ respondents' drawn for imputation, and the resultant value of the sample variance may be written following Eq. (7) as

$$\hat{V}_{+i} \doteq \frac{m}{n}[\bar{y}_1^2 + \hat{V}_1] + \left(1 - \frac{m}{n}\right)[\overline{y_{0i}^2} + 2\bar{y}_{0i}b_i + b_i^2] - \bar{y}_{+i}^2, \tag{25}$$

where $\overline{y_{0i}^2}$ is the mean of the square of the $n - m$ respondents' values drawn for imputation. The 95% interval for $\overline{Y}$ based on I imputations is

$$\bar{y}_+ \pm 2[\hat{V}_+/n + W_+]^{1/2}, \tag{26}$$

where

$$\bar{y}_+ = \sum_1^I \bar{y}_{+i}/I \quad \text{and} \quad \hat{V}_+/n = \sum_1^I \frac{\hat{V}_{+i}}{n}/I \tag{27}$$

with

$$W_+ = \sum_1^I (\bar{y}_{+i} - \bar{y}_+)^2/(I - 1). \tag{28}$$

The expectation of the center of the interval over repeated imputations is $\bar{y}_1$ because for each i, $E(\bar{y}_{0i}) = \bar{y}_1$ and $E(b_i) = 0$. Hence, the center of the interval is correct. The variance of each $\bar{y}_{+i}$ (conditional on M, D, Y) is

$$\text{Var}_*(\bar{y}_{+i}) = \left(\frac{n - m}{n}\right)^2 \left[\frac{\hat{V}_1}{n - m} + \frac{\hat{V}_1}{m}\right] = \frac{\hat{V}_1}{m}\left(\frac{n - m}{n}\right). \tag{29}$$

Consequently, the real variance of estimation of $\overline{Y}$ using $\bar{y}_+$ across repeated sampling and repeated multiple imputations is

$$\text{Var}_*(\bar{y}_+ \mid Y) = E\left(\frac{n - m}{nm} \hat{V}_1/I \mid Y\right) + \text{Var}(\bar{y}_1 \mid Y). \tag{30}$$

Comparing Eqs. (20) and (30) shows that the variance of $\bar{y}_+$ is larger than the variance of the unadjusted multiple imputation estimate $\bar{y}_*$ because of the added variance due to the b_i; Table 3 shows that for cases with $I > n/m$, the loss in efficiency of estimation is small.

TABLE 3

Relative Efficiency of $\bar{y}_+$; Multiple Imputation (Adj.)

Number of multiple imputations I	Proportion of sample observed								
	.1	.2	.3	.4	.5	.6	.7	.8	.9
1	.73	.75	.77	.80	.82	.85	.88	.91	.95
2	.83	.85	.86	.88	.89	.91	.93	.95	.98
3	.88	.89	.90	.91	.93	.94	.95	.97	.98
4	.90	.91	.92	.93	.94	.95	.96	.98	.99
5	.92	.93	.94	.95	.95	.96	.97	.98	.99
8	.95	.95	.96	.96	.97	.98	.98	.99	.99
10	.96	.96	.97	.97	.98	.98	.99	.99	1.00
15	.97	.97	.98	.98	.98	.99	.99	.99	1.00
20	.98	.98	.98	.99	.99	.99	.99	1.00	1.00

The advantage of the adjusted multiple imputation procedure is that on average we obtain the correct estimate of variance. That is, because $E_*(W_+) = \text{Var}_*(\bar{y}_{+i})$ and $E_*(\hat{V}_+/n) = E_*(\hat{V}_{+i}/n) = \hat{V}_1/n$, we have

$$E_*(\hat{V}_+/n + W_+) = \frac{\hat{V}_1}{n} + \frac{\hat{V}_1}{m}\left(1 - \frac{m}{n}\right) = \frac{\hat{V}_1}{m}. \qquad (31)$$

Even if n/N is not small, we still obtain the correct answer. In that case, the variance associated with each $\bar{y}_{+i}$ is $\hat{V}_1\left[(1/n) - (1/N)\right]$, which replaces V_1/n in Eq. (31) and thus leads to the estimate of variability $\hat{V}_1[(1/n) - (1/N)]$, which agrees with Eq. (3).

To summarize the effect of the adjusted randomly drawn multiple imputation procedure: (1) the expectation of the center of the interval is correct, and (2) the expectation of the width of the confidence interval is correct. Consequently, if the number of multiple imputations performed I is chosen to be large, then the resultant interval for $\bar{Y}$ will be correct. When I is small, the interval for $\bar{Y}$ will be correct in expectation, but it will vary somewhat; Table 3 summarizes this effect by showing the relative efficiency of $\bar{y}_+$ as a function of I and m/n. For only two multiple imputations, the efficiency (in standard deviations) of $\bar{y}_+$ relative to $\bar{y}_1$ is about 90% even with 50% of the sample missing. This result suggests that in a simple random sample or a relatively large hot-deck cell with at least a 50% response rate, two imputations per missing value should be adequate for practical purposes when estimating means.

3.   INDICATIONS OF EXTENSIONS

Of course multiple imputation methodology is not designed for the simple case treated in Section 2, since the correct inference is already available. The promise of the method lies in extensions to situations where the correct inference is not immediate. There are many possible extensions to the method of multiple imputations, Rubin (1978), for example, discusses multiple imputation procedures more generally; here we indicate ways in which some simple models can be used to incorporate nonresponse bias and handle multivariate and nonnormal Y.

3.1.   Nonresponse Bias — Confounded
Response Mechanism

Conceptually, a very important extension is to models with nonresponse bias, so that we can evaluate sensitivity of inferences to assumptions about the response mechanism. An easily implemented and easily communicated multiple imputation model that incorporates systematic differences between respondents and nonrespondents in a simple random sample is now described.

With no response bias, the small sample (Bayesian) multiple imputation scheme assuming normal data is to carry out the following procedure at each set of imputations.

For $i = 1, \ldots, I$

(a) Draw a χ^2_{m-1} random variable divided by $m - 1$, say x_i and let

$$\sigma_i^2 = \hat{V}_1/x_i.$$

(b) Draw a $N(0, 1)$ random variable, say, z_i and let

$$b_i = z_i \sqrt{\sigma_i^2/m}.$$

(c) Randomly draw with replacement $n - m$ values from the respondents; before imputing these values for the missing values:

(1) Divide each value by $\sqrt{x_i}$.
(2) Then add b_i to each value.

These three steps are identical to the adjusted multiple imputations of Section 2 except that x_i is drawn from a $\bar{y}^2_{m-1}/(m - 1)$ distribution rather than being set equal to 1; this is nearly the correct adjustment for small normal samples, and it leads essentially to a Student's t distribution for the imputed mean. The procedure is easily modified to reflect nonresponse bias.

Suppose first that it is suspected that the respondents' Y_i values are shifted from the nonrespondents' Y_i values. Then a shifting constant k_1 can reflect this. Replace step (c2) by

(c2') Add $b_i + k_1\sigma_i$ to each value.

The difference between the mean of the imputed values and the mean of the respondents' values will on average be k_1 standard deviations.

Suppose next that it is suspected that the nonrespondents' Y_i values have a different scale from the respondents' Y_i values. Then a scale factor k_2 can be used to reflect this; replace step (c1) by

(c1') Divide each value by $\sqrt{x_i}/k_2$.

The imputed values will then on average have k_2 times the standard deviation of the respondents' values.

Finally, suppose that it is suspected that the nonrespondents differ from respondents by a shape distortion reflected by a function $k_3(\cdot)$; then replace step (c) by

(c') Draw with replacement $n - n_1$ values from the respondents with probability proportional to $k_3(y_i)$.

The resulting imputed values will be skewed by the function $k_3(\cdot)$. For example, if $k_3(y_i) = y_i$, then larger values of y_i will be drawn for imputation with higher probabilities than smaller values. Such skewing might be appropriate for example with income items when it is suspected that nonresponse probabilities are proportional to actual income.

Notice that we have specified a simple, general family of response bias models defined by k_1 = shift bias, k_2 = scale bias, k_3 = shape bias, where $k_1 = 0$, $k_2 = 1, k_3(\cdot) \propto$ constant represents no nonresponse bias. Because this family is so easy to implement and to describe [e.g., the $(-.1, 1.5, \log)$ model implies a shift of $-.1$ standard deviations, an increase in scale by 50%, and probability proportional to $\log(y_i)$ for skewing], it may be useful in hot-deck contexts for exploring sensitivity to models. That is, perform two imputations under each of the three models $(0, 1, \text{cons.})$, $(-.1, 1.5, \log)$, $(-3, 2, Y)$, then calculate the resultant multiple imputation inference for each model and compare inferences. Of course, other families of models may also be of interest.

3.2. Multivariate and Nonnormal Data

With multivariate Y, more complicated models will be necessary. A simple generalization of the previous response bias model that may be appropriate with relatively large multivariate samples is to ignore step (a) to avoid drawing from a Wishart distribution, replace step (b) with a random draw from the multivariate normal with mean $\bar{y}_1$ and covariance s_1^2/m, and replace step (c') with the analogous step where $\mathbf{k}_1$ is a shift vector, $\mathbf{k}_2$ is a scale transformation matrix, and $k_3(\cdot)$ is a scalar function of a vector $\mathbf{y}$. Of course, in practice with multivariate response, it usually will not be realistic to assume normality. Also there will usually be different suspected reasons for unit and various types of item nonresponse.

If the respondent data are obviously nonnormal, it might be wise to transform to approximate normality before steps (a), (b), and (c) and then to "unwind" the transformation before actually imputing values [e.g., if $Z = \log Y$ is approximately normal, perform steps (a), (b), (c) on the Z data but let the imputed values be $\exp(Z)$]. Another method of drawing that is more appropriate for multivariate discrete data is the Bayesian bootstrap (Rubin, 1981), a simple simulation device that needs only a uniform random number generator.

Ideally, all models used for imputation will be based on careful data analyses of all available data. Coupling the analyses from such models with efficient Monte Carlo methods for randomly drawing from posterior distributions is the task that needs to be implemented in order for multiple imputation procedures to be truly useful in practice. Research is needed to determine appropriate ways to use multiple imputations in real-world complex surveys.

4. MODELING INDIVIDUAL SOCIAL SECURITY BENEFIT AMOUNTS FOR USE IN A MULTIPLE IMPUTATION PROTOCOL

This section and the next describe an application of multiple imputation. This section describes a two-stage model for predicting the Social Security benefits for a number of individuals surveyed during the Census Bureau's March 1973 Current Population Survey (CPS). Section 5 applies this model to produce multiple imputations for nonrespondents. This particular survey was used for this study because administrative data are available to validate results of the imputations. In Section 5, we not only compare the results of 100 applications of this two-stage protocol to these administrative data, but to the Census Bureau's 1973 CPS hot-deck procedure as well. Other recent work on missing CPS income data includes Oh and Scheuren (1980).

4.1. The CPS Data Base

The CPS has a multistage, stratified clustered sample design. It is a monthly household survey of over 50,000 households and about 150,000 individuals within these households. The Current Population Survey's principal goal is to estimate the labor force status of noninstitutionalized civilians at least 14 years of age. Every March CPS interview includes a series of (supplementary) income questions designed to ascertain all of the respondent's sources of income during the preceding calendar year.

At present the Census Bureau is using a modified hot-deck procedure to impute missing data items in the CPS [e.g., see Coder (1978) for details]. This procedure assigns the value of an item from a complete record to the record having the corresponding value absent. The complete record chosen is identical or nearly identical to the incomplete record as far as certain respondent-supplied characteristics are concerned. The third chapter, by Ford, in this part of the volume presents detailed descriptions of hot-deck procedures.

We have restricted our attention to a portion of the CPS–SSA–IRS Exact Match File (see Aziz, Kilss, and Scheuren, 1978); this file is based on the March 1973 CPS as well as administrative records of both the Social Security Administration (SSA) and the Internal Revenue Service (IRS) which were used to improve the reliability of the income data. Essentially, this file was created by matching individual CPS respondents to their 1972 tax return as well as their SSA earnings and benefit administrative information. The Match File, then, combines the probability sampling aspects of the CPS with the more reliable administrative records of the IRS and SSA.

TABLE 4

Number of Individuals by Response and Beneficiary Status

OASDI beneficiary status	Response status	
	Respondents	Nonrespondents
Total	999	59
Nonrecipients	200	10[a]
Recipients	799	49[a]
Average administrative benefit	$1819.50	$1886.08[a]

[a] These values were obtained from administrative records.

We considered only the 1128 individuals surveyed during the March 1973 CPS who had all of the following characteristics:

(1) At least 62 years of age as of December 1972
(2) Male
(3) In panels[1] 1, 2, or 5 of the March 1973 CPS
(4) Responded for themselves
(5) Had a usable administrative record

Characteristics (1)–(5) were chosen for reasons given in Herzog and Lancaster [1980, p. 72].

Of the 1128 individuals who satisfied the above criteria, 999 had no missing (CPS) income amounts of any kind. It is these 999 "respondents" whose data we shall use to construct our imputation protocol. Of the remaining 129 individuals, 59 failed to respond to the CPS questions on OASDI (old age-survivor and disability income) benefits and so had their OASDI benefit amounts imputed by the CPS hot deck. Our goal is to study the imputation of OASDI benefits for these 59 individuals, the "nonrespondents."

The terms "beneficiaries" and "recipients" are used to refer to those individuals whose administrative data indicated that they received some OASDI payments during calendar year 1972. Table 4 displays basic summary statistics.

The description of the imputation protocol is divided into three parts. First, we shall describe the construction of a multiple linear regression model to predict individual *recipient* OASDI benefit amounts. Next, we present a log-linear model to be used to predict OASDI recipiency status. Finally, in Section 5 we describe the use of our two-stage imputation protocol to predict the missing OASDI benefit amounts of the 59 nonrespondents. Although the prediction of OASDI amounts is accomplished by first predicting recipiency status from a log-linear model and second by using a regression model to predict the amount of benefits for those predicted to be recipients, the regression model is described

[1] In the CPS, there are eight panels, the number of the individual panels corresponding to the number of months each household in the panel has been included in the survey.

first because the regression model is used to construct one of the predictor variables used in the log-linear model.

4.2. A Multiple Linear Regression Model to Predict Individual OASDI Benefits in the March 1973 CPS

The data from the 799 recipient respondents were used to predict, using least squares regression, the benefits of recipient nonrespondents. The dependent variable was the natural logarithm of the amount of individual (administrative) SSA benefits. Fourteen characteristics were used as independent (predictor) variables in our regression models. The following seven numerical variables were employed:

1. Age (62, 63, ...)
2. Square of age^2
3. Reported income of rest of family
4. Reported individual income other than SSA benefits and earned income (to be defined)
5. D1 (to be defined)
6. D2 (to be defined)
7. Number of years of school (0, 1, ..., 16, ≥ 17).

In order to define $D1$ and $D2$, we let

$$X = \text{CPS reported wages for 1972}$$

and

$$Y = \text{the sum of reported farm and nonfarm self-employment income.}$$

We then define "earned income of an individual" as

$$Z = X + \max(0, Y).$$

For those individuals aged 72 and over we define $D1 = D2 = 0$. For the rest of the individuals who are between 62 and 71, we define

$$D1 = \begin{cases} 0, & Z \leq \$1680 \\ Z - \$1680 & \$1680 < Z \leq \$2880 \\ \$1200, & Z > \$2880 \end{cases}$$

and

$$D2 = \min[(\max(0, Z - \$2880)), \$6152],$$

where Z is as defined earlier.

---

^{2} Thus, under our models, the logarithm of benefit amounts is assumed to be a quadratic function of individual years of age.

TABLE 5

Coefficient Estimates and t-Statistics for Models Formed after the Deletion of Outliers

Variables	Panel 1		Panel 2		Panel 5		Panels 1, 2, 5	
	Coefficient estimate	t value	Coefficient estimate	t value	Coefficient estimate	t value	Coefficient estimate	t value
Constant	−281,505.40		−176,424.10		376,705.93		−441,249.32	
Age	28,759.28	4.8	26,276.96	3.7	10,108.28	1.3	32,630.97	7.4
Vet status	3,369.43	.8	8,083.44	1.6	9,143.17	1.8	5,531.54	1.8
Number of weeks worked								
0	15,815.40	2.2	9,703.17	1.3	−6,737.05	−.9	5,230.76	1.1
1–13	8,196.75	.8	−282.57	.0	−3,840.63	−.4	1,283.05	.2
14–26	11,331.35	1.3	−3,902.88	−.3	8,178.25	.7	6,357.15	.9
27–39	−41,522.56	−2.4	−21,555.24	−1.5	−28,971.67	−2.3	−23,293.29	−2.5
40–47	−19,606.74	−1.5	11,255.26	.6	7,667.32	.3	−31,287.57	−3.0
48–9	7,515.46	.3	−8,589.66	−.4	−5,010.58	−.2	1,108.57	.1
Number of years of school	577.42	1.0	−57.94	−.1	834.75	1.2	871.58	2.1
Martial/head of household status								
Single/head of primary household	15,995.39	.9	−20,430.43	−1.5	.00	.0	−543.96	.0
Single/not head of primary household	−537.73	−.1	−9,366.80	−1.0	−9,857.55	−1.1	−7,888.36	−1.3

228

Widower/head of primary household	-8,962.19	-.6	-7,781.58	.5	3,613.05	.2	-2,143.96	-.2
Widower/not head of primary household	-18,954.64	-1.7	-21,057.28	-2.0	1,739.31	.2	-14,302.77	-2.1
Other/head of primary household	-12,673.22	-1.3	-8,639.65	-.5	3,894.61	.4	-174.87	.0
Other/not head of primary household	-14,311.03	-2.5	-3,727.53	-.6	-3,291.48	-.5	-6,812.05	-1.7
Income of other family members	-1.23	-2.2	-.65	-1.5	-.01	-.1	-.13	-.6
Race/ethnicity status	-5,082.03	-.6	-10,151.50	-1.3	-18,904.06	-2.6	-16,623.67	-3.4
Insured status	-27,453.10	-6.0	-24,816.02	-5.3	-16,956.44	-3.7	-20,743.21	-7.0
Age squared	192.05	-4.7	-178.94	-3.8	-62.42	-1.2	-217.18	-7.3
D1	-15.52	-1.3	4.67	.3	-17.05	-1.4	-24.96	-3.2
Location								
Ring of SMSA	-6,790.25	-1.2	1,659.70	.3	-2,348.07	-.4	-4,399.04	-1.1
Urban non-SMSA	-3,730.32	-.6	-16,804.30	-2.5	-8,483.51	-1.1	-6,499.27	-1.5
Rural nonfarm	-22,369.54	-4.5	-11,077.84	-1.9	-17,343.91	-2.8	-16,314.20	-4.4
Rural farm	-28,118.78	-3.1	-28,141.63	-3.0	-29,672.61	-3.4	-30,480.74	-5.3
Other income of individual	.98	2.3	1.66	3.2	-.87	-1.3	.74	2.3
D2	-6.95	-1.8	-15.01	-3.3	-1.66	-.3	-7.35	-2.8
Interview type	9,335.21	.6	-224.75	.0	12,744.08	1.0	-1,130.10	-.2
Summary statistics								
Number of original observations	278		260		261		799	
Number of points deleted	3		9		4		16	
R^2 (of logs of benefits)	.4266		.3795		.2055		.2877	
Residual root mean square (of logs)	29,984		32,127		33,702		32,043	

The variables $D1$ and $D2$ were employed to aid in the prediction of benefits for those ages 62–71. The motivation for these particular definitions is as follows: In 1972, OASDI beneficiaries under age 72 could earn up to $1680 without having their OASDI benefits reduced. Benefits were reduced by half a dollar for each of the first $1200 earned in excess of $1680 and by one dollar for each dollar earned in excess of $2880. Those earning at least $6152 received no OASDI benefits. We hoped that the $D1$ and $D2$ variables would help us to incorporate the reduced benefit features into our model. Since those aged 72 or older were exempt from the reduced benefit provisions of the Social Security regulations, we set $D1 = D2 = 0$ for these individuals.

The seven "qualitative" independent variables used in our regression models were constructed so that those categories observed most frequently were generally assigned a value of 0.

(1) Race and ethnicity status (0 = white nonSpanish, 1 = other).
(2) Veteran's status (0 = nonveteran, 1 = veteran).
(3) Interview type (0 = interview conducted in person, 1 = otherwise).
(4) Insured status:

0   if "not insured,"
1   if "fully insured and eligible for disability,"
2   if "fully insured but not eligible for disability,"
3   if "currently insured only."

(5) Location [i.e., central city, ring of SMSA (Standard Metropolitan Statistical Area), urban non-SMSA, rural nonfarm, and rural farm]. Four 0–1 indicator variables are employed. All four indicator variables are set equal to 0 for individuals residing in a central city; otherwise, three of the indicators are set equal to 0 and the fourth, corresponding to the type of location of the individual, is assigned a value of 1.

(6) Number of weeks worked during calendar year 1972. This variable was partitioned in the Match File as 0, 1–13, 14–26, 27–39, 40–47, 48–49, and 50–52 weeks. Six 0–1 indicator variables were formed based on the number of weeks worked. All were set equal to 0 for individuals working at least 50 weeks; otherwise a single indicator, corresponding to the number of weeks worked, was set equal to 1.

(7) Marital and household status. Six indicator variables were formed. All six were set equal to 0 for individuals who were "married with spouse present." The other indicator variables corresponded to the following classifications:

(i)   single and head of household,
(ii)   single but not head of household,
(iii) widower and head of household,
(iv)   widower but not head of household,
(v)   other marital status and head of household, and
(vi)   other marital status but not head of household.

Plots of the predicted values versus the residual values in the initial analyses revealed a small number of outliers. A naive procedure was used to eliminate outliers. For each panel, we first constructed a regression model using all of the recipient values. We deleted all those cases whose residual values exceeded 2.5 times the sqaure root of the residual mean square (in absolute value). We repeated the above procedure (separately for each panel) until all of the residual values were less than 2.5 times the square root of the residual mean square (in absolute value). This process resulted in the elimination of three outliers from panel 1, nine from panel 2, and four from panel 5. The majority of the outlier values probably represent individuals who only received OASDI benefits for a few months of 1972 and, therefore, had an "artificially" low benefit level.

The summary statistics for each of the regression models formed after the deletion of outliers are shown in Table 5. It is interesting to note that the R^2 values decrease as the number of months in the sample increases. The combined model was used for prediction of imputed values.

Although many of the predictor variables were not significant at conventional levels (as evidenced by their nominal t statistics in Table 5), we left them in the final regression model because they did not detract from the accuracy of the predictions.

TABLE 6

Observed Frequency Counts for Those at Least 72 Years of Age

	Beneficiary status			
	Nonrecipient		Recipient	
Predicted recipient OASDI benefit amount	Earned income		Earned income	
	< $1680	≥ $1680	< $1680	≥ $1680
≤ $1250	5	0	13	0
$1251–$1500	7	0	58	5
$1501–$1750	5	0	113	5
$1751–$2000	1	0	101	5
> $2000	11	0	35	22

Model	Likelihood ratio (information) statistic (× 2)	D.F.	Probability of a larger value
Constant term only	35.74	9	.00
Income	31.35	8	.00
Benefits	10.03	5	.07
Income, benefits	.88	4	.93

4.3.   Log-Linear Models to Predict OASDI Recipiency Status in the March 1973 CPS

Log-linear models are used to predict the OASDI beneficiary status of the 59 nonrespondents from the data for the 999 respondents. The results are based on statistical analyses carried out by Lancaster (1979) at the Social Security Administration following principles in Gokhale and Kullback (1978).

During calendar year 1972, almost all U.S. citizens at least 72 years of age were entitled to OASDI benefits (irrespective of the extent of their prior contributions to the Social Security System). For this reason, separate models were used for those ages 62–71 and those at least 72 years of age.

The model developed by Lancaster for those at least 72 years of age contained two independent variables: earned income and predicted OASDI benefits, assuming the individual was a recipient. For the reasons given previously, earned income was partitioned into two levels: (1) less than $1680 and (2) greater than or equal to $1680. The predicted recipient OASDI benefit variable was partitioned into the five intervals shown in Table 6.

TABLE 7

Parameter Estimates for Contingency Table Models

Variable	Model for those 72+	Model for those 62–71
Constant	−2.046	−.620
Earned income less than $1680	.855	−.592
Predicted OASDI benefits		
$0–1250	.720	.582
$1251–1500	.136	−.151
$1501–1750	−.364	−.336
$1751–2000	−1.09	−.330
Age		
62		.681
63		.364
64		.394
65		−.251
66		−.317
67		.135
68		−.409
69		−.428
70		−.0157
Earned income—OASDI benefit interaction terms		
$0–1250		.125
$1251–1500		−.599
$1501–1750		−.0320
$1751–2000		.374

TABLE 8

Observed Frequency Counts for Those Aged 62–71

	Beneficiary status			
	Nonrecipient		Recipient	
Predicted recipient OASDI benefit amount	Earned income		Earned income	
	< $1680	≥ $1680	< $1680	≥ $1680
≤ $1250	5	96	8	23
$1251–1500	1	20	48	8
$1501–1750	4	7	91	15
$1751–2000	11	3	107	11
> $2000	20	4	127	4

Model	Likelihood ratio (information) statistic (× 2)	D.F.	Probability of a larger value
Constant term only	362.4	99	.00
Age	239.2	90	.00
Income benefits	94.8	90	.35
Income benefits, age	61.9	81	.94

The specific models considered are summarized in the lower portion of Table 6. The model involving both the earned income and predicted recipient OASDI benefit one-way marginals is the best of those considered. The parameter values for this model are shown in Table 7.

The model developed by Lancaster for those ages 62–71 consisted of three independent variables: earned income, predicted recipient OASDI benefit amounts, and an age variable partitioned into 10 categories—one for each of the individual ages 62–71. The basic data and specific contingency table models considered are summarized in Table 8. The parameter estimates for the model involving the earned income-predicted benefit amount two-way interaction variables together with the one-way age variable are shown in Table 7.

5. MULTIPLE IMPUTATION OF INDIVIDUAL OASDI BENEFIT AMOUNTS USING A TWO-STAGE PREDICTION SCHEME

In this section, we first describe the procedure used to generate 100 imputed benefit amounts (possibly $0) for each of the 59 nonrespondents. Then the results of applying the procedure are compared to the results of a two-imputation version of the 1973 CPS hot-deck procedure. Also these results are evaluated with respect to the administrative values available for nonrespondents.

5.1. The Prediction of Recipiency Status

The process employed to predict whether an individual was an OASDI recipient (i.e., recipiency status) consists of two basic steps carried out independently 100 times to produce 100 sets of imputed values, each value being 0 or 1. These steps are

(1)   The generation of an estimate for each of the two sets of parameters listed in Table 7. Each set of parameters is drawn from their posterior distribution, the first set for those at least 72 years of age and the second set for those 62–71 years of age. In this generation process, then, we are just drawing values from (or simulating) the distribution of the parameters given the observed respondent values.

(2)   The generation, for each of our 59 nonrespondents of an imputed benefit status using the 72+ or 62–71 model of step (1) with the log-linear parameter values drawn in step (1). Thus, each such imputed value will indicate whether an individual nonrespondent is an OASDI recipient.

The first step is carried out by assuming that (for each of the two models) the parameters have a multivariate normal distribution with posterior mean and variance given by large-sample likelihood theory. For each model, the mean of the distribution is the vector of parameter estimates of the model displayed in Table 7; the procedure described in Appendix A was used to estimate the variance–covariance matrix.

The second step of the procedure is carried out by first calculating the probability of being a recipient for each income–benefit–age cell using the parameters drawn in step (1). A uniform random number was generated for each nonrespondent (18 for the group over 72 years of age and 41 for the 62–71-year-old group). If the random number for a nonrespondent was less than the calculated probability, the nonrespondent was considered a recipient.[3]

---

[3] For each of the two models, we discarded all sets of imputed values for which the number of imputed recipients was outside a symmetric 90% confidence interval centered at the number of recipients expected under the model. This scheme was employed to avoid the prediction of values substantially different from those expected, while preserving the expected value and symmetry of the prediction process; i.e., it was felt to represent better the predictive distribution of values than the procedure without adjustment; see Herzog (1980, p. 79) for more details.

5.2. The Prediction of Individual OASDI Benefit Amounts

For each recipiency status imputed as 0, \$0 was imputed as the OASDI benefit amount. For each recipiency status imputed as 1, the regression model was used to predict OASDI benefit amounts. The process involved two basic steps:

(1) The generation of an estimate for each of the 28 coefficients of the combined regression model described in Section 4. Each set of parameters is drawn from the posterior distribution of the parameters of the basic model. Here again we are merely drawing values from (or simulating) the distribution of the parameters given the observed recipient respondent values.

(2) The generation, for each regression model of step (1), of an "imputed" benefit amount for each of the individuals predicted (by the log-linear model) to be recipients.

The first step is carried out by treating the vector of 28 regression coefficients as a random vector having a multivariate normal posterior distribution. The mean vector of this distribution is simply the vector of estimated coefficients of the basic model and is displayed in column 4 of Table 4. The variance–covariance matrix is just proportional to $\sigma^2(X'X)^{-1}$, where σ^2 is the residual mean square from the basic model and X is the 783-by-28 matrix of observations (e.g., see Anderson, 1958).

The second step of the procedure is carried out by first calculating the (mean) value predicted by the regression model for each of the individuals predicted to be recipients by the log-linear model. Each of these values is considered to be the mean of a normal distribution, while the residual mean square of the original regression model is employed as the variance. The value assigned to each of the individuals is obtained by randomly drawing a value from this normal distribution.[4]

The results of this process are summarized in Table 9, separately for those over 72 years of age (Part I of the table) and those 62–71 (Part II).

5.3. Comparing the Results of Our Imputation Protocol to Those Of the CPS Hot Deck

Since our two-stage model predicts administrative values whereas the CPS hot-deck predicts the answers that nonrespondents would have given had they

---

[4] The procedure we used to generate pseudorandom normal deviates is described in Appendix B. Also, the values were truncated by removing the 5% tail at each end of the distribution. This truncation scheme was employed for the same reasons as given in the previous footnote.

TABLE 9: Part I

Multiple Imputations for Those with Allocated OASDI Benefits and over 72 Years of Age[a]

Nonres. number	Admin. value	Hot-deck values		Model values		Collection of model values		
		First value	Second value	First value	Second value	Mean of all 100	Percent of recipiency	Standard error
1	1489	2085	2257	1400.50	1181.20	1555.01	99	420.56
2	2103	609	645	1650.17	1416.98	1719.53	95	596.43
3	2027	1968	2142	974.56	1019.94	1348.02	100	338.31
4	993	2059	2375	1858.02	2223.14	1596.13	96	516.88
5	0	2161	2025	3359.50	2656.24	2496.81	81	1444.67
6	2199	2296	2432	.00	1270.47	851.61	68	636.72
7	2487	1968	1839	2276.47	.00	1796.86	77	1120.00
8	2375	2271	2363	1885.66	.00	1949.05	98	560.80
9	1419	609	666	2781.50	3343.01	1773.27	72	1257.68
10	1854	0	2085	1692.57	2001.36	1938.99	100	468.77
11	2161	1603	1864	1497.99	2771.64	1873.20	98	566.98
12	2957	605	799	2255.92	.00	1725.20	73	1169.76
13	1187	2774	2348	1102.49	1778.75	1591.05	100	373.26
14	1835	791	797	1859.52	1585.78	1811.95	82	1000.65
15	887	1344	1609	2090.98	1316.64	1546.06	95	543.92
16	2375	1864	1603	2803.75	2391.59	1949.52	99	527.61
17	2384	0	2354	1688.80	1699.49	1756.03	84	920.13
18	2239	887	735	1164.78	1073.65	1260.98	95	429.37
Mean	1831.72	1438.56	1718.78	1796.84	1540.55	1696.63	89.56	789.26

[a] Each of the first six means is the arithmetic average of the corresponding column of benefit amounts. While the seventh is the arithmetic average of the percent of recipiency status. The mean of the last column is the square root of the arithmetic average of the squares of the standard errors (i.e., the variances).

responded, some adjustments were made to the hot deck so that both processes predict administrative values. Because it was no longer possible to use the original version of the 1973 Census hot deck, the following adjustment procedure was used. To each individual having a nonzero allocated OASDI amount, the administrative values of the two respondents whose reported CPS values were closest to the allocated amount were imputed. In the case of ties, a random (without replacement) choice was made. The individuals having zero allocated OASDI benefits were partitioned into six cells formed by cross-classifying age (62–64 and at least 65) and number of weeks worked during calendar year 1972 (0, 1–39, 40–52). The 193 respondents having zero reported OASDI amounts were partitioned in the same fashion as done for the nonrespondents. To each nonrespondent, we assigned the administrative value of each of two respondents selected randomly (without replacement) from the corresponding age–weeks worked cell. The procedure was such that no respondent value was selected more than once. The values chosen are displayed in columns three and four of Table 9.

Multiple Imputations for Those With Allocated OASDI Benefits and 62–71 Years of Age[a]

Nonres. number	Admin. value	Hot-deck values		Model values		Collection of model values		
		First value	Second value	First value	Second value	Mean of all 100	Percent of recipiency	Standard error
1	2027	1845	2613	.00	2438.27	1396.03	72	967.22
2	1047	1352	1548	.00	.00	834.67	51	866.56
3	2095	2613	2239	1692.40	1697.60	768.74	67	604.12
4	2112	2703	2685	1594.82	1753.41	1687.87	87	815.79
5	1947	2314	0	2142.06	1944.56	1065.70	60	929.66
6	2242	1870	815	2221.26	1941.71	1951.93	89	860.24
7	2341	2161	2025	.00	2711.00	1710.57	79	1025.43
8	2631	1877	1451	2852.47	2252.23	1939.90	84	1007.03
9	2597	0	2314	2530.61	1511.14	2144.34	85	1066.42
10	0	0	0	.00	2696.77	1737.49	73	1209.99
11	0	0	0	884.12	916.98	701.76	66	547.03
12	561	735	887	1355.60	1092.85	1463.35	78	898.53
13	2662	1778	666	1095.82	735.48	676.30	73	469.93
14	992	1546	993	1449.68	2090.34	1848.20	87	913.23
15	2204	1274	1035	1612.41	1536.66	1562.36	83	844.44
16	0	0	0	821.36	.00	415.71	63	346.64
17	1928	1378	1010	1452.45	2691.01	1934.42	90	811.03
18	2392	1718	2660	1319.26	.00	1101.59	61	957.19
19	2217	2018	1994	2491.58	1399.53	1868.86	81	1057.10
20	2685	2085	1920	2937.78	2679.56	2021.47	79	1184.73
21	1491	1279	1102	.00	1008.68	897.39	55	875.05
22	0	2604	0	1535.00	.00	712.36	64	577.65
23	1056	2058	1757	1411.18	1743.09	787.13	51	815.11
24	2343	2027	965	1471.62	1468.23	1477.34	80	861.49
25	0	2651	609	1781.91	1872.94	1437.02	87	686.19
26	1930	3103	2161	1845.74	1476.57	892.60	67	708.26
27	0	0	0	.00	1006.59	824.31	73	558.65
28	2169	2210	2314	2464.07	2355.40	1830.42	79	1065.30
29	2597	965	2027	1850.93	2270.65	1690.76	78	1013.98
30	848	1718	2315	1693.63	.00	1917.46	85	945.39
31	0	2411	2703	2476.77	2592.03	2157.13	89	941.29
32	2450	1438	1313	2073.52	1971.63	1945.88	84	1034.23
33	0	1568	1597	1819.68	2263.29	2124.97	81	1202.97
34	887	1031	1687	2724.71	1572.47	1713.04	81	951.13
35	410	1641	1990	.00	1027.45	765.01	62	657.56
36	0	2631	2597	2110.41	1588.93	984.78	57	924.42
37	1016	0	0	.00	919.83	547.86	70	398.13
38	1445	2199	2203	2110.66	1520.73	1118.53	57	1030.91
39	1774	2090	2239	1628.41	2537.47	1633.98	74	1090.76
40	2505	1313	1438	.00	2683.38	1828.96	84	935.59
41	1846	2523	2218	.00	2882.89	1968.68	84	1047.04
Mean	1449.93	1627.49	1465.61	1401.27	1630.52	1416.75	74.39	895.82

[a] Each of the first six means is the arithmetic average of the corresponding column of benefit amounts. While the seventh is the arithmetic average of the percent of recipiency status. The mean of the last column is the square root of the arithmetic average of the squares of the standard errors (i.e., the variances).

We now summarize the comparisons made between the results of our imputation protocol (labeled "Model") and those of the hot-deck procedure, as well as comparisons with administrative values. The bottom of Table 9 gives the average imputed value under each imputation procedure, separately for each age group. For the eighteen individuals at least 72 years of age, the average administrative value of $1831.72 was higher than both the average hot-deck value of $1578.67 (over both sets of imputations) and the average model value of $1696.63 (taken over 100 sets of imputations). The principal reason that the mean model value was lower than the average administrative value was that only 89.56% of the model values were predicted to be nonzero whereas in fact the true proportion was 17/18 or 94.44%.

For the 41 individuals ages 62–71, the average administrative value of $1449.93 was lower than the average hot-deck value of $1546.55 but slightly higher than the average model value of $1416.75. Again, a large part of the difference between the model and administrative values may be explained by the corresponding percents of recipiency: 32/41 = 77.05% for the actual values versus 74.39% for the model values. For each of the two age groups, the mean of the 100 model values was closer to the average administrative value than was the mean of the two sets of hot-deck values. Table 10 presents the mean absolute deviations between the administrative values and (i) the adjusted hot-deck values, and (ii) the model values. The mean absolute deviation of $738.91 resulting from the use of the mean of all 100 model values for all ages was lower than the mean absolute deviation of $832.09 resulting from the use of the mean of the two adjusted hot-deck values. Most of this difference is attributable to the

TABLE 10

Comparison of Imputation Methods

	Hot-deck		Model		
	First value	Mean of first two values	First value	Mean of first two values	Mean of all 100 values
Part I—imputations for those at least 72 years of age					
Mean absolute deviation	1055.83	937.00	839.80	939.89	653.80
Root mean squared deviation	1295.57	1121.95	1168.25	1212.30	867.51
Part II—imputations for those 62–71 years of age					
Mean absolute deviation	826.44	786.04	908.40	753.31	776.28
Root mean squared deviation	1132.57	1000.72	1174.89	966.61	933.60
Part III—imputations for all those at least 62 years of age					
Mean absolute deviation	896.42	832.09	887.47	810.23	738.91
Root mean squared deviation	1184.68	1039.21	1172.86	1047.69	913.94

TABLE 11

Precision of Hot-Deck Estimates versus Model Estimates

Age	Number of observations	Number of times mean of 2 hot-deck values is closer to admin. value than is mean of first two model values	Number of times mean of 2 hot-deck values is closer to admin. value than is mean of all 100 model values
≥ 72	18	7 (38.9%)	6[a] (33.3%)
62–71	41	20 (48.9%)	19 (46.3%)
All ≥ 62	59	27 (45.8%)	25 (42.4%)

[a] Using a one-sided test, this value is statistically significant at the 0.05 level.

data on those at least 72 years of age. In terms of the square roots of the mean squared deviation, the results were $1039.21 for the hot deck and $913.44 for the model. The latter result should not be particularly surprising since the ordinary least squares regression procedure used to construct the second stage of the imputation protocol minimizes the sum of the squared deviations. The use of the mean of all 100 model values rather than just the first two model values, also produced lower mean deviations for the combined group in both metrics.

We next determined on a case by case basis whether the mean of the two adjusted hot deck values was closer to the administrative value than (1) the mean of the first two model values or (2) the mean of all 100 model values. These results are shown in Table 11. For those at least 72 years of age, the mean of 100 model values was closer in 12 cases out of 18. Assuming that the values were generated independently for each nonrespondent (an assumption not quite true), we can "sign test" the (one-sided) null hypothesis that the mean of the two adjusted hot deck values is (more frequently) closer to the administrative value than is the mean of 100 model values. Using a 5% level of significance, we are just able to reject the null hypothesis. Thus, for those at least 72 years of age, the mean of 100 model values is "significantly" better than the mean of two adjusted hot deck values. Considering all 59 cases, the mean of 100 model values is closer in 34 instances or 57.6% of the time.

5.4. Comparing the Standard Errors of the Means Resulting from the Various Procedures

The standard errors of the mean benefit amounts for various collections of imputed values are shown in Parts I and II of Table 12. In accordance with the theory presented earlier in this chapter, the standard error of an estimate

TABLE 12: Part I

Standard Errors of the Means Produced by the Hot-Deck Procedure (Imputed Values Only)

Age group	Within-variance component only				Both components
	Administrative value	First value	Second value	Mean of first two values	First two values
62–71	152.74	133.65	139.09	118.61	178.06
≥ 72	169.26	200.06	160.03	159.19	268.48
All ages	119.48	110.77	108.61	94.93	111.34

contains two components: the average within-imputation variance and the between-imputation variance. Since the between-variance component is better estimated from 100 imputations than from two imputations, we feel that the best estimate of the standard error is the one based on all 100 model values. For the mean benefit amount for nonrespondents (for all ages) this standard error is 201.81. The within-component of the standard error is $128.32. This is obtained by taking the square root of the average of the 100 squared standard errors. Our best estimate, then, is that on the average, the use of only the within-component of the variance results in an estimated standard error for the mean value for nonrespondents that is about 36% too small. Also, there is a wide range of estimates of the within-variance component of the standard error, depending upon which estimate of the mean is used. If the mean of all 100 model values is employed (for all ages), the estimate is only $64.16, whereas, for the first model value, the estimate is $117.25. These differences are even more pronounced for those at least 72 years of age.

Since (in the absence of a replicated design in which the imputation process is carried out independently across replicates) the between component of the

TABLE 12: Part II

Standard Errors of the Means Produced by Model Procedure (Imputed Values Only)

Age group	Within-variance component only					Both variance components	
	First value	Second value	Mean of first two values	Mean of all 100 values	All 100 values	First two values	All 100 values
62–71	146.17	132.11	105.81	82.37	160.17	213.75	256.44
≥ 72	181.18	224.13	162.95	80.47	201.34	272.72	280.23
All ages	117.25	113.52	88.46	64.16	128.32	128.87	201.81

TABLE 12: Part III

Standard Errors of the Means for All Those Sampled Plus Hot-Deck Values

	Within-variance component only				Both components
Administrative value	First value	Second value	Mean of first two values	First two values	First two values
27.18	27.08	27.05	26.91	27.06	27.08

variance can only be estimated if there are at least two values imputed for each missing item, we strongly recommend that those imputing missing data items in complex sample surveys consider imputing at least two values for each missing item.

Unfortunately, even the imputation of two values for each missing item may not be enough if there is a lot of variation from one set of imputations to the next. For example, using only the first two sets of model imputed values, there is an estimated standard error of only 128.87 compared to a value of 201.81 for all 100 sets. The reason for the lack of stability of the estimates here presumably is due to the small sample which is sensitive to the prediction of beneficiary status.

Parts III and IV of Table 12 present the standard errors of the two sets of values formed by appending the administrative values of the individuals who had reported OASDI benefits (possibly for $0) to each set of imputed hot deck values and to each set of imputed model values. These results are the multiple imputation estimates of standard errors for those with benefits from the data set composed of all respondents and nonrespondents. Because only about 5% of those under consideration had imputed OASDI benefit amounts, there is not much difference among the various estimates of the standard errors. Nevertheless, the model results show that omitting the between component (i.e., that due to the imputation process) results in an almost 5% underestimate of the standard error.

TABLE 12: Part IV

Standard Errors of the Means for All Those Sampled Plus Model Values

	Within-variance component only				Both variance components	
First value	Second value	Mean of first two values	Mean of all 100 values	All 100 values	First two values	All 100 values
27.14	27.12	26.85	26.66	27.30	27.29	28.49

5.5. Nonresponse Bias

Thus far, the focus of this section has been on the use of multiple imputations to produce reasonable variance estimates and no mention has been made of including nonresponse bias in models, such as was discussed in Section 3. In fact, we have thus made the implicit assumption that there is no nonresponse bias. The decision not to include such models was motivated by the following: Of the 1128 surveyed individuals who had the five characteristics listed at the beginning of Section 4, there were 49 who received some social security benefits during calendar year 1972 but failed to answer the March 1973 CPS Social Security benefits question. The 49 individuals had an average OASDI administrative value of $1886 compared to an average predicted value of $1840—a difference of $46. Since this difference was quite small as a percentage of the actual average value and also as a percentage of the estimated standard errors, we felt it was not essential to adjust our regression model for this relatively small amount of bias. As for the predictive models of beneficiary status, 94.4% of the nonrespondents at least 72 years of age were beneficiaries as opposed to 90.4% predicted under the corresponding log-linear model; for those 62–71 years old, 78.0% of the nonrespondents were beneficiaries versus 74.9% predicted under the log-linear model. Although we might have improved our prediction process somewhat by adjusting our two log-linear models for these effects, we felt that such extensions were not essential for our purposes.

5.6. Conclusions

The explicit imputation procedure described in the last two sections took a tremendous amount of statistician time to complete. Yet, although it was very expensive, it only dealt with the prediction of a single variable. Thus, at this time, it is difficult to recommend the use of such an explicit modeling scheme for more than a few of the key variables of a sample survey. However, we do strongly recommend the imputation of at least two values for each missing value, regardless of the type of imputation protocol employed. For example, the imputation of multiple values should be quite straightforward in a hot deck scheme in which respondent values are selected at random within the appropriate cell. If it is desired to impute the closest value (according to a specified metric), the closest n values can be used as the n imputed values and randomly assigned among the n resulting data sets.

The use of multiple imputations is a relatively simple and straightforward way to estimate the component of the variance due to nonresponse, and ignoring this component can lead to underestimation of variability. Also, multiple imputation is the only way, within an imputation context, to investigate sensitivity to underlying models for nonresponse. Consequently, we expect multiple imputation to become a standard technique for handling nonresponse in sample surveys.

APPENDIX A

The estimated variance–covariance matrix is .25 times the inverse of the matrix $T'DT$ where the diagonal matrix D and the design matrix T will be defined. The factor .25 was employed for reasons given in Herzog [1980, p. 79], basically to make the results comparable to those of the CPS hot deck.

A.1.   The Diagonal Matrix D

The matrix D is the diagonal matrix whose main diagonal consists of the elements of the contingency table X written in "lexicographic order"; for example, if X is the 2×2 contingency table

$$\begin{bmatrix} X(1, 1) & X(1, 2) \\ X(2, 1) & X(2, 2) \end{bmatrix},$$

then D is the matrix

$$\begin{bmatrix} X(1, 1) & 0 & 0 & 0 \\ 0 & X(1, 2) & 0 & 0 \\ 0 & 0 & X(2, 1) & 0 \\ 0 & 0 & 0 & X(2, 2) \end{bmatrix}.$$

A.2.   The Design Matrix T

Let n denote the total number of observations (that is, n is the sum of all the entries in the contingency table) and τ is the (column) vector of parameters of the log-linear model under consideration; the vector τ consists of one constant term (which may be considered to be a normalizing parameter) and one parameter for each of the main effect and interaction terms included in the model. Let Ω denote the number of cells of the contingency table, $X(\omega)$ the estimated frequency count of the ωth cell of the fitted table ($\omega = 1, 2, \ldots, \Omega$), and $n\pi(\omega)$ the ωth cell of an appropriate reference table. Finally, let $W' = \left[\ln(X(1)/n\pi(1)), \ldots, \ln(X(\Omega)/n\pi(\Omega)) \right]$.

Then $T\tau = W$. The design matrix T consists entirely of zeros and ones. Each row of T corresponds to exactly one cell of the original contingency table, while each column is associated with exactly one of the parameters employed in the log-linear model.

For the saturated model of the 2×2 table, see Table 13. The design matrix T is simply the 4×4 matrix presented in Table 13.

TABLE 13

Cell	Constant term	Row effect	Column effect	Row–column interaction
(1, 1)	1	1	1	1
(1, 2)	1	1	0	0
(2, 1)	1	0	1	0
(2, 2)	1	0	0	0

APPENDIX B.   GENERATING THE PSEUDORANDOM NORMAL DEVIATES

The procedure described in Section 4 required a large number of pseudo-random normal deviates. In order to avoid exceeding computer storage capacity, these deviates were generated in five groups. Each group of normal deviates was produced using the APL programming language. We first drew $N = (1.4$ times the number of deviates required) uniform random numbers over the interval $(0, 1]$, using the APL query operator, ?. This is a multiplicative congruential random number generator. Each of the random numbers was computed to six decimal places. We then drew a random permutation of the integers from 1 to N in order to "shuffle" these random numbers. Next, we constructed $N - 2$ pairs of random numbers, thereby allowing us to consider each pair as a point in a Cartesian coordinate system. Using the polar method[5] of generating pseudorandom normal deviates (see Knuth, 1980), we transformed each point within the unit circle into two independent normal deviates. We were then able to extract the number of pseudorandom normal deviates required for our imputation procedure.

ACKNOWLEDGMENTS

We would like to thank D. Kasprzyk, R. Little, W. Madow, and F. Scheuren for helpful comments on an earlier version of this chapter. The primary support for this work was provided by the Social Security Administration as part of its development for handling nonresponse in the Survey of Income and Program Participation (SIPP).

[5] Frieden and Herzog (1979) have shown that for APL this scheme is the most efficient of three well-known methods.

REFERENCES

Anderson, T. W. (1958). *An Introduction to Multivariate Statistical Analysis*. New York: Wiley.

Aziz, F., Kilss, B., and Scheuren, F. (1978). 1973 Current Population Survey—Administrative Record Exact Match File Codebook. Report No. 4, Studies from Interagency Data Linkages. Washington, D.C.: Social Security Administration.

Coder, J. (1978). Income data collection and processing for the March incomes supplement to the current population survey. *Proceedings of the Survey of Income and Program Participation Data Processing Workshop*, DHEW.

Freiden, A., and Herzog, T. N. (1979). Generating normal random deviates in APL. *APL Quote Quad*. 9 (3), March.

Gokhale, D. V., and Kullback, S. (1978). *The Information in Contingency Tables*. New York: Dekker.

Hansen, M. H., Hurwitz, W. M., Madow, W. G. (1953). *Sample Survey Methods and Theory* (Vols. 1 and 2). New York: Wiley.

Herzog, T. N. (1980). Multiple imputation modeling for individual social security benefit amounts, Part 2. *American Statistical Association, Proceedings of the Section on Survey Research Methods*, pp. 404–407.

Herzog, T. N., and Lancaster, C. (1980). Multiple imputation modeling for individual social security benefit amounts, Part I. *American Statistical Association, Proceedings of the Section on Survey Research Methods*, pp. 398–403.

Knuth, D. C. (1980). *The Art of Computer Programming. Vol. 2: Seminumerical Algorithms* (2nd ed). Reading, Massachusetts: Addison-Wesley.

Lancaster, C. (1979). *Determining Social Security Recipiency for Imputation of Nonresponse in the CPS*. Social Security Administration Memorandum SRV–53, Washington, D.C., January 26.

Oh, H. Lock, and Scheuren, Frederick J. (1980). Estimating the variance impact of missing CPS income data. *American Statistical Association, Proceedings of the Section on Survey Research Methods*.

Rubin, D. B. (1977). Formalizing subjective notions about the effect of non-respondents in sample surveys. *Journal of the American Statistical Association* 72: 538–543.

Rubin, D. B. (1978). Multiple imputations in sample surveys—A phenomenological Bayesian approach to nonresponse. *Imputation and Editing of Faulty or Missing Survey Data*, U.S. Department of Commerce, Social Security Administration, Washington, D.C. (Also in the *1978 Proceedings American Statistical Association Section Survey Research Methods*.)

Rubin, D. B. (1979). Illustrating the use of multiple imputations to handle nonresponse in sample surveys. *Proceedings of the 1979 International Statistics Institute*, Manila.

Rubin, D. B. (1980). Handling Nonresponse in Sample Surveys by Multiple Imputation. U.S. Bureau of the Census Monograph.

Rubin, D. B. (1981). The Bayesian Bootstrap. *Annals of Statistics* 9: 130–134.

PART V

Imputation Methodology: Total Survey Error

CHAPTER 16

Introduction

Richard Platek
Gerald B. Gray

For a number of years various procedures of imputation for missing data due to nonresponse have been used in household surveys and censuses. The use of a particular procedure has been, to our knowledge, mostly justified on the ground of intuition and experience. It was often assumed that the probabilities of units responding were constant and the reduced sample size due to non-response was taken as the sample size specified. The nonresponse bias was largely ignored except when it could have been arrived at by means of intuitive feelings and limited information about the nonresponding units such as their sizes and geographic location. Although variations in response rates have been detected among units according to geographic areas and characteristics of units, the effect of individual units responding or not responding upon the bias and variance of the estimate has usually been insufficiently examined. To facilitate a detailed examination of the effect, we have developed methodology with respect to the bias and variance pertaining to several imputation procedures involving reweighting in adjustment cells,[1] the use of historical or census data, etc.

For any of the imputation procedures considered by us, the estimate of a total characteristic can be expressed as a Horvitz–Thompson estimate, namely, as a weighted sum of observed or imputed values of individual units, the weights being the inverse of selection probabilities. Both the observed and imputed values will be subject to error compared with the true values of the units. Consequently, the estimate may also be subject to error compared with the true characteristic total and some of the error may be the result of nonresponse. One component of error that frequently affects the estimate is the nonresponse

---

[1] Defined as balancing areas or weighting classes in the following chapter.

INCOMPLETE DATA
IN SAMPLE SURVEYS
Volume 2, Part V

bias. Ideally, to remove this bias, one would simply weight up each sample response by the inverse of the product of the selection and true response probabilities of each responding unit. This is an impossible procedure, since the true response probability is unknown for each unit. In practice, we employ average response probabilities or response rates in adjustment cells to adjust the weights to be used in the estimates of totals. In order to examine and develop the methodology which takes into account the error due to nonresponse in the context of total survey error, we have introduced a response, nonresponse model. In this model, when a unit responds, an observed value of a characteristic is obtained but when it fails to respond, the value of the characteristic is missing and an imputed value must be substituted for it.

The observed value of a characteristic for each respondent comprises two components, (i) the true value of the characteristic and (ii) the response error associated with the observed value consisting of both bias and response variance. Similarly, the imputed value for missing data consists of (i) the true value of the characteristics and (ii) the imputation error associated with it. The imputed value for nonrespondents may be obtained by one or more imputation procedures based on data from a variety of sources. Past census or administrative data, earlier survey data for the same unit, or current survey data for other units may be used as a source of an imputed value. The imputation error arising from any of these imputed values contains the errors of the source data, which may include sampling and response errors or even imputation error relative to the true value of the source data. Thus, the imputation error of the imputed value consists of both imputation bias and imputation variance. The imputation bias will be a function of the response bias of all observed values used in the imputation and of the differences between the true value of each of these observed values and that of the nonresponding unit. The imputation variance will depend upon a particular method of imputation and may be a simple response variance of the source data if it is a single observation or it may be a function of the sampling variance, the simple response variance, and the correlated response variance.

In approaching the problem of nonresponse and subsequent adjustment for it, we have assumed the existence of a covariance between the events of responding or not responding pertaining to pairs of units in the sample. For example, in a cluster containing households with similar characteristics, one would expect similar levels of difficulty in soliciting their cooperation as well as similar tendencies of being away from home, so that the probability of two units both responding is not merely the product of their response probabilities but in addition to this product the covariance between the events of the two units responding or not responding.

The methodology developed for the bias and variance of the estimates under different imputation procedures is based on a fundamental concept that a unit, if selected, responds or does not respond with a certain response probability attached to each unit. In other words, the population is not formed of respondents and nonrespondents in a dichotomous fashion, but rather of potential respondents with certain probabilities depending on the conditions under which the survey is conducted. The following methods of imputing for nonresponse will be dealt with at length:

(i)   Weighting method in adjustment cells
(ii) Duplication in adjustment cells
(iii) Historical or external source data substitution for missing data
(iv) Zero substitution method

These methods of imputation differ according to the manner in which survey data of responding units or external source data of the same unit are designated as a replacement for missing data. Thus, in the "weighting method" each missing record is replaced by the mean of all responding units in an adjustment cell. In the "duplication method" each missing record is replaced by another unit in the cell, namely, a similar type record for a unit that responded. In the "historical data substitution method" each missing record for a nonresponding unit is replaced by external source data, such as the census, pertaining to the same unit. Finally, in the "zero substitution method" each missing record is ignored or, by implication, zero is substituted for it. The various methods will result in different weight adjustments to the units in adjustment cells of which there are two basic types, namely (i) balancing areas, defined by design dependent geographic areas such as strata, clusters, or primary sampling units, and (ii) weighting classes defined by classes of units that are poststratified on the basis of partial responses or even limited data such as dwelling types or household size. A combination of these two types could also be used for imputation purposes, such as weighting classes within balancing areas or vice versa. In almost all cases, however, adjustment cells are mutually exclusive in the sense that a unit belongs to one and only one area or class. Then, to obtain an estimate in a cell, the weights determined by the inclusion probabilities are inflated by the inverse of the response rate in the relevant cell and the new weights are applied to all the respondents. Within a cell, the expected value of an estimate under any imputation procedure and its bias and variance may be derived by taking expected values in the following stages:

(i) E_1: expected value over all possible samples
(ii) E_2: expected value over all possible subsamples of respondents, given the sample, and finally
(iii) E_3: expected value over all possible responses, given the sample and the subsample of respondents

It is found that the expected value of the estimate over the three stages above contains two major components of bias: (i) response bias and (ii) imputation bias. A sampling bias does not exist in the estimates since weights before adjustments for nonresponses are defined by the inverses of the selection probabilities as determined at the design stage. The estimate of a characteristic total in an adjustment cell comprises two distinct portions; (i) a contribution to the estimate by the responding subsample and (ii) a contribution by the nonresponding subsample according to any one of several imputation procedures. The contribution by the responding subsample is assumed to be independent of the imputation procedure and will therefore contain response errors that are identical under each procedure. The nonresponding subsample, however, will contain different imputation errors according to the imputation procedure applied. The estimate for an area containing mutually exclusive cells may be added over the cells and consequently the two components of bias described may also be added over the cells.

The variance of an estimate based on any particular imputation procedure is found to contain the following components: (i) sampling variance, (ii) simple response variance, (iii) correlated response variance, (iv) variance component due to the variation in the events of responding or not responding pertaining to individual units, and (v) covariance component due to covariance between the events of responding or not responding pertaining to pairs of units. These components are further elaborated upon in the discussion of the variances in the following chapter that describes fully the various estimates. In addition to the variance components, the estimate of a total in an area consisting of several adjustment cells may be subject to covariances between the cells depending upon their definition. Unless the adjustment cell is a stratum or group of strata the covariance terms will include a sampling covariance. A sampling covariance may be nonexistent between cells that are defined below the stratum level if sampling with replacement instead of without replacement is undertaken at the cell level. There may also exist nonsampling covariance terms between cells similar to the covariance terms in (iii) and (v), the magnitude depending upon the extent to which the interactions of responses or tendencies to respond or not to respond among pairs of units cross the boundaries of the cells even if the cells lie in different strata. Apart from the imputation procedures described, other methods, such as regression techniques, could be used.

The estimation formula for each of the four methods of imputation is explained in detail in the following chapter. The expressions for the bias and variance of the estimate and a detailed discussion of the variance are included with each method. An overview of the estimates and their biases and practical uses of the methods is also included. Chapter 18 deals with a hypothetical example in which numerical values of the biases and variances under the four imputation procedures are obtained and analyzed. The methodology for the derivation of the bias and variance of the estimates is applied in an adjustment cell, and expressions for the variance within cells and the covariance between the cells are derived in Appendixes B and C.[2]

While there is some attempt to compare the biases and variances of the estimates under different imputation procedures and under different survey

---

[2] All references to appendixes refer to appendixes for Part V (Chapter 19).

conditions, the comparisons are mainly dealt with numerically in Chapter 18 dealing with the hypothetical example. The methodology of analysis is based on an adaptation of the bias and variance expressions to a two-stage sample in one stratum as given in Appendix D. In the example, 50 hypothetical dwellings were defined in a stratum consisting of one balancing area, and the dwellings were grouped into eight clusters of 3–10 dwellings. The characteristic analyzed in the example was the number of persons. A "true" dwelling size from 0 (vacant dwellings) to 9 persons was assumed for each of the 50 dwellings with a slight clustering effect. In each dwelling, response errors in the observed numbers of persons were assigned with an assumed probability of observing each error.

Small probabilities were also assigned to "vacancies." The "true" dwelling sizes were distributed roughly in proportion to the distribution in the census and probabilities of erroneously observed vacancies were assigned in such a manner as to conform roughly to a postcensus quality study where vacancies were analyzed. The response errors were assigned in such a manner that a tendency toward an undercount rather than an overcount occurs in the erroneous observations as revealed by some studies on census coverage.

On the basis of the analysis of the results from the hypothetical example, numerical comparisons between the biases, variances, and mean square errors of the estimates were observed. It can be seen that for different imputation procedures the biases are higher for some procedures than for others, while at the same time the variances for different sample sizes are lower. This would lead to interesting analysis and discussions pertaining to the relative components of mean square errors of the various estimates under different imputation procedures. Thus, at both the design stage and processing stage, the nonresponse and the resultant need for imputation must be considered carefully in relation to survey requirements, anticipated response rates, availability of external source data, and alternative strategies for dealing with nonresponse in the field and estimation stage.

Imputation for nonresponse or undercoverage of units for reasons other than nonresponse such as incomplete sample lists may also be undertaken by the use of combined or separate ratio estimators. Such an estimator is possible only when population totals may be more accurately estimated or are known from sources other than the sample, and in the case of the Canadian Labour Force Survey auxiliary characteristics such as projected populations by age and sex categories are assumed to be known. In the ratio estimator, the estimate for the auxiliary variable under the same imputation procedures as the survey variables may be carried out and a ratio estimate then obtained, with the survey weight adjusted by the ratio of the assumed population total of the auxiliary variable to its sample estimate.

In household surveys, imputation for nonresponse has usually been undertaken by weight adjustments or duplication of units in adjustment cells. For example, in the Canadian LFS, the cells are design-dependent areas defined as strata in large cities or the urban and rural portions of each selected primary sampling unit outside large cities. For about 30–40% of the nonrespondents in any given survey, the historical data, namely, the previous month's data, is substituted in place of missing data.

In the following sections, we deal with imputation methodology related to the estimates under the four imputation procedures. A detailed development of the expressions for biases, variances and covariances of these estimates will be found in Appendixes 1 to 3. The adaptation to a two-stage sample with respect to the hypothetical example will be found in Appendix 4. Finally, a glossary of terms is included as Appendix E.

CHAPTER 17

Imputation Methodology

Richard Platek
Gerald B. Gray

1. INTRODUCTION

Survey practitioners have long been able to design surveys to take into account the sampling variance and the cost of gathering the survey data by means of a judicious choice of cost-effective sample designs and estimation procedures subject to survey requirements. Survey statisticians have also addressed the problem of nonsampling errors such as response errors and errors due to nonresponse, both associated with data collection. There are many ways of dealing with the problem of response errors. For example, they may be avoided or minimized in the field by means of a well-organized survey data gathering organization, using well-trained interviewers and delineating assignments with a suitable workload for interviewers. Response errors may be also controlled, if not corrected for, through specially designed programs such as reinterview and observation to monitor the possible effect of such errors on the estimates. Nonresponse, especially the residual or hard-core types, is often a more difficult problem. It is true that at the data collection stage nonresponse can be reduced by persistent efforts of the interviewers and by motivation of nonrespondents to become respondents. At the design stage, the survey practitioner anticipating nonresponse usually increases the sample size above the original specifications to take into account the fact that a certain proportion of units will not respond. While this procedure is quite effective in reducing the variance, it may not reduce the bias resulting from nonresponse.

Regardless of the efficiency of interviewers in controlling nonresponse, and despite an increase in the sample size at the design stage, there will remain some

INCOMPLETE DATA
IN SAMPLE SURVEYS
Volume 2, Part V

point beyond which the nonresponse cannot be taken care of at a reasonable cost. Consequently, at the estimation stage, some compensation by imputation to replace the missing data of the nonresponding units must be carried out explicitly or implicitly to attempt to reduce the nonresponse bias.

2. ESTIMATION

There are many estimators in existence, but their appropriate choice depends upon the sample design and the availability of auxiliary information. Since in practice probability proportional to size (pps) sampling is frequently used, the Horvitz–Thompson estimator is often the most appropriate in sample surveys. Consequently, the Horvitz–Thompson estimator will be employed in the development of methodology pertaining to biases and variances due to nonresponse. It is assumed that a sample of n units is drawn by a probability proportional to size without replacement (ppswor) scheme from a population of N units in or more stages and in one or more strata. Only one characteristic will be dealt with at a time with a particular unit i possessing a true value X_i of the characteristic. The total $X = \sum_{i-1}^{N} X_i$ is to be estimated from the sample of n units.

2.1. Horvitz–Thompson Estimate
(Complete Response without Response Errors)

If every sampled unit responded and responded without error, then an unbiased estimate of the total X would be given by the Horvitz-Thompson estimate, namely, $\hat{X} = \sum_{i=1}^{n} X_i/\pi_i$, where π_i is the inclusion probability of unit i, and its variance would be given by

$$V(\hat{X}) = \sum_{i=1}^{N} X_i^2 \left(\frac{1}{\pi_i} - 1 \right) + \sum_{i \neq j}^{N} X_i X_j \left(\frac{\pi_{ij}}{\pi_i \pi_j} - 1 \right), \tag{1}$$

as derived by Horvitz and Thompson (1952). Here π_{ij} denotes the joint inclusion probability of units i and j.

Although Horvitz and Thompson derived the above variance on the assumption of a one-stage sample in one stratum, the variance expression $V(\hat{X})$ above may be also applied to estimates based on a multistage sample in one or more strata. The only restriction in formula (1) is that the selection probability of every unit should be known and fixed. The variance $V(\hat{X})$ in formula (1) is strictly the sampling variance of $\hat{X}$.

2.2. Estimate (Complete Response with Response Errors Present)

If every sampled unit responded but with some response error that may include both response bias and response variance, then X_i would be estimated by $x_i = X_i + {}_R\varepsilon_i$, the observed response for unit i, where ${}_R\varepsilon_i$ is the deviation of the observed response from the true value. The expected value of x_i or any other variable, such as an estimate of the total, is taken over three levels as defined in Chapter 16, namely, E_1, E_2, and E_3.

V_1, V_2, and V_3 are the corresponding variances, e.g., $V_1(x) = E_1 x^2 - (E_1 x)^2$. Beginning with E_3, we find that

$$E_3 x_i = X_i + ({}_R B_i),$$

where ${}_R B_i$ denotes the response bias for unit i.

$$V_3(x_i) = {}_R\sigma_i^2,$$

the response variance for unit i, which may also be written as

$$V_3(x_i) = E_3({}_R\varepsilon_i - {}_R B_i)^2.$$

The estimate of X under complete response but with response errors would then be given by

$$\hat{X} = \sum_{i=1}^{n} x_i/\pi_i = \sum_{i=1}^{n} \left[X_i + ({}_R\varepsilon_i) \right]/\pi_i, \tag{2}$$

and its expected value is given by

$$E\hat{X} = E_1 E_3 \hat{X}, \qquad E_3\hat{X} = \sum_{i=1}^{n} \left[X_i + ({}_R B_i) \right]/\pi_i. \tag{3}$$

In the case of complete response, but with response errors present,

$$E\hat{X} = E_1 E_3 \hat{X} = X + \sum_{i=1}^{N} ({}_R B_i) = X + B_R, \tag{4}$$

where B_R is the overall response bias of the estimate $\hat{X}$. E_2 is omitted since under complete response, there is no missingness pattern.

The expected value of $\hat{X}$ may also be written as $X + N\bar{B}_R$, where $\bar{B}_R$ is the mean response bias per unit, a parameter that is normally more easily estimable than individual response biases ${}_R B_i$. The mean response bias $\bar{B}_R$ may be estimated from specially designed studies such as a reinterview program in which a subsample of units is interviewed twice and the data reconciled whenever they are different.

The variance of $\hat{X}$, as defined in (2), is derived in Appendix B^1 [see Eq. (3) in Appendix B] by putting $\alpha_i \equiv 1$, $V(\delta_i) \equiv 0$, and $\mathrm{Cov}(\delta_i \delta_j) \equiv 0$ (see also G. Koch, 1973). The variance is given by

$$V(\hat{X}) = \sum_{i=1}^{N} (X_i + {}_RB_i)^2 \left(\frac{1}{\pi_i} - 1 \right)$$

$$+ \sum_{i \neq j}^{N} (X_i + {}_RB_i)(X_j + {}_RB_j)\left(\frac{\pi_{ij}}{\pi_i \pi_j} - 1 \right) \quad \text{(SV)}$$

$$+ \sum_{i=1}^{N} {}_R\sigma_i^2 \frac{1}{\pi_i} \quad \text{(SRV)}$$

$$+ \sum_{i \neq j}^{N} r_{2:ij} ({}_R\sigma_i)({}_R\sigma_j) \frac{\pi_{ij}}{\pi_i \pi_j} \quad \text{(CRV)} \qquad (5)$$

where $r_{2:ij}$ is the correlation between responses for units i and j; SV is sampling variance; SRV is simple response variance; and CRV is correlated response variance.

The parameters

$$ {}_R\sigma_i \quad \text{and} \quad r_{2:ij} \qquad (6)$$

are rarely estimable for individual units or individual pairs of units; however, average values of the parameters may be estimated at macro levels such as at stratum levels from interpenetrating samples with reinterview (see Fellegi, 1964, for example).

2.3. Estimation in the Presence of Nonresponse

Nonresponse occurs in nearly every survey, and some compensation for missing data due to nonresponse must be undertaken at the processing stage. The effects of nonresponse are an increase in the sampling variance which can be estimated and the presence of a nonresponse bias of unknown magnitude. This bias is caused by differences in the characteristics between respondents and nonrespondents. To study the bias, survey statisticians attempt to obtain the characteristics of nonrespondents by repeated "follow-ups," longitudinal studies of units over time where units have responded on only some occasions, or by an analysis of the nonresponding units from external sources.

To compensate for nonresponse at the processing stage, various imputation procedures have been used in practice, which may result in different magnitudes of the bias and of the variance. The expressions for the biases and variances as developed by us are based on the concept of response probabilities and the estimation formulae involves the following:

---

^{1} All references to appendixes refer to appendixes for Part V (Chapter 19).

(i) The use of cells for imputation (the cells may be either balancing areas or weighting classes)

(ii) The selection of responding units or external source data for imputation purposes within the cells

(iii) Adjustments in weights using estimated response probabilities within the cells

In deriving the biases and variances with respect to the various imputation procedures, the theoretical development in this chapter has adopted the unconditional approach, taking into account all possible survey conditions, including all sources of errors and all sizes of adjustment cells.

2.3.1. Balancing Areas

Balancing areas are frequently referred to as "design-dependent balancing areas" for imputation purposes. A balancing area is a geographic area in which a deficient sample arising from missing data is enlarged to a prescribed level by means of imputation for missing data. Commonly, a balancing area is a stratum, but it could be other design-dependent areas, such as primary sampling unit, cluster, or groups of strata. It could even be the entire sample. The balancing areas may be delineated before or after the survey is taken. The choice of balancing areas plays an important role in the attempt to reduce the mean square errors of estimates, since the bias and variance will usually be different among balancing areas depending upon the similarity of characteristics between respondents and nonrespondents and upon the variability of the characteristic in the population.

2.3.2. Weighting Classes

Weighting classes are defined by poststrata (strata defined after sampling) formed on the basis of information pertaining to respondents and nonrespondents in the sample. The information may be obtained from those partial nonrespondents for whom some characteristics are known even though the particular characteristic being estimated is not known for these units. The characteristics used in the poststrata could also be obtained from external sources. From the operational point of view, a weighting class is very similar to a balancing area except that the units having similar characteristics are grouped into classes or poststrata without regard to their geographic location or to the areas in the sample frame.

The choice of characteristics and the size of classes are quite important for the definition of classes, as the variance and bias of an estimate derived from the sample would depend upon the homogeneity of characteristics between respondents and nonrespondents and the nonresponse rates within the classes.

2.3.3. Response Probabilities

The development of the bias and the variance of the estimates under each imputation procedure considered by us is based on a fundamental concept that a unit, if selected, responds or does not respond with a certain response probability attached to that unit.

A particular unit i will be selected with inclusion probability π_i. The selected unit may either respond or not respond. If it responds, then $\delta_i = 1$; if it fails to respond, then $\delta_i = 0$ [see Eq. (7)]. The unit will respond with probability α_i, where $E\delta_i = \alpha_i$, or it will fail to respond with the complement probability $1 - \alpha_i$. The magnitude of the response probability α_i usually varies with the characteristics of the respondents, resulting in a correlation between the response probabilities and the characteristics of the respondents and consequently in a nonresponse bias in the estimate under most imputation procedures. In the case of an estimate of a census total in a cell containing respondents and nonrespondents with differing characteristics and different response probabilities, a one-to-one correspondence was demonstrated between the approach based on the differences in the characteristics and that based on the differences in response probabilities [Platek, Singh, and Tremblay (1977)].

In practice, response probabilities have been estimated by studying response patterns of units over time in continuous surveys together with their characteristics. Other sources for estimation of response probabilities have included reinterview surveys, administrative data sources and the previous census.

If response probabilities α_i were known for all units and if the main purpose of an estimation procedure were to avoid a nonresponse bias, the estimate of the total defined by $X = \sum_{i=1}^{N} X_i$, would be given by

$$\hat{X} = \sum_{i=1}^{n} \delta_i(X_i + {}_R\varepsilon_i)/(\pi_i\alpha_i). \tag{7}$$

The contribution to the above estimate by unit i exists only when $\delta_i = 1$. When $\delta_i = 0$, i.e., when unit i fails to respond, then $X_i + {}_R\varepsilon_i$ does not exist and $\delta_i(X_i + {}_R\varepsilon_i)$ equals zero. If $\alpha_i = 0$, then $\delta_i = 0$ and the whole expression $[\delta_i(X_i + {}_R\varepsilon_i)/\pi_i\alpha_i]$ and its expected value would be interpreted as zero. If some α_i do indeed equal zero while the corresponding $X_i \neq 0$, then a nonresponse bias would be unavoidable when using (7). Furthermore, if some α_i are close to zero while others are close to one, then there could be a very high variation in the weights $(\pi_i\alpha_i)^{-1}$, which could in turn result in a variance that is unacceptably high, possibly much higher than the variance of the estimates under any of the four imputation procedures considered by us.

2.3.4. Imputation Procedure in General

Before defining imputation procedures for any particular method, we shall consider an estimate under any imputation procedure, in general, defined by

$\hat{X}^G$, where

$$\hat{X}^G = \sum_{i=1}^{n} \left[\delta_i(X_i + {}_R\varepsilon_i) + (1 - \delta_i)(X_i + {}_{NR}\varepsilon_i) \right]\pi_i^{-1}, \qquad (8)$$

where $X_i + {}_{NR}\varepsilon_i$ is the imputed value for unit i when it fails to respond. Whatever the imputation procedure, the contribution to the estimate by unit i comes from an observed response $X_i + {}_R\varepsilon_i$ when unit i responds ($\delta_i = 1$) or from an imputed value $X_i + {}_{NR}\varepsilon_i$ when the unit fails to respond ($\delta_i = 0$). In the development of the bias and variance expressions, it is assumed that the whole sample of n units is partitioned into several balancing areas or weighting classes for imputation purposes. It is assumed that B cells (balancing areas or weighting classes) have been delineated and a typical cell is denoted by the subscript b. In order to illustrate the various imputation procedures as listed later, in Section 2.3.4, an example of a particular cell is presented in Table 1. The cell b contains a sample of n_b units representing a population of N_b units and the contribution

TABLE 1

Observed or Imputed Values for Cell Containing Selected Units[a]

Unit i	Selection prob. $\pi_i = n_b p_i$	True char. value X_i	Response status δ_i	Observed response $\delta_i(X_i + {}_R\varepsilon_i)$	Imputed value $(1 - \delta_i)(X_i + {}_{NR}\varepsilon_i)$	Use of historical data avail. imputed value $\delta_i'\delta_i''\delta_i''(X_i + {}_R\varepsilon_i')$		
1	π_1	X_1	1	$X_i + {}_R\varepsilon_i$	0	1	0	0
2	π_2	X_2	0	0	$X_2 + {}_{NR}\varepsilon_2$	1	1	$X_2 + {}_R\varepsilon_2'$
3	π_3	X_3	1	$X_3 + {}_R\varepsilon_3$	0	1	0	0
4	π_4	X_4	1	$X_4 + {}_R\varepsilon_4$	0	0	0	0
5	π_5	X_5	1	$X_5 + {}_R\varepsilon_5$	0	1	0	0
6	π_6	X_6	0	0	$X_6 + {}_{NR}\varepsilon_6$	0	0	0
7	π_7	X_7	1	$X_7 + {}_R\varepsilon_7$	0	1	0	0
8	π_8	X_8	0	0	$X_8 + {}_{NR}\varepsilon_8$	1	1	$X_8 + {}_R\varepsilon_8'$
9	π_9	X_9	1	$X_9 + {}_R\varepsilon_9$	0	1	0	0
10	π_{10}	X_{10}	1	$X_{10} + {}_R\varepsilon_{10}$	0	1	0	0
11	π_{11}	X_{11}	1	$X_{11} + {}_R\varepsilon_{11}$	0	0	0	0
12	π_{12}	X_{12}	0	0	$X_{12} + {}_{NR}\varepsilon_{12}$	0	0	0
$\vdots$								
n_b	π_{n_b}	X	1	$X_{n_b} + {}_R\varepsilon_{n_b}$	0	0	0	0
Total	n_b	X_{n_b}	m_b	—	—	—	m_b^1	—
Weighted total from sample	$\sum_{i=1}^{n_b} \pi^{-1}$	$\sum X_i \pi_i^{-1}$	—	$\hat{T}_b$	$\hat{X}_b^G - \hat{T}_b$	—	—	$\hat{T}_b''$

[a] Key: — = not relevant to methodology development; $\delta = 1$ or 0 according as sampled unit responded or did not respond; $\delta_i' = 1$ or 0 according as historical data available or not available; $\delta_i'' = (1 - \delta_i)\delta_i' = 1$ or 0 according as nonresponse occurs and historical data available or otherwise (nonresponse without historical data available or response).

to the estimate $\hat{X}^G$ by cell b is given by

$$\hat{X}_b^G = \sum_{i=1}^{n_b} \left[\delta_i(X_i + {}_R\varepsilon_i) + (1 - \delta_i)(X_i + {}_{NR}\varepsilon_i) \right] \pi_i^{-1}, \tag{9}$$

so that the estimate $\hat{X}^G$ equals the sum of the estimates over the B cells, or

$$\hat{X}^G = \sum_{b=1}^{B} \hat{X}_b^G.$$

The cell denoted by b contains n_b units in the sample representing N_b units in the population, where N_b may or may not be known. The selection probability π_i, the true characteristic value X_i, the response status ($\delta_i = 1$ or 0), the observed responses $X_i + {}_R\varepsilon_i$ when $\delta_i = 1$, and the imputed value $X_i + {}_{NR}\varepsilon_i$ when $\delta_i = 0$, are indicated for each unit. The last three columns pertain to the particular imputation procedure (historical data substitution method) and will be described later. The number of units in the cell, n_b, could be any number in practice although for illustrative purposes of several combinations of events twelve units were included.

Four particular imputations are dealt with in the development of biases and variances due to nonresponse:

   (i)   Weighting method
   (ii)   Duplication method
  (iii)   Historical data substitution
  (iv)   Zero substitution method

The definition and description for each of the above methods is included. The formulas for the estimate, using Table 1 as a guide, followed by the expected value and variance of the estimate are also presented.

3. WEIGHTING METHOD

There are several weighting methods of imputation which may be employed to enlarge a deficient sample in a cell as a result of missing data due to nonresponse. The method that is mainly considered in this chapter is the inflation of the sample weights by the inverse response rates in the cell. Implicitly, the imputed value for the missing data of each nonrespondent is the mean of all responding values in the cell, with some adjustments for selection probabilities, as seen in Eq. (11). In this weighting method of imputation, the simple response rate is defined as the proportion of the sample that responds, irrespective of the selection probabilities. Another weighting method could employ a weighted response rate, defined by the estimated proportion of the population in a cell that would be respondents. In the weighted response rates the inverse selection probabilities are applied to the selected units and to the responding units. The weighting method applying the unweighted response rate is considered first.

3.1. Estimate

The estimate of a total at a cell b level is given by

$$\hat{X}_b = \frac{n_b}{m_b} \sum_{i=1}^{n_b} \delta_i(X_i + {}_R\varepsilon_i)/\pi_i, \tag{10}$$

where m_b/n_b is the response rate for cell b and may be obtained from Table 1 by tallying all the δ_i of column 4 and dividing by the sample size n_b. If in fact the cell contained 12 units, where n_b would equal 12, the response rate would be 8/12 and only observed values of units 1, 3, 4, 5, 7, 9, 10 and 11 would be included in Eq. (10).

The estimate in Eq. (10) may be rewritten as a weighted sum of all observed or imputed values as defined by $\hat{X}_b^G$ in the estimation formula (8) at the cell b level. Thus, under this particular imputation procedure, the imputed value $X_i + {}_{NR}\varepsilon_i$, inserted for unit i, when unit i fails to respond or when ($\delta_i = 0$), is given by

$$X_i + {}_{NR}\varepsilon_i = \pi_i \Big[\sum_{j=1}^{n_b} \delta_j(X_j + {}_R\varepsilon_j)/\pi_j \Big]/m_b \tag{11}$$

or the mean of all observed responses, adjusted for varying selection probabilities. In the case of srs, $\pi_i \equiv \pi_j$ for all units and the imputed value would be the simple mean of all observed responses.

The imputation procedure would be repeated in every cell independently, so that

$$\hat{X} = \sum_{b=1}^{B} \hat{X}_b.$$

3.2. Expected Value of Estimate

The expected value of the estimate under the weighting procedure is given by

$$E\hat{X} = \sum_{b=1}^{B} E_1 E_2 E_3 \hat{X}_b,$$

where E_1 and E_3 are defined in Section 2.2.

As stated earlier, E_2 is the expected value over all possible missingness patterns within a cell, given the sample s. For a given sample of n_b units in the cell, there exists a missingness pattern of the events of responding and not responding, which may be indicated by a vector $\boldsymbol{\delta} = (\delta_1, \delta_2, \ldots, \delta_{n_b})$. In the case where $n_b = 12$, the missingness pattern would be indicated by the vector $\delta = (1,0,1,1,1,0,1,0,1,1,1,0)$. E_2 would be the expected value over all possible 2^{12} missingness patterns with their associated probabilities of occurrence. It is assumed in the development of the bias and variance that the probability of extremely deficient responses with m_b/n_b close to zero would be negligible. If, however, this is the case in practice, two or more balancing areas would have to be combined to permit the use of the weighting method.

The expected value of the estimate by the weighting method of imputation in cell b is developed in Appendix A and is given by

$$E\hat{X}_b \doteq X_b \quad \text{(true characteristic total)}$$

$$+ \bar{\alpha}_b^{-1} \sum_{i=1}^{N_b} \alpha_i(_RB_i) \quad \text{(response bias)}$$

$$+ \bar{\alpha}_b^{-1} \sum_{i=1}^{N_b} (\alpha_i - \bar{\alpha}_b)X_i \quad \text{(nonresponse or imputation bias)}, \quad (12)$$

where $\bar{\alpha}_b$ is the expected response rate or average response probability in cell b. It can be readily seen from the third line in (12) that the nonresponse or imputation bias will exist only when there is a correlation between response probabilities and the characteristic in the population. Otherwise one would be able to treat the responding sample as a random subsample of the complete sample. The biases of the weighting method along with the other imputation procedures will be discussed more fully in Section 8 and suggested ways of estimating the bias will be described.

3.3. Weighting Method Using Weighted Response Rates

When weighted response rates are used, the inflation factor applied to compensate for a deficient sample is given by the ratio

$$\frac{\sum_{i=1}^{n_b} \pi_i^{-1}}{\sum_{i=1}^{n_b} \delta_i \pi_i^{-1}}$$

in lieu of n_b/m_b, so that the estimation formula analogous to (10) is given by

$$\hat{X}_{bw} = \frac{\sum_{i=1}^{n_b} \pi_i^{-1}}{\sum_{i=1}^{n_b} \delta_i \pi_i^{-1}} \sum_{i=1}^{n_b} \delta_i(X_i + _R\varepsilon_i)\pi_i^{-1}, \quad (12a)$$

and its expected value by

$$E\hat{X}_{bw} = X_b + \bar{\alpha}_{bw}^{-1} \sum_{i=1}^{N_b} \alpha_i({}_R B_i) + \bar{\alpha}_{bw}^{-1} \sum_{i=1}^{N_b} (\alpha_i - \bar{\alpha}_{bw})X_i,$$

where $\bar{\alpha}_{bw} = \sum_{i=1}^{N_b} \alpha_i/N_b$, the simple average of the response probabilities in the cell.

$\bar{\alpha}_{bw}$ may be readily compared with the expected simple response rate $\bar{\alpha}_b$, given by $\sum_{i=1}^{N_b} \pi_i\alpha_i/\sum_{i=1}^{N_b} \pi_i$. By defining $E^*U_i = \sum_{i=1}^{N_b} \pi_iU_i/En_b$ and $\text{Cov}^*(U_i, V_i) = E^*(U_i, V_i) - E^*(U_i)E^*(V_i)$, we may show that

$$\bar{\alpha}_{bw} = \bar{\alpha}_b + (En_b/N_b)\, \text{Cov}^*(\alpha_i, \pi_i^{-1}). \qquad (12b)$$

Thus if large units respond with higher probability than small units within a cell, $\text{Cov}^*(\alpha_i, \pi_i^{-1}) < 0$ and $\bar{\alpha}_{bw}^{-1} > \bar{\alpha}_b^{-1}$. In such a case, $\hat{X}_{bw} > \hat{X}_b$.

However, this does not mean that $\hat{X}_{bw}$ is less biased than $\hat{X}_b$, since, under some survey conditions, $\hat{X}_b$ might contain only response bias while $\hat{X}_{bw}$ would also contain imputation biases. Such a situation would arise when

$$\text{Cov}^*\big[\alpha_i(X_i + {}_R B_i)\pi_i^{-1}\big] = 0$$

while $\text{Cov}^*(\alpha_i, \pi_i^{-1}) < 0$. It should be noted that, with self-weighting design, $\bar{\alpha}_{bw} = \bar{\alpha}_b$ and the two estimates above are identical.

3.4. Variance of Estimate

The variance of the estimate $\hat{X} = \sum_{b=1}^{B} \hat{X}_b$ is given by

$$V(\hat{X}) = \sum_{b=1}^{B} V(\hat{X}_b) + \sum_{b \neq c} \text{Cov}(\hat{X}_b, \hat{X}_c),$$

where the variance in $\hat{X}_b$ is derived in Section B.2.3 in Appendix B by obtaining $E_1E_2E_3(\hat{X}_b^2)$, and is given by

$$V(\hat{X}_b) = E_1E_2E_3(\hat{X}_b^2) - \big[E_1E_2E_3(\hat{X}_b)\big]^2.$$

Similarly, the covariance expression is derived by taking the expected value of $\hat{X}_b\hat{X}_c$ (i) E_1, over all possible samples, (ii) E_2, over all possible missingness patterns, and (iii) E_3, over all possible responses in two distinct cells b and c, so that

$$\text{Cov}(\hat{X}_b, \hat{X}_c = E_1E_2E_3(\hat{X}_b\hat{X}_c) - \big[E_1E_2E_3(\hat{X}_b)\big]\big[E_1E_2E_3(\hat{X}_c)\big].$$

3.5. Variance of Estimate in a Cell

The variance of an estimate under the weighting imputation procedure is derived in Appendix B and is given by

$$V(\hat{X}_b)$$

$$= \bar{\alpha}_b^{-2} V_s \left\{ \sum' \pi_i^{-1} \left[\alpha_i f_b(i) + \frac{T_b}{En_b} \pi_i \right] \right\} \quad \text{(sampling variance SV)}$$

$$+ \bar{\alpha}_b^{-2} \sum_i \pi_i^{-1} [\alpha_i^2 + V(\delta_i)] (_R\sigma_i^2) \quad \text{(simple response variance SRV)}$$

$$+ \bar{\alpha}_b^{-2} \sum_{i \neq j} \pi_{ij} \pi_i^{-1} \pi_j^{-1} \quad \text{(correlated response variance CRV)}$$

$$\cdot \left[\alpha_i \alpha_j + \text{Cov}(\delta_i, \delta_j) \, r_{2ij} (_R\sigma_i)(_R\sigma_j) \right]$$

$$+ \bar{\alpha}_b^{-2} \sum_i \pi_i^{-1} V(\delta_i) f_b(i) f_b(i) \quad \begin{array}{l}\text{(variance component contri-} \\ \text{buted by the variances } V(\delta_i) \text{ in} \\ \text{the events of responding or not} \\ \text{responding among units VR}\bar{\text{R}})\end{array}$$

$$+ \bar{\alpha}_b^{-2} \sum_{i \neq j} \pi_{ij} \pi_i^{-1} \pi_j^{-1} \quad \begin{array}{l}\text{(covariance component contri-} \\ \text{buted by the covariances be-}\end{array}$$

$$\cdot \text{Cov}(\delta_i, \delta_j) \, f_b(i) f_b(j) \quad \begin{array}{l}\text{tween } \delta_i \text{ and } \delta_j, \text{ the events of} \\ \text{responding or not responding} \\ \text{among pairs of units CVR}\bar{\text{R}}), \quad (13)\end{array}$$

where

$$T_b = \sum_{i=1}^{N_b} \alpha_i (X_i + {}_RB_i), \qquad f_b(i) = X_i + {}_RB_i - \frac{T_b}{En_b \bar{\alpha}_b} \pi_i,$$

and $\sum$ and $\sum'$ denote, respectively, the sum over N_b and n_b units in cell number b. $\bar{\alpha}_b$ is the expected response rate in cell b, i.e., $E_1 E_2(m_b/n_b)$, En_b is the expected sample size in cell b and $En_b = E_1 n_b$, and $\sum_{i \neq j}$ denotes the sum over all $N_b(N_b - 1)$ pairs of units in cell b. The definitions of $_R\sigma_i^2$ and $r_{2:ij}$ were given in Section 2.2 and after formula (5), respectively.

If the expression $\alpha_i f_b(i)$ is abbreviated by B_i in the sampling variance SV of $V(\hat{X}_b)$ just given, then $V_s[\sum'_i \pi_i^{-1} B_i]$ denotes the Horvitz–Thompson variance expression, given by

$$V_s\left[\sum'_i \pi^{-1} B_i \right] = \sum_i \left(\frac{1}{\pi_i} - 1 \right) B_i^2 + \sum_{i \neq j} \left(\frac{\pi_{ij}}{\pi_i \pi_j} - 1 \right) B_i B_j. \quad (14)$$

When n_b is constant, B_i simplifies to $\alpha_i f_b(i)$, or

$$\alpha_i \left(X_i + {}_R B_i - \frac{T_b \pi_i}{n_b \bar{\alpha}_b} \right)$$

in the sampling variance component of $V(\hat{X}_b)$. $\sum$ is taken over all N_b units.

3.6. Variance of Estimate (Weighting Method) Using Weighted Response Rates

The five variance components for $\hat{X}_{bw}$ are almost the same as those for $\hat{X}_b$ except that the factor $\bar{\alpha}_b^{-2}$ is replaced by $\bar{\alpha}_{bw}^{-2}$. Other changes in (13) are as follows: $f_b(i)$ would be replaced by $f_{bw}(i)$, where

$$f_{bw}(i) = X_i + {}_R B_i - \frac{T_b}{N_b \bar{\alpha}_{bw}},$$

$T_b \pi_i / E n_b$ would be replaced by T_b / N_b. The variance of $\hat{X}_{bw}$ is approximately $\bar{\alpha}_{bw}^{-2} / \bar{\alpha}_b^{-2}$ times that of $\hat{X}_b$, since one would expect SV, VR$\bar{\mathrm{R}}$, and CVR$\bar{\mathrm{R}}$ to be of about the same magnitude as in (13) except for the factor $\bar{\alpha}_{bw}^{-2}$.

3.7. Covariance of Estimates between Cells

When more than one cell exists, a covariance may exist between estimates of different cells. A sampling covariance may exist unless a census is taken or unless the cells are defined in different strata. However, two nonsampling covariance components may exist and these would include terms containing covariances between responses of different cells and terms containing covariances between the events of responding or not responding. The nonsampling covariance components may exist even if the cells occur in different strata, for example, when interviewer assignments cross stratum boundaries and an interviewer effect is present in the response errors (see Fellegi, 1964). Even with different interviewers, a correlation between response errors may prevail because of common training techniques applied to a group of interviewers. More discussion about the covariance and ways of reducing it will be included in a general discussion about the various imputation procedures.

The covariance between the estimates X_b and X_c pertaining to distinct cells b and c is derived in Appendix 2 [see Eq. (21) in Appendix B] and is given by

$$\text{Cov}(\hat{X}_b, \hat{X}_c)$$

$$= \bar{\alpha}_b^{-1}\bar{\alpha}_c^{-1}\,\text{Cov}_s\left\{\sum_i' \pi_i^{-1}\left[\alpha_i f_b(i) + \pi_i \frac{T_b}{En_b}\right],\right. \qquad \text{(sampling covariance SCV)}$$

$$\left. \cdot \sum_j' \pi_j^{-1}\left[\alpha_j f_c(i) + \pi_j \frac{T_c}{En_c}\right]\right\}$$

$$+ \bar{\alpha}_b^{-1}\bar{\alpha}_c^{-1}\sum_i\sum_j \pi_{ij}\pi_i^{-1}$$

(covariance component contributed by the covariance between the responses $X_i + {}_R\varepsilon_i$ and $X_j + {}_R\varepsilon_j$ of individual pairs of units CRV)

$$\cdot \left[\alpha_i\alpha_j + \text{Cov}(\delta_i, \delta_j)\right] r_{2ij}({}_R\sigma_i)({}_R\sigma_i)$$

$$+ \bar{\alpha}_b^{-1}\bar{\alpha}_c^{-1}\sum_i\sum_j \pi_{ij}\pi_i^{-1}\pi_j^{-1}$$

(covariance component contributed by the covariances between δ_i and δ_j the events of responding or not responding among pairs of units CVR$\bar{\text{R}}$).   (15)

$$\cdot \text{Cov}(\delta_i, \delta_j)\, f_b(i) f_c(j)$$

$\text{Cov}_s[\sum_i' B_i\pi_i^{-1}, \sum_i' B_j\pi_h^{-1}]$ is the sampling covariance between $\hat{B}_b$ and $\hat{B}_c$, estimates of $\sum_{i=1}^{N_b} B_i$ and $\sum_{j=1}^{N_c} B_j$, in two distinct cells b and c, and is given by

$$\text{Cov}_s\left[\sum_i' B_i\pi_i^{-1}, \sum_j' B_j\pi_j^{-1}\right] = \sum_i\sum_j\left(\frac{\pi_{ij}}{\pi_i\pi_j} - 1\right) B_i B_j. \qquad (16)$$

$\sum_j'$ and $\sum_j$ denote summation over n_c and N_c units, respectively, in cell c; otherwise, the notation is identical to that used in (13). If b and c denote distinct strata or cells in different strata, $\pi_{ij} \equiv \pi_i\pi_j$ and Cov_s as in (16) would equal zero.

3.8.   Discussion about the Variance of the Estimate under "Weighting Method"

The estimate $\hat{X}$ under the "weighting method" is subject to as many as five variance and covariance components within a cell and, when the selected sample is divided up into more than one cell, it is subject to as many as three components between cells.

The sample variance of $\hat{X}$ may be obtained by summing the sampling variance given by (13) over the B cells and the sampling covariance given by (16) over the $B(B - 1)$ pairs of cells and the sampling variance may be rewritten as

$$V_1(E_2 E_3 \hat{X}) = V_s \left[\sum_{b=1}^{B} \bar{\alpha}_b^{-1} \left(\sum_{i \in b}' \pi^{-1} A_i \right) \right] = V_s \left(\sum_{i}' \pi_i^{-1} \bar{\alpha}_b^{-1} A_i \right), \qquad (16a)$$

where

$$A_i = \alpha_i \left(X_i + {}_R B_i - \frac{T_b \pi_i}{En_b \bar{\alpha}_b} \right) + \frac{T_b}{En_b} \pi_i$$

and $\sum_{i \in b}'$ denotes summation over n_b sampled units in cell b. The double summation $\sum_{b=1}^{B} \sum_{i \in b}'$ is equivalent to the summation $\sum_i'$ over all n sampled units; hence, the two forms for V_s in (16a). The sampling variance of $\hat{X}$ will increase as the expected response rates $\bar{\alpha}_b$ decrease among the cells but not by as much as one would expect by the inverse sample size rule. This may be seen by expanding the sampling variance using various average parameters. The sampling variance would depend upon the manner in which cells are delineated for imputation purposes, the homogeneity of characteristics within cells as well as the sample design for the selection of n units. The sampling variance may be expected to increase as the variation in α_i increases within cells.

The nonsampling variances consist of four components, two of which are related to response errors. The simple and correlated response variances SRV and CRV will exist whether or not there is nonresponse, although their magnitude will be affected by the expected nonresponse rate. The SRV may be written as

$$\mathrm{SRV}(\hat{X}) = \sum_{b=1}^{B} \bar{\alpha}_b^{-2} \sum_{i \in b} \alpha_i ({}_R \sigma_i^2), \qquad (16b)$$

where $\bar{\alpha}_b$ = expected response rate in cell b, α_i = response probability for unit $i = E_i$, ${}_R \sigma_i^2$ = simple response variance for unit i, given that unit i responds. Since $V(\delta_i) = \alpha_i(1 - \alpha_i)$, α_i may be rewritten as $\alpha_i^2 + \delta_i$, so that the simple response variance in cell b will be roughly inversely proportional to the expected response rate $\bar{\alpha}_b$ in the cell, as one can see by noting that $\bar{\alpha}_b^{-2} \alpha_i$ will average $\bar{\alpha}_b^{-1}$ in cell b. For a given set of survey conditions, the same relation may hold for the correlated response variance CRV since, within a cell, the CRV equals approximately the simple response variance times a factor $(En_b - 1) \bar{r}_{2b}$, where $\bar{r}_{2b}$ is the average correlation between responses in cell b. The correlated response variation will exist only if the individual correlations $r_{2ij} \neq 0$ and the average $\bar{r}_{2b} \neq 0$. The correlation will be close to zero under conditions of self-enumeration with little or no interchange of respondents about survey data. When professional interviews are employed, however, correlations between response errors may exist and will usually be positive within an assignment.

The remaining two components of nonsampling error deal with those pertaining to nonresponse. If there were always full response, then δ_i and α_i would equal one and $V(\delta_i)$ and $\mathrm{Cov}(\delta_i, \delta_j)$ would equal zero so that the two components VR$\bar{\mathrm{R}}$ and CVR$\bar{\mathrm{R}}$ would be zero. When nonresponse occurs and with some probability other than one for the units, the VR$\bar{\text{R}}$ component will most certainly exist in the case of the use of interviewers to gather the survey data, whether by telephone or personal interviewing the units in an interview assignment. In the case of self-enumeration, CVR$\bar{\text{R}}$ will likely be zero unless there is some communication about the survey among the units.

4. DUPLICATION METHOD

The "duplication method" of imputation is one in which the deficiency in the sample in a cell due to nonresponse is made up by duplicating all or a subsample of respondents. The duplication is equivalent to applying integral weights to the respondents. For example, if the response rate in a cell equals 3/7, one third of the respondents, selected at random, will be duplicated three times or given a weight of 3, while the remaining 2/3 will be duplicated twice or given a weight of 2. The method is essentially equivalent to the weighting method except that the inverse response rate in a cell is truncated to an integer and the integral weight or the weight plus one is applied to the sample weights in the cell among the respondents. The difference between the duplication and weighting methods lies largely in their application. The weighting is primarily applied in the case of complete nonresponse of units, whereas the practical application of the duplication is largely in the case of partial nonresponse. Here, similar record substitution rather than weighting by an inverse response rate in a cell must be undertaken to ensure consistent data among several characteristics. When partial nonresponse occurs, that is, for some but not all questions in a survey, the weighting method would result in different weights being applied to different questions according to the response rate by question, an undesirable situation since inconsistent data would result among the different questions. However, the use of similar record substitution inherent in the duplication method would avoid inconsistency in the weighted-up data among the different questions.

In the development of the bias and variance of the estimate under the duplication method, we have considered sampling without replacement rather than with replacement since most of the surveys in practice utilize sampling without replacement.

4.1. The Estimate

The estimate of total is given by $\hat{X}^{\text{D}} = \sum_{b=1}^{B} \hat{X}_b^{\text{D}}$, where at the cell level,

$$\hat{X}_b^{\text{D}} = \sum_{i=1}^{n_b} \delta_i w_i (X_i + {}_{\text{R}}\varepsilon_i)/\pi_i. \qquad (17)$$

Here, $\hat{X}_b^{\text{D}}$ refers to the estimate under the duplication method and $w_i = [n_b/m_b + 1]$ for $n_b (\text{mod } m_b)$ responding units, selected at random for m_b respondents. If the first $n_b(\mathrm{mod}\ m_b)$ respondents formed a random subsample from m_b respondents, then $w_i = \left[n_b/m_b + 1 \right]$ for $i = 1, 2, \ldots, n_b(\mathrm{mod}\ m_b)$. Here $[\ ]$ denote the expression within the square bracket truncated to an integer. For the remainder of the respondents, namely, $i = n_b(\mathrm{mod}\ m_b) + 1, \ldots, m_b$, the weight $w_i = \left[n_b/m_b \right]$.

Turning again to the general estimation formula $\hat{X}_b^G$, we note that the imputed value $X_j + {}_{\mathrm{NR}}\varepsilon_j$ is given by the response of another unit in the sample in cell b that responded, or

$$X_j + {}_{\mathrm{NR}}\varepsilon_j = \pi_j(X_i + {}_{\mathrm{R}}\varepsilon_i)/\pi_i,$$

where unit i is said to be the "donor" record for unit j. If the response rate exceeds $1/2$ in the cell, the donor records do not have to be used more than once. In this case, if a responding unit such as i is used as a donor to replace missing data of a nonresponding unit such as j, then $w_i = 2$; otherwise, $w_i = 1$ in the estimate given by (17).

On the other hand, if the response rate is less than $1/2$, then every unit will become a donor record at least once; and, in general, a responding unit will be a donor record, either $\left[n_b/m_b \right]$ times or $\{\left[n_b/m_b \right] - 1\}$ times.

In Table 1, if we take n_b to be 12 as before in the case of the weighting method, we have a sample size of 12 with 8 respondents, so that $w_i = 2$ for 12 (mod 8) or 4 respondents and $w_i = 1$ for the remaining $8 - 4$ or 4 respondents. We have 4 nonrespondents, namely, units 2, 6, 8, 12, and the procedure under the duplication method is to search within the cell for a "donor" record to replace each missing value according to some rule. There are several rules that may be applied to search for "donor" records and we shall deal with one of these, namely, the use of the "next" available responding unit in a cell according to the order in which the units are listed (in this case in numerical sequence from 1 to 12). When the response rate exceeds $1/2$ as it does in the cell referred to in Table 1, a donor unit is said to be "available" if it has not already been used for a missing unit. In this case, a unit would not be used more than once as a donor record. By this rule, the "donor" records for missing units would be units 3, 7, 9, and 1, so that in effect $w_i = 2$ for these responding units and $w_i = 1$ for the remaining responding units, those numbering 4, 5, 10, and 11. The imputed values for units 2, 6, 8, and 12 are respectively given by

$$X_2 + {}_{\mathrm{NR}}\varepsilon_2 = \pi_2 \frac{X_3 + {}_{\mathrm{R}}\varepsilon_3}{\pi_3},$$

$$X_6 + {}_{\mathrm{NR}}\varepsilon_6 = \pi_6 \frac{X_7 + {}_{\mathrm{R}}\varepsilon_7}{\pi_7},$$

$$X_8 + {}_{\mathrm{NR}}\varepsilon_8 = \pi_8 \frac{X_9 + {}_{\mathrm{R}}\varepsilon_9}{\pi_9},$$

and

$$X_{12} + {}_{\mathrm{NR}}\varepsilon_{12} = \pi_{12} \frac{X_1 + {}_{\mathrm{R}}\varepsilon_1}{\pi_1}.$$

When units vary greatly in size as they often do in pps sampling, imputations from other respondents must be scaled by the size of the units; hence, the factors π_i/π_j, etc., as in the above example for substituted responses in place of missing values. When simple random sampling without replacement is undertaken, i.e., when selection probabilities are equal for all the units, no such scaling as above is necessary.

4.2. Expected Value of Estimate

In a cell with n_b units of which m_b responded, the integral weights

$$\left[\frac{n_b}{m_b} + 1\right] \quad \text{and} \quad \left[\frac{n_b}{m_b}\right]$$

are assumed to be assigned at random to $n_b(\text{mod } m_b)$ and $\left[m_b - n_b(\text{mod } m_b)\right]$ respondents subsampled at random. In practice, however, the units may not be sorted in a random order. With the application of such a rule as "the nearest record available," the subsample of respondents to be duplicated the number of times given by either $\left[n_b/m_b + 1\right]$ or $\left[n_b/m_b\right]$ may not actually be a random subsample with the nonrandom arrangement of the units (for example, in serial number order; see Bailar and Bailar, 1978). Consequently, the method of selecting the nearest record available for imputation purposes is in effect duplication within very small weighting classes defined after the sample is taken. To simplify the development of the bias and variance of the estimate under the duplication method, we shall assume that the sample has been split up into distinct cells with cell b containing n_b units in the sample representing N_b units in the population. We shall assume also that the $n_b(\text{mod } m_b)$ units to be duplicated $\left[(n_b/m_b) + 1\right]$ times rather than $\left[n_b/m_b\right]$ times would be subsampled at random.

Under this assumption, $E_4 w_i/i = n_b/m_b$ for all i and the bias of the estimate is identical to that of the estimate under the weighting method. E_4 refers to the operation of taking expected values over all possible subsamples of $n_b(\text{mod } m_b)$ respondents to be assigned weights of $\left[(n_b/m_b) + 1\right]$, so that $E_4 \hat{X}_b^D = \hat{X}_b$, the estimate under the weighting method, and $E\hat{X}_b^D = E_1 E_2 E_3 E_4 \hat{X}_b^D = E\hat{X}_b$ as stated in (12). The operation V_4 is the corresponding variance, where

$$V_4(\hat{X}_b^D) = E_4(\hat{X}_b^D)^2 - \left[E_4(\hat{X}_b^D)\right]^2.$$

4.3. Variance of Estimate

Under the assumptions just stated, the variance of the estimate contains an additional component to the five variance components pertaining to the weighting, or $V(\hat{X}^D) = EV_4(\hat{X}^D) + V(\hat{X})$.

4.4. Variance of the Estimate at the Cell Level

At the cell level, $V(\hat{X}_b^D) = EV_4(\hat{X}_b^D) + V(\hat{X}_b)$, where $V(\hat{X}_b)$ is the variance of the estimate under the weighting method, given by expression (13). $V_4(\hat{X}_b^D)$ is the conditional variance of $\hat{X}_b^D$, given the sample, missingness pattern, and responses and $EV_4(\hat{X}_b^D) = E_1 E_2 E_3 V_4(\hat{X}_b^D)$. The additional variance to that of the estimate under the weighting procedure is derived in Appendix 3 [see Eq. (10) in Appendix C] and is given by

$$EV_4(\hat{X}_b^D) = Ef(m_b, n_b) \frac{1}{En_b\bar{\alpha}_b} \sum_i \alpha_i^2 (X_i + {}_R B_i)^2 \pi_i^{-1}$$

$$- \frac{\sum_{i \neq j} \alpha_i \alpha_j (X_i + {}_R B_i)(X_j + {}_R B_j) \pi_{ij} \pi_i^{-1} \pi_j^{-1}}{En_b\bar{\alpha}_b(En_b\bar{\alpha}_b - 1) + V(m_b)} \quad \text{(SV)}$$

$$+ Ef(m_b, n_b) \frac{1}{En_b\bar{\alpha}_b} \sum_i [\alpha_i^2 + V(\delta_i)]_R \sigma_i \pi_i^{-1} \quad \text{(SRV)}$$

$$- \frac{Ef(m_b, n_b) \sum_{i \neq j} [\alpha_i \alpha_j + \text{Cov}(\delta_i, \delta_j)] r_{2ij} ({}_R \sigma_i)({}_R \sigma_j) \pi_{ij} \pi_i^{-1} \pi_j^{-1}}{En_b\bar{\alpha}_b(En_b\bar{\alpha}_b - 1) + V(m_b)}$$

$$\text{(CRV)}$$

$$+ Ef(m_b, n_b) \frac{1}{En_b\bar{\alpha}_b} \sum_i V(\delta_i)(X_i + {}_R B_i)^2 \pi_i^{-1} \quad \text{(V}\bar{\text{R}}\text{)}$$

$$- \frac{Ef(m_b, n_b) \sum_{i \neq j} \text{Cov}(\delta_i, \delta_j)(X_i + {}_R B_i)(X_j + {}_R B_j) \pi_{ij} \pi_i^{-1} \pi_j^{-1}}{En_b\bar{\alpha}_b(En_b\bar{\alpha}_b - 1) + V(m_b)}$$

$$\text{(CVR}\bar{\text{R}}\text{).} \quad (18)$$

Here,

$$f(m_b, n_b) = m_b \left(\frac{n_b}{m_b} - \left[\frac{n_b}{m_b} \right] \right) \left(1 - \frac{n_b}{m_b} + \left[\frac{n_b}{m_b} \right] \right),$$

i.e., the sample size that responded times the conditional variance of the weight w_i to be assigned to unit i, given the response rate m_b/n_b.

$$Ef(m_b, n_b) = En_b\bar{\alpha}_b(\bar{\alpha}_b^{-1} - [\bar{\alpha}_b^{-1}])([\bar{\alpha}_b^{-1}] + 1 - \bar{\alpha}_b^{-1})$$

$$+ En_b \sum_W P_r(W)\{(W - [\bar{\alpha}_b^{-1}])[2 - (2[\bar{\alpha}_b^{-1}] + 1)E'(m_b/n_b)]$$

$$- (W - [\bar{\alpha}_b^{-1}])^2 E'(m_b/n_b)\},$$

which may be explained as the product of the expected sample size $En_b\bar{\alpha}_b$ and the variance of the weight w_i, taken over all possible response rates m_b/n_b. Here, $[\bar{\alpha}_b^{-1}]$ is the integer portion of $\bar{\alpha}_b^{-1}$ and $\bar{\alpha}_b^{-1} - [\bar{\alpha}_b^{-1}]$ is the decimal portion of $\bar{\alpha}_b^{-1}$; $P_r(W)$ is the probability that the response rate lies between $1/(W + 1)$ and $1/W$, where W is a positive integer or inverse response rate, truncated to an integer. $E'(m_b/n_b)$ is the conditional expected value of m_b/n_b, given that it lies between $1/(W + 1)$ and $1/W$. The sum $\sum_W$ is taken over all permissible values of W in the sense that the probability $P_r(W)$ is not negligible or in the sense that the response rate is not unacceptably low so as to discard the survey data or to necessitate a change in the structure of adjustment cells.

In many household surveys, the response rate nearly always lies between $1/2$ and 1, so the $P_r(W)$ may be negligible for $W > 1$. When the nonresponse rate may be less than $1/2$, the truncated inverse response rate W sometimes equals or exceeds 2, and provision for this case has been made in the methodology developed here.

Other symbols used in (13) have been defined earlier in connection with the variance under the weighting methods.

4.5. Covariance between Estimates of Different Cells

For a given sample, missingness pattern, and observed responses, the procedure of duplication of units, that is, the selection of the subsample for assignment of weights $[(n_b/m_b) + 1]$ as opposed to $[n_b/m_b]$, is independent in each cell. Consequently, there is no conditional covariance between the estimates of different cells, given the sample, missingness patterns, and observed responses.

Hence, for estimates $\hat{X}_b^D$ and $\hat{X}_c^D$ pertaining to different cells b and c, $\text{Cov}_4(\hat{X}_b^D, \hat{X}_c^D) = 0$, so that $\text{Cov}(\hat{X}_b^D, \hat{X}_c^D)$ equals $\text{Cov}(\hat{X}_b, \hat{X}_c)$, as stated in (15) for the weighting method.

4.6. Discussion about the Additional Variance Due to Duplication

Since the variance of the estimate due to duplication has been shown to be a variance that is an addition to the variance of $\hat{X}$, the estimate under the weighting procedure, nearly all of the comments about $V(\hat{X})$ apply also to $V(\hat{X}^D)$.

The additional variance components would be expected to add about 10–15% to the sampling and nonsampling components of variance. Hansen, Hurwitz, and Madow (1953) showed that the sampling variance under duplication instead of weighting in the case of srswor would increase by as much as just over 10% for a 2/3 response rate.

5. HISTORICAL DATA SUBSTITUTION METHOD

The "historical data substitution method" is one in which historical or external sources such as census, earlier survey, or administrative data are substituted for a unit to replace missing data caused by nonresponse. The following two types of historical data substitution method procedures may be considered:

(i)   One type, for which historical or external source data are available for all units which have failed to respond

(ii)   Another, for which the external source data is available for some but not all units, and imputation by another method, e.g., weighting must also be applied

To deal with the second type of imputation procedure, we have introduced a concept of the probability of availability of external source data, a concept similar to that of response probability when the historical data are obtained from other surveys or censuses. However, when administrative data are used as the external source for imputation procedures, the concept resembles the probability of coverage of the unit in the administrative records. When historical or external source data are not available for every unit, then one must use another imputation procedure together with the historical data substitution; an example of another method could be weighting. Sometimes a correlation exists between the events of nonresponding in the current survey and the non-availability of external source data, a correlation which is taken into account in the development of the variance under case (ii). This correlation may be low or negligible when census or administrative data are used but very high when the previous month's survey data whenever it exists are used to replace current month's nonresponses.

5.1.   Estimate: Case (i)

When external source data are available for every unit, then the imputed value for missing data would be given by $X_i + {}_R\varepsilon_i'$, the observed value in the preceding survey, census, or administrative data file. The estimate would be given by

$$\hat{X}' = \sum_{i=1}^{n} \left[\delta_i(X_i + {}_R\varepsilon_i) + (1 - \delta_i)(X_i + {}_R\varepsilon_i') \right] \pi_i^{-1}, \qquad (19)$$

where ${}_R\varepsilon_i'$ is the response error of the historical or external source data relative to the true value for the unit.

As in the case of estimates under any imputation procedure, the general estimation formula $\hat{X}^D$ defined in (8) may be applied to derive $\hat{X}'$ by substituting $X_i + {}_{NR}\varepsilon_i = X_i + {}_R\varepsilon_i'$, where the imputed value for unit i that failed to respond is the historical or external source data.

When external source data are available for every unit as in (19), there is no need for balancing areas or weighting classes since no weighting or duplication is undertaken, only substitution of data pertaining to the same unit when it fails to respond.

5.2. Expected Value of the Estimate: Case (i)

The expected value of the estimate, given in (19), is derived in Appendix 1 [see Eq. (12) in Appendix A] for the case of the historical substitution and weighting methods. To adapt Eq. (2) in Appendix A to this case, $\alpha_i'' = 1 - \alpha_i$ and $\bar{\alpha}_b'' = 1 - \bar{\alpha}_b$. The expected value is given by

$$E\hat{X}' = X \qquad \text{(true characteristic total)}$$

$$+ \sum_{i=1}^{N} \alpha_i ({}_R B_i) \qquad \text{(response bias, due to respondents)}$$

$$+ \sum_{i=1}^{N} (1 - \alpha_i)({}_{NR}B_i') \qquad \begin{array}{l}\text{(imputation bias, due to historical data} \\ \text{substitution; bias of historical data rela-} \\ \text{tive to current true value).} \end{array} \qquad (20)$$

In formula (20), ${}_{NR}B_i' = E({}_R \varepsilon_i')$ and is the nonresponse bias of the external source data for unit i, relative to the current value pertaining to the unit. As in the case of the expected value of the estimates under the weighting method, $E\delta_i$ or α_i is the response probability and $E(1 - \delta_i)$ or $(1 - \alpha_i)$ is the nonresponse probability.

5.3. Variance of the Estimate: Case (i)

The variance of the estimate under the historical data substitution method (when available for all units) is derived in Appendix B [see Eq. (3) and Section B.3.2 in Appendix B]. The variance is given by

$$V(\hat{X}') = V_s \{ \sum_{i=1}^{n} [\alpha_i(X_i + {}_R B_i) + (1 - \alpha_i)(X_i + {}_{NR}B_i')]\pi_i^{-1} \} \qquad \text{(SV)}$$

$$+ \sum_{i=1}^{N} \{ [\alpha_i^2 + V(\delta_i)]_R \sigma_i^2 $$

$$+ \sum_{i=1}^{N} [(1 - \alpha_i)^2 + V(\delta_i)]_{NR} \sigma_i'^2 \} \pi_i^{-1} \qquad \text{(SRV)}$$

$$+ \sum_{i \neq j}^{N} \pi_{ij}\pi_i^{-1}\pi_j^{-1} \{ [\alpha_i\alpha_j + \text{Cov}(\delta_i, \delta_j)]r_{2ij}({}_R\sigma_i)({}_R\sigma_j) $$

$$+ [(1 - \alpha_i)(1 - \alpha_j) + \text{Cov}(\delta_i, \delta_j)]r_{4ij}({}_{NR}\sigma_i')({}_{NR}\sigma_j') $$

$$+ [\alpha_i(1 - \alpha_j) - \text{Cov}(\delta_i, \delta_j)]r_{3ij}({}_R\sigma_i)({}_{NR}\sigma_j') $$

$$+ [(1 - \alpha_i)\alpha_j - \text{Cov}(\delta_i, \delta_j)]r_{3ji}({}_{NR}\sigma_i')({}_R\sigma_j) \} \qquad \text{(CRV)}$$

$$+ \sum_{i=1}^{N} \pi_i^{-1} V(\delta_i)({}_R B_i - {}_{NR}B_i')^2 \qquad \text{(VR\bar{R})}$$

$$+ \sum \pi_{ij}\pi_i^{-1}\pi_j^{-1} \text{Cov}(\delta_i, \delta_j)({}_R B_i - {}_{ND}B_i')({}_D B_i - {}_{NR}B_j') \qquad \text{(CVR\bar{R})}. \qquad (21)$$

The symbols, α_i, $_R\sigma_i^2$, and r_{2ij} in this expression were defined with the variance of the estimate under the weighting method of imputation. $_R B_i$ and $_{NR} B_i'$ have also been previously defined. Other symbols in (21) are to be defined and explained.

$_{NR}\sigma_i'^2 = W(_R\varepsilon_i' - _{NR}B_i')^2 = $ simple response variance pertaining to historical data responses for unit i. $r_{3ij} = $ correlation coefficient between $_R\varepsilon_i$ and $_R\varepsilon_j'$ or between $X_i + _R\varepsilon_i$, the responses of unit i of current survey and $X_j + _R\varepsilon_j'$ responses for historical or external source data of unit j. In many cases $r_{3ij} = 0$, but in the case of continuous surveys with the same interviewer covering both units i and j on several occasions, the correlation r_{3ij} could exist. $r_{4ij} = $ correlation coefficient between $_R\varepsilon_i'$ and $_R\varepsilon_j'$, the response errors of historical or external source data pertaining to units i and j, and is analogous to r_{2ij}, the correlation between $_R\varepsilon_i$ and $_R\varepsilon_j$.

When external source data are missing for some units and other imputation procedures must be resorted to, then the sample of n units may, for some imputation procedures such as the weighting method, be delineated in adjustment cells in the same manner as described for the weighting method.

5.4. Estimate: Case (ii)

Here, the weighting method is applied when external source data are only available for some of the nonresponding units. The estimate of a total at the cell b level, when historical data are substituted for missing values or when the weighting method is resorted to in the absence of historical or external source data, is given by

$$\hat{X}_b' = \frac{n_b}{m_b + m_b'} \sum_{i=1}^{n_b} \left[\delta_i(X_i + _R\varepsilon_i) + (1 - \delta_i)\delta_i'(X_i + _R\varepsilon_i') \right]\pi_i^{-1}, \qquad (22)$$

where $\delta_i' = 1$ or 0 according as historical or external source data are available or not available for unit i; $m_b = $ nonrespondents for current survey data, with historical or external source data $= \sum_i' (1 - \delta_i)\delta_i'$; and $X_i + _R\varepsilon_i' = $ observed response for historical data for unit i, given that $\delta_i = 0$ and $\delta_i' = 1$.

The estimate as defined in (22) is equivalent to the weighting method, where observed responses from external sources are used whenever possible to replace missing data. One may refer to the ratio $(m_b + m_b')/n_b$ as the adjusted response rate.

The general estimation formula $\hat{X}^G$ or its cell b contribution $\hat{X}_b^G$ may be applied to the combined historical substitution and weighting method as described above with one of the following substitutions for a missing value due to nonresponse:

$$X_i + _{NR}\varepsilon_i = \begin{cases} X_i + _R\varepsilon_i' & \text{when } \delta_i' = 1 \quad \text{(historical data available)} \\[2mm] \pi_i \sum_{j=1} \left[\delta_j(X_j + _R\varepsilon_j) + (1 - \delta_j)\delta_j'(X_j + _R\varepsilon_j') \right]\pi_j^{-1}/(m_b + m_b') \\[2mm] \quad\quad \text{when } \delta_i' = 0 \quad \text{(historical data not available)}. \end{cases}$$

To illustrate the estimation procedure from Table 1, three additional columns relevant to the procedure have been provided, and these include δ_i', $(1 - \delta_i)\delta_i'$ or δ_i'', and the imputed historical data $X_i + {}_R\varepsilon_i'$ if $\delta_i' = 1$ and 0 if $\delta_i' = 0$. Historical data may be available (i.e., $\delta_i' = 1$) but it is not needed for imputation purposes when $\delta_i = 1$ since an observed response $X_i + {}_R\varepsilon_i$ is already available for estimation.

Possibly the estimate of the total could have been improved from the variance point of view if historical data were used along with current observed responses as for example, in composite estimation. However, any possible method of improving the current estimate by external source data other than for imputation purposes is another issue that is not relevant in this discussion.

Among the nonresponding units in Table 1, numbers 2, 6, 8, and 12, only units 2 and 8 contain historical data that are available for imputation purposes. Then $X_2 + {}_{NR}\varepsilon_2 = X_2 + {}_R\varepsilon_2'$ and $X_8 + {}_{NR}\varepsilon_8 = X_8 + {}_R\varepsilon_8'$.

If cell b contains 12 units, the imputed values for the remaining 2 non-respondents, numbers 6 and 12, are given by the mean of the 10 respondents, adjusted by size, and including the 2 units with historical data available, or

$$\frac{X_6 + {}_{NR}\varepsilon_6}{\pi_6} = \frac{X_{12} + {}_{NR}\varepsilon_{12}}{\pi_{12}} = \frac{1}{10}\left[\frac{X_i + {}_R\varepsilon_1}{\pi_1} + \frac{X_2 + {}_R\varepsilon_2'}{\pi_2} + \frac{X_3 + {}_R\varepsilon_3}{\pi_3} + \cdots\right].$$

In general,

$$X_i + {}_{NR}\varepsilon_i = \pi_i \frac{1}{m_b + m_b'} \sum_{j=1}^{n_b} \left\{\delta_j \frac{X_j + {}_R\varepsilon_j}{\pi_j} + (1 - \delta_j)\delta_j' \frac{X_j + {}_R\varepsilon_j'}{\pi_j}\right\}$$

when the historical data and weighting methods of imputation are effected. The additional "respondents," based on available historical data, include m_b' of them, given by $\sum_j (1 - \delta_j)\delta_j'$ or by $\sum_j \delta_j''$.

5.5. Expected Value of the Estimate: Case (ii)

The expected value of the estimate $\hat{X}_b'$ under the combined historical data substitution and weighting methods is derived in Appendix A [see Eq. (2) in Appendix A] and is given by

$$E\hat{X}_b' = X_b \qquad\qquad \text{(true characteristic total)}$$

$$+ \sum_{i=1}^{N_b} \alpha_{i.R}B_i(\bar{\alpha}_b + \bar{\alpha}_b'')^{-1} \qquad \text{(response bias due to respondents)}$$

$$+ \sum_{i=1}^{N_b} \alpha_{i.NR}''B_{i.}'(\bar{\alpha}_b + \bar{\alpha}_b'')^{-1} \qquad \text{(imputation bias, due to historical data substitution; response bias of historical observed value relative to current true value)}$$

(Equation Continues)

$$+ \left[\sum_{i=1}^{N_b} (\alpha_i - \bar{\alpha}_b) X_i \right.$$

(imputation bias, due to
weighting applied to enlarge
the deficient sample).

$$+ \left. \sum_{i=1}^{N_b} (\alpha_i'' - \bar{\alpha}_b'') X_i \right] (\bar{\alpha}_b + \bar{\alpha}_b'')^{-1} \tag{23}$$

In the above expression, $\alpha_i = E\delta_i$ as in the weighting method; $\alpha_i'' = E\delta_i''$, where $\delta_i'' = (1 - \delta_i)\delta_i'$; $\bar{\alpha}_b = \sum_{i=1}^{N_b} \pi_i \alpha_i / En_b$ or the expected response rate in cell b; $\bar{\alpha}_b'' = \sum_{i=1}^{N_b} \pi_i \bar{\alpha}_i'' / En_b$ or the expected increase in response rate in b due to availability of historical records among nonrespondents; $En_b = \sum_i \pi_i$ or the expected sample size in b; and $_{NR}B_i' = E(_R\varepsilon_i')$, where $_R\varepsilon_i'$ is the response error of the historical data, compared with the true value X_i. The remaining symbols were defined in the subsection on weighting method. When historical data are available for all units, whether they respond or do not respond, then $\alpha_i'' = 1 - \alpha_i$ and $\bar{\alpha}_b'' = 1 - \bar{\alpha}_b$ and the bias in (23) would reduce to the bias in (20) at the cell b level. In this case, the component of imputation bias, due to weighting, given in the last line of (23) would be zero, since $\alpha_i + \alpha_i'' = \bar{\alpha}_b + \bar{\alpha}_b'' = 1$.

5.6. Variance of the Estimate: Case (i) or (ii)

The variance of the estimate is the sum of variances over the B cells and the sum of the $B(B - 1)$ covariances between them, or

$$V(\hat{X}') = \sum_{b=1}^{B} V(\hat{X}_b') + \sum_{b \neq c} \text{Cov}(\hat{X}_b', \hat{X}_c').$$

5.7. Variance of the Estimate at the Cell Level: Case (ii)

The variance of the estimate at the cell b under the combined historical data substitution and weighting method is derived in Appendix B [see Eqs. (19) and (20), Table 12 and Section B.5]. The variance is given by

$$V(\hat{X}_b') = (\bar{\alpha}_b + \bar{\alpha}_b'')^{-2} V_s \left\{ \sum' \left[\alpha_i f_b'(i) + \alpha_i'' f_b''(i) + \frac{T_b + T_b''}{En_b} \pi_i \right] \pi_i^{-1} \right\} \tag{SV}$$

$$+ (\bar{\alpha}_b + \bar{\alpha}_b'')^{-2} \sum_i \{ [\alpha_1^2 + V(\delta_i)] \, _R\sigma_i^2$$

$$+ \alpha_i''^2 + V(\delta_i'') \, _{NR}\sigma_i'^2 \} \pi \qquad \text{(SRV)}$$

$$+ (\bar{\alpha}_b + \bar{\alpha}_b'')^{-2} \sum_{i \neq j} \pi_{ij} \pi_i^{-1} \pi_j^{-1} \{ [(\alpha_i \alpha_j + \text{Cov}(\delta_i, \delta_j)] r_{2ij} (_R\sigma_i)(_R\sigma_j)$$

(*Equation Continues*)

$$+ \left[\alpha_i \alpha_j'' + \mathrm{Cov}(\delta_i, \delta_j'') \right] r_{3ij}(_R\sigma_i)(_{NR}\sigma_j')$$

$$+ \left[\alpha_i'' \alpha_j + \mathrm{Cov}(\delta_i'', \delta_j) \right] r_{3ji}(_{NR}\sigma_i')(_R\sigma_j)$$

$$+ \left[\alpha_i'' \alpha_j'' + \mathrm{Cov}(\delta_i'', \delta_j'') \right] r_{4ij}(_{NR}\sigma_i')(_{NR}\sigma_j') \} \qquad (CRV)$$

$$+ (\bar{\alpha}_b + \bar{\alpha}_b'')^{-2} \sum_i \pi_i^{-1} \left[V(\delta_i) f_b'(i) f_b'(i) + 2\, \mathrm{Cov}(\delta_i, \delta_i'') f_b'(i) f_b''(i) \right.$$

$$\left. + V(\delta_i'') f_b''(i) f_b''(i) \right] \qquad (VR\bar{R})$$

$$+ (\alpha_b + \alpha_b'')^{-2} \sum_{i \neq j} \pi_{ij} \pi_i^{-1} \pi_j^{-1}\, \mathrm{Cov}(\delta_i, \delta_j) f_b'(i) f_b'(j)$$

$$+ \mathrm{Cov}(\delta_i, \delta_j'') f_b'(i) f_b''(j) + \mathrm{Cov}(\delta_i, \delta_j) f_b''(i) f_b'(j)$$

$$+ \mathrm{Cov}(\delta_i'', \delta_j'') f_b''(i) f_b''(j) \right] \qquad (CVR\bar{R}), \qquad\qquad (24)$$

where

$$f_b'(i) = X_i + {}_R B_i - \pi_i \frac{T_b + T_b''}{En_b(\bar{\alpha}_b + \bar{\alpha}_b'')},$$

$$f_b''(i) = X_i + {}_{NR} B_i' - \pi_i \frac{T_b + T_b''}{En_b(\bar{\alpha}_b + \bar{\alpha}_b'')},$$

$$T_b = \sum_i \alpha_i (X_i + {}_R B_i) \qquad \text{(as before for the weighting method)},$$

$$T_b'' = \sum_i \alpha_i'' (X_i + {}_{NR} B_i'),$$

$$\alpha_i'' = E\delta_i'' = E(1 - \delta_i)\delta_i'; \qquad \bar{\alpha}_b'' = \sum_i \pi_i \alpha_i'' / En_b.$$

Many of the symbols used in the variance expression for (24) were defined earlier in connection with (21). A couple of additional covariances such as $\mathrm{Cov}(\delta_i, \delta_j'')$ and $\mathrm{Cov}(\delta_i'', \delta_j'')$ appear in (24) that did not exist in (21); they are summarized in the following and explained more fully in Appendix B. $\mathrm{Cov}(\delta_i, \delta_j'')$ is the covariance between δ_i, the event of responding or not responding, and δ_j'', the event of availability or nonavailability of external source data, given that the unit fails to respond. $\mathrm{Cov}(\delta_i'', \delta_j'')$ is the covariance between $(1 - \delta_i)\delta_i'$ and $(1 - \delta_j)\delta_j'$, the events of not responding and availability of historical records for units i and j.

5.8.   Covariance between Estimates of Different Cells

As in the case of the estimate under the weighting procedure, a covariance may exist between estimates under the historical data substitution method for different cells. The covariance is derived in Appendix B [see Eq. (21), Table 12, and Section B.5] and is given here for case (ii), when weighting is resorted to in case of nonavailability of historical or external source data:

$$\text{Cov}(\hat{X}'_b, \hat{X}'_c) \doteq (\bar{\alpha}_b + \bar{\alpha}''_b)^{-1}(\bar{\alpha}_c + \bar{\alpha}''_c)^{-1}$$

$$\cdot \text{Cov}_s \left\{ \sum_{i=1}^{n_b} \left[\alpha_i f_b(i) + \alpha''_i f''_b(i) + \frac{T_b + T''_b}{En_b(\bar{\alpha}_b + \bar{\alpha}''_b)} \pi_i \right] \pi_i^{-1}, \right.$$

$$\left. \sum_{j=i}^{n_c} \left[\alpha_j f'_b(j) + \alpha''_j f''_c(j) + \frac{T_c + T''_c}{En_c(\bar{\alpha}_c + \bar{\alpha}''_c)} \pi_j \right] \pi_j^{-1} \right\} \qquad \text{(SCV)}$$

$$+ (\bar{\alpha}_b + \bar{\alpha}''_b)^{-1}(\bar{\alpha}_c + \bar{\alpha}''_c)^{-1} \sum_{i=1}^{N_b} \sum_{j=i}^{N_c} \pi_{ij} \pi_i^{-1} \pi_j^{-1}$$

$$\cdot \left\{ [\alpha_i \alpha_j + \text{Cov}(\delta_i, \delta_j)] r_{2ij}(_R\sigma_i)(_R\sigma_i) \right.$$

$$+ [\alpha_i \alpha''_j + \text{Cov}(\delta_i, \delta''_j)] r_{3ij}(_R\sigma_i)(_{NR}\sigma'_j)$$

$$+ [\alpha''_i \alpha_j + \text{Cov}(\delta''_i, \delta_j)] r_{3ji}(_{NR}\sigma'_i)(_R\sigma_j)$$

$$\left. + [\alpha''_i \alpha''_j + \text{Cov}(\delta''_i, \delta''_j)] r_{4ij}(_{NR}\sigma'_i)(_{NR}\sigma'_j) \right\} \qquad \text{(CRV)}$$

$$+ (\bar{\alpha}_b + \bar{\alpha}''_b)^{-1}(\bar{\alpha}_c + \bar{\alpha}''_c)^{-1} \sum_{i=1}^{N_b} \sum_{j=i}^{N_c} \pi_{ij} \pi_i^{-1} \pi_j^{-1}$$

$$\cdot \text{Cov}(\delta_i, \delta_j) f'_b(i) f'_c(j)$$

$$+ \text{Cov}(\delta_i, \delta''_j) f'_b(i) f''_c(j) + \text{Cov}(\delta''_i, \delta_j) f''_b(i) f'_c(j)$$

$$+ \text{Cov}(\delta''_i, \delta''_j) f''_b(i) f''_c(j)] \qquad \text{(CVRR)}. \qquad (25)$$

The definitions of all symbols used have already been given; for example, SCV is the sampling covariance defined in Section 3.5.

5.9. Discussion of the Variance of the Estimate under the Historical Substitution Method

The estimate $\hat{X}'$ under case (i), when historical or external data are available for every unit, is subject to five components of variance, SV, SRV, CRV, VRR̄, and CVRR̄, as noted in (21). The sampling variance will depend largely on the sample design but may increase slightly with the use of more historical data. The SRV comprises two subcomponents, one due to response variances of current survey data and the other due to response variances of historical data. The SRV may be written as

$$\text{SRV} = \sum_i \pi_i^{-1} [\alpha_i(_R\sigma_i)^2 + (1 - \alpha_i)(_{NR}\sigma'_i)^2],$$

so that as the individual response probabilities α_i change, the SRV will depend upon the magnitude of the simple response variances of the historical data relative to those of current survey data. If the survey conditions employed for data collection for the historical data are similar to those for current survey data, one would expect little change in SRV as the expected response rate $\bar{\alpha}$ changes, but the SRV would increase or decrease with a decrease in the response rate according as $_{NR}\sigma_i'$ tends to be higher or lower than $_R\sigma_i'$.

The correlated response variance CRV comprises four subcomponents, the first line, involving r_{2ij}, the correlation between responses of the current survey, being the most important subcomponent. The second subcomponent, involving r_{4ij}, the correlation between responses based on historical data, would only be a significant contribution to $V(\hat{X}')$ if the expected response rate $\bar{\alpha}_b$ were low. The third and fourth subcomponents involving r_{3ij} and r_{3ji} would be close to zero if the current and historical data are obtained in different periods without any interrelated effects of their respective survey conditions.

The remaining components $VR\bar{R}$ and $CVR\bar{R}$, depend upon the extent to which the response biases of historical data and current survey data differ as well as the nonresponse rate, which affects the magnitude of $V(\delta_i)$. Quite often the historical data and current survey data refer to different periods, so that the values of $_RB_i - {_{NR}}B_i'$ may all tend to be of similar sign. In such a case, $VR\bar{R}$ could be an important contribution to $V(\hat{X}')$. The covariance component $CVR\bar{R}$ will occur only if the events of responding and not responding are correlated among the units, a condition that may frequently occur in interviewer's assignment.

The estimate $\hat{X}'$ under case (ii), when historical data are available only for some of the units, is also subject to five components, the last two, $VR\bar{R}$ and $CVR\bar{R}$, containing terms involving the variation in δ_i and δ_i'', the events of responding/not responding and availability/nonavailability of historical data. The SV may be slightly lower than for case (i) because of the ratio estimation procedure inherent in the weighting method, but in the event that the SV is lower, its smaller magnitude is more than made up by a relatively high component $VR\bar{R}$, the fourth major component of (24). The SRV and CRV will increase by approximately a factor $(\bar{\alpha}_i + \bar{\alpha}_b'')^{-1}$ over the magnitudes of these components for case (i). The fifth component, $CVR\bar{R}$, contains four subcomponents, the first involving $Cov(\delta_i, \delta_j)$, which is likely the most important, since the covariance is that between the response status of units i and j in the current month, while $Cov(\delta_i\delta_j'')$ and $Cov(\delta_i''\delta_j)$ are the covariances between the response status of the current and historical period and consequently will likely be close to zero. $Cov(\delta_i''\delta_i'')$ may be written as $Cov[(1 - \delta_i)\delta_i', (1 - \delta_j)\delta_j']$, which is a covariance between the combined nonresponse status in the current month and response status of the historical period for units i and j, and while the covariance may exist because of the covariances between δ_i and δ_j and between δ_i' and δ_j', one would expect $Cov(\delta_i'', \delta_j'')$ to be smaller than $Cov(\delta_i, \delta_j)$.

Most of the parameters in the variance expressions (21) and (24) cannot be estimated at the unit level, but their average values may be estimated; for example, $\bar{\alpha}_b$, the expected response rate in cell b, may be readily estimated by m_b/n_b; and similarly $\bar{\alpha}_b''$, by m_b'/n_b. The average of the average response variances

σ_{2ij}^2, viz., $\bar{\sigma}_{Rb}^2$, and of the r_{2ij}, viz., $\bar{r}_{2b}$, may be obtained, as mentioned earlier, by interpenetrating samples with reinterview.

In a similar manner, average response variances $(\bar{\sigma}_{NR:b}')^2$ and average correlations $\bar{r}_{4b}$, the average of the $\bar{r}_{4ij}$, may be obtained for the historical data. The average correlations $\bar{r}_{3b}$, which would be nonzero only in the case of historical data obtained from a previous survey with identical interviewing techniques, will be less than $\bar{r}_{2b}$ and $\bar{r}_{4b}$ and may be obtained from interpenetrating samples with reinterview taken on two occasions for similar units; otherwise, it may be assumed equal to zero

Individual covariances between the events of responding or not responding pertaining to a pair of units, $\text{Cov}(\delta_i, \delta_j)$, cannot be estimated but, upon writing

$$\text{Cov}(\delta_i, \delta_j) = r_{1ij}\sqrt{V(\delta_i)V(\delta_i)},$$

average correlations $\bar{r}_{1b}$ may be obtained through studies of measures of homogeneity in interviewer assignments treated as clusters, using the response/nonresponse status δ_i as the variable. Similarly $\bar{r}_{1b}'$ and $\bar{r}_{1b}''$, the average of the correlations $\bar{r}_{1ij}'$ and r_{1ij}'', may be obtained, where the correlations are defined as follows:

$$\text{Cov}(\delta_i, \delta_j'') = r_{1ij}'\sqrt{V(\delta_i)}\sqrt{V(\delta_j'')},$$

$$\text{Cov}(\delta_i'', \delta_j'') = r_{1ij}''\sqrt{V(\delta_i'')}\sqrt{V(\delta_j'')}.$$

6. ZERO SUBSTITUTION METHOD

The "zero substitution method" of imputation is one in which the missing data due to nonrespondents are ignored at the estimation stage. Implicitly in many cases, this would mean substitution of zero for missing data. It may seem at the first glance that the zero substitution method is the least practical of all imputation methods. However, a closer examination of the method reveals that it may be applied under the following conditions:

(a) A very high response rate occurs in a survey, so that the Horvitz–Thompson estimate may be applied without any further adjustments. In such a case, the underestimate from the zero substitution method may result in an estimate with lower mean square error and less costly to produce than an estimate under any other imputation procedure.

(b) A mean per unit in an area is estimated, using only infomation from respondents and making no other adjustments for missing data. The procedure is a special case of the weighting method described earlier with the whole sample as one balancing area. In such a case when m units respond out of a sample of n units selected by srswor procedure, the mean may be estimated by

$\bar{x} = \sum_{i=i}^{m} x_i/m$, which may be also written as $\bar{x} = (n/m) \sum_{i=i}^{m} x_i/n$, thus showing the equivalence of the estimation of the mean per responding unit and the application of the weighting method.

(c)   The total estimate for an area is obtained by the ratio estimation procedure, where the ratio is calculated between two estimates of which is based on the zero substitution method, as in (a). The numerator of the ratio pertains to the survey variable, while the denominator pertains to the auxiliary variable. The estimate of the survey and auxiliary variables may separately be underestimates, but the ratio between them is not necessarily an underestimate of the true ratio. Ratio estimation using survey and auxiliary variable estimates can also be obtained by other imputation procedures. However, it may happen that the particular ratio estimate as based on the zero substitution method for the two variables is the simplest and least costly to calculate without increasing the mean square error as compared with ratio estimates based on other imputation procedures.

Adjustment cells are redundant in the case of the zero substitution method, since no values other than "zero" are substituted for missing values. For comparison purposes with other methods of imputation, however, one may conceive of an application of the above procedure within an area or class.

6.1.   The Estimate

The estimate of a total of a characteristic [the survey variable in an area with N units, derived from a sample of n units, with some nonresponding under the zero substitution method as in (a)] is given by

$$\hat{T} = \sum_{i=1}^{n} \delta_i(X_i + {}_R\varepsilon_i)\pi_i^{-1}.$$

At cell b level (even though redundant for the above imputation procedure), the estimate would be given by

$$\hat{T}_b = \sum_{i=1}^{n_b} \delta_i(X_i + {}_R\varepsilon_i)\pi_i^{-1},$$

where symbols have been defined earlier.

In applying the general estimation $\hat{X}^G$, we note that $X_i + {}_{NR}\varepsilon_i = 0$ for estimate $\hat{T}$, and in Table 1, all of the imputed values $X_i + {}_{NR}\varepsilon_i$, for units 2, 6, 8, and 12, would be zero instead of being functions of respondents values in the balancing area or external source data.

Another form of an estimate by the zero substitution method would be the substitution of zero for missing data when a unit fails to respond and no historical data are available. For each nonrespondent with the historical data available, it would be substituted in place of the missing data. In such a case, the estimate would be given by

$$\hat{T} + \hat{T}'' = \sum_{i=1}^{n} \left[\delta_i(X_i + {}_R\varepsilon_i)\pi_i^{-1} + (1 - \delta_i)\delta_i'(X_i + {}_R\varepsilon_i')\pi_i^{-1} \right]$$

or at the cell b level,

$$\hat{T}_b + \hat{T}_b'' = \sum_{i=1}^{n_b} \left[\delta_i(X_i + {}_R\varepsilon_i)\pi_i^{-1} + (1 - \delta_i)\delta_i'(X_i + {}_R\varepsilon_i')\pi_i^{-1} \right].$$

When the general estimate $\hat{X}^G$ is applied to $\hat{T} + \hat{T}''$, $X_i + {}_{NR}\varepsilon_i$ equals $X_i + {}_R\varepsilon_i'$ when $\delta_i' = 1$ and equal 0 when $\delta_i' = 0$.

The comments about the practicality and application of the above estimate are the same as in the case of $\hat{T}$ or $\hat{T}_b$ alone. With historical data used whenever possible, however, the "response" rate (where response is also extended to the historical data) would be higher than with current survey data alone, so that if historical data are available, the use of $\hat{T} + \hat{T}''$ in practice would be preferable.

6.2. Expected Value of the Estimate

The expected value of the estimate $\hat{T} + \hat{T}''$ may be derived from (23), the expected value of $\hat{X}_b'$, by making the quantity $\bar{\alpha}_b + \bar{\alpha}_b''$ equal to 1 in (23) without altering the individual α_i or α_i'' and treating the whole sample as one balancing area. This substitution is justified on the grounds that units may or may not respond; they may or may have historical data available if they fail to respond, but no additional weighting by a factor $n_b/(m_b + m_b')$ is undertaken.

Then the expected value [derived in Appendix A—see Eq. (2)—with $\bar{\alpha}_b + \bar{\alpha}_b'' = 1$] is given by

$$E(\hat{T} + \hat{T}'') = X \qquad \text{(true characteristic total)}$$

$$+ \sum_{i=1}^{N} \left[\alpha_i({}_R B_i) + \alpha_i''({}_{NR} B_i') \right] \qquad \text{(response bias due to respondents an bias of historical data, relative to current value)}$$

$$+ \sum_{i=1}^{N} \left[(\alpha_i + \alpha_i'') - 1 \right] X_i \qquad \text{(imputation bias due to substitution of zero in place of missing current response or historical value). \qquad (26)}$$

The expected value of $\hat{T}$ alone may be readily derived from (26) by putting $\alpha_i' \equiv 0$ for all i. In the particular case when historical data are available for all units, $\alpha_i + \alpha_i'' \equiv 1$ for all i and (26) becomes identical to (20).

6.3. Variance of the Estimate

The variance of the estimate $\hat{T} + \hat{T}''$ is derived in Appendix B [see Eq. (3) and Table 12], and is given by $V[(\hat{T} + \hat{T}'')]$, where

$$V[(\hat{T} + \hat{T}'')] = V_s\{ \sum_{i=1}^{n} [\alpha_i(X_i + {}_RB_i) + \alpha_i''(X_i + {}_{NR}B_i')]\pi_i^{-1}\} \qquad \text{(SV)}$$

$$+ \sum_{i=1}^{N} [\pi_i^{-1}\{\alpha_i^2 + V(\delta_i)\}({}_R\sigma_i^2)$$

$$+ [\alpha_i''^2 + V(\delta_i'')]({}_{NR}\sigma_i'^2)\} \qquad \text{(SRV)}$$

$$+ \sum_{i \neq j}^{N} \pi_{ij}\pi_i^{-1}\pi_j^{-1}\{[\alpha_i\alpha_j + \text{Cov}(\delta_i, \delta_j)]r_{2ij}({}_R\sigma_i)({}_R\sigma_j)$$

$$+ [\alpha_i\alpha_j'' + \text{Cov}(\delta_i, \delta_j'')]r_{3ij}({}_R\sigma_j')$$

$$+ [\alpha_i''\alpha_j + \text{Cov}(\delta_i'', \delta_j)]r_{3ji}({}_{NR}\sigma_i')({}_R\sigma_j)$$

$$+ [\alpha_i''\alpha_j'' + \text{Cov}(\delta_i'', \delta_j'')]r_{4ij}({}_{NR}\sigma_i')({}_{NR}\sigma_j')\} \qquad \text{(CRV)}$$

$$+ \sum_{i=1}^{N} \pi_i^{-1}\{V(\delta_i)(X_i + {}_RB_i)^2$$

$$+ 2\,\text{Cov}(\delta_i, \delta_i'')(X_i + {}_RB_i)(X_i + {}_{NR}B_i')$$

$$+ V(\delta_i'')(X_i + {}_{NR}B_i')^2]\} \qquad \text{(VR}\bar{\text{R}})$$

$$+ \sum_{i \neq j}^{N} \pi_{ij}\pi_i^{-1}\pi_j^{-1}\{\text{Cov}(\delta_i, \delta_j)(X_i + {}_RB_i)(X_j + {}_RB_j)$$

$$+ \text{Cov}(\delta_i, \delta_j'')(X_i + {}_RB_i)(X_j + {}_{NR}B_i')$$

$$+ \text{Cov}(\delta_i'', \delta_j)(X_i + {}_{NR}B_i')(X_j + {}_RB_j)$$

$$+ \text{Cov}(\delta_i'', \delta_j'')(X_i + {}_{NR}B_i')(X_j + {}_{NR}B_j')\} \qquad \text{(CVR}\bar{\text{R}}). \quad (27)$$

The variance of the estimate $\hat{T}$ alone may be easily derived from this by putting all δ_i'' and all α_i'' equal to zero. Then $V(\delta_i'') = 0$, and likewise $\text{Cov}(\delta_i, \delta_j'')$, $\text{Cov}(\delta_i'', \delta_j)$, and $\text{Cov}(\delta_i'', \delta_j'')$ all equal zero when the estimate $\hat{T}$ is considered alone.

The variance then simplifies to the following:

$$V(\hat{T}) = V_s\{\sum_i{}' \left[\alpha_i(X_i + {}_RB_i)\right]\pi_i^{-1}\} \qquad \text{(SV)}$$

$$+ \sum_{i=1}^{N} \pi_i^{-1}\left[\alpha_i^2 + V(\delta_i)\right]({}_R\sigma_i^2) \qquad \text{(SRV)}$$

$$+ \sum_{i=j}^{N} \pi_{ij}\pi_i^{-1}\pi_j^{-1}\left[\alpha_i\alpha_j + \text{Cov}(\delta_i, \delta_j)\right]r_{2ij}({}_R\sigma_i)({}_R\sigma_j) \qquad \text{(CRV)}$$

$$+ \sum_{i=1}^{N} \pi_i^{-1}V(\delta_i)(X_i + {}_RB_i)^2 \qquad \text{(VR\bar{R})}$$

$$+ \sum_{i=j}^{N} \pi_{ij}^{-1}\pi_i^{-1}\pi_j^{-1}\,\text{Cov}(\delta_i, \delta_j)(X_i + {}_RB_i)(X_j + {}_RB_j) \qquad \text{(CVR\bar{R}). \quad (28)}$$

6.4. Discussion about the Variance of the Estimate under the Zero Substitution Method

We shall deal below with both estimates $\hat{T}$ and $\hat{T} + \hat{T}''$, the latter using historical data whenever it is available for nonrespondents and zero whenever it is not available. Both estimates are subject to five components of variance, as can be seen in (27) and (28).

The variance of $\hat{T} + \hat{T}''$ depends upon the overall expected response rate, including the adjustment for available historical records, namely, $\bar{\alpha}_b + \bar{\alpha}_b''$, and would be roughly proportional to its size. The variance is lower than it would be for complete response only because of the smaller estimate than under complete response. The smaller variance, however, is more than compensated for by a larger bias than in the case of the estimate under complete response, so that the resultant mean square error of $\hat{T} + \hat{T}''$ would be larger than it would be for the estimate with full response. The large bias in either estimate $\hat{T}$ or $\hat{T} + \hat{T}''$ is due to the underestimate that arises from the substitution of zero in place of true values of characteristics that are not zero.

Many of the parameters in $V(\hat{T})$ and $V(\hat{T} + \hat{T}'')$ are the same as those in $V(\hat{X}_b)$ and $V(\hat{X}_b'')$, respectively, and the same comments that were stated in the variance of the estimate under the weighting method and the historical data substitution data method apply to the variances of $\hat{T}$ and $\hat{T} + \hat{T}''$.

7.   RATIO ESTIMATION

Ratio estimation may be used to reduce the bias due to nonresponse, which may exist in the numerator and denominator of the ratio estimate but which

may cancel out or at least be greatly reduced when the ratio of two biased estimates is obtained. Whatever imputation procedure is used to estimate both X
and Y, respectively, the total of the survey variable characteristic and the total
of the auxiliary variable characteristic, the ratio estimate for X would be given by

$$\hat{X}_{(R)}^G = Y(\hat{X}^G/\hat{Y}^G),$$

where $\hat{X}^G$ and $\hat{Y}^G$ are estimates of X and Y under any imputation procedure
and are given by (8).

The use of ratio estimate is appropriate when an auxiliary variable Y has
a known total and a high correlation exists between the values of the characteristics X_i and Y_i. The use of ratio estimate is not appropriate when $\hat{X}^G$ and
$\hat{Y}^G$ are obtained from different respondents because the correlation between
$\hat{X}^G$ and $\hat{Y}^G$ would be considerably lower than in the case when the estimates of
X and Y are based on the same respondents. For example, if there exist partial
respondents who respond for the y characteristic but not for the characteristic
and the zero substitution method is employed separately to estimate X and Y,
then $\hat{T}_y$, the estimate of the total of the y variables, will be based on more
respondents than $\hat{T}$. Here, T_y, which is the expected value of $\hat{T}_y$, corresponds
to T with X_i replaced by Y_i. In such a case, the ratio $\hat{T}_x/\hat{T}_y$ would be a serious
underestimate of the ratio X/Y and there would also exist sampling and nonsampling variance. Consequently, the ratio estimation procedure is usually
appropriate for estimating totals only when common respondents as well as a
common imputation procedure are applied to estimate X and Y separately.

7.1. Expected Value of the Ratio Estimate

If we neglect the ratio estimate bias, the expected value of a ratio estimate
$\hat{X}_{(R)}^G$ is given by

$$E\hat{X}_{(R)}^G = Y(E\hat{X}^G/E\hat{Y}^G), \tag{29}$$

and, for each imputation procedure, the bias of $\hat{X}^G$ is obtained from $X - E\hat{X}^G$
as in expressions (12) for the weighting and duplication methods, (20) for
historical data substitution [case (i)], (23) for historical data substitution [case
(ii)], and (26) for the zero substitution method. $Y - E\hat{Y}^G$ may be obtained by
substituting Y_i for X_i and interpreting all parameters as referring to the auxiliary
variable instead of the survey characteristics X_i.

7.2. Variance of the Ratio Estimate

The variance of a ratio estimate is given by

$$V(\hat{X}_{(R)}^G) = Y^2 \left(\frac{EX^G}{E\hat{Y}^G}\right)^2 V\left(\hat{X}^G - \frac{EX^G}{EY^G}\hat{Y}^G\right),$$

where

$$\hat{X}^G - \frac{E X^G}{E Y^G} \hat{Y}^G = \sum_i \pi_i^{-1} \left\{ \delta_i \left[X_i + {}_R\varepsilon_{ix} - \frac{E\hat{X}^G}{E\hat{Y}^G}(Y_i + {}_R\varepsilon_{iy}) \right] \right.$$

$$\left. + (1 - \delta_i)\left[X_i + {}_{NR}\varepsilon_{ix} - \frac{E\hat{X}^G}{E\hat{Y}^G}(Y_i + {}_{NR}\varepsilon_{iy}) \right] \right\}. \quad (30)$$

In (30), additional symbols pertaining to the survey and auxiliary variables have been defined. For example, ${}_R\varepsilon_{ix} = {}_R\varepsilon_i$ (as defined earlier) and ${}_R\varepsilon_{iy} =$ the response error for characteristic y; similarly, for other variables and parameters.

$V[\hat{X}^G - (E\hat{X}^G/E\hat{Y}^G)\hat{Y}^G]$ is the variance of the "adjusted" estimate for ratio estimation procedure given in square brackets, where $\hat{X}^G$ and $\hat{Y}^G$ are estimates of X and Y under any imputation procedure such as any one of the procedures considered by us; the same imputation procedure would be employed for $\hat{X}^G$ and $\hat{Y}^G$, and it shall be assumed that the same missingness pattern exists for the x and y characteristic data.

Whatever the imputation procedure, $V[\hat{X}^G - (E\hat{X}^G/E\hat{Y}^G)\hat{Y}^G]$ will be identical to $V(\hat{X}^G)$ with the parameters and variables pertaining to $[X_i + {}_R\varepsilon_{ix} - P(Y_i + {}_R\varepsilon_{iy})]$ instead of $X_i + {}_R\varepsilon_i$, where $P = E\hat{X}^G/E\hat{Y}^G$. The simple response variance $({}_R\sigma_i)^2$ employed in the nonsampling variance components would be replaced by $[{}_R\sigma_{i(x-Py)}]^2$, which may be expanded into

$$[{}_R\sigma_{i(x-Py)}]^2 = ({}_R\sigma_{ix})^2 - 2Pr_{2:iixy}({}_R\sigma_{ix})({}_R\sigma_{iy}) + P^2({}_R\sigma_{iy})^2,$$

where $r_{2:iixy}$ is the correlation between $X_i + {}_R\varepsilon_{ix}$ and $Y_i + {}_R\varepsilon_{iy}$.

To illustrate the analogy between the variance of the ratio estimate and that of the simple estimate, we shall consider the ratio estimate when $\hat{X}$ and $\hat{Y}$ are both obtained under the weighting method. The ratio estimate of X under the weighting method is given by $\hat{X}_{(R)} = Y\hat{P}$, where $\hat{P} = \hat{X}/\hat{Y}$, estimating the ratio X/Y with a ratio estimate bias as well as a response and imputation bias for each of $\hat{X}$ and $\hat{Y}$. We shall denote $E\hat{X}/E\hat{Y}$ by P, which is not necessarily X/Y. Then

$$V(\hat{X}_{(R)}) = Y^2(E\hat{X}/E\hat{Y})^2 V(X - P\hat{Y}),$$

where

$$V(\hat{X}_b - P\hat{Y}) = \sum_b V(\hat{X}_b - P\hat{Y}_b) + \sum_{b \neq c} \text{Cov}(\hat{X}_b - P\hat{Y}_b, \hat{X}_c - P\hat{Y}_c),$$

$$V(\hat{X}_b - P\hat{Y}_b) = \bar{\alpha}_b^{-2} V_s \left\{ \pi_i^{-1} \left[f_{b(x-Py)}(i) + \frac{T_{bx} - PT_{by}}{En_b}\pi_i \right] \right\} \quad (SV)$$

$$+ \bar{\alpha}_b^{-2} \sum_i \pi_i^{-1}[\alpha_i^2 + V(\delta_i)][{}_R\sigma_i(x - Py)]^2 \quad (SRV)$$

$$+ \bar{\alpha}_b^{-2} \sum_{i \neq j} \pi_{ij}\pi_i^{-1}\pi_j^{-1}$$

(*Equation Continues*)

$$\cdot \left[\alpha_i \alpha_j + \text{Cov}(\delta_i, \delta_j)\right] r_{2 : ij(x - Py)} \left[_R \sigma_{i(x - Py)}\right]\left[_R \sigma_{j(x - Py)}\right]$$

$$+ \bar{\alpha}_b^{-2} \sum_i \pi_i^{-1} V(\delta_i) \left[f_{b(x - Py)}(i)\right]^2 \qquad (\text{VR}\bar{\text{R}})$$

$$+ \bar{\alpha}_b^{-2} \sum_{i = j} \pi_{ij} \pi_i^{-1} \pi_j^{-1} \text{Cov}(\delta_i, \delta_j) \left[f_{b(x - Py)}(i)\right]\left[f_{b(x - Py)}(i)\right]. \quad (31)$$

As defined before, $T_{bx} = T_b = \sum \alpha_i (X_i + {}_R B_{ix})$, $T_{by} = \sum \alpha_i (Y_i + {}_R B_{iy})$, and

$$f_{b(x - Py)}(i) = (X_i + {}_R B_{ix}) - P(Y_i + {}_R B_{iy}) - \frac{T_{bx} - P T_{by}}{E n_b \bar{\alpha}_b}.$$

The corresponding covariance between the adjusted estimates in cells b and c should be evident from adopting (16) to derive $\text{Cov}(\hat{X}_b - P\hat{Y}_b, \hat{X}_c - P\hat{Y}_c)$.

7.3.   Discussion of the Variance of the Ratio Estimate

If $\hat{X}$ and $\hat{Y}$ are highly correlated when taking into account both the sampling and nonsampling covariances between $\hat{X}$ and $\hat{Y}$, then the ratio estimate will have a lower variance than the corresponding simple estimate regardless of the imputation procedure undertaken. As is well known from sampling theory (Cochran, 1963, for example), the efficiency of the ratio estimate relative to the simple estimate depends upon the correlation between the estimates of the survey and auxiliary characteristics, in this case between $\hat{X}$ and $\hat{Y}$, and the ratio estimate is superior when

$$r_{\hat{X}, \hat{Y}} > \tfrac{1}{2} CV(\hat{Y})/CV(\hat{X}),$$

when $\hat{X}$ and $\hat{Y}$ are both positive. Here $CV(\hat{X})$ is the coefficient of variation of X or $\sqrt{V(\hat{X})}/E\hat{X}$, and similarly for $\hat{Y}$. $\text{Cov}(\hat{X}, \hat{Y})$ may be derived from the following equation:

$$V(\hat{X} - P\hat{Y}) = V(\hat{X}) - 2P \text{Cov}(\hat{X}, \hat{Y}) + P^2 V(\hat{Y}). \qquad (32)$$

The imputation procedure as well as the sample design could have an effect on the magnitude of the correlation between $\hat{X}$ and $\hat{Y}$.

8.   OVERVIEW OF THE ESTIMATES AND THEIR BIASES

The estimates under any of the imputation procedures described so far may be interpreted as variations in weighting methods even though we reserved the term for a specific procedure. The estimate may be stated as an application of weights to observed responses, where the weights include not only the inverse selection probabilities but also the inverses of estimated response probabilities.

In algebraic terms, the estimate under most imputation procedures, including those described in this paper, may be written as

$$\hat{X}^G = \sum_{i=1}^{n} \left[\delta_i x_i + (1 - \delta_i)\delta_i' x_i' \right](\pi_i^{-1} \hat{\alpha}_i^{-1}). \tag{33}$$

x_i and x_i' are defined by $X_i + {}_R\varepsilon_i$ and $X_i + {}_{NR}\varepsilon_i'$; other symbols have been defined earlier.

In Table 2, $\sum_i' = \sum_{i=1}^{n_b}$, summation over the n_b sampled units in cell b. The variable δ_i' is defined in the glossary of terms (see definition in Appendix E21).

The estimated response probability pertaining to the ratio estimate as in each of the two earlier cases may also be regarded as an estimate of the compound probability of both response and coverage. An underestimate of X or Y from the sample alone may occur even after imputation for nonresponse is applied because of a lack of coverage of some units. Ratio estimation, however, will result in an imputation for missing data due to undercoverage. We have only dealt with a combined ratio estimate for simplicity but the methodology could be easily extended to a separate ratio estimate.

The bias in the estimates under all imputation procedures, apart from the response bias, results from the estimated response probability differing from the true response probabilities and a correlation between the value of the

TABLE 2

Estimated Response Probability $\hat{\alpha}_i$ by Imputation Procedure

Procedure	Estimate response probability	Other comments
Weighting method	$\hat{\alpha}_i = m_b/n_b$	$m_b = \sum_i'\delta_i,\ \delta_i' \equiv 0$
Duplication method	$\hat{\alpha}_i = [n_b/m_b]^{-1}$ or $[n_b/m_b + 1]^{-1}$	$m_b = \sum_i'\delta_i,\ \delta_i' \equiv 0$
Historical data substitution		
Case (i)	$\hat{\alpha}_i = 1$	$\delta_i' \equiv 1$
Case (ii)	$\hat{\alpha}_i = (m_b + m_b')/n_b$	$m_b' = \sum_i'(1 - \delta_i)\delta_i'$
Zero substitution		
Case (i): $\hat{T}$	$\hat{\alpha}_i = 1$	$\delta_i' \equiv 0$
Case (ii): $\hat{T} + \hat{T}''$	$\hat{\alpha}_i = 1$	
Ratio estimate		
Weighting method (both x and y variables)	$\hat{\alpha}_i = (\hat{Y}/Y)(m_b/n_b)$	$m_b = \sum_i'\delta_i,\ \delta_i \equiv 0$
Zero substitution method [Case (i), both x and y variables]	$\hat{\alpha}_i = \hat{T}_y/Y$	$\delta_i' \equiv 0$

characteristic and the true response probabilities. By delineating cells for imputation purposes, for example, strata or clusters, one attempts to employ estimated response probabilities as close to the true values as possible. The most
common procedure is to employ response rates which are equivalent to estimates of average response probabilities in adjustment cells, where it would be
expected that the response probabilities and the characteristics would be
homogeneous compared with the whole area represented by all sampled units.
Since the bias is additive over the delineated B cells, one may discuss the bias
at the cell level and reflect on the sum of the individual biases at the area level.

Depending on the magnitude and sign of the response probabilities, it
would seem that in most cases, the bias of greatest magnitude occurs in the case
of the zero substitution method. The nonresponse or imputation bias at the
cell level is observed to be $\sum_{i=1}^{N_b} (1 - \alpha_i)X_i$ and a great underestimate of X_b
will occur if the response bias $\sum_{i=1}^{N_b} \alpha_i(_RB_i)$ is also negative. However, if the
$_RB_i$ are positive, the response bias will offset and may even nullify the large
negative imputation bias. It should be noted that when a mean per unit or ratio
estimate is obtained, the bias will not necessarily be of the greatest magnitude
(see Section 5.9).

A response bias of slightly higher magnitude of $\bar{\alpha}_b^{-1} \sum_{i=1}^{N_b} \alpha_i(_RB_i)$ occurs in
the case of weighting method, but the imputation bias $\bar{\alpha}_b^{-1} \sum_{i=1}^{N_b} (\alpha_i - \bar{\alpha}_b)X_i$ is
expected to be much lower in magnitude than $\sum_{i=1}^{N_b} (1 - \alpha_i)X_i$, since some α_i
will exceed $\bar{\alpha}_b$ while others will not. The imputation bias may also be written
$\bar{\alpha}_b^{-1}En_b \, \mathrm{Cov}_b^*(\alpha_i, X_i/\pi_i)$, and in this expression, the covariance between the response probabilities and the characteristic may be high or low depending on
how the response probabilities are related to the characteristics.

The response bias and imputation bias due to historical substitution present
in the combined historical substitution and weighting methods of imputation
may be observed to be

$$(\bar{\alpha}_b + \bar{\alpha}_b'')^{-1} \sum_{i=1}^{N_b} \left[\alpha_i(_RB_i) + \alpha_i''(_{NR}B_i')\right].$$

The imputation bias $_{NR}B_i'$ may tend to be higher in magnitude than $_RB_i$, since
historical data may tend to be "further from the truth" than current data. In
any case, $\alpha_i(_RB_i) + \alpha_i''(_{NR}B_i')$ is higher than $\alpha_i(_RB_i)$ unless $_RB_i$ and $_{NR}B_i'$ are of
opposite signs, but the higher magnitude of the bias component may be more
than offset by a factor $(\bar{\alpha}_b + \bar{\alpha}_b'')^{-1}$, which is lower than $\bar{\alpha}_b^{-1}$. Finally, in comparing
the imputation biases

$$\bar{\alpha}_b^{-1} \sum_{i=1}^{N_b} (\alpha_i - \bar{\alpha}_b)X_i \qquad \text{and} \qquad (\bar{\alpha}_b + \bar{\alpha}_b'')^{-1} \sum_{i=1}^{N_b} (\alpha_i + \alpha_i'' - \bar{\alpha}_b - \bar{\alpha}_b'')X_i,$$

we note again the factor $(\bar{\alpha}_b + \bar{\alpha}_b'')^{-1}$ is smaller than $\bar{\alpha}_b^{-1}$. It is somewhat difficult
to compare $(\alpha_i + \alpha_i'' - \bar{\alpha}_b - \bar{\alpha}_b'')X_i$ and $(\alpha_i - \bar{\alpha}_b)X_i$. In many situations, as for
example, when response probabilities are high (say, greater than 0.85), the
$\alpha_i + \alpha_i''$ would be closer to one than α_i and may have smaller variability between

the units. The small variability in the $\alpha_i + \alpha_i''$ compared with the α_i may in turn be reflected in smaller covariances between $\alpha_i + \alpha_i''$ and X_i/π_i than between α_i and X_i/π_i, resulting in a lower imputation bias due to weighting when historical data are substituted whenever possible as opposed to only the application of the weighting method.

9. FURTHER DISCUSSION ABOUT THE VARIANCES

For all the particular imputation procedures considered, there are five variance components, designated SV, SRV, CRV, VR$\bar{\text{R}}$, and CVR$\bar{\text{R}}$. Comparisons between the variances may be more easily considered by comparing individual components than studying the variances in total.

The SRV and CRV of $\hat{T}_b$ is lower than those of $\hat{X}_b$ by a factor of $\bar{\alpha}_b^{-2}$, while SV, VR$\bar{\text{R}}$, and CVR$\bar{\text{R}}$ may be expected to be lower for $\hat{X}_b$, which may be written as $n_b(\hat{T}_b/m_b)$, than for $\hat{T}_b$ because of the high correlation between $\hat{T}_b$ and m_b when applying the ratio estimation procedure while only a simple weight inflation is employed in $\hat{T}_b$, the zero imputation estimate. Offsetting the potential variance reduction, however, is the inflation of terms in the three components by the factor $\bar{\alpha}_b^{-2}$, a factor which does not exist in the variance components of $\hat{T}_b$.

The duplication method automatically results in an increase in the variance compared with the weighting method, the extent of which is unknown but will always exist in the context of variable response rates, since the weight n_b/m_b will not always be an integer. One would expect the increase $EV_4(\hat{X}_b^{\text{D}})$ to be of the order of 10% of $V(\hat{X}_b)$ in view of the methodology on the variance of duplication versus weighting for srs estimates derived by Hansen *et al.* (1953).

One would expect most of the variance components of $V(\hat{X}_b')$ to be lower than those of $V(\hat{X}_b)$ because of the use of more information in the estimation by the historical data substitution method. However, the decrease in the variances depends largely on the correlation between current and historical data and or the relation between response variances of historical data and those of current data.

To complete the study of comparisons between the methods, one would have to consider the mean square errors of the estimates, which include also the square of the biases along with the sampling and nonsampling variance. While one may conjecture differences in variance components as we have done here, it is difficult to compare the total variances and even more difficult to compare mean square errors. Consequently, we have set up in the next chapter a hypothetical example with what we feel are realistic parameters at the unit (dwelling) level and calculated the variances, biases, and mean square errors under different imputation procedures.

REFERENCES AND BIBLIOGRAPHY

Bailar, J. C. III, and Bailar, B. A. (1978). Comparison of two procedures for imputing missing survey values. In *Imputation and Editing of Faulty or Missing Survey Data*, pp. 65–75. Selected papers presented at 1978 ASA Meeting, compiled by Social Security Administration.

Cochran, W. G. (1963). *Sampling Techniques* (2nd ed.). New York: Wiley.

Fellegi, I. P. (1964). Response variance and its estimation. *Journal of the American Statistical Association* 59: 1016–1041.

Hansen, M. H., Hurwitz, W. N., and Madow, W. G. (1953). *Sample Survey Methods and Theory* (Vol. 11), pp. 139–141. New York: Wiley.

Horvitz, D. G., and Thompson, D. J. (1952). A generalization of sampling without replacement from a finite universe. *Journal of the American Statistical Association* 47: 663–685.

Koch, G. (1973). An alternative approach to multivariate response error models for sample survey data with applications to estimators involving sub-class means. *Journal of the American Statistical Association* 68: 906–913.

Platek, R., Singh, M. P., and Tremblay, V. (1977). Adjustment for non-response in surveys. *Survey Methodology* 3(1): 1–24. (Statistical Services Field, Statistics Canada.)

CHAPTER 18

Hypothetical Example
with Imputation Procedures

Richard Platek
Gerald B. Gray

1. HYPOTHETICAL POPULATION

A hypothetical population of 50 households was made up with 8 clusters of 3–10 households in each. The characteristic for each household was its size, and the sizes were distributed among the 50 households in approximately the same distribution as in the 1976 census, including vacants so that the sizes ranged from 0 (vacant households) to 9.

Response probabilities from almost 1 for large households to as low as .72 for small households of one person were designated in such a manner that the correlation between response probabilities and the size of households was positive though not unrealistically large. The overall expected response rate was taken as .874, resulting in an average nonresponse rate of 12.6%, a not too unrealistic level of nonresponse in household surveys when interviewers are used.

Response errors of -2, -1, $+1$, and $+2$ were assumed possible in each unit with assigned probabilities of attaining each error. Also, it was assumed that the probability of obtaining accurate counts in large households was lower than in smaller households. In addition, small probabilities of calling households vacant when in fact they are occupied were assigned for every household. If X_i denotes the size of the household, then an erroneously declared vacant household would result in a response error of $-X_i$. The probabilities of observing response errors of various magnitudes result in the calculations of the response bias $_RB_i$

INCOMPLETE DATA
IN SAMPLE SURVEYS
Volume 2, Part V

and response variance $_R\sigma_i^2$ for each household. A tendency toward an undercount was assumed.

2. HYPOTHETICAL EXAMPLE

The purpose of the hypothetical example is two fold: (a) to compare the mean square errors of estimates by the different imputation procedures and (b) to demonstrate the feasibility of calculating the various measures given in Tables 6–9. Even with the use of average parameters such as average variances and correlation coefficients, it appears difficult to compare the variances pertaining to the estimates by the different imputation procedures without recourse to actual numbers. Further developmental work in the expressions in terms of the average parameters may render possible simple comparisons between the theoretical variances on the basis of various responses rates, sampling and response variances, and the magnitude to the various correlation coefficents, but such an analysis lies in the future.

A two-stage design such as in the hypothetical example is a realistic one since cities often contain block faces of varying sizes and the strata may be very large or small depending upon the conditions of the survey being undertaken. In the example, the stratum size is small compared with many large household surveys.

An average correlation of responses between households in different clusters and within clusters is assumed rather than assigning individual correlation coefficients between every pair of households in the stratum. The same holds true for the correlation between the events of responding or not responding between households. Empirical data on realistic value of correlation coefficients is lacking, so the best we could do under these circumstances was to assume an average correlation coefficient of .05 within clusters and .02 in distinct clusters. The coefficients may lean toward higher rather than lower values than these in practice, and later on we may reexamine the nonsampling variance components with higher correlation coefficients.

The sample design in the example was as follows: a selection of 2, 3, 4, and 5 clusters out of 8 by ppswor scheme and within each selected cluster, a selection of 2 or 3 dwellings by srswor scheme. The biases and variances of the estimates under each imputation procedure were calculated for each of the eight above cases, using expressions derived in Appendixes A–C[1] and adapted to the above sample design in Appendix D.

The hypothetical example of 50 units with the relevant parameters is given in the following. The parameters sizes of households, response probabilities, probabilities of errors in the observed sizes, and the resultant response biases and response variances are given in Table 3.

[1] All references to appendixes refer to appendixes to Part V (Chapter 19).

TABLE 3

Hypothetical Population of Units in Stratum Probability
of Observed Deviation from True Value[a]

i	X_i	α_i	$p(-X_i)$	$p(-2)$	$p(-1)$	$p(0)$	$p(+1)$	$p(+2)$	$_RB_i$	$_R\sigma_i^2$
1										
1	5	.84	.005	.15	.205	.58	.06		−.47	.7691
2	3	.86	.01	.09	.16	.69	.04	.01	−.31	.5939
3	2	.78		.08	.12	.80			−.28	.3616
SUM	10	2.48							−1.06	1.7246
2										
1	1	.89			.07	.90	.03		−.04	.0984
2	2	.83		.01	.10	.85	.04		−.08	.1736
3	2	.91		.02	.14	.78	.06		−.12	.2656
4	1	.72			.03	.95	.02		−.01	.0499
5	6	.98	.055	.05	.15	.7	.095		−.185	.590775
6	0	.94				.95	.05		.05	.0475
7	3	.93	.03	.02	.15	.75	.05		−.23	.4971
SUM	15	6.20							−.615	1.722875
3										
1	2	.92		.04	.02	.93	.01		−.09	.1819
2	3	.84	.01	.03	.13	.7	.08	.05	−.04	.6184
3	1	.82			.1	.89	.01		−.09	.1019
4	2	.91		.01	.12	.84	.03		−.11	.1779
5	3	.83	.015	.005	.06	.9	.02		−.095	.225975
6	8	.99	.005	.10	.20	.665	.02	.01	−.40	.8200
SUM	19	5.31							−.825	2.126075
4										
1	1	.79			.19	.8	.01		−.18	.1676
2	2	.86		.09	.02	.88	.01		−.19	.3539
3	2	.84		.05	.01	.94			−.11	.1979
4	3	.88	.01	.07	.1	.8	.02		−.25	.4275
5	5	.77	.005	.01	.065	.86	.06		−.05	.2875
6	4	.93	.008	.002	.05	.92	.02		−.066	.201644
7	4	.77	.008	.01	.14	.83	.012		−.18	.2876
8	0	.92				.9	.1		.10	.09
9	3	.83	.006	.004	.06	.92	.01		−.076	.134224
10	6	.90	.005	.005	.04	.93	.02		−.06	.2564
SUM	30	8.49							−1.062	2.404268
5										
1	2	.89		.025	.08	.86	.03	.005	−.09	.2219
2	1	.92			.08	.91	.01		−.07	.0851
3	3	.83	.009	.002	.05	.93	.009		−.072	.142816
4	4	.94	.01	.04	.09	.84	.02		−.19	.3939
5	3	.83	.05	.01	.13	.78	.03		−.27	.5771
SUM	13	4.41							−.692	1.420816

(*Continued next page*)

TABLE 3 (*Continued*)

i	X_i	α_i	$p(-X_i)$	$p(-2)$	$p(-1)$	$p(0)$	$p(+1)$	$p(+2)$	$_R B_i$	$_R \sigma_i^2$
6										
1	7	.94	.004	.06	.1	.75	.08	.006	−.156	.615664
2	2	.97		.03	.08	.88	.01		−.13	.1931
3	4	.94	.007	.023	.05	.9	.02		−.104	.263184
4	9	.92	.002	.028	.08	.8	.08	.01	−.054	.471084
5	4	.88	.009	.021	.08	.83	.06		−.098	.358396
6	5	.83	.01	.04	.1	.78	.07		−.16	.5544
7	6	.84	.003	.01	.04	.94	.007		−.071	.189959
8	5	.90	.004	.016	.05	.89	.04		−.062	.250156
SUM	42	7.22							−.835	2.895943
7										
1	1	.72			.05	.94	.01		−.04	.0584
2	2	.94		.03	.03	.93	.01		−.09	.1536
3	4	.88	.01	.01	.05	.92	.01		−.1	.25
4	5	.86	.008	.012	.07	.86	.05		−.084	.360944
SUM	12	3.40							−.304	.822944
8										
1	2	.80		.04	.05	.89	.02		−.11	.2179
2	0	.92				.94	.06		.06	.0564
3	4	.90	.01	.02	.08	.87	.02		−.14	.3204
4	3	.84	.015	.005	.06	.9	.02		−.095	.225975
5	7	.96	.003	.017	.05	.91	.015	.005	−.08	.2935
6	4	.87	.006	.014	.05	.93			−.102	.191595
7	2	.90		.04	.01	.95			−.09	.1619
SUM	22	6.19							−.557	1.467771
SUM	163	43.70							−5.95	14.585292

 " Symbols used in the hypothetical population:

i = household = (i, i_2), where i = cluster no. and i_2, the household within cluster.
X_i = true value of characteristic (size of household in terms of numbers of individuals within household i).
α_i = response probability pertaining to household i.
d_i = response error $_R\varepsilon_i$ in the observed number of individuals (values of $-2, -1, 0, +1, +2$, and $-X_i$ were assumed.
Pr(d_i) = probability of response error d_i.
Pr($-X_i$) = probability of household being erroneously declared vacant (unless household is actually vacant; i.e., when $X_i = 0$).
$_R B_i$ = response bias = $\sum_{d_i} \text{Pr}(d_i)d_i$.
$_R\sigma_i^2$ = response variance = $\sum_{d_i} \text{Pr}(d_i)d_i^2 - {_R}B_i^2$.
SUM = sum over all units in a cluster and finally over all clusters.

A guide to the calculations is presented in Section 5 at the end of the chapter after the analysis of mean square errors of the estimates under the different imputation procedures.

3. NUMERICAL DATA OBTAINED FROM HYPOTHETICAL EXAMPLE

The bias, sampling variance, nonsampling variance, and the mean square errors have been calculated for the estimates of the total number of individuals in the hypothetical stratum for various sample sizes (see Table 4). In the estimates, $w = t./n_1 n_2$, where $t. = 50$ (households), $n_1 =$ number of clusters selected (out of $N_1 = 8$), and $n_2 =$ number of households selected in each selected cluster (out of t_i in cluster i). $_R\varepsilon_i =$ error in observed count of individuals in household $\mathbf{i}$; $\mathbf{i} = (i, i_2)$; $\delta_i = (1 - \delta_i)\delta_i' = 1$ or 0 according as historical data (assumed to be the same as current data) are available or not given that the unit does not respond. We have assumed that $E\delta_i'' = (1 - \alpha_i)\alpha_i'$, neglecting the possible correlation between δ_i and δ_i'. In practice, a correlation may exist between δ_i and δ_i', since historical data may be less likely available for nonrespondents than respondents as, for example, in the case of refusals in continuing surveys.

The true number of individuals in this hypothetical stratum was 163 and the total bias as in Table 6 is relative to this total. Since the biases at individual levels have been assumed to be independent of both the sample selected and the sample size, the total biases of the various estimates, along with their response and imputation components are independent of the sample size. In practice, this condition may not always hold as we have pointed out in the development of the expected value of the estimate $\hat{X}_b^1$ in Appendix A.

The sampling and nonsampling variances have been calculated in Tables 7 and 8, respectively, by the appropriate formulas stated in earlier sections. Finally, in Table 9, the mean square error, defined as the sum of the square of the bias, the sampling variance, and the non-sampling variance, is provided. The variances and mean square errors have been calculated for different sample sizes of 2–5 clusters and 2 or 3 households in each selected cluster.

Formulas (1)–(3) in Appendix D were used to calculate the sampling and nonsampling variances, while the bias may be obtained from Eq. (12) or (26) in Chapter 17 with i replaced by vector $\mathbf{i}$.

TABLE 4

Estimates Obtained for the Hypothetical Stratum and Assumptions

(i)	Without response error and full response	$\hat{X} = w \sum_i' X_i$
(ii)	With response error but full response	$\hat{X} = w \sum_i' (X_i + {}_R\varepsilon_i)$
(iii)	Zero substitution method of imputation	$\hat{T}_b = w \sum_i' \delta_i (X_i + {}_R\varepsilon_i)$
(iv)	Weighting method	$\hat{X}_b = [(n_1 n_2)/\sum_i' \delta_i]\hat{T}_b$
(v)	Historical substitution and weighting methods $\alpha_i' = 1/3$	$\hat{X}_b = [(n_1 n_2)/\sum_i' (\delta_i + \delta_i'')](\hat{T}_b + \hat{T}_b'')$
(vi)	As in (v) but $\alpha_i' = 2/3$	As in (v) with higher values of α_i'
(vii)	Duplication method	$\hat{X}_b^D = w \sum_i' \delta_i w_i (X_i + {}_R\varepsilon_i)$, $w_i = 1$ or 2

TABLE 5

Reference for Formula and Substitutions to Obtain Biases, Sampling,
and Nonsampling Variances[a]

	Estimate	Bias	Substitution in Eqs. (1)–(3) in Appendix D to sampling and nonsampling variances			
			$\bar{\alpha}_b$	$\bar{\alpha}_i$	$f(\mathbf{i})$	$_R\sigma_i$
(i)	Without response error and full response	No bias	1	1	X_i	0
(ii)	With response error, but with full response	Eq. (12) in Chapter 17 with $\alpha_i = \bar{\alpha}_b = 1$	1	1	$X_i + {}_RB_i$	$_R\sigma_i$
(iii)	Zero substitution for nonresponse	Eq. (26) in Chapter 17 with $\alpha_i'' = 0$	1	α_i	$X_i + {}_RB_i$	$_R\sigma_i$
(iv)	Weighting method of imputation	Eq. (12) in Chapter 17	$\bar{\alpha}_b$	α_i	$X_i + {}_RB_i - c$	$_R\sigma_i$
(v)	Historical substitution method and weighting (1/3 records available)	Eq. (12) in Chapter 17 with α_i replaced by $\alpha_i + (1 - \alpha_i)(1/3)$	$\bar{\alpha}_b + \alpha_b''$	$\alpha_i + \alpha_i''$	$X_i + {}_RB_i - c'$	$_R\sigma_i$
(vi)	As in (v) (2/3 records available)	Eq. (12) in Chapter 17 α_i replaced by $\sigma + (1 - \alpha_i)(2/3)$	$\bar{\alpha}_b + \alpha_b''$	$\alpha_i + \alpha_i''$	$X_i + {}_RB_i - c'$	$_R\sigma_i$
(vii)	Duplication method	As in (iv)	For the duplication method, an additional sampling and nonsampling variance component is added to those pertaining to the weighting method and consequently must be dealt with in a special way. See description of estimate by duplication method in Chapter 17.			

[a] As given in Tables 6–8. $c = \sum_i \alpha_i (X_i + {}_RB_i)/\sum_i \alpha_i$ and $c' = \sum_i (\alpha_i + \alpha_i'')(X_i + {}_RB_i)/\sum_i (\alpha_i + \alpha_i'')$.

TABLE 6

Bias of Estimate[a]

	Estimate	Response bias	Imputation bias	Total bias
(i)	Without response error and full response	0	0	0
(ii)	With response error but full response	-5.95	0	-5.95
(iii)	Zero substitution method of imputation	-5.20	-18.77	-23.97
(iv)	Weighting method of imputation	-5.95	2.02	-3.93
(v)	Historical substitution and weighting (1/3 records available)	-5.95	1.29	-4.67
(vi)	As in (v) (2/3 records available)	-5.95	.62	-5.34
(vii)	Duplication method	-5.95	2.02	-3.93

[a] Compared with "true" total of 163. Assumptions: (1) The ratio estimate bias inherent in weighting procedure is omitted in the above results. (2) The bias is assumed to be independent of both the sample selected and the sample size.

TABLE 7

Sampling Variances

	Estimate	No. hhlds[a]	Number of first-stage units selected			
			$n_1 = 2$	$n_1 = 3$	$n_1 = 4$	$n_1 = 5$
(i)	Without response error	2	2570.71	1578.62	1079.11	785.37
	and full response	3	1764.46	1041.12	675.98	462.87
(ii)	With response error but	2	2504.92	1536.42	1046.90	758.74
	with full response	3	1732.57	1021.52	660.73	449.80
(iii)	Zero substitution method	2	2176.66	1338.81	918.17	664.38
		3	1488.62	880.11	574.15	389.17
(iv)	Weighting method	2	2664.98	1641.70	1125.70	821.89
		3	1823.55	1080.75	704.99	485.31
(v)	Historical substitution	2	2604.00	1601.52	1095.62	797.77
	and weighting methods (1/3 records available)	3	1789.03	1058.21	688.14	471.79
(vi)	As in (v) (2/3 records	2	2551.19	1566.74	1069.58	776.90
	available)	3	1759.04	1038.54	673.51	460.04
(vii)	Duplication method	2	2855.08	1771.01	1223.54	900.57
		3	1948.98	1166.31	769.84	537.52

[a] No. hhlds = number of selected households in each selected cluster $= n_2$.

TABLE 8

Nonsampling Variances

	Estimate	No. hhlds[a]	Number of first-stage units selected			
			2	3	4	5
(i)	Without response error	2	0	0	0	0
	and full response	3	0	0	0	0
(ii)	With response error but	2	197.14	135.80	105.12	86.72
	with full response	3	139.12	97.12	76.12	63.52
(iii)	Zero substitution for	2	983.63	673.83	518.87	425.94
	nonresponse	3	688.73	477.22	371.42	307.98
(iv)	Weighting method of	2	500.88	338.04	256.06	207.76
	imputation	3	343.02	232,81	177.67	144.62
(v)	Historical substitution	2	391.15	264.97	201.87	164.02
	method and weighting (1/3 records available)	3	269.35	183.77	140.97	115.30
(vi)	As in (v) (2/3 records	2	290.23	197.78	151.54	123.81
	available)	3	201.60	138.69	107.23	88.36
(vii)	Duplication method	2	611.51	412.07	312.22	252.29
		3	416.64	282.10	214.71	174.28

[a] See note to Table 7.

TABLE 9

Mean Square Errors

	Estimate	Number of households	Number of first-stage units selected			
			2	3	4	5
(i)	Without response error	2	2570.71	1578.62	1079.11	785.37
	and full response	3	1764.46	1041.12	675.98	462.87
(ii)	With response error but	2	2737.46	1707.62	1187.43	907.86
	with full response	3	1907.09	1154.04	772.25	548.72
(iii)	Zero substitution for	2	3734.85	2587.20	2011.60	1664.88
	nonresponse	3	2751.91	1931.89	1520.13	1271.71
(iv)	Weighting method of	2	3181.30	1995.18	1397.74	1045.09
	imputation	3	2182.01	1329.00	898.10	645.37
(v)	Historical substitution	2	3016.96	1888.30	1319.30	983.60
	method and weighting	3	2080.19	1263.79	850.92	608.90
	(1/3 records available)					
(vi)	As in (v) (2/3 records	2	2869.94	1793.04	1249.64	929.23
	available)	3	1989.16	1205.85	809.26	576.92
(vii)	Duplication method	2	3482.03	2198.53	1551.20	1168.31
		3	2381.06	1463.84	999.98	727.24

The reference and adaptation of the formulas to the data of Tables 6–8 are given in Table 5.

4.   ANALYSIS OF TABLES 6–9

4.1.   Bias

The response bias is of course zero in the case of the estimate based on true observations and full response. As soon as response errors are taken into account, the response bias of -5.95 compared with 163 represents a 3.65% undercount in the case of all estimated containing response errors except the zero substitution method with a response bias of -5.20. The apparently constant response bias of -5.95 only occurs because of rounding and the lack of correlation between the response probability and the response bias. The deflation of the response bias to -5.20 for the zero substitution method from -5.95 is due to the fact that the response bias is only $\sum_i \alpha_{i.R} B_i$ instead of $\bar{\alpha}^{-1} \sum \alpha_{i.R} B_i$, so that it has been deflated by the overall response rate of about .874.

The imputation bias is observed to be 2.02 for the weighting and duplication method, representing a $+1.24\%$ bias compared with the true value of 163. The imputation bias gradually drops by about 1/3 and 2/3 with the use of historical records (assumed identical to current ones) for the two cases of the use of historical records. The positive bias arises in all cases because of a positive correlation between response probabilities and household sizes.

A high underestimate results from zero substitution for missing data, as one would expect, and the imputation bias of -18.77 represents an 11.5% underestimate of the total count. The smaller underestimate than the 12.6% expected nonresponse rate results from the negative correlation between the nonresponse probability and the characteristic.

The total bias, the sum of the response bias and the imputation bias, is clearly the worst in the case of the zero substitution method because of the underestimation that occurs for both responses and substitution of zero values. If there had been a tendency to overestimate in each response, there would have been some compensating biases for the case of zero substitution. However, the positive imputation bias did compensate in part for the negative response bias for the other imputation procedures. It should be noted that the total bias will not necessarily decrease as the response rate increases since the response bias and imputation bias may be of opposite sign. In such a case, the response bias may be about the same for a wide range of response rates while the imputation bias, decreasing with an increase in the response rate, will offset the response bias to a lesser extent as the response rate approaches one.

4.2. Sampling Variance

The sampling variance is roughly inversely proportional to the sample size, although in finite populations such as in this small stratum of 50 units, the decrease tends to be faster than indicated by the inverse sample size relation. As one would expect, whatever estimate is employed, the sampling variance is highest for a sample of only 4 households (2 clusters, 2 households in each) and lowest for a sample of 15 households (5 clusters, 3 households in each), and in all cases the ratio is about 5.5 or 5.6 to 1 compared with 3.75 to 1 for the ratio of the inverse sample sizes.

The sampling variances for the case of estimates without nonresponse but with response errors are slightly lower (by about 3%) than the variances for the estimates without any response errors.

Sampling variances tend to be roughly proportional to the size of the estimates and the 3% drop is in line with the 3.65% average underestimate when response errors are taken into account. As nonresponse tends to reduce the sample size, the sampling variances increase from the variances of the estimate without nonresponse by only $6\text{--}8\%$ to the estimates with imputation by weighting. This result is surprising in view of the expected reduction of the sample by about 12.6% as a result of nonresponse. We are unable to account for this discrepancy. A possible contributing factor to this discrepancy may lie in the effect of the positive correlation between $\hat{T}_b$ and m_b, which helps to reduce the variance of the ratio estimate $(n_b/m_b)\hat{T}_b$. This correlation may be accentuated by the positive correlation between the response probabilities and the sizes of the households in the stratum. As historical records are employed to the extent possible (1/3 and 2/3 assumed available), the sampling variance decreases from the variance under the weighting method by about 2% for the 1/3 available case and 4% for the 2/3 available case.

Not surprising is the minimum sampling variance for all cases that occur among the estimates by the zero substitution method in view of the estimates smaller than those for other cases and the variances are about 13 to 14% below the variances of the estimates with only response errors. However, the sampling variances are almost 20% below those for the estimates by the weighting method of imputation.

4.3.   Nonsampling Variances

If we ignore the correlated effects, the nonsampling variances are roughly inversely proportional to the sample size, and this relation holds for finite as well as infinite populations, since nonsampling variances occur among census estimates. Since our assumed correlation coefficients of .05 and .02 are quite conservative, the bulk of the nonsampling variances are due to the errors among individual units rather than pairs of units in this stratum. We find the ratio of the nonsampling variances for the smallest sample (4 households) to those for the largest sample (15 households) to be slightly more than 3 to 1 compared with the 3.75 ratio of the sample sizes. Therefore the correlated effect had some impact on the relation between nonsampling variance and sample size.

The zero substitution method clearly resulted in estimates with the highest nonsampling variances compared with the estimates by the other methods. Apparently, in this example, the contribution of the nonsampling variance component $\sum_i V(\delta_i)(X_i + {}_R B_i)^2 \pi_i^{-1}$ contributed to the high variance. In the weighting method the corresponding component became $\sum_i V(\delta_i)(X_i + {}_R B_i - c)^2 \pi_i - 1$, where $c = T_b / \sum \alpha_i$ and the contribution was considerably lower. There is no guarantee that the same situation would hold in all cases though one would expect the component to tend to be lower in the case of weighting since $(X_i + {}_R B_i - c)^2$ tends to be lower than $(X_i + {}_R B_i)^2$.

In the case of the imputation by weighting the nonsampling variances are about 20–30% of the sampling variances, the higher percentage occurring with the higher sample sizes. As historical data become available (in our example, equivalent to higher response rates), the nonsampling variances decrease approximately in a linear trend with the availability of historical data until the minimum nonsampling variance (except for the ideal case of neither response nor imputation error) occurs with the presence of only response variance of 8–15% of the sampling variance (see full response/response errors in Tables 6–9).

4.4   Mean Square Error

In this example, the sampling variances of the different estimates differ only marginally, except for the zero substitution method with the lowest sampling variance. The minimum sampling variance, however, is more than offset by the maximum bias and maximum nonsampling variance, resulting in a maximum mean square error for the zero substitution method estimates compared with the others. As in the case of the nonsampling variance, the trend in the mean square error for the various estimates is approximately a linear decrease as the effective response rate increases.

The mean square error of an estimate under the duplication method contains the mean square error of the estimate under the weighting method plus additional sampling and nonsampling variance components attributable solely to duplication. It can be seen from Table 9 that the additional mean square error of the estimate or the combined additional sampling and nonsampling variance ranges from 10 to 12% above the MSE of the estimate under the weighting method as the sample size increases from 4 to 15 dwellings. The additional mean square error may be decomposed into an additional sampling variance ranging from 7 to 11% and an additional nonsampling variance of about 20% over the corresponding variances under the weighting method.

5. GUIDE TO CALCULATION FOR TABLES 6–9

To calculate the bias and variance of the various estimates according to the formulas of Appendix D require 3 stages, as follows:

Stage 1

(a)   Calculate of $_RB_i$, $_R\sigma_i^2$, $V(\delta_i)$ for each unit (household) e.g., for $i = (1, 1)$:

$$_RB_i = .005(-5) + .15(-2) + .205(-1) + .06(+1) = -.47,$$

$$_R\sigma_i^2 = .005(25) + .15(4) + .205(1) + .06(1) - .47^2 = .7691.$$

During this stage of the calculations, the following relevant parameters for the variances are also obtained [data refer to $i = (1, 1)$]:

$$a_i = \begin{cases} X_i = 5 \\ \alpha_i = .84 \\ \sqrt{V(\delta_i)} = \sqrt{.84 \times .16} = .366606 \\ X_i + {_RB_i} = 5 - .47 = 4.53 \\ \alpha_i(X_i + {_RB_i}) = .84 \times 4.53 \\ \sqrt{V(\delta_i)}(X_i + {_RB_i}) = 1.660725 \\ _R\sigma_i = .876983 \\ \alpha_{iR}\sigma_i = .84 \times .876, 983 \\ \sqrt{V(\delta)}{_R\sigma_i} = .366, 606 \times .876983 \end{cases}$$

At the same time, $\sum_{i_2 \in i} a_i$ and $\sum_{i_2 \in i} a_i^2$ are being obtained and recorded at the cluster level. Here a_i refers to any of the relevant parameters listed.

(b)   Sums and sums of squares are recorded at each cluster level and and over all clusters. Whatever the parameters, the sum $a_i = \sum_{i_2 \in i} a_i$ and the sum of squares $\sum_{i_2 \in i} a_i^2$ are obtained for cluster i. Then $a = \sum_i a_i$ and $\sum_i a_i^2$ are obtained over all units (households) in the stratum.

The calculations are provided for cluster 1 and overall clusters in Table 10.

(c)   Finally before proceeding to stage 2, the sums and sums of squares pertaining to $a_i = \alpha_i(X_i + {}_R B_i - c)$ and $\sqrt{V(\delta_i)}(X_i + {}_R B_i - c)$ are obtained with $c = \sum_i \alpha_i(X_i + {}_R B_i)/\sum_i \alpha_i$. These calculations are needed in order to calculate $V(\hat{X}_b)$, the variance of the estimate due to weighting method. These are

	Cluster 1 level		Stratum level	
a_i	a_i	$\sum_{i_2 \in i} a_i^2$	$a.$	$\sum_i a_i^2$
$\alpha_i(X_i + {}_R B_i - c)$	$-.429598$	2.76122	0	164.781576
$\sqrt{V(\delta_i)}(X_i + {}_R B_i - c)$	$-.281451$	$.639986$	-3.053386	16.718745

Stage 2

Calculations of

$$g(a_i) = \sum_{i>j} \pi_{ij}[(a_i a_j)/(t_i t_j)] \quad \text{and} \quad h(a_i) = \sum_i [1/(t_i - 1)][a_i^2 - \sum_{i_2 \in i} a_i^2],$$

two relevant expressions in the variance formulas, are obtained for all parameters a_i listed; $g(a_i)$ must be obtained separately for each sample size n_1, since π_{ij} in the joint inclusion probability of clusters i and j and varies with n_1. π_{ij}

TABLE 10

Parameter	Cluster 1 level		Stratum level	
a_i	a_i	$\sum_{i_2 \in i} a_i^2$	$a.$	$\sum_i a_i^2$
X_i	10	38	163	739
α_i	2.48	2.0536	43.7	38.391
$\sqrt{V(\delta_i)}$	1.127839	.4264	15.842762	5.309
$X_i + {}_R B_i$	8.94	30.7154	157.050	694.2527
$\alpha_i(X_i + {}_R B_i)$	7.4602	21.631257	137.02587	563.009284
$\sqrt{V(\delta_i)}(X_i + {}_R B_i)$	3.306624	4.136897	47.348306	60.783919
${}_R \sigma_i$	2.248964	1.7246	25.634243	14.585292
$\alpha_{iR} \sigma_i$	1.868463	1.201923	22.513091	11.403055
$\sqrt{V(\delta_i)}_R \sigma_i$	.838012	.236923	7.979407	1.463156
$t_i = 1$	3	—	50	—

have been calculated for a ppswor sampling scheme where the selection procedure is pps systematic with units in random order and π_{ij} may be exactly calculated by a computer program for any given sizes of units, any N_1, the total number of clusters up to about 13 or 14,[2] and for any sample size n_i such that $\pi_i < 1$.

An example of π_{ij} in the case of $n_1 = 3$ is given as a triangular matrix:

$i\backslash j$	2	3	4	5	6	7	8
1	.05267	.04267	.08733	.03467	.05933	.03067	.05267
2	—	.11467	.20933	.09467	.15933	.07267	.13667
3	—	—	.17533	.08067	.13333	.05867	.11467
4	—	—	—	.14533	.25600	.11733	.20933
5	—	—	—	—	.10733	.04267	.09467
6	—	—	—	—	—	.08533	.15933
7	—	—	—	—	—	—	.07267

Values of $g(a_i)$ and $h(a_i)$ as calculated for parameters relevant to the variance of $\hat{X}_b$, the estimate by the weighting method, are given in Table 11.

Stage 3

We now proceed to the final stage, stage 3, to calculate the sampling and nonsampling variance, and in the case of the variance of the estimate by the weighting method,

$V_1(E\hat{X}_b) =$ sampling variance   (as in Table 7)

$$= \bar{\alpha}^{-2}\left\{\frac{t.}{n_1 n_2}\left[\sum_i a_i^2 + (n_2 - 1)h(a_{ii})\right] + 2\frac{t_.^2}{n_1^2}g(a_{ii}) - a_1^2\right\},$$

TABLE 11

	$g(a_i)$ by value of n_1				
Parameter a_i	$n_1 = 2$	$n_1 = 3$	$n_1 = 4$	$n_1 = 5$	$h(a_i)$
$\alpha_i(X_i + {}_RB_i - c)$	−.124460	−.372246	−.754389	−1.243486	10.521706
$\sqrt{V(\delta_i)}(X_i + {}_RB_i - c)$	−.013586	−.040583	−.084741	−.139503	2.684842
$\alpha_{i\,R}\sigma_i$	.202176	.606325	1.213077	2.021634	10.158392
$\sqrt{V(\delta_i)}_R\sigma_i$	.025363	.076096	.152137	.253797	1.308352

[2] For larger $N.$, the running time on the computer to calculate π_{ij} is excessive. One may then employ the Hartley and Rao (1962) asymptotic expression.

where

$$a_{ii} = \alpha_i(X_i + {}_RB_i - c)$$

$$= .874^{-2} \left\{ \frac{50}{n_1 n_2} \left[164.781576 + (n_2 - 1)(10.521706) \right] \right.$$

$$+ 2 \times \frac{2500}{n_1^2} \times \left. \begin{cases} -.124460 | n_1 = 2 \\ -.372240 | n_1 = 3 \\ -.754389 | n_1 = 4 \\ -1.243486 | n_1 = 5 \end{cases} - 0 \right\}$$

and the nonsampling variance of $\hat{X}_b$ as in Table 8 is given by

$$E_1 V(X_b | \mathbf{i}) = \bar{\alpha}^{-2} \left\{ \frac{t.}{n_1 n_2} \left[\sum_{k=2}^{4} a_{ki}^2 + (n_2 - 1) \sum_{K=2}^{4} \bar{r}_{Kw}'' h(a_{K\mathbf{i}}) \right] \right.$$

$$+ \left. 2 \frac{t_.^2}{n_1^2} \sum_{K=2}^{4} \bar{r}_{KB}'' g(a_{K\mathbf{i}}) \right],$$

where $a_{2i} = \sqrt{V(\delta_i)}(X_i + {}_RB_i - c)$, $a_{3i} = \alpha_{iR}\sigma_i$, and $a_{4i} = \sqrt{V(\delta_i)}_R\sigma_i$; $\bar{r}_{2w}'' = \bar{r}_{1w}$ (taken as .05), $\bar{r}_{3w}'' = \bar{r}_{2w}$ (taken as .05), and $\bar{r}_{4w}'' = \bar{r}_{1w}\bar{r}_{2w}$, or .0025; $\bar{r}_{2B}'' = \bar{r}_{1B}$ (taken as .02), $\bar{r}_{3B}'' = \bar{r}_{2B}$ (taken as .02), and $\bar{r}_{4B}'' = \bar{r}_{2B}\bar{r}_{1B} = .0004$. Then

$$E_1 V(\hat{X}_b)$$

$$= .874^{-2} \times \frac{50}{n_1 n_2} \left[16.718745 + 11.403055 + 1.463156 \right]$$

$$+ (n_2 - 1)$$

$$\times \left[\bar{r}_{1w} \times 2.684842 + \bar{r}_{2w} \times 10.158392 + \bar{r}_{1w}\bar{r}_{2w} \times 1.308352 \right] + 2 \times \frac{2500}{n_1^2}$$

$$\times \left[\bar{r}_{1B} \times \begin{pmatrix} -.013586 \\ -.040583 \\ -.08474 \\ -.139503 \end{pmatrix} + \bar{r}_{2B} \times \begin{pmatrix} .202176 \\ .606325 \\ 1.213077 \\ 2.021634 \end{pmatrix} + \bar{r}_{1B}\bar{r}_{2B} \times \begin{pmatrix} .025363 \\ .076096 \\ .152137 \\ .253797 \end{pmatrix} \begin{matrix} | n_1 = 2 \\ | n_1 = 3 \\ | n_1 = 4 \\ | n_1 = 5 \end{matrix} \right],$$

Bias $\hat{X}_b$

$$= \bar{\alpha}^{-1} \sum_i \alpha_i(X_i + {}_RB_i) - \sum_i X_i$$

$$= .874^{-1} \times 139.02589 - 163$$

$$= -3.93 \quad \text{(as in Table 6)},$$

and finally $\text{MSE}(X_b) = V_1(E\hat{X}_b / \mathbf{i}) + E_1 V(\hat{X}_b / \mathbf{i}) + 3.93^2$ (as in Table 9).

REFERENCE

Hartley, H. O., and Rao, J. N. K. (1962). Sampling with unequal and without replacement. *Annals of Mathematical Statistics* 33: 350–374.

CHAPTER 19

Appendixes to Part V

Richard Platek
Gerald B. Gray

APPENDIX A.
EXPECTED VALUE OF THE ESTIMATES
UNDER VARIOUS IMPUTATION PROCEDURES

We begin with the derivation of the expected value of the estimate under the combined historical substitution and weighting methods since this procedure is the most general of all the imputation procedures considered by us. The expected value of the estimates under the other procedures may be derived from it with the appropriate substitutions.

A.1. Expected Value of Estimate
(Combined Historical Substitution and Weighting Methods)

The estimate under the combined historical substitution and weighting methods is given in Chapter 17, Eq. (22), is given as

$$\hat{X}'_b = \frac{n_b}{m_b + m'_b} \sum_{i=1}^{n_b} [\delta_i(X_i + {}_R\varepsilon_i) + (1 - \delta_i)\delta'_i(X_i + {}_R\varepsilon'_i)]\pi_i^{-1}, \qquad (1)$$

where $\delta_i = 1$ or 0 according as unit i responds or not, and $\delta'_i = 1$ or 0 according as historical data are available or not for unit i. The expression $(1 - \delta_i)\delta'_i$ may be given by δ''_i.

Here n_b is the total sample size in balancing area b and may be subject to variation—hence the use of the symbols En_b and $V(n_b)$ in the methodological

INCOMPLETE DATA
IN SAMPLE SURVEYS
Volume 2, Part V

developments that follow. The responding sample size m_b may be also written as $\sum_{i=1}^{n_b} \delta_i$, and the expected responding sample size, given the sample, is the following:

$$E_2 m_b \big| s = \sum_{i=1}^{n_b} \alpha_i \big| s,$$

where it is assumed for the moment that the response probability depends upon the sample.

In turn, the unconditional expected value of the responding sample size is given by

$$E_1 E_2 m_b \big| s = \sum_{i=1}^{N_b} \pi_i \alpha_i = E n_b \bar{\alpha}_b,$$

where $\bar{\alpha}_b$ is the expected response rate and $En_b = \sum_{i=1}^{N_b} \pi_i$. Here E_1 is taken over all s, including i, and in turn over all units i in the population.

It may happen that the response bias and response variance as well as the response probability pertaining to unit i depend upon the sample. Even if they depend upon the sample, they may be averaged over all possible samples that include i so that an overall response bias, etc., pertaining to unit i exists. To simplify the methodological development, we have assumed that

$$\alpha_i \big| s = \alpha_i, \qquad _R B_i \big| s = _R B_i, \qquad \text{and} \qquad _R \sigma_i^2 \big| s = _R \sigma_i^2.$$

The operator E will be taken as E_1, E_2, E_3, i.e., the expected value over all possible responses, missingness patterns, and samples.

In the same manner as for m_b, m_b'' may be written as $m_b'' = \sum_{i=1}^{n_b} \delta_i''$ and $Em_b'' = En_b \bar{\alpha}_b''$.

Neglecting the product and ratio estimate bias and writing (1) using the δ_i and δ_i'' notation, we find that

$$E\hat{X}_b' \doteq \frac{En_b}{E(m_b + m_b')} E \sum_{i=1}^{n_b} \left[\delta_i (X_i + _R \varepsilon_i) + \delta_i'' (X_i + _{NR} \varepsilon_i') \right] \pi_i^{-1}$$

$$= \frac{En_b}{En_b(\bar{\alpha}_b + \bar{\alpha}_b'')} E_1 \sum_i{}' \left[\alpha_i (X_i + _R B_i) + \alpha_i'' (X_i + _{NR} B_i') \right] \pi_i^{-1}$$

$$= (\bar{\alpha}_b + \bar{\alpha}_b'')^{-1} \sum_i \left[\alpha_i (X_i + _R B_i) + \alpha_i'' (X_i + _{NR} B_i') \right]$$

$$= X_b + (\bar{\alpha}_b + \bar{\alpha}_b'')^{-1} \sum_i \left[\alpha_{i.} \, _R B_i + \alpha_{i.}'' \, _{NR} B_i' \right]$$

$$+ \sum_{i=1} (\alpha_i + \alpha_i'' - \bar{\alpha}_b - \bar{\alpha}_b'') X_i. \tag{2}$$

Here and henceforth, $\sum_i$ means $\sum_{i=1}^{N_b}$ while $\sum_i'$ means $\sum_{i=1}^{n_b}$. It may be recalled that $\delta_i'' = (1 - \delta_i)\delta_i'$, so that

$$E\delta_i'' = \alpha_i'' = E(1 - \delta_i)\delta_i' = (1 - \alpha_i)\alpha_i' - \text{Cov}(\delta_i \delta_i').$$

A covariance $\text{Cov}(\delta_i \delta_i')$ may exist between the events of responding or not responding and the nonavailability of historical records since nonrespondents in an earlier survey may be more likely to be nonrespondents also in the current survey than respondents in the earlier survey.

A.2. Application of Formula (2) to Other Methods of Imputation

Formula (2) may be utilized to derive the biases of the estimates under all of the imputation procedures by applying simplifications in the formula.

For the weighting and duplication methods alone, it is necessary only to substitute $\alpha_i'' \equiv 0$ and $\bar{\alpha}_b'' = 0$ in (12) in Chapter 17 to derive $E\hat{X}_b$ or $E\hat{X}_b^D$.

For the zero substitution method, case (i) when no historical data are used, all $\alpha_i \equiv 0$ and $\bar{\alpha}_b'' = 0$ as in the weighting method, but also $\bar{\alpha}_b^{-1}$ may be interpreted as one, since no additional weighting is applied; however, the individual response probabilities α_i must be included in (2). For case (ii), the values of α_i' and α_i'' are to be employed in (2), but the expected weight adjustment for the deficient sample, namely, $(\bar{\alpha}_b + \bar{\alpha}_b'')^{-1}$, would be taken as one to derive $E(\hat{T}_b + \hat{T}_b'')$. The overall biases of the estimates $\hat{T}$ and $\hat{T} + \hat{T}''$ are then obtained by summing the biases over the cells.

A.3. Relation between Imputation Bias and Covariance between Characteristic and Response Probabilities

An imputation bias occurs only when there is a covariance between the characteristics and response probabilities in a cell, as will be shown. The imputation bias, due to weighting, viz.,

$$(\bar{\alpha}_b + \bar{\alpha}_b'')^{-1} \sum_{i=1} (\alpha_i + \alpha_i'' - \bar{\alpha}_b - \bar{\alpha}_b'')X_i,$$

may be also written by defining

$$\text{Cov}_b^*(b_i c_i) = E_b^*(b_i c_i) - (E_b^* b_i)(E_b^* c_i) = E_b^*(b_i - E_b^* b_i)(c_i - E_b^* c_i), \qquad (3)$$

where $E_b^* b_i = \sum_{i=1} \pi_i b_i / \sum_{i=1} \pi_i = \sum_{i=1} \pi_i / En_b$, and similarly for other expressions. The summation over N_b units i, viz., $\sum_{i=1}^{N_b} (\alpha_i + \alpha_i'' - \bar{\alpha}_b - \bar{\alpha}_b'')X_i$, may be written as $\sum_{i=1}^{N_b} \pi_i(\alpha_i + \alpha_i'' - E_b^* \alpha_i - E_b^* \alpha_i'')X_i / \pi_i$, noting that $\bar{\alpha}_b = E_b^* \alpha_i$ by definition, and similarly for $\bar{\alpha}_b''$. Also $E_b^* X_i / \pi_i = (En_b)^{-1} X_b$ by definition and summation.

Since $E_b^*(\alpha_i + \alpha_i'' - E_b^* \alpha_i - E_b^* \alpha_i'') = 0$, then the imputation bias may be written as

$$(\bar{\alpha}_b + \bar{\alpha}_b'')^{-1} \sum_{i=1} (\alpha_i + \alpha_i'' - \bar{\alpha}_b - \bar{\bar{\alpha}}_b'')X_i$$

$$= (\bar{\alpha}_b + \bar{\alpha}_b'')^{-1} En_b \, \text{Cov}_b^*(\alpha_i + \alpha_i'', X_i / \pi_i). \qquad (4)$$

APPENDIX B.
VARIANCE OF ESTIMATES UNDER DIFFERENT IMPUTATION PROCEDURES

The variances of the estimates under the different imputation procedures all contain components pertaining to the variance of the estimate under the zero substitution method, and consequently we begin with the development of the estimate under the zero substitution method.

B.1.   Zero Substitution Method: Case (i)

As in Chapter 17, the estimate of the total for the zero substitution method [case (i)] in cell b is given by

$$\hat{T}_b = \sum_i{}' \delta_i(X_i + {}_R\varepsilon_i)\pi_i^{-1}. \tag{1}$$

The expected value of $\hat{T}_b$ over all samples, missingness patterns, and responses is given by

$$E\hat{T}_b = \sum_i \alpha_i(X_i + {}_RB_i), \qquad \text{say} \quad T_b. \tag{2}$$

Now

$$V(\hat{T}_b) = E_1[V(\hat{T}_b)|S] + V_1[E\hat{T}_b|S]$$

$$= \text{nonsampling and sampling variance with } E_1 \text{ and } V_1 \text{ taken over all possible samples.}$$

$$E\hat{T}_b|S = \sum_i{}' \alpha_i(X_i + {}_RB_i)\pi_i^{-1}.$$

$$V(\hat{T}_b)|S = \sum_i{}' V[\delta_i(X_i + {}_R\varepsilon_i)]\pi_i^{-2}$$

$$+ \sum_{i\neq j}{}' \text{Cov}[\delta_i(X_i + {}_R\varepsilon_i), \delta_j(X_j + {}_R\varepsilon_j)]\pi_i^{-1}\pi_j^{-1}$$

$$= \sum_i{}' \{E[\delta_i^2(X_i + {}_R\varepsilon_i)^2] - \alpha_i^2(X_i + {}_RB_i)^2\}\pi_i^{-2}$$

$$+ \sum_{i\neq j}{}' \{E[\delta_i(X_i + {}_R\varepsilon_i)\delta_j(X_j + {}_R\varepsilon_j)]$$

$$- \alpha_i(X_i + {}_RB_i)\alpha_j(X_j + {}_RB_j)\}\pi_i^{-1}\pi_j^{-1}.$$

$\sum_i{}'$ means $\sum_{i=1}^{n_b}$ and $\sum_{i\neq j}{}'$ means $\sum_{i\neq j}^{n_b}$. Similarly, $\sum_{i\neq j}$ means $\sum_{i\neq j}^{N_b}$.

$$V(\hat{T}_b)|S = \sum_i{}' \{\alpha_i[(X_i + {}_RB_i)^2 + {}_R\sigma_i^2] - \alpha_i^2(X_i + {}_RB_i)^2\}\pi_i^{-2}$$

$$+ \sum_{i\neq j}{}' \{[\alpha_i\alpha_j + \text{Cov}(\delta_i\delta_j)][(X_i + {}_RB_i)(X_j + {}_RB_j) + r_{2ij}({}_R\sigma_i)({}_R\sigma_j)]$$

$$- \alpha_i\alpha_j(X_i + {}_RB_i)(X_j + {}_RB_j)\}\pi_i^{-1}\pi_j^{-1}.$$

Hence

$$E_1 V(\hat{T}_b)|S = \sum_i \left[\alpha_i(1 - \alpha_i)(X_i + {}_R B_i)^2 + \alpha_i({}_R \sigma_i^2)\right]\pi_i^{-1}$$

$$+ \sum_{i \neq j} \left[\mathrm{Cov}(\delta_i \delta_j)(X_i + {}_R B_i)(X_j + {}_R B_j)\right.$$

$$+ (\alpha_i \alpha_j + \mathrm{Cov}(\delta_i \delta_j \; r_{2ij}({}_R \sigma_i)({}_R \sigma_j)\right]\pi_{ij}\pi_i^{-1}\pi_j^{-1}$$

$$= \text{nonsampling variance component.}$$

The covariance between the events of responding or not responding, namely, $\mathrm{Cov}(\delta_i, \delta_j)$, is discussed fully in Section 4 of this appendix.

The sampling variance component of the estimate by the zero substitution method is given by

$$V_1(E\hat{T}_b|S) = V_s\left[\sum_i{}' \alpha_i(X_i + {}_R B_i)\pi_i^{-1}\right],$$

where V_s is the Horvitz–Thompson variance defined by formula (14) in Chapter 17. One may apply Eq. (14) in Chapter 17 by putting $B_i = \alpha_i(X_i + {}_R B_i)$. Hence,

$$V(\hat{T}_b) = V_s\left[\sum_i{}' \alpha_i(X_i + {}_R B_i)\pi_i^{-1}\right]$$

$$+ \sum_i \left[V(\delta_i)(X_i + {}_R B_i)^2 + (\alpha_i^2 + V(\delta_i)) {}_R \sigma_i^2\right]\pi_i^{-1}$$

$$+ \sum_{i \neq j} \{\mathrm{Cov}(\delta_i \delta_j)(X_i + {}_R B_i)(X_j + {}_R B_j)$$

$$+ \left[\alpha_i \alpha_j + \mathrm{Cov}(\delta_i \delta_j)\right] r_{2ij}({}_R \alpha_i)({}_R \alpha_j)\}\pi_{ij}\pi_i^{-1}\pi_j^{-1}, \tag{3}$$

where $V(\delta_i) = \alpha_i(1 - \alpha_i)$.

In a similar manner, when two cells b and c are considered,

$$\mathrm{Cov}(\hat{T}_b, \hat{T}_c) = \mathrm{Cov}_S\left[\sum_i{}' \alpha_i(X_i + {}_R B_i)\pi_i^{-1}, \sum_{j=1}{}' \alpha_j(X_j + {}_R B_j)\pi_j^{-1}\right]$$

$$+ \sum_{i=1}^{N_b} \sum_{j=1}^{N_c} \{\mathrm{Cov}(\delta_i \delta_j)(X_i + {}_R B_i)(X_j + {}_R B_j)$$

$$+ \left[\alpha_i \alpha_j + \mathrm{Cov}(\delta_i \delta_j)\right] r_{2ij}({}_R \sigma_i)({}_R \sigma_j)\}\pi_{ij}\pi_i^{-1}\pi_j^{-1}. \tag{4}$$

This sampling covariance arises only because of the sampling without replacement scheme from finite populations since two balancing areas contain different units.

B.2.　Zero Substitution Method: Case (ii)

If we consider the zero substitution method of imputation [case (ii)], when historical data are available for some but not all nonresponding units, then

$$\hat{T}_b + \hat{T}_b'' = \sum_i{}' \left[\delta_i(X_i + {}_R \varepsilon_i) + \delta_i''(X_i + {}_{NR} \varepsilon_i')\right]\pi_i^{-1}, \tag{5}$$

TABLE 12

Symbol/expression in $V(\hat{T}_b)$	To be read in $V(\hat{T}_b + \hat{T}_b'')$ as
$\sum_i' \alpha_i(X_i + {}_RB_i)$	$\sum_i' [\alpha_i(X_i + {}_RB_i) + \alpha_i''(X_i + {}_{NR}B_i')]$
$V(\delta_i)(X_i + {}_RB_i)^2$	$V[\delta_i(X_i + {}_RB_i) + \delta_i''(X_i + {}_{NR}B_i')]$
$\mathrm{Cov}(\delta_i\delta_j)(X_i + {}_RB_i)(X_j + {}_RB_j)$	$\mathrm{Cov}[\delta_i(X_i + {}_RB_i) + \delta_i''(X_i + {}_{NR}B_i'),$
	$\delta_j(X_j + {}_RB_j) + \delta_j''(X_j + {}_{NR}B_j')]$
$\alpha_i^2({}_R\sigma_i^2)$	$\alpha_i^2({}_R\sigma_i^2) + \alpha_i''^2({}_{NR}\sigma_i'^2) + 2\alpha_i\alpha_i'' r_{3ii}({}_R\sigma_i)({}_{NR}\sigma_i')$
$V(\delta_i)({}_R\sigma_i^2)$	$V(\delta_i)({}_R\sigma_i^2) + V(\delta_i'')({}_{NR}\sigma_i'^2) + 2\,\mathrm{Cov}(\delta_i\delta_i'')\, r_{3ii}({}_R\sigma_i)({}_{NR}\sigma_i')$
	where $\mathrm{Cov}(\delta_i\delta_i'') = -\alpha_i\alpha_i''$
$\alpha_i\alpha_j r_{2ij}({}_R\sigma_i)({}_R\sigma_j)$	$\alpha_i\alpha_j r_{2ij}({}_R\sigma_i)({}_R\sigma_j) + \alpha_i\alpha_j'' r_{3ij}({}_R\sigma_i)({}_{NR}\sigma_j')$
	$+ \alpha_i''\alpha_j r_{3ji}({}_{NR}\sigma_i')({}_R\sigma_j) + \alpha_i''\alpha_j'' r_{4ij}({}_{NR}\sigma_i')({}_{NR}\sigma_j')$
$\mathrm{Cov}(\delta_i\delta_j)\, r_{2ij}({}_R\sigma_i)({}_R\sigma_j)$	$\mathrm{Cov}(\delta_i\delta_j)\, r_{2ij}({}_R\sigma_i)({}_R\sigma_j) + \mathrm{Cov}(\delta_i\delta_j'')\, r_{3ij}({}_R\sigma_i)({}_{NR}\sigma_j')$
	$+ \mathrm{Cov}(\delta_i''\delta_j)\, r_{3ji}({}_{NR}\sigma_j')({}_R\sigma_j') + \mathrm{Cov}(\delta_i''\delta_j'')\, r_{4ij}({}_{NR}\sigma_i')({}_{NR}\sigma_j')$

where

$$\delta_i'' = (1 - \delta_i)\delta_i'. \tag{6}$$

Then $V(\hat{T}_b + \hat{T}_b'')$ is essentially the same as $V(\hat{T}_b)$ with the substitutions in formula (3) given in Table 12.

B.3. Weighting Method

The estimate by the weighting method as stated in Chapter 17 may be written as

$$\hat{X}_b = (n_b/m_b)\hat{T}_b. \tag{7}$$

Hence, using Taylor series expansion and treating $\hat{X}_b$ as a product ratio estimator, we find that

$$\mathrm{Rel}\ V(\hat{X}_b) = \mathrm{Rel\ Var}\ n_b +)\mathrm{Rel\ Var}\ \hat{T}_b + \mathrm{Rel\ Var}\ m_b + 2\ \mathrm{Rel\ Cov}(n_b, \hat{T}_b)$$
$$- 2\ \mathrm{Rel\ Cov}(n_b, m_b) - 2\ \mathrm{Rel\ Cov}(m_b, \hat{T}_b). \tag{8}$$

Neglecting the product ratio estimate bias, we note from Eq. (2) in Appendix A that, by putting α_i'' and $\bar{\alpha}_b''$ both equal to zero and rewriting the equation as

$$E\hat{X}_b = \bar{\alpha}_b^{-1} \sum_{i=1}^{N_b} \alpha_i(X_i + {}_RB_i) = \bar{\alpha}_b^{-1} T_b, \tag{9}$$

$$V(\hat{X}_b)/[\bar{\alpha}_b^{-2} T_b^2] = V(n_b)/(En_b)^2 + V(\hat{T}_b)/T_b^2 + V(m_b)/(Em_b)^2$$
$$+ 2\ \mathrm{Cov}(n_b, \hat{T}_b)/(En_b T_b) - 2\ \mathrm{Cov}(n_b, m_b)/(En_b Em_b)$$
$$- 2\ \mathrm{Cov}(m_b, \hat{T}_b)/(Em_b T_b),$$

or

$$V(\hat{X}_b) = \bar{\alpha}_b^{-2} \left[\frac{T_b^2}{(En_b)^2} V(n_b) + V(\hat{T}_b) + \frac{T_b^2}{(Em_b)^2} V(m_b) + 2 \frac{T_b}{En_b} \text{Cov}(n_b, \hat{T}_b) \right.$$

$$\left. - 2 \frac{T_b}{En_b} \frac{T_b}{Em_b} \text{Cov}(n_b, m_b) - 2 \frac{T_b}{Em_b} \text{Cov}(m_b, \hat{T}_b) \right], \tag{10}$$

or

$$V(\hat{X}_b) \doteq \bar{\alpha}_b^{-2} V \left(\hat{T}_b + \frac{T_b}{En_b} n_b - \frac{T_b}{Em_b} m_b \right)$$

$$\doteq \bar{\alpha}_b^{-2} V \left[\sum_i{}' \delta_i (X_i + {}_R\varepsilon_i) \pi_i^{-1} + \frac{T_b}{En_b} n_b - \frac{T_b}{En_b \bar{\alpha}_b} \sum_i{}' \delta_i \right], \tag{11}$$

noting from Appendix A that $Em_b = En_b \bar{\alpha}_b$.

$$V(\hat{X}_b) = \bar{\alpha}_b^{-2} \left[\left(\frac{T_b}{En_b} \right)^2 V(n_b) + 2 \frac{T_b}{En_b} \text{Cov} \left(n_b, \hat{T}_b - \frac{T_b}{En_b} \bar{\alpha}_b^{-1} m_b \right) \right.$$

$$\left. + V \left(\hat{T}_b - \frac{T_b}{En_b \bar{\alpha}_b} m_b \right) \right]. \tag{12}$$

The variance of the sample size $V(n_b)$ is strictly a sampling variance and $V_S(n_b) = \sum_{i \neq j} \pi_{ij} - En_b(En_b - 1)$, where $En_b = \sum_{i=1}^{N_b} \pi_i$. Note that $V_S(n_b)$ may be derived from Eq. (14) in Chapter 17 by putting $B_i = \pi_i$.

$$\text{Cov} \left(n_b, \hat{T}_b - \frac{T_b}{En_b} \bar{\alpha}_b^{-1} m_b \right) = E \left[n_b E \left(\hat{T}_b - \frac{T_b}{En_b} \bar{\alpha}_b^{-1} m_b \right) \middle| n_b \right]$$

$$- En_b \left(T_b - \frac{T_b}{En_b} \bar{\alpha}_b^{-1} En_b \bar{\alpha}_b \right), \tag{13}$$

$$E\hat{T}_b | n_b = E \sum_i{}' \delta_i (X_i + {}_R\varepsilon_i) \pi_i^{-1} = \sum_i{}' \alpha_i (X_i + {}_R B_i) \pi_i^{-1},$$

and

$$Em_b | n_b = E \sum_i{}' \delta_i = \sum_i{}' \alpha_i.$$

Thus, $\text{Cov}(n_b, T_b - (T_b/En_b)\bar{\alpha}_b^{-1} m_b)$ is entirely contributed by sampling errors in $\hat{T}_b - (T_b/En_b)\bar{\alpha}_b^{-1} m_b$, so that $\text{Cov}(n_b, \hat{T}_b - (T_b/En_b)\bar{\alpha}_b^{-1} m_b)$ is given by

$$\text{Cov}_S \left[n_b, \sum_i{}' \alpha_i (X_i + {}_R B_i) \pi_i^{-1} - \frac{T_b}{En_b} \bar{\alpha}_b^{-1} \sum_i{}' \alpha_i \right], \tag{14}$$

where Eq. (16) in Chapter 17 may be utilized by putting $B_i = \pi_i$ and

$$C_i = \alpha_i (X_i + {}_R B_i) - \frac{T_b}{En_b} \bar{\alpha}_b^{-1} \pi_i \alpha_i = \alpha_i \left(X_i + {}_R B_i - \frac{T_b}{En_b} \pi_i \bar{\alpha}_b^{-1} \right).$$

It remains to derive

$$V\left(\hat{T}_b - \frac{T_b}{En_n\bar{\alpha}_b}\, m_b\right).$$

$V(\hat{T}_b)$ has already been derived in (3).

$$V(m_b) = V(\sum_i {}' \delta_i) = E_1 V(\sum_i {}' \delta_i)|S + V_1(E \sum_i {}' \delta_i|S)$$

$$= E_1\Big[\sum_i {}' V(\delta_i) + \sum_{i \neq j} {}' \operatorname{Cov}(\delta_i\delta_j)\Big] + V_1(\sum_i {}' \alpha_i).$$

$V_1(\sum'_i \alpha_i) = V_S(\sum'_i \alpha_i)$ is obtained by putting $B_i = \pi_i\alpha_i$ in Eq. (14) in Chapter 17. Hence,

$$V(m_b) = \sum_i \pi_i V(\delta_i) + \sum_{i \neq j} \pi_{ij} \operatorname{Cov}(\delta_i\delta_j) + V_S(\sum {}' \alpha_i), \qquad (15)$$

$$\operatorname{Cov}(\hat{T}_b, m_b) = E_1\big[\operatorname{Cov}(\hat{T}_b, m_b|S)\big] + \operatorname{Cov}_1(E\hat{T}_b|S, Em_b|S)$$

$$= E_1\Big\{\operatorname{Cov}\big[\sum_i {}' \delta_i(X_i + {}_R\varepsilon_i)\pi_i^{-1}\big], \sum_i {}' \delta_i\big|S\Big\}$$

$$+ \operatorname{Cov}_S\Big[\sum_i {}' \alpha_i(X_i + {}_R B_i)\pi_i^{-1}, \sum_i {}' \alpha_i\Big],$$

where Cov_S is defined by

$$\operatorname{Cov}_S\Big[\sum_i {}' A_i\pi_i^{-1}, \sum_i {}' B_i\pi_i^{-1}\Big]$$

$$= \sum_i \left(\frac{1}{\pi_i} - 1\right) A_i B_i + \sum_{i \neq j} \left(\frac{\pi_{ij}}{\pi_i\pi_j} - 1\right) A_i B_j \qquad \text{(sampling covariance). (15a)}$$

Put $A_i = \alpha_i(X_i + {}_R B_i)$ and $B_i = \alpha_i$ in Cov_S in (15a). Confining our attention to the given sample S, we find that

$$\operatorname{Cov}\Big[\sum_i {}' \delta_i(X_i + {}_R\varepsilon_i)\pi_i^{-1}, \sum_i {}' \delta_i\Big]\Big|S$$

$$= \sum {}' V(\delta_i)(X_i + {}_R B_i)\pi_i^{-1} + \sum_{i \neq j} {}' \operatorname{Cov}(\delta_i\delta_j)(X_i + {}_R B_i)\pi_i^{-1},$$

since

$$E(X_i + {}_R\varepsilon_i)\delta_i\delta_j = \begin{cases} X_i + {}_R B_i & \text{if } \delta_i = \delta_j = 1, \text{ whether } i = j \text{ or } i \neq j \\ 0 & \text{otherwise.} \end{cases}$$

Hence,

$$E_1 \, \mathrm{Cov}\Big[\sum_i{}' \delta_i(X_i + {}_R\varepsilon_i)\pi_i^{-1}, \sum_i{}' \delta_i\Big]\Big|S$$

$$= \sum_i V(\delta_i)(X_i + {}_RB_i) + \sum_{i \neq j} \pi_{ij}\pi_i^{-1} \, \mathrm{Cov}(\delta_i\delta_j)(X_i + {}_RB_i).$$

Therefore,

$$\mathrm{Cov}(\hat{T}_b, m_b) = \mathrm{Cov}_S\Big[\sum_i{}' \alpha_i(X_i + {}_RB_i \, \pi_i^{-1}, \sum_i{}' \alpha_i\Big]$$

$$+ \sum_i V(\delta_i)(X_i + {}_RB_i)$$

$$+ \sum_{i \neq j} \pi_{ij}\pi_i^{-1} \, \mathrm{Cov}(\delta_i\delta_j)(X_i + {}_RB_i). \tag{16}$$

Thus,

$$V\left(\hat{T}_b - \frac{T_b}{En_b\bar{\alpha}_b} \, m_b\right)$$

$$= V(\hat{T}_b) - 2\frac{T_b}{En_b\bar{\alpha}_b} \, \mathrm{Cov}_S(E\hat{T}_b|S, \sum_i{}' \alpha_i) - 2\frac{T_b}{En_b\bar{\alpha}_b} \Big[\sum_i V(\delta_i)(X_i + {}_RB_i)$$

$$+ \sum_{i \neq j} \pi_{ij}\pi_i^{-1} \, \mathrm{Cov}(\delta_i\delta_j)(X_i + {}_RB_i)\Big]$$

$$+ \left(\frac{T_b}{En_b\bar{\alpha}_b}\right)^2 \Big[V_S(\sum_i{}' \alpha_i) + \sum_i \pi_i V(\delta_i) + \sum_{i \neq j} \pi_{ij} \, \mathrm{Cov}(\delta_i\delta_j)\Big] \tag{17}$$

$$= V_S\left[\sum_i{}' \alpha_i(X_i + {}_RB_i)\pi_i^{-1} - \frac{T_b}{En_b\bar{\alpha}_b} \sum{}' \alpha_i\right]$$

$$+ \sum_i \pi_i V(\delta_i)\left[(X_i + {}_RB_i)^2\pi_i^{-2} - 2\frac{T_b}{En_b\bar{\alpha}_b}(X_i + {}_RB_i)\pi_i^{-1} + \left(\frac{T_b}{En_b\bar{\alpha}_b}\right)^2\right]$$

$$+ \sum_i [\alpha_i^2 + V(\delta_i)]({}_R\sigma_i^2) + \sum_{i \neq j} \pi_{ij} \, \mathrm{Cov}(\delta_i\delta_j)$$

$$\cdot \left[(X_i + {}_RB_i)(X_j + {}_RB_j)\pi_i^{-1}\pi_j^{-1} - \frac{T_b}{En_b\bar{\alpha}_b}(X_i + {}_RB_i)\pi_i^{-1}\right.$$

$$\left. - \frac{T_b}{En_b\bar{\alpha}_b}(X_j + {}_RB_j)\pi_j^{-1} + \left(\frac{T_b}{En_b\bar{\alpha}_b}\right)^2\right]$$

$$+ \sum_{i \neq j} [\alpha_i\alpha_j + \mathrm{Cov}(\delta_i\delta_j)]r_{2ij}.({}_R\sigma_i)({}_R\sigma_j)\pi_{ij}. \tag{18}$$

Hence, the sampling variance of the estimate by the weighting method of imputation is given by

$$
\begin{aligned}
V_1(\hat{X}_b) = \bar{\alpha}_b^{-2} \Bigg\{ & V_s\bigg[\sum_i{}' \alpha_i(X_i + {}_R B_i)\pi_i^{-1} - \frac{T_b}{En_b\bar{\alpha}_b} \sum_i{}' \alpha_i \bigg] \\
& + \left(\frac{T_b}{En_b}\right)^2 V_s(m_b) + 2\frac{T_b}{En_b}\text{Cov}_S\Big[n_b, \sum_i{}' \alpha_i(X_i + {}_R B_i)\pi_i^{-1}\Big] \\
& - 2\frac{T_b}{En_b\bar{\alpha}_b}\text{Cov}_S\Big(n_b, \sum_i{}' \alpha_i\Big) \Bigg\} \\
= \bar{\alpha}_b^{-2} V_S\bigg[& \sum_i{}' \alpha_i(X_i + {}_R B_i)\pi_i^{-1} - \frac{T_b}{En_b\bar{\alpha}_b} \sum_i{}' \alpha_i + \frac{T_b}{En_b}n_b \bigg]. \quad (19)
\end{aligned}
$$

Note that $\text{Cov}_S(n_b, \sum_i{}' \alpha_i)$, for example, would be derived from $\text{Cov}_S(\sum_i{}' A_i\pi_i^{-1}, \sum_i{}' B_i\pi_i^{-1})$ by putting $A_i = \pi_i$ and $B_i = \pi_i\alpha_i$, and the four nonsampling variance/covariance components are given by

$$
\begin{aligned}
E_1 V(\hat{X}_b)|S = & \bar{\alpha}_b^{-2} \sum_i \pi_i^{-1}[\alpha_i^2 + V(\delta_i)]\,{}_R\sigma_i^2 \quad (\text{SRV}) \\
& + \bar{\alpha}_b^{-2} \sum_{i\neq j} \pi_{ij}\pi_i^{-1}\pi_j^{-1}[\alpha_i\alpha_j + \text{Cov}(\delta_i, \delta_j)]\,r_{2ij}({}_R\sigma_i)({}_R\sigma_j) \quad (\text{CRV}) \\
& + \bar{\alpha}_b^{-2} \sum_i \pi_i^{-1} V(\delta_i)\bigg[(X_i + {}_R B_i) - \pi_i\frac{T_b}{En_b\bar{\alpha}_b}\bigg]^2 \quad (\text{VR}\bar{\text{R}}) \\
& + \bar{\alpha}_b^{-2} \sum_{i\neq j} \pi_{ij}\pi_i^{-1}\pi_j^{-1}\,\text{Cov}(\delta_i, \delta_j)\bigg\{\bigg[(X_i + {}_R B_i) - \pi_i\frac{T_b}{En_b\bar{\alpha}_b}\bigg] \\
& \qquad\qquad \cdot\bigg[(X_j + {}_R B_j) - \pi_j\frac{T_b}{En_b\bar{\alpha}_b}\bigg]\bigg\} \quad (\text{CVR}\bar{\text{R}}). \quad (20)
\end{aligned}
$$

The sampling variance and the four nonsampling variance/covariance components are defined in Chapter 17 in the section dealing with the bias and variance of the estimate under the weighting method. The additional sampling and nonsampling variance of the estimate under duplication instead of weighting is derived in Appendix C.

A covariance may exist between the estimated totals of different balancing areas or weighting classes b and c and $\text{Cov}(\hat{X}_b, \hat{X}_c)$ is therefore given by

$$
\begin{aligned}
& \text{Cov}(\hat{X}_b, \hat{X}_c) \\
& \doteq \bar{\alpha}_b^{-1}\bar{\alpha}_c^{-1}\Bigg\{ \text{Cov}_S\bigg(E\hat{T}_b|S - \frac{T_b}{En_b\bar{\alpha}_b}\sum_i{}' \alpha_i + \frac{T_b}{En_b}n_b, \\
& \qquad\qquad E\hat{T}_c|S - \frac{T_c}{En_c\bar{\alpha}_c}\sum_j{}' \alpha_j + \frac{T_c}{En_c}n_c \bigg) \qquad\qquad (\text{sampling covariance})
\end{aligned}
$$

(*Equation Continues*)

$$+ \sum_i \sum_j \pi_{ij} \pi_i^{-1} \pi_j^{-1}$$

(correlated response variance between balancing areas)

$$\cdot [\alpha_i \alpha_j + \text{Cov}(\delta_i \delta_j)] r_{2ij}(_R \sigma_i)(_R \sigma_j)$$

$$+ \sum_i \sum_j \pi_{ij} \pi_i^{-1} \pi_j^{-1} \text{Cov}(\delta_i, \delta_j)$$

(covariance due to covariance between the events of re-

$$\cdot \left(X_i + {_R B_i} - \frac{\pi_i T_b}{E n_b \bar{\alpha}_b} \right) \left(X_j + {_R B_j} - \frac{\pi_j T_c}{E n_c \bar{\alpha}_c} \right) \Big\}$$

sponding or not responding). (21)

In (21), $\sum_i = \sum_{i=1}^{N_b}$ as before, but $\sum_j = \sum_{j=1}^{N_c}$. $\sum'_i = \sum_{i=1}^{n_b}$ as before, but $\sum'_j = \sum_{j=1}^{n_c}$.

B.4. Discussion of the Covariance between the Events of Responding and Not Responding

The covariance between the events of responding and not responding among units i and j was given by $\text{Cov}(\delta_i, \delta_j)$. The units i and j may both respond ($\delta_i = \delta_j = 1$); both may fail to respond ($\delta_i = \delta_j = 0$); or one may respond and the other fail to respond ($\delta_i = 1, \delta_j = 0$ or vice versa). Unit i responds with probability α_i, which may not be known in practice and similarly unit j with probability α_j. If these two units respond or do not respond independently of each other, then the probability that both units respond is simply the product of the response probabilities $\alpha_i \alpha_j$, where $\text{Cov}(\delta_i, \delta_j) = 0$. However, depending upon the geographic proximity of the units and the interval of time between personal interview of the two units, there could be a relation between the events of responding and not responding between the two units, with the result that the probability of both responding deviates from the product of the individual probabilities. In fact, $E(\delta_i \delta_j) = \text{Pr}(\delta_i = \delta_j = 1)$ for $\delta_i \delta_j$ equals zero if at least one of δ_i or δ_j equals zero and $E(\delta_i \delta_j) = \alpha_i \alpha_j + \text{Cov}(\delta_i \delta_j)$ by definition of covariance. Hence, the probability that both units respond equals $\alpha_i \alpha_j + \text{Cov}(\delta_i \delta_j)$. In a similar manner, the probability that neither unit responds equals $(1 - \alpha_i)(1 - \alpha_j) + \text{Cov}(1 - \delta_i), (1 - \delta_j)$, or $(1 - \alpha_i)(1 - \alpha_j) + \text{Cov}(\delta_i \delta_j)$; the probability of unit i responding and unit j not responding equals $\alpha_i(1 - \alpha_j) - \text{Cov}(\delta_i \delta_j)$. If a covariance between the events of responding or not responding exists, it is most likely positive, and the closer geographically the units i and j, the larger the covariance. For example, in an apartment building, tenants with similar life styles may tend to be at home or away from home simultaneously, so that as an interviewer attempts to contact respondents in the apartment building repeatedly, he may be very successful or unsuccessful in obtaining the survey data. The covariance may be expected to drop as the geographic distance between the pairs of units increases, for even if the life style of the two units is similar, the interviewing schedule planned by the interviewer may be distinct enough to minimize or eliminate the relation between the events of responding and not responding. Also, with increasing distance between units, the chance of distinct interviewers being assigned to units i and j is greater and the more independent the events of responding and not responding become.

There is even a possible case of a negative covariance between the events of responding and not responding for a pair of units. If two individuals happen to be special coworkers in a plant such that only one can be absent at a time, then the probability of both persons being nonrespondents would be much lower than the product of the probabilities of nonresponse, viz., $(1 - \alpha_i)(1 - \alpha_j)$, and consequently the covariance would be negative.

B.5.   Historical Data Substitution and Weighting

Formulas (19)–(21) dealing with the weighting method of imputation alone may be adapted to the combined historical substitution and weighting methods by replacement of the symbols as noted in Section 3 in this appendix.

In addition to the replacements listed in (6), $X_i + {}_R B_i$ would be replaced by $X_i + {}_R B_i'$, where ${}_R B_i'$ is defined by

$$(\alpha_i + \alpha_i'')\,{}_R B_i' = \alpha_{i.}\,{}_R B_i + \alpha_{i.}''\,{}_{NR} B_i'. \tag{22}$$

Also, T_b would be replaced by

$$T_b + T_b'' = \sum_i \left[\alpha_i (X_i + {}_R B_i) + \alpha_i'' (X_i + {}_{NR} B_i') \right]. \tag{23}$$

APPENDIX C.
ADDITIONAL VARIANCE OF ESTIMATE
UNDER THE DUPLICATION AS OPPOSED
TO THE WEIGHTING METHOD OF IMPUTATION

In the duplication method, as pointed out in Chapter 17, the estimate is given by

$$\hat{X}_b^D = (W_b + 1) \sum_{i=1}^{d_b m_b} (X_i + {}_R \varepsilon_i)\pi_i^{-1} + W_b \sum_{i=d_b m_b + 1}^{m_b} (X_i + {}_R \varepsilon_i)\pi_i^{-1}, \tag{1}$$

where $n_b = W_b m_b + d_b m_b$, with W_b an integer and d_b a decimal. The most important case occurs in practice in many household surveys when $m_b/n_b > 0.5$, and in this case, $W_b = 1$.

For any response rate m_b/n_b, the weight w_i attached to responding unit i equals W_b with probability $1 - d_b$ and $W_b + 1$ with probability d_b. Hence, $E_4 w_i = W_b(1 - d_b) + d_b(W_b + 1) = W_b + d_b = n_b/m_b$, where E_4 is the expectation over all possible random assignments of the integral weights W_b and $W_b + 1$ to $(1 - d_b)m_b$ and $d_b m_b$ respondents, respectively. V_4 is the corresponding variance.

Then

$$E_4(\hat{X}_b^D) = E_4 \sum_{i=1}^{m_b} w_i(X_i + {}_R\varepsilon_i)\pi_i^{-1} = (n_b/m_b)\hat{T}_b = \hat{X}_b, \tag{2}$$

the estimate pertaining to the weighting method of imputation, and $V_4(X_b^D) = E_4(\hat{X}_b^D)^2 - \hat{X}_b^2$. Now

$$(\hat{X}_b^D)^2 = \sum_{i=1}^{m_b} w_i^2(X_i + {}_R\varepsilon_i)^2\pi_i^{-2} + \sum_{i \neq j}^{m_b} w_i w_j(X_i + {}_R\varepsilon_i)(X_j + {}_R\varepsilon_j)\pi_i^{-1}\pi_j^{-1}.$$

It can be shown that

$$E_4 w_i^2 = (n_b/m_b)^2 + d_b(1 - d_b)$$

and

$$E_4 w_i w_j = (n_b/m_b)^2 - d_b(1 - d_b)/(m_b - 1).$$

Hence

$$V_4(\hat{X}_b^D) = d_b(1 - d_b) \sum_{i \neq 1}^{m_b} (X_i + {}_R\varepsilon_i)^2\pi_i^{-2}$$

$$- \frac{d_b(1 - d_b)}{m_b - 1} \sum_{i \neq j}^{m_b} (X_i + {}_R\varepsilon_i)(X_j + {}_R\varepsilon_j)\pi_i^{-1}\pi_j^{-1}. \tag{3}$$

Since $E_4\hat{X}_b^D = \hat{X}_b$, $V(\hat{X}_b^D) = E_1 E_2 E_3 V_4(\hat{X}_b^D) + V(\hat{X}_b)$, where $V(\hat{X}_b)$ has been derived in Eqs. (19) and (20) in Appendix B.

$E_1 E_2 E_3 V_4(\hat{X}_b^D)$ represents the additional variance component due to duplication as opposed to weighting, while $V_4(\hat{X}_b^D)$ is the additional variance for a given sample, missingness pattern, and set of responses. The decimal d_b may be written as $(n_b/m_b) - [n_b/m_b]$, where $[n_b/m_b]$ denotes the integral weight W_b. If we denote m_b/n_b, the observed response rate, as $\hat{\bar{\alpha}}_b$, then $d_b = \hat{\bar{\alpha}}_b^{-1} - [\hat{\bar{\alpha}}_b^{-1}]$, and

$$V_4(\hat{X}_b^D) = (\hat{\bar{\alpha}}_b^{-1} - [\hat{\bar{\alpha}}_b^{-1}])(1 - \hat{\bar{\alpha}}_b^{-1} + [\hat{\bar{\alpha}}_b^{-1}]) \left[\sum_{i=1}^{m_b} (X_i + {}_R\varepsilon_i)^2\pi_i^{-2} \right.$$

$$\left. - \frac{1}{m_b - 1} \sum_{i \neq j}^{m_b} (X_i + {}_R\varepsilon_i)(X_j + {}_R\varepsilon_j)\pi_i^{-1}\pi_j^{-1} \right]. \tag{4}$$

To evaluate $E_1 E_2 E_3 V_4(\hat{X}_b^D)$ properly is a difficult task, since the expected value of $[\ \ ]$ involves the conditional expectation, given m_b and n_b, and in turn will involve the conditional expections of δ_i given m_b and n_b. Some restrictive assumptions will be required.

Returning to Eq. (4) above, we note that the expressions

$$\frac{1}{m_b}\sum_{i=1}^{m_b}(X_i + {}_R\varepsilon_i)^2\pi_i^{-2} \quad \text{and} \quad \frac{1}{m_b(m_b-1)}\sum_{i\neq j}^{m_b}(X_i + {}_R\varepsilon_i)(X_j + {}_R\varepsilon_j)\pi_i^{-1}\pi_j^{-1} \quad (5)$$

should not vary extensively as m_b changes and may not be strongly correlated with m_b. Hence to simplify the evaluation of $E_1E_2E_3V_4(\hat{X}_b^D)$, we shall define $f(\hat{\bar{\alpha}}_b) = (\hat{\bar{\alpha}}_b^{-1} - W_b)(1 - \hat{\bar{\alpha}}_b^{-1} + W_b)n_b\hat{\bar{\alpha}}_b$, where $n_b\hat{\bar{\alpha}}_b = m_b$, and assume that $f(\hat{\bar{\alpha}}_b)$ is uncorrelated with either of the above expressions.

Then we may derive the expected values $E_1E_2E_3$ for all three terms involved separately before pulling them together.

$$E_1E_2E_3\frac{1}{m_b}\sum_{i=1}^{m_b}(X_i + {}_R\varepsilon_i)^2\pi_i^{-2} = \frac{1}{En_b\bar{\alpha}_b}\sum_i \alpha_i[(X_i + {}_RB_i)^2 + {}_R\sigma_i^2]\pi_i^{-1},$$

omitting the ratio estimate bias.

$$E_1E_2E_3\frac{1}{m_b(m_b-1)}\sum_{1=j}^{m_b}(X_i + {}_R\varepsilon_i)(X_j + {}_R\varepsilon_j)\pi_i^{-1}\pi_j^{-1}$$

$$\doteq \frac{\sum_{i\neq j}[\alpha_i\alpha_j + \text{Cov}(\delta_i,\delta_j)][(X_i + {}_RB_i)(X_j + {}_RB_j) + r_{2ij}({}_R\sigma_i)({}_R\sigma_j)]\pi_{ij}\pi_i^{-1}\pi_j^{-1}}{En_b\bar{\alpha}_b(En_b\bar{\alpha}_b - 1) + V(m_b)},$$

(6)

again neglecting the ratio estimate bias. The variance of the responding sample size, viz., $V(m_b)$, has been obtained in Eq. (15) in Appendix B.

Turning now to $f(\hat{\bar{\alpha}}_b)$, we note that $Ef(\hat{\bar{\alpha}}_b)$, where $E = E_1E_2E_3$, may be difficult to obtain if W_b takes on several values over the possible observed ranges of the response rate $\hat{\bar{\alpha}}_b$; but under the assumption of a normal distribution of $\hat{\bar{\alpha}}_b^{-1}$ with expected value $\bar{\alpha}_b^{-1}$ and variance $V(\hat{\bar{\alpha}}_b^{-1})$, it should be possible to find $Ef(\hat{\bar{\alpha}}_b)$ when W_b may vary.

$$V(\bar{\alpha}_b^{-1}) \doteq \bar{\alpha}_b^{-2}[V_s(n_b)/(En_b)^2 - 2\,\text{Cov}_s(n_b, \sum_i' \alpha_i)/En_b\bar{\alpha}_b + V(m_b)/(En_b\bar{\alpha}_b)^2], \quad (7)$$

where $V_s(n_b)$ is given in Eq. (13) in Appendix B. $\text{Cov}_s(n_b, \sum_i' \alpha_i)$ may be derived from $\text{Cov}_s(\sum_i' \pi_i^{-1}A_i, \sum_i' \pi_i^{-1}B_i)$ by putting $A_i = \pi_i$ and $B_i = \pi_i\alpha_i$. $V(m_b)$ is given by Eq. (15) in Appendix B.

$E\hat{\bar{\alpha}}_b^{-1} \doteq \bar{\alpha}_b^{-1}$, and if we denote $[\bar{\alpha}_b^{-1}]$, the integral value of $\bar{\alpha}_b^{-1}$, by $\overline{W}_b$, then the expression $f(\hat{\bar{\alpha}}_b)$ may be rewritten as

$$f(\hat{\bar{\alpha}}_b) = n_b\hat{\bar{\alpha}}_b[\hat{\bar{\alpha}}_b^{-1} - \overline{W}_b - (W_b - \overline{W}_b)][1 - \hat{\bar{\alpha}}_b^{-1} + \overline{W}_b + (W_b - \overline{W}_b)]$$

$$= n_b\{1 + 2\overline{W}_b - \overline{W}_b(\overline{W}_b + 1)\hat{\bar{\alpha}}_b - \hat{\bar{\alpha}}_b^{-1} + (W_b - \overline{W}_b)$$

$$\cdot [2 - \hat{\bar{\alpha}}_b(2\overline{W}_b + 1)] - (W_b - \overline{W}_b)^2\hat{\bar{\alpha}}_b\}. \quad (8)$$

The probability of an observed integral value W_b occurring is just the probability that the response rate $\hat{\bar{\alpha}}_b$ or m_b/n_b lies in the range between $1/(W_b + 1)$ and $1/W_b$, or $\Pr(W_b) = \Pr[1/(W_b + 1) < \hat{\bar{\alpha}}_b \leq 1/W_b]$, and the probability may be approximately evaluated on the assumption of a normal distribution for the response rate. Hence,

$$Ef(\hat{\bar{\alpha}}_b) \doteq En_b[1 + 2\overline{W}_b - (\overline{W}_b + 1)\overline{W}_b\bar{\alpha}_b - \bar{\alpha}_b^{-1}]$$

$$+ En_b \sum_{W_b} \Pr(W_b)(W_b - \overline{W}_b)$$

$$\cdot \left\{ 2 - [2\overline{W}_b + 1 + (W_b - \overline{W}_b)] - E\hat{\bar{\alpha}}_b \left| \left(\frac{1}{W_{b+1}} < \hat{\bar{\alpha}}_b \leq \frac{1}{W_b} \right) \right. \right\}$$

$$= En_b\bar{\alpha}_b(\bar{\alpha}_b^{-1} - \overline{W}_b)(1 + \overline{W}_b - \bar{\alpha}_b^{-1})$$

$$+ En_b \sum_{W_b} \Pr(W_b)(W_b - \overline{W}_b)[2 - (2\overline{W}_b + 1)E\hat{\bar{\alpha}}_b | W_b]$$

$$- En_b \sum_{W_b} \Pr(W_b)(W_b - W_b)^2 E\hat{\bar{\alpha}}_b | W_b, \tag{9}$$

where $E\hat{\bar{\alpha}}_b | W_b = E\hat{\bar{\alpha}}_b | (1/W_{b+1} < \hat{\bar{\alpha}}_b \leq 1/W_b)$. Here, $W_b = [\hat{\bar{\alpha}}_b^{-1}$ and $\overline{W}_b = [\bar{\alpha}_b^{-1}]$ and n_b is assumed to be independent of W_b and $\hat{\bar{\alpha}}_b$.

In this $\sum_{W_b} \Pr(W_b)$ is taken over all possible observed integral values to the point where $\Pr(W_b)$ becomes negligible or to the point at which the observed response rate $\hat{\bar{\alpha}}_b$ becomes unacceptably low for the subject matter data being obtained so as to discard the data.

In the case where $\Pr(W_b) = 0$ for $W_b > 1$, $\overline{W}_b = 1$ and $Ef(\hat{\bar{\alpha}}_b)$ reduces to $En_b(3 - 2\bar{\alpha}_b - \bar{\alpha}_b^{-1}) = En_b\bar{\alpha}_b \cdot (2 - \bar{\alpha}_b^{-1})(\bar{\alpha}_b^{-1} - 1)$. $E\hat{\bar{\alpha}}_b | (1/W_{b+1} < \hat{\bar{\alpha}}_b \leq 1/W_b)$ may be obtained by assuming a normal distribution for the response rate $\hat{\bar{\alpha}}_b$, where $E\hat{\bar{\alpha}}_b = \bar{\alpha}_b$ and

$$V(\hat{\bar{\alpha}}_b) \doteq (En_b)^{-2}[V(m_b) - 2\bar{\alpha}_b^{-1}\,\mathrm{Cov}_s(m_b, n_b) + \bar{\alpha}_b^{-2}V_s(n_b)],$$

noting that $V(m_b)$ is given in Eq. (15) in Appendix B.

Then $EV_4(\hat{X}_D)$ is the additional variance due to duplication as opposed to weighting in cell b and is given by

$$EV_4(\hat{X}_b^D)$$

$$\doteq Ef(\hat{\bar{\alpha}}_b) \left\{ \frac{1}{En_b\bar{\alpha}_b} \sum_i \alpha_i[(X_i + {}_RB_i)^2 + {}_R\sigma_i^2]\pi_i^{-1} \right.$$

$$\left. - \frac{\sum_{i \neq j}\pi_{ij}\pi_i^{-1}\pi_j^{-1}[\alpha_i\alpha_j + \mathrm{Cov}(\delta_i, \delta_j)][(X_i + {}_RB_i)(X_j + {}_RB_j) + r_{2ij}({}_R\sigma_i)({}_R\sigma_j)]}{En_b\bar{\alpha}_b(En_b\bar{\alpha}_b - 1) + V(m_b)} \right\},$$

$$\tag{10}$$

where $Ef(\hat{\bar{\alpha}}_b)$ is derived in (9) and $V(m_b)$ derived in Eq. (15) in Appendix B.

APPENDIX D.
ADAPTATION OF VARIANCE OF ESTIMATES
TO A TWO-STAGE SAMPLE DESIGN
AS A HYPOTHETICAL EXAMPLE

The expressions for the variances under the different imputation procedures were derived in Appendix B and described in Chapter 17 for any sample design where Horvitz–Thompson estimators are applied. In this section, the variances of the estimates under the different imputation procedures are adapted to a two-stage sample design, as applied to the hypothetical example where first-stage units (clusters) are selected by a ppswor scheme and the second-stage units (households) are selected by the srswor scheme. The average correlations (those referring to responses and those referring to events of responding or not responding) are split up into (i) "between-cluster average correlations," referring to the average correlation coefficient between all possible pairs of units in different clusters, averaged over all pairs of clusters, and (ii) "within-cluster average correlations," referring to the average between all possible pairs of units within clusters, averaged over all clusters. One would usually expect higher correlation coefficients within clusters than between clusters, since effects, whatever they may be, as for example, response errors, might be more alike within clusters than between clusters; hence, the distinction between the two correlations.

The variance of $\hat{X}_b$, $\hat{X}'_b$, $\hat{T}_b$, and $\hat{X}_b^{\mathrm{P}}$ may be adapted to two-stage design by rewriting unit i as $\mathbf{i} = (i, i_2)$, so that π_i is replaced by $\pi_i \pi_{i_2/i}$, where π_i is the probability of selection of cluster i, and it equals $n_1 t_i / t$ when n_1 clusters out of N_1 are selected and cluster i contains t_i dwellings. The conditional probability of household i_2 being selected in cluster i, viz., $\pi_{i_2/i}$, equals n_2/t_i when n_2 dwellings are selected so that the overall probability of selection of unit (i, i_2) equals $n_1 n_2/t.$, $t.$ being the total number of units in the stratum.

The variance of $\hat{X}_b$, the estimate by the weighting method of imputation, may be adapted from Eq. (13) in Chapter 17 to the two-stage sample by the following substitutions and splitting up the variances and covariances into between- and within-cluster components.

$i \rightarrow \mathbf{i}$ (unit i replaced by vector $\mathbf{i}$, denoted by i, i_2), where i denotes clusters and i_2, a unit within i. Similarly $j \rightarrow \mathbf{j}$.

$\pi_j \rightarrow \pi_{\mathbf{i}} = n_1 n_2/t.$

$$\pi_{ij} \rightarrow \pi_{\mathbf{ij}} = \begin{cases} \pi_{ij}(n_2/t_i)(n_2/t_j) & \text{when } \mathbf{i} \text{ and } \mathbf{j} \text{ are in distinct clusters} \\ \pi_i n_2(n_2 - n_1)/[t_i(t_i - 1)] & \text{when } \mathbf{i} \text{ and } \mathbf{j} \text{ are in the same cluster.} \end{cases}$$

π_{ij} must be derived by Connor's (1966) method for each value of n_1. Then

$$V(\hat{X}_b) = V_1(\hat{X}_b) + E_1 V(\hat{X}_b),$$

$$V_1(\hat{X}_b) = \text{sampling variance}$$

(Equation Continues)

$$= \bar{\alpha}^{-2}\left[\frac{t.}{n_1 n_2}\sum_i a_{1i}^2 + 2\frac{t.^2}{n_1^2}g(a_{1i.}) + t.\frac{n_2^{-1}}{n_1 n_2}h(a_{1i}) - a_{1..}^2\right] \quad (1)$$

where

$$g(a_{1i.}) = \sum_{i<j}\frac{a_{1i.}}{t_i}\frac{a_{1j.}}{t_j}\pi_{ij},$$

$$h(a_{1i}) = \sum_i\frac{1}{t_i-1}(a_{1i.}^2 - \sum_{i_2\in i}a_{1ii_2}^2),$$

$$a_{1i} = \alpha_i f(i), \quad \text{where} \quad f(i) = X_i + {}_R B_i - T_b/(t.\,\bar{\alpha}).$$

Here $\bar{\alpha}$ is the expected response rate, or average response probability, of all $t.$ units in the stratum. The nonsampling variance is given in terms of the following notation:

$$a_{2i} = \alpha_{i.\,R}\sigma_i,$$

$$a_{3i} = \sqrt{V(\delta_i)}{}_R\sigma_i,$$

$$a_{4i} = \sqrt{V(\delta_i)}f(i), \quad \text{where} \quad f(i) = X_i + {}_R B_i - T_b/(t.\,\bar{\alpha}).$$

Then

$$E_1 V(\hat{X}_b) = \text{nonsampling variance component}$$

$$= \left\{\frac{t.}{n_1 n_2}\sum_{k=2}^4\sum_i a_{ki}^2 + 2\frac{t.^2}{n_1^2}\left[\bar{r}_{2B}g(a_{2i.})\right.\right.$$

$$+ \bar{r}_{1B}\bar{r}_{2B}g(a_{3i.}) + \bar{r}_{1B}g(a_{4i.})\right]$$

$$+ t.\frac{n_2^{-1}}{n_1 n_2}\left[\bar{r}_{2W}h(a_{2i}) + \bar{r}_{1W}\bar{r}_{2W}h(a_{3i} + \bar{r}_{1W}h(a_{4i})\right]\right\}\bar{\alpha}^{-2}, \quad (2)$$

where $g(a_{ki.})$ and $h(a_{ki})$ are defined in the same way as $g(a_{1i.})$ and $h(a_{1i})$ in relation to the sampling variance.

$\bar{r}_{2B}$ = average between-cluster correlation between responses of pairs of households.

$\bar{r}_{2W}$ = average within-cluster correlation between responses of pairs of households.

$\bar{r}_{1B}$ = average cluster correlation between the events of responding and not responding pertaining to pairs of households.

r_{1W} = average within-cluster correlation between the events of responding and not responding pertaining to pairs of households.

$V(\hat{X}_b')$, the variance of the estimate of the combined historical substitution and weighting methods, may be written approximately as $V(\hat{X}_b)$ in (1) and (2) by increasing $\bar{\alpha}$ by $\bar{\alpha}''$ and assuming the historical value identical to the current information, so that the response bias and response variance of the historical data are the same as the current value. Such an assumption will make the use of historical data somewhat better than it really is in practice, as one would expect the historical data to deviate more widely from the true value than current data. However, such an assumption would provide an upper bound to the improvement that one may expect through the use of historical data combined with weighting as opposed to weighting alone as an imputation method.

The variance of $\hat{T}_b$, the estimate by the zero substitution method, may be obtained from $V(\hat{X}_b)$ as in (1) and (2) by setting $\bar{\alpha} = 1$ but maintaining α_i unchanged in the formula and redefining $f(i) = (X_i + {}_RB_i)$.

Finally, when duplication as opposed to weighting is undertaken, it should be remembered that $V(\hat{X}_b^D) = V(\hat{X}_b) + EV_4(\hat{X}_b^D)$, so that we need only consider the additional variance due to duplication in place of weighting. In any sample design where Horvitz–Thompson estimates are applied, $EV_4(\hat{X}_b^D)$ is given by Eq. (17) in Chapter 17 and may be readily adapted to a two-stage design in a similar manner as $V(\hat{X}_b)$. We shall confine our attention to the case where the response rate exceeds one-half, so that the weight w_i is either one or two. Then by applying the same definitions for a_{ki} for $j = 1, 2, 3, 4$ and functions $g(a_{ki.})$ and $h(a_{ki.})$,

$$
EV_4(\hat{X}_b^D) = (2 - \bar{\alpha}^{-1})(\bar{\alpha}^{-1} - 1)\left\{\frac{t.}{n_1 n_2} \sum_i a_{1i}^2 \right.
$$

$$
+ \frac{t.}{n_1 n_2} \sum_{k=2}^{4} a_{ki}^2 - \frac{n_1 n_2 \bar{\alpha}}{n_1 n_2 \bar{\alpha}(n_1 n_2 \bar{\alpha} - 1) + V(m_b)}
$$

$$
\cdot \left\{\frac{2t_.^2}{n_1^2} g(a_{1i.}) + t. \frac{n_2^{-1}}{n_1 n_2} h(a_{1i}) \right.
$$

$$
+ 2 \frac{t_.^2}{n_1^2} \left[\bar{r}_{2B} g(a_{2i.}) + \bar{r}_{1B}\bar{r}_{2B} g(a_{3i.}) + \bar{r}_{1B} g(a_{4i.})\right]
$$

$$
\left.\left.+ t. \frac{n_2^{-1}}{n_1 n_2} \left[\bar{r}_{2W} h(a_{2i}) + \bar{r}_{1W}\bar{r}_{2W} h(a_{3i}) + \bar{r}_{1W} h(a_{4i})\right]\right\}\right\}. \tag{3}
$$

$V(m_b)$ is obtained from Eq. (15) in Appendix B and may also be adapted to the two-stage design as follows:

$$
V(m_b) = \left(\frac{n_1 n_2}{t.}\right)^2 \left[\frac{t.}{n_1 n_2} \sum_i \alpha_i^2 + 2 \frac{t_.^2}{n_1^2} g(\alpha_{i.}) + \frac{t.(n_2 - 1)}{n_1 n_2} h(\alpha_i) - \alpha_.^2\right]
$$

$$
+ \left(\frac{n_1 n_2}{t.}\right)^2 \left[\frac{t.}{n_1 n_2} \sum_i V(\delta_i) + 2 \frac{t_.^2}{n_1^2} g(\sum_{i2\epsilon i} \sqrt{V(\delta_i)})\bar{r}_{1B}\right.
$$

$$
\left.+ \frac{t.(n_2 - 1)}{n_1 n_2} h(\sqrt{V(\delta_i)})\bar{r}_{1W}\right]. \tag{4}
$$

In formula (3), the expressions involving a_{1i} and a_{1i} comprise the sampling variance component, while the remaining expressions comprise the nonsampling variance components of $EV_4(\hat{X}_b^D)$.

In formula (4), the two terms in brackets are the sampling and nonsampling variance components, respectively, of $V(m_b)$.

APPENDIX E.
GLOSSARY OF TERMS

(1) *Unit*   A unit is an abbreviation of ultimate population unit; it may be a household, individual, establishment, store, etc., generally the unit for which basic survey data is gathered. A unit will be denoted by i.

The following definitions refer to a unit as defined by (1) or to pairs of units in the case of covariance definitions unless otherwise specified.

(2) *Characteristic*   Each unit has characteristics which are subject to survey inquiry. The characteristic may be employment status, marital status, simple head count, income, or any other qualitative or quantative value.

(3) *Characteristic Value*   Each characteristic of a unit has some value attached to it such as 1 or 0 according as the unit has or has not *some* characteristic (e.g., unemployed or other than unemployed) or the actual dollar value of the income of the unit. X_i denotes "true" value of *some* characteristic pertaining to unit i.

(4) *Sampling Unit*   A sampling unit may be a well-defined area, household, cluster, etc., that may be sampled by some specified sampling procedure. In multistage sampling, units are frequently "areas," while the ultimate sampling unit is a household or an individual in the case of household surveys.

(5) *Response Error*   The response error of a selected unit is the deviation of the observed characteristic value from the true characteristic value in the course of the survey inquiry. For example, if the X_i characteristic is "unemployed" and the unit is an individual whose "true" status is "unemployed," then $X_i = 1$. If the response to the question of unemployment status by the selected unit i is "other than unemployed," then the response error is -1. In general, the response error for unit i is denoted by $_R\varepsilon_i$.

(6) *Response Bias*   The response bias of an observed characteristic for a selected unit is the expected value of response errors over all possible survey conditions, given that the selected unit responds. The response bias is given by

$$E_{R}\varepsilon_i | i = {}_R B_i, \qquad \text{or} \qquad [(X_i + {}_R B_i) = X_i].$$

For example, if, as in definition (5), unit i is actually unemployed and an erroneous response of "other than unemployed," viz., $_R\varepsilon_i = -1$, is provided by the unit with probability 0.3, then $_R\varepsilon_i = 0$ with probability 0.7 and $_R\varepsilon_i = -1$ with probability 0.3 and $_RB_i = -1 \times 0.3 = -0.3$.

(7) *Response Variance*   The response variance of an estimate for a characteristic value for a unit is the variance of response errors under all possible survey conditions. The response variance pertaining to unit u is given by

$$E(_R\varepsilon_i - _RB_i)^2 | i = _R\sigma_i^2.$$

For example, in the example of the unit i being unemployed as in definitions (5) and (6), the response variance equals $3(-1 + 3)^2 + .7(0 + .3)^2$, or $_R\sigma_i^2 = .21$.

(8) *Correlated Response Variance* (pertaining to a pair of units)   The correlated response variance of observed characteristic values pertaining to a pair of units is the covariance between the response errors pertaining to the two units in the pair. In general, the covariance is given by

$$E(_R\varepsilon_i - _RB_i)(_R\varepsilon_j - _RB_j) | i, j = r_{2ij}(_R\sigma_i)(_R\sigma_j),$$

where r_{2ij} is the correlation coefficient between the response errors of units i and j.

(9) *Events of Responding and Not Responding*   A unit may or may not respond or it may respond producing data of such dubious quality that it must be discarded. The event of responding or not responding is denoted by a variable δ_i, where $\delta_i = 1$ if unit i responds to provide data of acceptable quality. Otherwise, $\delta_i = 0$, i.e., if the unit does not respond or fails to provide data of acceptable quality. We shall simplify the possible events to a response or nonresponse. A unit that responds is termed a responding unit as opposed to a nonresponding unit or one that does not respond.

(10) *Response Probability*   The response probability of a unit is the probability in that the unit will provide data of acceptable quality, i.e., the probability that $\delta_i = 1$ is α_i.

(11) *Variance of the Event of Responding or Not Responding*   The variance of the event of responding or not responding pertaining to unit i is $V[\delta_i | i]$ and it may be readily verified that $V[\delta_i] = E\delta_i^2 - (E\delta_i)^2 = \alpha_i - \alpha_i^2 = \alpha_i(1 - \alpha_i)$. We shall often use $V(\delta_i)$ instead of $V(\delta_i | i)$ to refer to this variance.

(12) *Covariance between the Events of Responding and Not Responding between Units*   The covariance between the events of responding and not responding between units in a pair is $\text{Cov}[\delta_i\delta_j | i, j]$, where i and j denote two distinct units in a pair. The covariance may also be written as

$$\text{Cov}[\delta_i\delta_j | i, j] = r_{1ij}\sqrt{V(\delta_i)V(\delta_j)},$$

where r_{1ij} denotes the correlation coefficient between the events of responding and not responding pertaining to the pair of units.

(13) *Imputation* (for missing values)   Imputation is the procedure of substituting a characteristic value for a missing value of a nonresponding unit. This substitution may be explicit or implicit depending upon the procedure employed.

(14) *Imputation Error* Whatever imputation procedure is used to sub-stitute a missing value for a unit, the imputation error is the deviation of the imputed value from the true value of a characteristic for the unit, given that the unit does not respond. In general, the imputation error is denoted by $_{NR}\varepsilon_i$ and the error may be explicit or implicit, depending upon the procedure employed.

(15) *Adjustment Cell* An adjustment cell is a balancing area or weighting class as defined in Chapter 17.

(16) *Missingness Pattern* (cell level) The missingness pattern is the vector of events of responding or not responding pertaining to the sampled units. The vector is denoted by

$$\boldsymbol{\delta} = (\delta_1, \delta_2, \ldots, \delta n_b)$$

in cell b, which contains n_b sampled units.

(17) *Response or Nonresponse Rate* (cell level) The response rate is the proportion of the sample that responded in a cell or group of cells. If m_b units out of n_b selected units responded in cell b, then the response rate is m_b/n_b, or in percentage terms $100 m_b/n_b$. The nonresponse rate is the complement of the response rate of $1 - m_b/n_b$.

(18) *Weighting Method* (cell level) The weighting method of imputation is one of inflating the original weight or inverse sampling fraction by the inverse of the response rate in a cell. If the response rate in cell b is m_b/n_b, then the survey data of the area are further weighted by the factor n_b/m_b.

(19) *Duplication Method* (of imputation) The duplication method of im-putation is one of replacing missing data of a sampled nonresponding unit with the response of another sampled unit in a cell. If, as mentioned in the definition of weighting method, m_b units responded out of n_b sampled units with a response rate at least $1/2$, then $n_b - m_b$ responding units will have a weight of 2 along with their original weight, while $2m_b - n_b$ responding units will carry only their original weight.

(20) *Historical Substitution Method* (of imputation) The historical sub-stitution method of imputation is one of replacing missing data of a sampled nonresponding unit with census or other historical data pertaining to the same unit. This method of imputation is possible only if historical data are available.

(21) *Event of Availability or Nonavailability of Historical Data* Historical data for a unit may or may not be available. The variable δ_i' denotes the presence or absence of historical data for unit i, so that $\delta_i' = 1$ or 0 according as the data are available or not for substitution in the event that the unit does not respond. Another variable δ_i'' denotes the combined event of nonresponse and the use or availability of historical data or other than this combined event. Thus, $\delta_i'' = 1$ if unit i fails to respond ($\delta_i = 0$) and historical data are available for substitution ($\delta_i' = 1$). In fact, $\delta_i'' = (1 - \delta_i)\delta_i'$ and $\delta_i + \delta_i''$ denotes the event of responding or not responding and using historical data so that $\delta_i + \delta_i'' = 1$ or 0 according as unit i contains current or historical data or does not respond and contains no historical data.

(22) *Probability of Availability of Historical Data*   As mentioned in definition (21), the historical data may or may not be available, and the probability of its availability is given by $E\delta_i'|i = \alpha_i'$. Since $\delta_i + \delta_i'' = \delta_i + (1 - \delta_i)\delta_i'$, it follows that $E(\delta_i + \delta_i)|i = \alpha_i + [(1 - \alpha_i)\alpha_i' - \text{Cov}(\delta_i\delta_i')]$, the probability of response or nonresponse and the possible use of historical data. The quantity $[(1 - \alpha.)\alpha_i' - \text{Cov}(\delta_i\delta_i')]$ is frequently abbreviated by α_i'' in the development of the imputation methodology involving the use of historical data.

(23) *Unit Substitution Method* (of imputation)   The unit substitution method of imputation is one of substituting another unit that was not originally sampled. The method is possible only in the case of sample surveys rather than a census, where every unit is taken anyway.

(24) *Zero Substitution Method*   Zero substitution is the method of doing nothing to compensate for missing data or, by implication, substituting zero for each missing value of nonresponding units.

(25) *Characteristic Total in an Area* (group of cell level)   The characteristic total in an area consisting of a cell or group of cells in the sum of the individual characteristic values of all the units in the area. In general, the total is denoted by $X = \sum_i X_i$. Specifically, in cell b, $X_b = \sum_{i \in b} X_i$.

(26) *Estimate of Characteristic Total for an Area* (group of cell level)   The estimate of a characteristic total for an area as in (25) is the weighted sample estimate, using the Horvitz–Thompson estimator. If a sampled unit i is selected with probability π_i by any probability sample design, $X_i + {}_R\varepsilon_i$ is the response if the unit responds and $X_i + {}_{NR}\varepsilon_i$ is the substituted value according to some imputation procedure if the unit does not respond. The estimated characteristic total in an area is given by

$$X = \sum_i t_i[(\delta_i(X_i + {}_R\varepsilon_i) + (1 - \delta_i)(X_i + {}_{NR}\varepsilon_i)]\pi_i^{-1},$$

where $t_i = 1$ or 0 according as unit is sampled or not sampled. $Et_i|i = \pi_i.$. In cell b,

$$X_b = \sum_{i=1}^{n_b} [\delta_i(X_i + {}_R\varepsilon_i) + (1 - \delta_i)(X_i + {}_{NR}\varepsilon_i)]\pi_i^{-1}.$$

(27) *Bias of an Estimate of a Total*   The bias of an estimate of the total as defined in (26) is the difference between the expected value of the estimate and the true total in an area. The expected value is taken over all possible samples and over all the various missingness patterns and responses that may occur under all possible survey conditions.

(28) *Response Bias of an Estimate of a Total*   The response bias of an estimate is the component of the bias obtained according to definition (27), contributed by the response biases at the unit levels [see definition (6)].

(29) *Imputation of Bias of an Estimate of a Total*   The imputation bias of an estimate is the remaining component of bias of the estimate as obtained in (27) upon removal of the response bias [see definition (28)].

(30) *Variance of an Estimate of a Total*   The variance of an estimate of the total as defined in (26) is the expected value of the square of the difference between the estimate and its expected value; the expected values are taken over all possible samples and over all possible missingness patterns and responses that may occur under all possible survey conditions.

(31) *Sampling Variance of an Estimate of a Total*   The sampling variance is the expected value of the square of the difference between the conditional expected value of the estimate, given the sample, and its overall expected value, taken over all possible samples.

(32) *Nonsampling Variance of an Estimate of a Total*   The nonsampling variance of an estimate of a total is the variance component of the variance as defined in (30) after the sampling variance as defined in (31) has been removed.

(33) *Simple Response Variance of an Estimate of a Total*   The simple response variance of an estimate of a total is the weighted sum of the response variances pertaining to estimated characteristic values of units [see definition (7)], where each weight is the product of the response and inverse selection probabilities. The simple response variance of an estimate is one component of nonsampling variance defined in (32).

(34) *Correlated Response Variance of an Estimate of a Total*   The correlated response variance of an estimate of a total is the weighted sum of the correlated response variances pertaining to pairs of units [see definition (8)], taken over all pairs of units, where each weight is the product of the joint inclusion probability, the joint response probability, and the inverse inclusion probabilities of the two units. The correlated response variance of an estimate is another component of nonsampling variance, defined in (32). The joint response probability pertaining to two units is the probability that both units respond, given that they are selected. The joint response probability for units i and j, given that are both selected, equals $\alpha_i \alpha_j + \text{Cov}(\delta_i \delta_j)$.

REFERENCES AND BIBLIOGRAPHY

Connor, W. S. (1966). An exact formula for the probability that two specified sampling units will occur in a sample drawn with unequal probabilities and without replacement. *Journal of the American Statistical Association* 61: 384–390.

Platek, R., and Gray, G. B. (1978). Non-response and imputation, *Survey Methodology* 4: (2): 144–177.

Szameitat, K., and Zindler, H. J. (1965). The reduction of errors in statistics by automatic corrections. *Bulletin of the International Statistical Institute, Proceedings of 35th Session, Belgrade* 41, pp. 395–417.

PART VI

Superpopulation Models
for Nonresponse

CHAPTER 20

Introduction

Roderick J. A. Little

1. CONCEPTUAL FRAMEWORK

In Part IV, Chapter 12, Rubin distinguished two systems of inference for sample surveys, which he called the randomization approach and the model-based approach. In the randomization approach the item values are treated as fixed, and inferences are based on the distribution generated by the sampling mechanism, which determines which items are sampled. In the model-based approach inferences are based on a stochastic model for the item values in the population. We review here methods for handling nonresponse derived from *parametric* models for the item values. This introductory chapter provides a brief overview of the material and indicates relations with the randomization based methods discussed in Part IV.

We adopt a notation similar to that of Rubin. Let y represent the set of item values in the population, d a set of binary variables indicating which units are sampled and which units are not sampled (the *sampling mechanism*), and r a set of binary variables indicating which units respond if sampled and which do not respond if sampled (the *response mechanism*). In the absence of nonresponse, the randomization approach bases inferences on the distribution of d given y, which for probability sampling is known. The extension of the randomization approach so as to handle nonresponse specifies a distribution for d and r given y. In Chapter 13 of Part IV, Scheuren and Oh describe this as *quasi-randomization*, since the distribution of r is assumed to correspond to another stage of random sampling but the probabilities are assumed rather than known as in the case of randomization.

INCOMPLETE DATA
IN SAMPLE SURVEYS
Volume 2, Part VI

In contrast, the model-based approach described here specifies a joint distribution for d, r, and y, indexed by a set of unknown parameters θ. This joint distribution induces a distribution for the observed components of d, r, and y, that is, the sample indicators, the response indicators of sampled units, and the item values of variables which are sampled and are recorded. After observing the data, this distribution defines a likelihood which is used to derive inferences about unknown parameters θ in the model, for example, by the method of maximum likelihood. This leads to predictive inferences about the unknown y values, and hence to inferences about population quantities such as the population mean or total.

The main difficulties of this approach concern the formulation of a suitable model for the distribution of d, r, and y and computational and inferential problems arising from the fact that the likelihood has a complicated form.

2. IGNORABLE AND NONIGNORABLE SAMPLING AND RESPONSE MECHANISMS

A key concept in the model building part of the process is *ignorability*, as discussed in Part IV, Chapter 12. If the sampling mechanism is ignorable, then the distribution of the sample indicators d does not affect inferences about the item variables y and can be omitted from the model. If the response mechanism is ignorable, then the distribution of the response indicators r does not affect inferences about the item variables y and can be omitted from the model. Detailed conditions for when the sampling mechanism and the response mechanism are ignorable are given in Section 2 of Chapter 21. A key aspect of these conditions is that the probability of being sampled, and the probability of response if sampled, should not depend on item values y which have not been recorded.

For probability sampling designs the sampling mechanism is ignorable provided design variables are recorded for analysis. All methods considered here assume that this is the case. However, the response mechanism is not under the control of the sampler, and may or may not be ignorable. In Chapter 20 we derive methods under the assumption that the response mechanism is ignorable. In Chapter 21 we discuss models for the response mechanism when it is not ignorable. A major problem with nonignorable models is that y values are only observed for units which respond, and hence the scope for testing the model for the response mechanism r with the available data is very limited. Hence these models may be more useful for sensitivity analyses rather than for providing single inferences for quantities of interest.

3. AN EXAMPLE OF AN IGNORABLE MODEL:
REGRESSION FOR A SINGLE INCOMPLETE ITEM

All the methods discussed in Part IV of this volume are based on an assumption that the response mechanism is ignorable. We conclude by introducing one of the ignorable models discussed in the next chapter and relating it to the weighting method for handling nonresponse described in Part IV, Chapter 13.

Suppose that there is a single item variable subject to nonresponse, and let y_i denote the value of this item for unit i of the population. Let $x_{i1}, x_{i2}, \ldots, x_{ik}$ denote the values for unit i for k variables recorded for all units in the sample. These variables may be sample design variables available for all units in the population, such as variables indicating strata, or they may be item variables completely recorded in the sample. The *normal linear regression* model specifies that, given $x_{i1}, \ldots, x_{ik}$, values of y_i are independent over units and follow a normal distribution with mean

$$E(y_i | x_{i1}, \ldots, x_{ik}) = \beta_0 + \sum_{j=1}^{k} \beta_j x_{ij}$$

and variance σ^2.

The parameters $(\beta_0, \beta_1, \ldots, \beta_k, \sigma^2)$ of this model are not population quantities, which could in principle be measured by a complete census of the population. Rather they represent a simplified structure for the relation between y_i and $x_{i1}, \ldots, x_{ik}$ in the population. In *analytic* surveys such structures are of primary interest, and the parameters are important in their own right. In *descriptive* surveys population quantities such as means or totals are of primary interest, and the parameters are intermediate quantities for predicting non-sampled and nonresponding items. Often inferences about parameters differ from inferences about finite-population quantities by finite-population correction factors. If these are small, it is often convenient to ignore them and to focus on the parameters rather than the quantities. This approach is generally adopted in Chapters 20 and 21.

If the response mechanism is ignorable, then maximum likelihood estimates $(\hat{\beta}_0, \hat{\beta}_1, \ldots, \hat{\beta}_k, \bar{\sigma}^2)$ of the parameters are obtained by least squares linear regression of y_i on $x_{i1}, \ldots, x_{ik}$ using responding units in the sample. The resulting estimates of nonresponding y values in the sample take the form

$$\hat{y}_i = \hat{\beta}_0 + \sum_{j=1}^{k} \hat{\beta}_j x_{ij},$$

where $(x_{i1}, \ldots, x_{ik})$ are values of the x variables for the nonresponding unit.

A special case of this model occurs when the x_{ij} are dummy variables indicating $k + 1$ weighting classes. Let

$$x_{ij} = \begin{cases} 1 & \text{if} \quad \text{unit } i \text{ is in weighting class } j \\ 0 & \text{otherwise.} \end{cases}$$

By the theory of dummy variable regression, the resulting estimate $\hat{y}_i$ is the sample mean of the weighting class to which unit i belongs. Thus the predicted values under this form of the regression model are the weighting class means. If the population totals in the weighting classes are known, the resulting model-based estimator of the population mean of the y_i is the poststratified estimator discussed in Part IV, Chapter 13. If the weighting-class totals are unknown, the resulting estimator is the weighting-class estimator discussed in the same chapter. Model-based estimates of standard errors condition on the number of observed units in each class and lead to the correct inferences under the assumption of simple random sampling within strata (cf. Herzog and Rubin, Part IV, Chapter 15).

The regression model provides more flexible methods for using covariate information to predict missing values y_i than the quasi-randomization approach of Part IV, since it is not restricted to categorical x variables indicating weighting classes. Continuous x variables can be included in the regression model. Furthermore the fitted values y_i can be smoothed by omitting interactions between categorical and/or continuous x variables, on the basis of statistical tests for the regression coefficients. The regression method can also be extended to handle a set of incomplete y variables with different patterns of response. Maximum likelihood methods for these cases are reviewed in Sections 2 and 3 of Chapter 21. Models for the case where y is itself a categorical variable are reviewed in Section 4 of Chapter 21.

The Ignorable Case

Roderick J. A. Little

1. INTRODUCTION

1.1. Preliminaries

In this chapter and the next, item and unit nonresponse are discussed in the context of parametric superpopulation models. The analysis involves methods of parametric statistics such as linear regression, maximum likelihood, and Bayes estimation, rather than methods developed specifically for finite population sampling, as presented in texts such as Cochran (1963) or Kish (1965). Accordingly the reader is expected to have some familiarity with these methods, and in particular, with the basic theory of maximum likelihood estimation. For accounts of these methods the reader is referred to texts such as Kendall and Stuart (1967) and Cox and Hinkley (1974, Chapter 9).

Some notation will be used consistently in these chapters. Latin letters will be used to denote random variables which are scalar, vector, or matrix-valued according to context. Probability density functions of continuous random variables and distribution functions of discrete random variables will be denoted by the symbol f, and densities for different random variables will be distinguished by their arguments. Parameters will be denoted by Greek letters $(\theta, \phi, \psi, \ldots)$. For example, suppose x and y have a joint distribution indexed by the parameter θ. Then the probability density function of this joint distribution is denoted $f(x, y; \theta)$. The probability density functions of the marginal distributions of x and y are denoted $f(x; \theta)$ and $f(y; \theta)$, respectively. The probability density function of the conditional distribution of x given y is denoted $f(x|y; \theta)$. This notation is not technically perfect, since the form of a function $f(\ )$ is not determined by its argument. However it is simple and

INCOMPLETE DATA
IN SAMPLE SURVEYS
Volume 2, Part VI

suffices for our purposes. Likelihoods will be denoted by the symbol L and log-likelihoods by the symbol l. To emphasize that these are functions of the parameters with the data fixed, parameters are written as the first argument. For example, the likelihood of θ based on data (x, y) is

$$L(\theta; x, y) = \text{const.} f(x, y; \theta) \quad \text{for all} \quad \theta,$$

and $l(\theta; x, y) = \ln L(\theta; x, y)$. Finally, the likelihood derived from the conditional distribution of x given y is written $L(\theta; x|y)$.

1.2. Superpopulation Modeling

As has been noted in Part I, Chapter 1, there are two quite different approaches to statistical inference in survey sampling. Under the *fixed population model*, the values of the items for units of the population are treated as fixed but unknown and inferences are based on the randomization distribution induced by taking a probability sample of units in the population. Under the *superpopulation model*, the items in the population are assumed to have a distribution over a sample space of populations, which is sometimes called the *superpopulation distribution*, and inferences are based on this distribution rather than the sampling distribution which determines the sample selection.

The discussion in the previous chapters has centered largely on the fixed population model, although occasional reference is made to superpopulation distributions. In the next two chapters, methods for handling item and unit nonresponse will be considered entirely from the superpopulation point of view.

In their discussion of superpopulation models, Cassel, Särndal, and Wretman (1977) indicate five alternative interpretations of the superpopulation concept:

(1) The finite population is actually drawn from a larger universe.

(2) The population distribution is modeled to describe a random mechanism or process in the real world; such models are frequently used in econometric or sociometric model building.

(3) The distribution is considered as a prior distribution reflecting subjective belief, as in a Bayesian approach. The unobserved population values may be looked upon as unknown values for which we seek the posterior distribution, given the sample.

(4) The distribution is used simply as a mathematical device to make explicit the theoretical derivations. For example, one might be interested in identifying models under which certain estimates have optimal properties.

(5) The superpopulation approach is a device for incorporating the treatment of nonsampling errors in survey sampling.

The relative merits of these interpretations for complete sample survey data vary with the context and with the interpreter and have been the subject of some argument (Johnson and Smith, 1969). In the context of sample survey data with nonresponse the same considerations apply, with nonresponse included as an additional component of nonsampling error.

The extension of the superpopulation model from complete to incomplete data is conceptually trivial. The superpopulation distribution of the complete data is simply replaced by the superpopulation distribution of the data which have been observed. In its simplest form, the argument is as follows. Suppose that the data are sampled from a set of population items y. The superpopulation model specifies that y is stochastic with a probability distribution belonging to a certain family of distributions $\mathscr{D}$. Often this family is characterized as having a probability density function $f(y; \theta)$ of known form indexed by an unknown k-dimensional parameter θ. For example, suppose there are N population units and a single item variable. Then y can be written as a row vector $(y_1, \ldots, y_N)$, where y_i is the value of the item variable for unit i of the population. If the superpopulation model specifies that $y_1, \ldots, y_N$ are independently normally distributed with mean μ and variance σ^2, then $\theta = (\mu, \sigma^2)$ and $f(y; \theta)$ is a product of normal density functions over the population items. That is,

$$f(y; \theta) = \prod_{i=1}^{N} \{(2\pi\sigma^2)^{-1/2} e^{(-1/2)(y_i - \mu)^2/\sigma^2}\}. \tag{1}$$

Now let y_s denote the items that are sampled and $y_{\bar{s}}$ the items that are not sampled. Then in the absence of nonresponse, inference may under certain circumstances be based on y_s and its superpopulation distribution $f(y_s; \theta)$, obtained by averaging $f(y; \theta)$ over the nonsampled items:

$$f(y_s; \theta) = \int f(y; \theta)\, dy_{\bar{s}}. \tag{2}$$

For the simple model (1) this leads to a product of normal densities over the sampled units, that is,

$$f(y_s; \theta) = \prod_{i \text{ sampled}} \{(2\pi\sigma^2)^{-1/2} e^{-(1/2)(y_i - \mu)^2/\sigma^2}\}.$$

In the presence of nonresponse, let p denote the set of sampled items that are present and m the set of sampled items that are missing. Then the data consist of p, and inference may under certain circumstances be based on the superpopulation distribution $f(p; \theta)$ of p obtained by averaging $f(y_s; \theta)$ over the missing items:

$$f(p; \theta) = \int f(y_s; \theta)\, dm = \int f(y; \theta)\, dy_{\bar{s}}\, dm, \tag{3}$$

from Eq. (2). For model (1), this leads to a product of normal densities over the responding units, and thus effectively treats response as another stage of random sampling. More generally, suppose that there are K items and let p_i denote the items present for unit i. If we assume a model where the items are identically and independently distributed over units, then

$$f(y; \theta) = \prod_{i=1}^{N} f(y_i; \theta), \tag{4}$$

and Eq. (3) leads to

$$f(p; \theta) = \prod_{i \text{ sampled}} f(p_i; \theta). \tag{5}$$

That is, inference is based on the marginal distribution of the present items in each unit.

Three characteristics of this basic formulation should be noted. First, a crucial element is the selection of an appropriate family of superpopulation distributions $\mathscr{D}$. If the population under study cannot be modeled by a distribution in the chosen class, then inferences under the superpopulation model may be biased by an unknown amount. In survey sampling, sample sizes are often large, and consequently bias introduced by the wrong choice of $\mathscr{D}$ can easily outweigh gains in precision obtained by modeling the population values. For further discussion see, for example, Hansen, Madow and Tepping (1978). Second, basing inferences in the absence of nonresponse on the marginal distribution (2) involves a hidden assumption that the sample selection procedure is ignorable. Broadly speaking, this assumption implies that the probability of selecting a particular sample should not depend on the values of the population items, y. This assumption is generally satisfied by probability sampling designs, but may not be valid for other selective methods, such as purposive or quota sampling. Hence the superpopulation model approach does not conflict with the desire for probability sampling. Finally, basing inferences in the presence of nonresponse on (3) involves the crucial assumption that the response mechanism is ignorable, or, in other words, that we can ignore the mechanism that caused some of the sampled items to be missing.

A more detailed account of these assumptions is deferred until Chapter 21, where the superpopulation model is extended to include distributions for the sample selection and for the pattern of missing values. For the present chapter we shall confine discussion to one elaboration of the basic model of great practical importance, namely, the inclusion of sample design variables.

Sampling statisticians rarely select units from the population by simple random sampling, but make extensive use of existing information on the population to construct complex sampling schemes based on clustering and stratification. It is clearly advisable to take into account the information used to design the sample in the superpopulation model used to analyze the sample.

A common class of models which fails to incorporate this information makes the assumption that the set of items for unit i $(i = 1, \ldots, N)$ is independent and identically distributed, as in Equation (4). This model corresponds to simple random sampling of units from the superpopulation and hence effectively ignores aspects of the population exploited by stratification or clustering of the sample design. Equation (1) is a special case of the model for a normal item variable.

In order to model the effects of stratification or clustering, we introduce a set of *sample design variables*

$$z = \{z_i; i = 1, \ldots, N\},$$

which are assumed to be known for all units of the population. For example, the values of z_i may indicate strata or primary sampling units. Then the superpopulation model specifies the conditional distribution of population items y given the design variables z, with probability density function $f(y|z; \theta)$. It may then be appropriate to model conditional independence between the units, that is,

$$f(y|z; \theta) = \prod_{i=1}^{N} f(y_i|z_i; \theta). \tag{6}$$

If the z_i identify strata, this model reflects stratification of the population values which the sampler exploits by using a stratified sample design. For example, for the case of a single item variable with J strata, we may replace the model (1) by a model that specifies a normal distribution with mean μ_j and variance σ_j^2 within the stratum for which $z_i = j$. The corresponding form of (2) is then

$$f(y|z; \theta) = \prod_{j=1}^{J} \prod_{\{i:z_i = j\}} \{(2\pi\sigma_j^2)^{-1/2} e^{-(1/2)(y_i - \mu_j)^2/\sigma_j^2}\}.$$

If the z_i identify clusters, the model can be adapted to reflect within cluster correlation in the population values, as in the random effects model of Scott and Smith (1969).

Given the superpopulation distribution $f(y|z; \theta)$, we assume as before that the distribution of the sampled units y_s, $f(y_s|z; \theta)$, can be obtained by averaging over the nonsampled items $y_{\bar{s}}$ and that the distribution of the responding items p, $f(p|z; \theta)$, can be obtained by averaging over the missing items, m. That is,

$$f(y_s|z; \theta) = \int f(y|z; \theta) \, dy_{\bar{s}}, \tag{7}$$

$$f(p|z; \theta) = \int f(y_s|z; \theta) \, dm. \tag{8}$$

Under the conditional independence model (6) these distributions can be written

$$f(y_s|z; \theta) = \prod_{i \text{ sampled}} f(y_i|z_i; \theta_i),$$

$$f(p|z; \theta) = \prod_{\substack{i \text{ sampled and} \\ \text{observed}}} f(p_i|z_i; \theta_i),$$

where p_i is the set of items observed in unit i. As shown formally in Chapter 22, the expression (8) is valid for surveys with differential response rates between strata, but does not model more crucial situations where the responding units are a biased sample of sampled units within strata. Superpopulation models for this form of unit nonresponse are deferred until Chapter 22.

It should be noted that most of the examples of incomplete data methods reviewed here are based on models of the form (4), reflecting the fact that they were not developed in a survey sampling context. However, the extension to models of the population which take account of clustering and stratification is feasible in principle, although real-world examples are not common in the literature.

1.3. Forms of Inference Based on the Superpopulation Distribution

It is convenient to distinguish two forms of inference based on the super-population distribution $f(p|z;\theta)$:

Case 1: Inference for the Superpopulation Parameters θ In certain situations the unknown parameters of the superpopulation model are themselves of primary interest. This is generally not the case in descriptive surveys where simple population statistics such as means and totals are required, but rather in analytic surveys where multivariate statistics such as factor scores or regression coefficients are under study. However, even in the former case the estimation of θ is often required as an intermediate step towards estimating the population statistics (see case 2). Inference about θ can be based on the sampling distribution of p, as in a classical sampling theory approach, or on the likelihood of θ given the data p,

$$L(\theta;p|z) \propto f(p|z;\theta) \qquad \text{for all} \quad \theta,$$

as in a likelihood or Bayesian analysis.

Case 2: Inference for Population Values More commonly interest is not in the population parameters but in some function of the population item values, such as the sample total $\sum_{i=1}^{N} y_i$. In general we can represent any such population quantity as a known function $t(y)$ of the population values y. The superpopulation distribution of y induces a distribution for t, with density $f(t;\theta)$, and the conditional distribution of t given the present items p, with density $f(t|p;\theta)$.

If θ were known, a possible estimate of t would be the mean of this conditional distribution,

$$t^*(\theta) = E\{t|p;\theta\} = \int tf(t|p;\theta)\,dt. \qquad (9)$$

However, in practice θ is unknown. One possibility is to substitute an estimate $\hat{\theta}$ of θ, leading to

$$t = t^*(\hat{\theta}). \tag{10}$$

Inferences may be based on the properties of t in repeated samplings from the superpopulation distribution (Royall, 1971). An alternative, (and, in the author's opinion, a more natural) approach is to introduce a prior distribution $\pi(\theta)$ for the unknown parameters θ. Inference about θ is based on its posterior distribution given the data p, found by Bayes's theorem:

$$f(\theta|p) = f(p;\theta)\pi(\theta)\bigg/\int f(p;\theta')\pi(\theta')\,d\theta'. \tag{11}$$

Inference about t is based on its predictive distribution, obtained by averaging $f(t|p;\theta)$ over the posterior distribution of θ, that is,

$$f(t|p) = \int f(t|p;\theta)f(\theta|p)\,d\theta. \tag{12}$$

A possible point estimate of t is the mean of its predictive distribution $f(t|p)$. For asymmetric distributions other measures, such as the median or the mode, may be preferable. In large samples this Bayesian analysis may be simplified by the following approximation. Assume asymptotic normality; the mean of the predictive distribution is approximately

$$\hat{t}_\pi = E(t|p;\hat{\theta}_\pi), \tag{13}$$

where $\hat{\theta}_\pi$ is the mode of the posterior distribution of θ. This leads to inferences of the same form as (10). For discussions of Bayesian predictive inferences and its equivalence with sampling theory methods in large samples, see Geisser (1971), Aitchison (1975).

EXAMPLE 1: INFERENCE FOR A POPULATION TOTAL.   Suppose that $t = \sum_{i=1}^{N} y_i$, the population total for a single item. Then the mean of t given θ and the data is

$$t^*(\theta) = E\{\sum y_i|p;\theta\} = \sum_{i\text{ observed}} y_i + \sum_{i\text{ missing}} E(y_i|p;\theta) + \sum_{\substack{i\text{ not}\\ \text{sampled}}} E(y_i|p;\theta).$$

Hence $t^*(\theta)$ is the sum of the observed items and the predicted values of the nonsampled and missing items. If θ is replaced by an estimate $\hat{\theta}$ we obtain the estimate of t,

$$t = \sum_{i\text{ observed}} y_i + \sum_{\substack{i\text{ sampled}\\ \text{and missing}}} \hat{y}_i + \sum_{\substack{i\text{ not}\\ \text{sampled}}} \hat{y}_i,$$

where $\hat{y}_i = E(y_i|p;\theta)$, evaluated at $\theta = \hat{\theta}$.

Hence the estimate of the population total involves fitted values for the nonsampled and missing items, which depend on the estimate of θ. In subsequent sections we shall be mainly concerned with the estimation of θ, using standard incomplete data methods in the statistical literature. The role of the fitted values $\hat{y}_i$ is a special feature of finite-population inference which will be emphasized in the course of the discussion.

1.4. Estimating the Superpopulation Parameters

Two broad approaches to parameter estimation from incomplete data can be distinguished in the statistics literature. The first is to adapt estimates developed for the hypothetical complete data y_s, with missing values filled in or imputed by intuitively sensible estimates. For example, the estimates are chosen to approximate as closely as possible the true values, as in mean imputation, or to reflect as far as possible the distribution of the missing item, as in random imputation or certain hot-deck procedures. Standard methods are then applied to the data completed in this way. The sampling properties of these estimates should be based of course on the distribution $f(p|z; \theta)$ rather than on the distribution of y_s, and where possible, inferences developed in this way should allow for this difference.

The second approach derives estimates directly from the likelihood of the incomplete data p, using the method of maximum likelihood or Bayesian techniques.

In general, the early theoretical statistical literature on incomplete data follows the first of these approaches, except for simple patterns of missing values [see, for example, Afifi and Elashoff (1966)]. This probably reflects the fact that missing values were a problem for applied statisticians before formal methods for handling them had been written down, and thus early methods inevitably treated the problem by discarding incomplete observations or by imputation of the missing values. Thus early theoretical formulations tended to follow the same pattern. Another reason is that methods based on the likelihood of the incomplete data often involved excessive computation before the development of electronic computers. The more recent model-based literature is less subject to these constraints and hence has also considered likelihood-based estimates which require iterative calculations and use the incomplete data in an efficient way.

Both approaches will be examined here. Although they represent quite different ways of looking at the problem, we shall show that the resulting estimates are often in agreement.

1.5. Maximum Likelihood Estimation for Incomplete Data

In this section we review standard large-sample theory for the estimation of an $r \times 1$ vector of parameters θ by the method of maximum likelihood. We assume that the sampling mechanism and the response mechanism are ignorable, so that the distribution of the observed items takes the form

$$f(p|z; \theta) = \int f(y_s|z; \theta) \, dm$$

of Eq. (8). Likelihood methods are based on the likelihood function, or equivalently its logarithm

$$l(\theta; p|z) = \log f(p|z; \theta),$$

considered as a function of θ.

A *Maximum Likelihood (ML) estimate* of θ,

$$\hat{\theta} = \hat{\theta}(p),$$

is defined as a value of θ which maximizes $l(\theta; p|z)$. The *expected information matrix* $J(\theta)$ is defined as the $r \times r$ matrix with (j, k)th element

$$J_{jk}(\theta) = -E \frac{\partial^2 l(\theta; p|z)}{\partial \theta_j \, \partial \theta_k},$$

with expectation over the distribution of p. Under mild regularity conditions, $\hat{\theta}$ is a consistent, asymptotically efficient estimate of θ and has an asymptotic r-variate normal distribution with mean θ and covariance matrix $J^{-1}(\theta)$, the inverse of the expected information matrix. In practice $J(\theta)$ is estimated by $J(\hat{\theta})$, or by the *information matrix* $I(\theta; p|z)$, with (j, k)th element

$$I_{jk}(\theta; p|z) = -\frac{\partial^2 l(\theta; p|z)}{\partial \theta_j \, \partial \theta_k},$$

evaluated at $\theta = \hat{\theta}$.

Bayesian motivation for the ML estimate is based on the fact that the posterior distribution of θ in large samples can be approximated by an r-variate normal distribution with mean $\hat{\theta}(p)$ and covariance matrix $I^{-1}(\hat{\theta}; p|z)$, the inverse of the information matrix evaluated at $\theta = \hat{\theta}$. The large-sample results are numerically similar to the analysis based on the sampling distribution of $\hat{\theta}(p)$, differing only in probabilistic interpretation. See, for example, Cox and Hinkley (1974), Section 10.6.

Useful discussions of ML estimation with incomplete data are given by Hartley (1958), Hartley and Hocking (1971), Orchard and Woodbury (1972) and Dempster, Laird and Rubin (1977). Certain general characteristics of the problem are worth noting.

1.6.   Existence and Asymptotic Properties of Maximum Likelihood Estimates

For many important superpopulation models, including special cases of the multivariate linear model and the log-linear models for contingency tables, the complete data have a distribution belonging to the regular exponential family. Consequently the complete data ML estimate is the unique solution of the likelihood equations and has the desired asymptotic properties. In contrast, the incomplete data p often have a distribution outside the regular exponential family, and it is possible for the likelihood function to have multiple stationary values. Hence, one can not always be certain that a given solution of the likelihood equation is the ML estimate. Because examples in the literature are largely artificial, the extent to which this is a problem in real data sets is largely unknown. Nevertheless, the analyst should be aware of the possibility of this difficulty (Murray, 1977).

Asymptotic theory for incomplete data patterns is not highly developed. One complicating issue is how to generalize the notion of letting the sample size tend to infinity in the context of incomplete data patterns. A weak condition is to let the proportion of incomplete units tend to zero as the sample size increases (Press and Scott, 1976). A more appropriate asymptotic theory is obtained by allowing the proportion of units with each observed pattern of response to remain constant as the sample size increases. A question of more practical importance concerns how much data is required for asymptotic theory to be relevant, and whether t-type approximations can be developed for small samples (Little, 1979).

Very little is known about these questions. However, in sample surveys we are often in the fortunate position where the number of units is large and asymptotic theory can be expected to apply. Also it should be noted that randomization inferences for finite populations are also based on large-sample approximations, which are often less likely to be valid since design unbiased estimators (such as the Horvitz–Thompson estimator of the population total) do not reduce the number of parameters to be estimated from the data.

1.7. The Pattern of Missing Data

In general, the likelihood of the observed data p is a much more complicated function than the likelihood of the complete data y_s. For complete data the likelihood equations can often be solved directly or by readily available statistical subroutines. When data are incomplete, iterative methods are often required to maximize the likelihood.

The complexity of the likelihood depends on the pattern of the missing data. Indeed, for certain patterns the likelihood factors into components, each of which can be maximized separately by complete data methods. For other patterns no such simplification occurs, but an organization of the cases by pattern of missingness still helps the estimation procedure. Hence it is desirable to classify the patterns of missing values. Also a distinction needs to be made between algorithms designed for maximizing the likelihood for any pattern of missing values (Section 2) and those designed for a particular pattern of missing data (Section 3).

1.8. Algorithms for Finding Maximum Likelihood Estimates

In situations where the ML estimates require iterative calculation, standard numerical methods for maximizing functions such as Newton–Raphson or the method of Scoring (where the expected information is used to modify estimates at each step) can be used (see, for example, Kendall and Stuart, 1973.) However, an alternative algorithm for incomplete data deserves special study. This algorithm, termed the EM (expectation maximization) algorithm by Dempster *et al.* (1977), is based on a theorem relating the observed data log-likelihood $l(\theta; p|z)$ to the complete data log-likelihood $l(\theta; y_s|z)$ and produces algorithms which are often natural extensions of complete data methods. We shall see that certain methods based on filling in the missing values can be viewed as particular cases of the EM algorithm for data with a multivariate normal distribution. The EM algorithm is discussed in Section 3.3.

2. METHODS FOR SPECIAL PATTERNS OF INCOMPLETE DATA

2.1. Introduction

This section discusses methods which have been developed for particular patterns of incomplete multivariate data. Section 3 develops techniques which apply to any pattern of missing values.

In both these sections the examples concern exclusively the estimation of the means and covariance matrix of the variables, and functions of these parameters such as regression coefficients. For ML estimation, the hypothetical complete data are assumed to be a random sample from the multivariate normal distribution with mean μ and covariance matrix Σ. For methods based on imputing the missing values, the assumption of normality is not necessarily made explicit, but often underlies the form of the imputed values.

This concentration on multivariate normal examples reflects an emphasis in the literature, and may disappoint the applied statistician who knows that data rarely fit this theoretically convenient mold. The following points are worth stating for the defence.

1. Transformations (such as the logarithm for positive data) can be used to improve the validity of the assumption.

2. The multivariate normal provides a general baseline model, which can be elaborated in particular cases if necessary. For example, an important characteristic of the distribution is that the regression of any single variable on the others is linear and additive. For particular data sets this basic model may be elaborated to include polynomial terms or interactions, and methods for handling incomplete data developed in Sections 2.3 and 3.2 can be applied to such models as necessary. (However, very little literature on this topic is known to this author).

3. The multivariate normal assumption can be made more realistic by transformations of variables or by splitting the data into subgroups by dis-aggregating with respect to categorical variables such as those defining strata. Also, some weakening of multivariate normality is possible in the case of multiple regression, as explained in Example 8.

Despite these remarks, the fact remains that often data from surveys are available in a cross-tabular form for which multivariate normality is clearly not an appropriate distributional assumption. Examples with discrete multivariate data are discussed in Section 4.

2.2. The Bivariate Case

The first data pattern considered is perhaps the simplest case of item non-response, but it is nevertheless important and repeatedly serves to illustrate the main ideas of Chapters 21 and 22.

EXAMPLE 2: BIVARIATE DATA WITH MISSING VALUES FOR ONE VARIABLE. The data consist of n observations $\{(y_{i1}, y_{i2}), i = 1, \ldots, n\}$ on two random variables y_1 and y_2 and $n_1 - n$ observations $\{y_{i1}, i = n + 1, \ldots, n_1\}$ on y_1 alone. The values of y_2 for the unpaired observations can be regarded as missing data. The data are represented diagrammatically in Fig. 1.

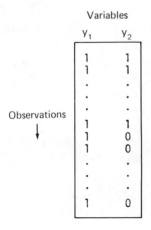

Fig. 1. *Incomplete data pattern for Example 2*

Suppose that the paired observations are a random sample from the bivariate distribution of y_1 and y_2, with means (μ_1, μ_2), variances $(\sigma_{11}, \sigma_{22})$, and covariance σ_{12}, and the unpaired observations are a random sample from the marginal distribution of y_1, with mean μ_1 and variance σ_{11}. The problem is to estimate the parameters

$$\theta = (\mu_1, \sigma_{11}, \mu_2, \sigma_{22}, \sigma_{12})$$

or functions of these such as the correlation $\rho = \sigma_{12}(\sigma_{11}\,\sigma_{22})^{-1/2}$.

Even for this simple example there are a surprising number of options. One of the simplest is to discard the unpaired observations and form sample means and covariances from the paired observations, giving estimates

$$\tilde{\mu}_j = \bar{y}_j \equiv \frac{1}{n}\sum_{i=1}^{n} y_{ij} \qquad (j = 1, 2),$$

$$\tilde{\sigma}_{jk} = s_{jk} \equiv \frac{1}{n}\sum_{i=1}^{n}(y_{ij} - \bar{y}_j)(y_{ik} - \bar{y}_k) \qquad (j, k = 1, 2),$$

(14)

where the factor $1/n$ in the second expression can be replaced by $1/(n-1)$ if the sample covariances are adjusted for degrees of freedom, an adjustment which is omitted from now on for simplicity of exposition. The estimates $\tilde{\mu}_1$ and $\tilde{\sigma}_{11}$ clearly waste information in the unpaired values of y_1 and should be replaced by

$$\hat{\mu}_1 = \frac{1}{n_1}\sum_{i=1}^{n_1} y_{i1},$$

$$\hat{\sigma}_{11} = \frac{1}{n_1}\sum_{i=1}^{n_1}(\bar{y}_{i1} - \hat{\mu}_1)^2.$$

(15)

Wilks (1932) proposes estimating the means and variances by $\hat{\mu}_1, \tilde{\mu}_2, \hat{\sigma}_{11}$, and $\tilde{\sigma}_{22}$ and debates whether to estimate σ_{12} or ρ from the paired observations.[1] The latter leads to the estimates of ρ and σ_{12}

$$\tilde{\rho} = \tilde{\sigma}_{12}(\tilde{\sigma}_{11}\,\tilde{\sigma}_{22})^{-1/2}, \qquad \tilde{\sigma}'_{12} = \tilde{\rho}(\hat{\sigma}_{11}\,\tilde{\sigma}_{22})^{1/2} = \tilde{\sigma}_{12}(\hat{\sigma}_{11}/\tilde{\sigma}_{11})^{1/2}, \quad (16)$$

whereas the former gives the alternative estimates

$$\tilde{\rho}' = \tilde{\sigma}_{12}(\hat{\sigma}_{11}\,\tilde{\sigma}_{22})^{-1/2} \qquad \text{and} \qquad \tilde{\sigma}_{12}. \tag{17}$$

Wilks compares the asymptotic variances of these estimates and finds (16) preferable to (17). Matthai (1951) notes that unlike $\tilde{\rho}$ the estimate $\tilde{\rho}'$ in (17) has the unfortunate property that it does not always lie between -1 and 1.

Both these authors were aware that, apart from $\hat{\mu}_1$ and $\hat{\sigma}_{11}$, none of these estimators is asymptotically efficient. An alternative approach which leads to

---

[1] In fact Wilks considered the more general pattern with unpaired observations on both variables. His analysis is simplified for the special case of this example.

Roderick J. A. Little

asymptotically efficient estimates is to assume bivariate normality of y_1 and y_2 and to estimate the parameters by maximum likelihood.

The likelihood of $\theta = (\mu_1, \mu_2, \sigma_{11}, \sigma_{12}, \sigma_{22})$ is the product of the bivariate normal density for the n paired observations and the normal density of the $n_1 - n$ unpaired observations. Lord (1955) found explicit expressions for the ML estimates of θ by solving the likelihood equations. However, Anderson (1957) introduced an ingenious simplification of the likelihood which greatly simplifies the calculations, and this is now presented.

Consider the alternative set of parameters $\phi = (\mu_1, \sigma_{11}, \beta_{20.1}, \beta_{21.1}, \sigma_{22.1})$ corresponding to the factorization of the bivariate normal distribution of y_1 and y_2 into the marginal distribution of y_1 and the conditional distribution of y_2 given y_1. That is,

$$f(y_1, y_2; \theta) = N(y_1; \mu_1, \sigma_{11})N(y_2; \beta_{20.1} + \beta_{21.1}y_1, \sigma_{22.1}), \qquad (18)$$

where $N(\ ; \mu, \sigma^2)$ denotes the normal density with mean μ and variance σ^2.

The probability density of the data p factorizes as

$$f(p; \theta) = f_1(y_{11}, \ldots, y_{n_1,1}; \theta)f_2(y_{12}, \ldots, y_{n2}|y_{11}, \ldots, y_{n_1,1}; \theta).$$

The first factor f_1 is the density of the marginal distribution of $y_{11}, \ldots, y_{n_1,1}$, and hence depends on μ_1 and σ_{11} only. The second factor is the density of the conditional distribution of $y_{12}, \ldots, y_{n2}$ given $y_{11}, \ldots, y_{n_1,1}$. Since the observations are independent, this term is independent of $y_{n+1,1}, \ldots, y_{n_1,1}$, and depends on $\beta_{20.1}$, $\beta_{21.1}$, and $\sigma_{22.1}$ only. Hence taking logarithms, the log-likelihood partitions into

$$l(\mu_1, \sigma_{11}, \beta_{20.1}, \beta_{21.1}, \sigma_{22.1}; p)$$

$$= l_1(\mu_1, \sigma_{11}; y_{11}, \ldots, y_{n_1,1})$$

$$+ l_2(\beta_{20.1}, \beta_{21.1}, \sigma_{22.1}; y_{12}, \ldots, y_{n2}|y_{11}, \ldots, y_{n1}). \qquad (19)$$

Note that both the log-likelihoods on the right-hand side of (19) correspond to complete data problems: l_1 is the log-likelihood for a random sample of size n_1 from the normal distribution, and l_2 is the log-likelihood for the normal linear regression of y_2 on y_1 based on n complete observations. Also, the components l_1 and l_2 involve distinct sets of parameters, and hence the overall log-likelihood is maximized by maximizing each component separately.

Thus maximizing l_1, we obtain ML estimates $\hat{\mu}_1, \hat{\sigma}_{11}$ of μ_1 and σ_{11}, as given in Eq. (15). Maximizing l_2, we obtain ML estimates of $\beta_{20.1}$, $\beta_{21.1}$, and $\sigma_{22.1}$, viz.,

$$\hat{\beta}_{21.1} = s_{12}/s_{11},$$

$$\hat{\beta}_{20.1} = \bar{y}_2 - (s_{12}/s_{11})\bar{y}_1, \qquad (20)$$

$$\hat{\sigma}_{22.1} = s_{22} - s_{12}^2/s_{11}.$$

Thus we have simple closed form estimates of ϕ. It remains to express θ as a function of ϕ, or, more explicitly, μ_2, σ_{22}, and σ_{12} as functions of μ_1, σ_{11}, $\beta_{20.1}$, $\beta_{21.1}$, and $\sigma_{22.1}$. The required connecting equations are

$$\sigma_{12} = \beta_{21.1}\sigma_{11}, \qquad \mu_2 = \beta_{20.1} + \beta_{21.1}\mu_1, \qquad \sigma_{22} = \sigma_{22.1} + \beta_{21.1}^2\sigma_{11}.$$

Hence ML estimates of θ are given by (15) and

$$\begin{aligned}
\hat{\mu}_2 &= \hat{\beta}_{20.1} + \hat{\beta}_{21.1}\hat{\mu}_1 = \bar{y}_2 + (s_{12}/s_{11})(\hat{\mu}_1 - \bar{y}_1), \\
\hat{\sigma}_{22} &= \hat{\sigma}_{22.1} + \hat{\beta}_{21.1}^2\hat{\sigma}_{11} = s_{22} - s_{12}^2/s_{11} + (s_{12}^2/s_{11}^2)\hat{\sigma}_{11}, \\
&= s_{22} + (s_{12}^2/s_{11}^2)(\hat{\sigma}_{11} - s_{11}), \\
\hat{\sigma}_{12} &= \hat{\beta}_{21.1}\hat{\sigma}_{11} = s_{12}(\hat{\sigma}_{11}/s_{11}).
\end{aligned} \tag{21}$$

The key to the solution is the decomposition of the log-likelihood Eq. (19), which also clarifies some interesting aspects of the data. The observations on y_2 do not affect the log-likelihood of the mean and variance of y_1, and hence do not carry any information about these parameters. Similarly, the incomplete observations on y_1 convey no information about the parameters of the regression of y_2 on y_1. However, the observations on y_1 do convey information on the mean and variance of y_2 when there are extra observations on y_1. The ML estimates of μ_2, σ_{22}, and σ_{12} based on the n complete observations alone are $\bar{y}_2$, s_{22}, and s_{12}, respectively. The extent to which these are modified by the extra data on y_1 is clear from (21).

The data pattern in Fig. 1 is familiar in the sampling context. A certain characteristic y_2 is measured for a sample of the population, and an estimate of the mean of y_2 is required. A correlated characteristic y_1 is available for a larger sample, or for the whole population. A common method for exploiting this is to regress y_2 on y_1 using the pairs of observations, and then to use the regression equation to predict values of y_2 where y_1 is present and y_2 missing. Then the average of the observed and predicted values of y_2 is called a regression estimate of the mean of y_2.

The predicted values for nonsampled values of y_2 are

$$\hat{y}_{i2} = \bar{y}_2 + (s_{12}/s_{11})(y_{i1} - \bar{y}_1),$$

and hence the regression estimate of μ_2 is

$$\frac{1}{n_1}\left(\sum_{\substack{i \text{ sampled}}} y_{i2} + \sum_{\substack{i \text{ not} \\ \text{sampled}}} \hat{y}_{i2} \right),$$

and this can easily be shown to be exactly equal to $\hat{\mu}_2$. Thus this regression estimate of μ_2 is the ML estimate under the assumption that y_1 and y_2 are bivariate normally distributed.

Returning to the case where values of y_2 are missing for the sample, note that if interest lies in the estimation of the population total of y_2, then this can be estimated as

$$t = \sum_{i=1}^{n} y_{i2} + \sum_{i=n+1}^{n_1} \hat{y}_{i2} + (N - n_1)\hat{\mu}_2,$$

where $N - n_1$ is the number of units in the population which have not been sampled.

2.3. Factorizing the Likelihood

The factorization of the likelihood in Example 2 can be formulated more generally to solve a much wider class of problems. The generalization was sketched for the normal distribution in Anderson's (1957) paper and described further by Bhargava (1962). Extensions to other patterns and distributions were given by Rubin (1974).

The log-likelihood $l(\theta; p)$ of θ based on the incomplete data may be a complicated function with no obvious maximum. However, in some circumstances an alternative parameterization ϕ can be found such that the log-likelihood of ϕ decomposes into components

$$l(\phi; p) = l_1(\phi_1; p_1) + l_2(\phi_2; p_2) + \cdots + l_k(\phi_k; p_k), \qquad (22)$$

where

  (i) $\phi_1, \phi_2, \ldots, \phi_k$ are *distinct*, in the sense that the joint parameter space of $(\phi_1, \phi_2, \ldots, \phi_k)$ is the product of the individual parameter spaces of ϕ_j, $j = 1, \ldots, k$.

  (ii) The components $l_j(\phi_j; p_j)$ correspond to likelihoods for complete data problems (or more generally, for easier incomplete data problems).

If a decomposition with these properties can be found, then since $\phi_1, \ldots, \phi_k$ are distinct, $l(\phi; p)$ can be maximized by maximizing $l_j(\phi_j; p_j)$ separately for each j. If $\hat{\phi}$ is the resulting ML estimate of ϕ, the ML estimate of any function $\theta(\phi)$ of ϕ is obtained by substituting $\hat{\phi}$ for ϕ, that is, $\hat{\theta} = \theta(\hat{\phi})$ (Kendall and Stuart, 1967, Section 18.5).

Equation (19) is clearly a special case of (22) with $k = 2$, $\phi_1 = (\mu_1, \sigma_{11})$, and $\phi_2 = (\beta_{20.1}, \beta_{21.1}, \sigma_{22.1})$. Further examples are now given.

EXAMPLE 3: A SPECIAL K-VARIATE CASE. An obvious elaboration of Example 2 is to replace the variables y_1 and y_2 in Fig. 1 by blocks of variables, so that y_1 represents a set of r variables which are always observed and y_2 a set of $K - r$ variables which are observed for units $i = 1, \ldots, n$ and missing thereafter. Suppose that $(y_1 : y_2)$ is multivariate normal with mean μ and covariance matrix Σ and that the parameters are written in the partitioned form

$$\mu = (\mu_1 : \mu_2), \qquad \Sigma = \begin{pmatrix} \Sigma_{11} & \Sigma_{12} \\ \Sigma_{21} & \Sigma_{22} \end{pmatrix},$$

corresponding to the variable blocks. Then ML estimates are obtained using the factorization of the distribution of (y_1, y_2) into the normal distribution of y_1, with mean μ_1 and covariance matrix Σ_{11}, and the conditional distribution of y_2 given y_1, with mean $\Sigma_{21}\Sigma_{11}^{-1}(y_1 - \mu_1)$ and covariance matrix $\Sigma_{22.1} = \Sigma_{22} - \Sigma_{21}\Sigma_{11}^{-1}\Sigma_{12}$. The estimates are direct matrix analogs of (15) and (20). That is, in obvious generalized notation,

$$\hat{\mu}_1 = \frac{1}{n_1} \sum_{i=1}^{n_1} y_{i1}, \qquad \hat{\Sigma}_{11} = \frac{1}{n_1} \sum_{i=1}^{n_1} (y_{i1} - \hat{\mu}_1)(y_{i1} - \hat{\mu}_1)^{\mathrm{T}},$$

$$\hat{\mu}_2 = \bar{x}_2 + s_{21}s_{11}^{-1}(\hat{\mu}_1 - \bar{y}_1), \tag{23}$$

$$\hat{\Sigma}_{21} = s_{21}s_{11}^{-1}\hat{\Sigma}_{11},$$

$$\hat{\Sigma}_{22} = s_{22} - s_{21}s_{11}^{-1}(\hat{\Sigma}_{11} - s_{11})s_{11}^{-1}s_{12}.$$

An interesting application of these estimates occurs in stratified sampling without nonresponse, where y_1 represents stratifying variables present for the whole population and y_2 represents sampled items. To allow for stratification, inference about the parameters (μ_2, Σ_{22}) of the marginal distribution of y_2 should be based on $\hat{\mu}_2$ and $\hat{\Sigma}_{22}$, rather than on the means and covariance matrix of the sampled items. The estimate $\hat{\mu}_2$ is a poststratified mean (Demets and Halperin, 1977; Holt, Smith and Winter, 1980).

A simple extension of this idea relates methods of mean imputation and weighting discussed in earlier chapters to the model based estimates of Eq. (23). Suppose that y_1 is a set of dummy variables indicating strata and y_2 is an item variable which is missing for some sampled items. By a well-known property of dummy variable regression, the regression of y_2 on y_1 results in a fitted value equal to the observed mean for each stratum. Thus the expression for $\hat{\mu}_2$ in (23) is identical to a poststratified estimate of μ_2 where the stratum mean has been imputed for missing values. Furthermore, if y_1 represents a large set of stratifying variables, then individual stratum means might be based on small sample sizes and hence have a large variance. Then a regression of y_2 on y_1 which omits interactions between stratifying variables may lead to improved estimates of missing values.

The reader may justifiably query the multivariate normality assumption when y_1 is a set of dummies indicating strata. However, this assumption is not necessary since it can be shown (Rubin, 1974) that a variable like y_1 which is observed for all units can be held fixed without affecting the ML estimates of the regression of y_2 on y_1. We return to this point in Example 7.

EXAMPLE 4: MONOTONE DATA PATTERNS. A further extension involves the generalization of the pattern in Fig. 1 to monotone data patterns.[2] A data pattern is monotone if the observations and variables can be arranged so that for each observation i, y_{ij} observed implies y_{ik} observed for all $k < j$. The general

---

[2] Described as *nested* patterns by Hartley and Hocking (1971).

case is illustrated in Fig. 2, where each symbol $y_1, y_2, \ldots, y_K$ may represent a single variable or a block of variables.

The relevance of this data pattern to sample surveys may be demonstrated by elaborating the stratified sample problem just considered. Once again, let y_1 represent stratifying variables present for all units in the population; let y_2 represent item variables observed for all units of the sample, and let y_3 represent an item variable subject to nonresponse. Then the resulting data have the pattern of Fig. 2 with $K = 3$ variables.

An appropriate parameterization for the pattern in Fig. 2 corresponds to the factorization

$$f(y_1, \ldots, y_k; \phi) = f_1(y_1; \phi_1)f_2(y_2|y_1; \phi_2) \cdots f(y_K|y_1, \ldots, y_{K-1}; \phi_K), \quad (24)$$

where ϕ_j are the parameters of the conditional distribution of y_j given $y_1, \ldots,$ y_{j-1} and are estimated using the rectangle of data consisting of the values of $y_1, y_2, \ldots, y_j$ for all observations where $y_1, \ldots, y_j$ are observed. If the parameters ϕ_j are distinct, they can be estimated by complete data methods.

EXAMPLE 5: AN EXAMPLE WITH REAL DATA. Common sources of monotone data patterns are panel studies where individuals are lost to follow-up. Marini, Olsen and Rubin (1980) analyze data of this kind based on a 15-year follow-up of students in 10 Illinois high schools, originally studied by Coleman (1961).

The data, restricted for our purposes to female respondents, consist of four blocks of variables. The first block, w, contains variables obtained from the questionnaire administered to individuals in the original study in 1957. These

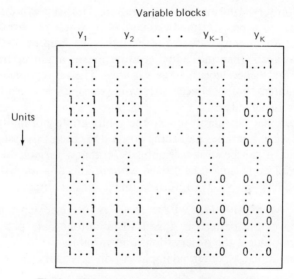

Fig. 2. *The monotone data pattern of Example 4.*

variables are effectively 100% observed. The second block, x, consists of variables measured for all respondents in the 15-year follow-up study. Of all female respondents to the original survey, 79% responded to the follow-up, and thus the subset of variables x are regarded as 79% observed. The data for the 15-year follow-up survey were collected in several phases, and for economic reasons some variables were measured only for respondents in the first phase. These variables form the third block, y, and were recorded for 51.5% of the original female sample. The three blocks w, x, and y, form a monotone pattern as in Fig. 2, with $K = 3$, $y_1 = w$, $y_2 = x$, $y_3 = y$.

A fourth block of variables, z, consists of a small number of items measured by a questionnaire mailed to the parents of all students in the original adolescent sample. Of these parents, 65% responded. Since w is completely observed, all those who responded to the variables in z also responded to the variables in w. However, those who responded to the variables in z did not necessarily respond to the variables in x and y, and those who responded to the variables in x and y did not necessarily respond to the variables in z. Hence when all four variable blocks are considered, the overall data pattern is not completely monotone, as illustrated in Table 1. Since the data do not have a monotone pattern, the method of factorizing the likelihood cannot be used to find ML estimates.

Iterative methods for finding ML estimates are given in Section 3. However, by sacrificing a relatively small amount of data monotone patterns can be obtained. Two monotone patterns are examined. First, the values of z for patterns C and E (marked with asterisks) are omitted, leaving a monotone pattern with w more observed than x, x more observed than y, and y more observed than z. Second, the values of x for patterns B and D and the values of y for pattern B (marked with daggers) are omitted, leaving a monotone pattern with w more observed than z, z more observed than x, and x more observed than y. For the first of these patterns, the likelihood factorizes into components

TABLE 1

Data Pattern for Follow-Up Study

	Variable blocks					
Pattern	*w*	*x*	*y*	*z*	*Number of cases*	*Cases* (%)
A	1	1	1	1	1594	36.6
B	1	1†	1†	0	648	14.9
C	1	1	0	1*	722	16.6
D	1	1†	0	0	469	10.8
E	1	0	0	1*	499	11.5
F	1	0	0	0	420	9.6
					4352	100.0

TABLE 2

Maximum Likelihood Estimates of Means and Standard Deviations Obtained for
the Total Original Sample and Comparisons with Two Alternative Sets of Estimates

Variable	Maximum likelihood estimates for total sample (n = 4352)		Estimates based on data for pattern A only (n = 1594)			
	Mean μ_{ML}	s.d. σ_{ML}	Mean μ_A	s.d. σ_A	$\dfrac{(\mu_A - \mu_{ML}) \times 100}{\sigma_{ML}}$	$\dfrac{(\sigma_A - \sigma_{ML}) \times 100}{\sigma_{ML}}$
Variables measured during adolescence: (w)						
Father's education	11.702	3.528	12.050	3.469	9.9	−1.6
Mother's education	11.508	2.947	11.864	2.868	12.1	−2.6
Father's occupation	6.115	2.904	6.407	2.868	10.1	−1.2
Intelligence	106.625	12.910	109.034	11.174	18.7	−13.4
College preparatory curriculum	.411	.492	.528	.499	23.4	1.4
Time spent on homework	1.589	.814	1.633	.795	5.4	−2.3
Grade point average	2.324	.773	2.594	.701	34.9	−9.3
College plans	.488	.500	.595	.491	21.4	−1.8
Friends' college plans	.512	.369	.572	.354	16.3	−4.1
Participation in extra-curricular activities	.413	.492	.492	.500	15.8	1.6
Membership in top leading crowd	.088	.283	.131	.338	8.6	19.4
Membership in intermediate leading crowd	.170	.376	.198	.399	5.6	6.1
Smoking/drinking	.570	1.032	.483	.935	−8.4	−9.4
Dating frequency at time of survey	4.030	4.802	3.701	4.523	−6.8	−5.8
Liking for self	2.366	.525	2.364	.515	−.4	−1.9
Grade in school	2.432	1.048	2.496	1.064	6.1	1.5
Variables measured for all follow-up respondents (x)						
Educational attainment	13.625	2.295	14.196	2.204	24.9	−4.0
Occupational prestige	44.405	13.008	47.056	12.745	20.4	−2.0
Marital status	.940	.238	.940	.237	.0	−.4
Number of children	1.991	1.306	1.928	1.242	−4.8	−4.9
Age	30.629	1.221	30.726	1.152	7.9	−5.6
Father's occupational prestige	43.998	14.821	44.782	14.333	5.3	−3.2
Variables measured only for initial questionnaire respondents to the follow-up (y)						
Personal esteem	3.128	.377	3.148	.373	5.3	−1.1

TABLE 2 (*Continued*)

Variable	Maximum likelihood estimates for total sample (n = 4352)		Estimates based on data for pattern A only (n = 1594)			
	Mean μ_{ML}	s.d. σ_{ML}	Mean μ_A	s.d. σ_A	$(\mu_A - \mu_{ML}) \times 100$ σ_{ML}	$(\sigma_A - \sigma_{ML}) \times 100$ σ_{ML}
Dating frequency during last two years of high school	4.374	3.408	4.213	3.352	−4.7	−1.6
Number of siblings	2.219	1.748	2.055	1.660	−9.4	−5.0
Variables measured on parents' questionnaire (z)						
Family income	4.092	1.530	4.215	1.570	8.0	2.6
Parental encouragement to go to college	.714	.434	.754	.431	8.0	−.7
Number of children in family of origin	3.039	1.539	2.975	1.551	−4.2	.8

corresponding to the marginal distribution of w and the conditional distributions of x given w, y given w and x, and z given w, x, and y. Thus ML estimates for this pattern are obtained by the following procedure.

(1) Calculate the means and covariance matrix for the w variables, from all observations.

(2) Calculate the multivariate linear regression of x on w, from all observations with x and y present.

(3) Calculate the multivariate linear regression of y on w and x, from all observations with w, x, and y present.

(4) Calculate the multivariate linear regressions of z on w, x, and y, from all observations with w, x, y, and z present.

ML estimates of other parameters, such as the means of x, y, and z, are obtained as functions of the estimates obtained in (1)–(4) by "pivoting" or "sweeping" operations. (See, for example, Dempster, 1969, Sec. 4.3.2.) An analogous procedure provides ML estimates for the other pattern. Comparison revealed only small differences between the estimates for these two monotone data sets, and subsequently estimates from the first pattern were treated as approximating ML estimates for all the data.

In Table 2 ML estimates of the means and standard deviations of variables calculated by maximum likelihood are compared with estimates based on the data for pattern A only. Considerable differences are evident. For several variables (college preparatory curriculum, grade point average, college plans,

TABLE 3

Descriptive Statistics for Variables Measured during Adolescence by Response to the Follow-Up, Response to the Initial Follow-Up Questionnaire, and Response to the Parents' Questionnaire

Variable	Patterns A, B, C, D, E, F — Total adolescent sample (T)	Patterns A, B, C, D vs patterns E, F — Total follow-up respondents (R)	Nonrespondents to follow-up (NR)	$(R-T) \times 100 / \sigma_T$	Patterns A, B vs patterns C, D, E, F — Initial follow-up respondents (R)	Nonrespondents to initial questionnaire (NR)	$(R-T) \times 100 / \sigma_T$	Patterns A, C, E vs patterns B, D, F — Parents responded (R)	Parents did not respond (NR)	$(R-T) \times 100 / \sigma_T$
Father's education										
Mean	11.702	11.762	11.464	1.7	12.108	11.253	11.5	11.730	11.649	.8
s.d.	3.528	3.532	3.506	.1	3.565	3.432	1.1	3.446	3.677	-2.3
Mother's education										
Mean	11.508	11.589	11.197	2.8	11.847	11.136	11.5	11.583	11.367	2.5
s.d.	2.947	2.943	2.944	-.1	2.983	2.863	1.2	2.846	3.124	-3.4
Father's occupation										
Mean	6.115	6.161	5.935	1.6	6.444	5.755	11.3	6.117	6.111	.1
s.d.	2.905	2.904	2.902	.0	2.930	2.831	.9	2.868	2.973	-1.3

Intelligence										
Mean	106.625	107.393	103.562	6.0	109.536	103.433	22.5	106.771	106.358	1.1
s.d.	12.912	12.546	13.868	-2.8	12.362	12.749	-4.3	11.817	14.706	-8.5
College preparatory curriculum										
Mean	.411	.439	.306	5.7	.500	.316	18.1	.454	.333	8.7
s.d.	.492	.496	.461	.8	.500	.465	1.6	.498	.471	1.2
Time spent on homework										
Mean	1.589	1.598	1.553	1.1	1.648	1.526	7.2	1.589	1.588	.0
s.d.	.814	.814	.816	.0	.813	.811	-.1	.802	.837	-1.5
Grade point average										
Mean	2.324	2.415	1.972	11.8	2.549	2.082	29.1	2.402	2.178	10.1
s.d.	.773	.737	.808	-4.7	.707	.768	-8.5	.757	.781	-2.1
College plans										
Mean	.488	.510	.402	4.4	.576	.393	17.6	.522	.426	6.8
s.d.	.500	.500	.491	.0	.494	.489	-1.2	.500	.495	.0
Friends' college plans										
Mean	.542	.533	.431	5.7	.573	.445	16.5	.525	.488	3.5
s.d.	.369	.362	.382	-1.9	.359	.368	-2.7	.363	.379	-1.6

educational attainment, occupational prestige) means based on the complete observations are .2–.35 standard deviations higher than estimates based on all the data.

Table 3 reveals why the two sets of estimates in Table 2 are discrepant. Means of the completely observed items w are calculated for the whole sample, and for subgroups of the sample with different patterns of response, and they reveal systematic differences. As in many follow-up studies, the group responding to follow-up are not a random subsample of the original sample. In such cases methods which throw away the incomplete observations are not only statistically inefficient but are also biased. Methods such as maximum likelihood which use the incomplete units can eliminate or reduce this bias. We return to this point in Chapter 22, Example 2.

Other patterns of incomplete data where a factorization of the likelihood is possible are noted by Rubin (1974). Specifically, suppose that the variables can be arranged into three blocks (y_1, y_2, y_3) such that

(a) y_3 is *more observed* than y_1, in the sense that for any unit in which y_1 is at least partially observed, y_3 is fully observed.

(b) y_2 and y_1 are *never jointly observed*, in the sense that for any unit where y_1 is at least partially observed, y_2 is completely missing.

(c) The rows of y_1 given y_3 are conditionally independent with the same set of parameters.

The pattern is illustrated in Fig. 3.

Then Rubin shows that the log-likelihood of the data decomposes into two components:

$$l(\theta; p) = l_1(\phi_{23}; p_2, p_3) + l_2(\phi_{1.3}; p_1 | p_3), \qquad (25)$$

where p_1, p_2, and p_3 are observed values within the variable blocks y_1, y_2, and y_3, respectively, ϕ_{23} represents parameters of the joint distribution of y_2 and y_3, and $\phi_{1.3}$ represents parameters of the conditional distribution of y_1 given y_3.

The parameters ϕ_{23} and $\phi_{1.3}$ are often distinct, as ϕ_{23} can be reparameterized (in the obvious notation) as $\phi_{2.3}$ and ϕ_3 and the parameters $\phi_{1.3}$,

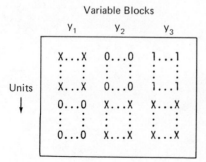

Fig. 3. *Data pattern, where* (a) y_3 *is more observed than* y_1 *and* (b) y_2 *and* y_1 *are never observed together.* X *denotes observed or missing.*

$\phi_{2.3}$, and ϕ_3 are also often distinct. An interesting aspect of this example is that ϕ_{23} and $\phi_{1.3}$ are not a complete reparameterization of θ, in that some distinct parameters are missing, namely, the parameters of conditional association (for example, partial correlation) between y_1 and y_2. These parameters do not appear in the log-likelihood, and hence are inestimable from the data.

EXAMPLE 6: A THREE-VARIABLE EXAMPLE. A special case of the pattern given above consists of three variables y_1, y_2, y_3 and n_1 observations $\{(y_{i1}, y_{i3});$ $i = 1, \ldots, n_1\}$ on y_1 and y_3, n_2 observations $\{(y_{i2}, y_{i3}); i = n_1 + 1, \ldots, n_1 + n_2\}$ on y_2 and y_3. If these three variables follow a multivariate normal distribution, then the likelihood factorizes into components involving $n_1 + n_2$ observations on the marginal distribution of y_3, with 2 parameters, n_1 observations on the conditional distribution of y_1 given y_3, with 3 parameters, and n_2 observations on the conditional distribution of y_2 given y_3, with 3 parameters. These three distributions involve 8 distinct parameters, whereas the original multivariate normal distribution involves 9 parameters, 3 means, 3 variances, and 3 covariances. The missing parameter in the reparameterization is the conditional covariance of y_1 and y_2 given y_3, which is not estimable from the data. This example was first analysed by Lord (1955). The factorization (25) of the likelihood was noted by Anderson (1957).

3.   METHODS FOR GENERAL PATTERNS OF MISSING DATA

3.1.   Introduction

We have seen that for certain special patterns of missing data the problem of maximizing the likelihood can be transformed into a set of complete data problems with standard solutions. In many situations the data do not conform to such a structured pattern of missingness, and these methods do not apply. In this section we turn to methods which can be applied to any pattern of missing values. In contrast to the last section, where explicit expressions for maximum likelihood estimates can be derived for normal models, in this section the computations are iterative and closed-form expressions are not available.

The general considerations of Section 3.3 can be motivated by the following important example.

3.2.   Estimation of a Vector of Means and Covariance Matrix

EXAMPLE 7: ESTIMATING MEANS AND COVARIANCE MATRIX FROM INCOMPLETE DATA. Suppose that the hypothetical complete data y is an $N_s \times K$ matrix such that y_{ij} is the value of the jth item for the ith unit, for $i = 1, \ldots, N_s$,

$j = 1, \ldots, K$. The N_s units constitute a random sample from a K-variate distribution with means $\mu = (\mu_1, \ldots, \mu_K)$ and covariance matrix $\Sigma = (\sigma_{jk})$. The data consists of present values $p = (p_1, \ldots, p_N)$, where p_i is the set of present values for observation i. The objective is to estimate μ and Σ from these incomplete data.

Two well-known elementary approaches to this problem are (a) to discard incomplete units and estimate μ and Σ from the sample means and covariances of the complete units and (b) to estimate the means and variance of each variable y_j from all the units for which y_j is observed, and the covariance of y_j and y_k from all the units for which both y; and y_k are observed.

The first procedure seems highly inefficient if the number of incomplete units is large, and is inoperable if the number of complete units is less than $K + 1$. The second procedure is considered by Glasser (1964). It appears to make more use of the available data, but it can give very poor results, as demonstrated in simulation studies reported by Haitovsky (1968).

A more promising approach is to fill in the missing values with appropriate estimates, and form sample means and covariance matrix from the completed data. If for each variable y_j, missing values y_{ij} are estimated by the mean of y_j over all observations with y_j present, the resulting estimate of μ_j is the same as in method (b). The estimated covariance matrix is positive definite, but is not a consistent estimate of Σ.

This method is greatly improved by using the present values in an incomplete unit to predict the missing values in that unit. Recall that for the special pattern of Example 2, the ML solution estimates the missing values of y_2 by a linear regression of y_2 on y_1. Buck (1960) proposed the following extension of this idea to the present problem:

Step 1:   Estimate μ and Σ by $\tilde{\mu}$ and $\tilde{\Sigma}$, the sample means and covariance matrix of the complete observations.

Step 2:   For each incomplete observation i, calculate the linear regressions of the missing variables m_i on the present variables p_i, from $\tilde{\mu}$ and $\tilde{\Sigma}$. Then use the resulting regression equations to predict the missing values m_i as linear functions of the present variables p_i. This yields the completed data matrix $\hat{y} = (\hat{y}_{ij})$, where

$$\hat{y}_{ij} = \begin{cases} y_{ij}, & y_{ij} \text{ present} \\ \tilde{\mu}_j + \sum_{l \in p_i} \tilde{\beta}_{jl.p_i}(y_{il} - \tilde{\mu}_l), & y_{ij} \text{ missing,} \end{cases}$$

and $\tilde{\beta}_{jl.p_i}$ is the partial regression coefficient on y_j on y_l given variables p_i, calculated from $\tilde{\Sigma}$.

Step 3:   Calculate the means and sum of squares and cross-products (SCP) matrix of the completed matrix $\hat{y}$:

$$\hat{\bar{y}}_j = \frac{1}{N_s} \sum_{i=1}^{N_s} \hat{y}_{ij} \qquad\qquad (j = 1, \dots, K),$$

$$U_{jk} = \sum_{i=1}^{N_s} (\hat{y}_{ij} - \hat{\mu}_j)(\hat{y}_{ik} - \hat{\mu}_k), \qquad (j, k = 1, \dots, K).$$

Step 4:   Calculate final estimates

$$\hat{\mu}_j = \hat{\bar{y}}_j,$$

$$\hat{\sigma}_{jk} = (U_{jk} + \sum_{i=1}^{N_s} c_{ijk})/N_s,$$

where the correction term c_{ijk}, calculated from $\tilde{\Sigma}$, is the residual covariance (variance if $j = k$) of y_j and y_k given the variables p_i present in observation i if y_{ij} and y_{ik} are both missing, and zero otherwise.

The correction terms c_{ijk} in step 4 are required for estimates of the covariance matrix to allow for the fact that some of the values $\hat{x}_{ij}$ have been imputed. Buck gave the adjustment terms for the variances but omitted the terms for the covariances required when both variables are missing. We shall refer to the corrected procedure as Buck's method.

The computational requirements to calculate the regression coefficients $\tilde{\beta}_{jk.p_i}$ and the residual covariance terms c_{ijk} are not nearly as severe as one might think because all these values are obtained by simple "pivoting" or "sweeping" operations on the covariance matrix. See, for example, Dempster (1969, Sec. 4.3.2) or Beale (1970).

It can be shown that Buck's method is equivalent to maximum likelihood under multivariate normality for the special case of monotone data discussed in Example 3. Further links with the ML solution will be established in Section 3.3.

The maximum likelihood solution for an arbitrary pattern of missing values was presented by Trawinski and Bargmann (1964) for the following slightly more general problem.

EXAMPLE 8:   MULTIVARIATE LINEAR REGRESSION WITH MISSING VALUES. Suppose that for the data of the previous example interest lies not in the means and covariance matrix of a set of K variables but rather in the parameters of the linear regression of a subset of s of these variables, on the remaining $r = K - s$ variables. Writing $Y = (y_1, \dots, y_s)$ for the set of regressand variables, and $Z = (Z_1, \dots, Z_r)$ for the set of regressors, the relation between Y and Z may be described by the multivariate linear regression model

$$E(Y|Z) = b_0 + BZ, \qquad \operatorname{Var}(Y|Z) = \Sigma_{y.z},$$

where b, B, and $\Sigma_{y.z}$ are matrices of parameters. Example 7 can be viewed as a special case of this model with $r = 0$, $K = s$.

A series of papers by Afifi and Elashoff (1967, 1969a, 1969b) compared the efficiency and sampling properties of various simple estimators for the special case of one response variable and one regressor. For the general K-variable case, the problem can be conveniently viewed as an extension of the previous example. With complete data, the least squares estimates of the regression parameters are well-known functions of the sample means and covariance matrix, calculated by "sweeping" on the covariance matrix. With incomplete data, estimates of b_0, B, and $\Sigma_{y.z}$ can be obtained by calculating these functions with the sample means and covariance matrix replaced by estimates of μ and Σ as in Example 7.

In particular, if we can find estimates of μ and Σ which are ML are under the model which assumes that (Y, Z) are multivariate normally distributed, then the resulting estimates of b_0, B, and $\Sigma_{y.z}$ are also maximum likelihood. Rubin (1974) points out that in this situation the multivariate normality assumption can be weakened, in that any regressor variable which has no missing values can be considered fixed. This is important if the regressor variables include, for example, variables indicating strata in an analysis of covariance. Such variables are not usually missing, and so can be held fixed.

EXAMPLE 7 CONTINUED. We now discuss ML estimates of μ and Σ under the assumption that the data are an incomplete random sample from the K-variate normal distribution.

The data can be arranged into T patterns, so that the tth pattern has n_t observations from a q_t-variable normal distribution with mean $\mu_t = D_t\mu$ and covariance matrix $\Sigma_t = D_t\Sigma D_t^T$, where D_t is a $q_t \times K$ matrix of 0's and 1's, indicating the variables missing and present, respectively. The sufficient statistics consist of the $q_t \times 1$ vector of sample means $\hat{\mu}_t$ and the $q_t \times q_t$ sample covariance matrix S_t for each distinct pattern t. The log-likelihood is $l = \sum_{t=1}^{T} l_t$, where writing tr for the trace and det for the determinant of a matrix,

$$l_t = -\tfrac{1}{2}n_t \log \det \Sigma_t - \tfrac{1}{2} \operatorname{tr} n_t\Sigma_t^{-1}\{S_t + (\hat{\mu}_t - \mu_t)(\hat{\mu}_t - \mu_t)^T\}.$$

Maximum likelihood estimates of μ and Σ can be obtained by differentiating l with respect to the elements of μ and Σ and solving the likelihood equations by iterative techniques such as the scoring algorithm (Trawinski and Bargmann, 1964). Hartley and Hocking (1971) derive the likelihood equations in the elegant form

$$W_\mu\mu = \sum_{t=1}^{T} D_t^T W_{\mu_t}\hat{\mu}_t, \tag{26}$$

$$W_\delta\delta = \sum_{t=1}^{T} C_t^T W_{\delta_t}(\hat{\delta}_t + h_t), \tag{27}$$

where δ, $\hat{\delta}_t$, and h_t are Σ, S_t, and $(\hat{\mu}_t - \mu_t)(\hat{\mu}_t - \mu_t)^T$, respectively, rewritten as vectors, W_μ and W_δ are the expected information matrices of μ and δ, respectively, and C_t is a matrix analogous to D_t for covariances, defined so that $\delta_t = C_t\delta$.

Equations (26) and (27) are equivalent to the iterating equation for the scoring algorithm. Strategies for the solution of these equations can be developed which lead to noniterative solutions for monotone data patterns, as in Example 4. The form of the equations (26) and (27) is similar for other incomplete data problems; for example, Hocking and Oxspring (1971, 1974) obtain parallel equations for incomplete multinomial data, and apply them to partially categorized contingency tables.

An important aspect of this estimation procedure is that the expected information matrices of μ and δ, W_μ and W_δ, have to be inverted at each iteration. By standard maximum likelihood theory, these supply estimates of the asymptotic covariance matrices of the ML estimates $\hat{\mu}$ and $\hat{\Sigma}$. However, in another sense the inversion of W_δ is less attractive, since it can involve a considerable computational task. For the K-variable case, W_δ is a matrix of dimension of $K(K + 1)/2$ and for a problem with 30 variables has over 100,000 elements!

Section 3.3 provides an alternative method for finding ML estimates which avoids the inversion of W_δ and provides a useful link with alternative estimation procedures given for this example. [Hocking and Marx (1979) present another algorithm which avoids the inversion of W_δ.]

3.3. The Missing Information Principle and the EM Algorithm

In this section we discuss a property of maximum likelihood estimates for incomplete data which provides a link with the problem of maximum likelihood estimation for the hypothetical complete data log-likelihood $l(\theta; y_s)$. We revert to the general notation of Section 1.2, with design variables z omitted for notational clarity.

Recalling our earlier partition of y_s into present data p and missing data m, we write the log-likelihood of the (hypothetical) complete data as $l(\theta; p, m)$. Since m is missing, we might consider eliminating it by averaging $l(\theta; p, m)$ over the conditional distribution of m given p. However, this distribution also depends on θ, which of course is unknown.

Suppose we choose any value of θ_a of θ and then average $l(\theta; p, m)$ over the conditional distribution of m given p evaluated at $\theta = \theta_a$. The resulting averaged log-likelihood

$$l^*(\theta; p, \theta_a) = E_m[l(\theta; p, m)|p; \theta_a] \tag{28}$$

is a function of p, θ and θ_a, but not m. Let

$$\theta_b = \phi(\theta_a) \tag{29}$$

be the value of θ which maximizes $l^*(\theta; p, \theta_a)$. The transformation defined by this process has the following properties:

(a) The maximum likelihood estimate $\hat{\theta}$ of $l(\theta; p)$ is a solution of the equation

$$\theta = \phi(\theta); \tag{30}$$

in other words, $\hat{\theta}$ is a fixed point of the transformation ϕ.

(b) Any solution of (30) is a maximum or other stationary value of the log-likelihood $l(\theta; p)$.

Thus one route to the ML estimate (or at least to a stationary value of the likelihood) is to find a fixed point of the transformation ϕ. This result was noticed for particular problems by several authors, including Hartley (1958), Baum, Petrie, Soules and Weiss (1970), Hartley and Hocking (1971), and Sundberg (1974). It was first formulated in general terms by Orchard and Woodbury (1972), who termed it a missing information principle. The formulation given here appears in Beale and Little (1975).

Most of these authors considered a particular procedure for solving the fixed point equation (30), namely, to iterate on Eq. (29). That is, we proceed as follows:

  (i)   Find an initial estimate θ_a.
  (ii) Calculate the averaged log-likelihood (28).
  (iii) Find θ_b to maximize the averaged likelihood.
  (iv) Substitute $\theta_a = \theta_b$ and return to step (ii); iterate until convergence.

The heart of this process involves an expectation step (ii) and a maximization step (iii), and hence it is termed the EM (expectation maximization) algorithm by Dempster, Laird, and Rubin (1977). This paper gives applications of the algorithm to a wide variety of situations, including algorithms for methods such as factor analysis and variance component estimation, which are not usually considered as problems of incomplete data. The authors also demonstrate that each cycle of the algorithm increases the likelihood and discuss conditions for convergence and the rate at which convergence is achieved.

The usefulness of the EM algorithm naturally depends on how easy the E and M steps are to compute in particular problems. An important special case, discussed by Sundberg (1974), and Dempster, Laird, and Rubin (1977) is when the distribution of the complete data y_s belongs to the regular exponential family

$$f(y_s; \theta) = B(y_s) \exp\{\theta^T t(y_s)\}/A(\theta), \tag{31}$$

where A and B are scalar functions, θ is an $r \times 1$ vector consisting of the so-called *natural* parameters, and $t(y_s)$ is an $r \times 1$ vector of complete data sufficient statistics. The complete data log-likelihood of θ is then

$$l(\theta; y_s) = -\log A(\theta) + \theta^T t(y_s). \tag{32}$$

The E step consists of finding

$$l^*(\theta; p, \theta_a) = E[l_1(\theta; y_s)|p; \theta_a] = -\log A(\theta) + \theta^T t_a,$$

where $t_a = E[t(y_s)|p; \theta_a]$ is the expected value of the sufficient statistics given p, evaluated at $\theta = \theta_a$. The M step consists in maximizing

$$l^*(\theta; p, \theta_a) = -\log A(\theta) + \theta^T t_a, \tag{33}$$

which is now identical to the complete data log-likelihood (31) except that $t(y_s)$ has been replaced by its "estimate" t_a. Thus the EM algorithm involves the following steps:

(i)   Find an initial estimate of the natural parameters θ_a.
(ii) Estimate the sufficient statistics $t(y_s)$ by t_a, the expected value given p evaluated at $\theta = \theta_a$.
(iii) Maximize the complete data likelihood with $t(y_s)$ replaced by t_a, obtaining θ_b.
(iv) Replace θ_a by θ_b and return to step (ii), iterating to convergence.

We now apply the EM algorithm to the multivariate normal example.

EXAMPLE 7 CONTINUED.   Suppose as before that the hypothetical complete data $y = (y_{ij})$ is a random sample from the K-variate normal distribution, with mean μ and covariance matrix Σ.

This belongs to the regular exponential family (31), with sufficient statistics $t(y_s)$ given by the sample means

$$\bar{y}_j = \frac{1}{N_s} \sum_{i=1}^{N_s} y_{ij}, \qquad j = 1, \ldots, K,$$

and the *uncorrected* sample sum of squares and cross-products (SCP) matrix d, with (j, k)th element

$$d_{jk} = \sum_{i=1}^{N_s} y_{ij} y_{ik}, \qquad j, k = 1, \ldots, K.$$

The complete data maximum likelihood estimates are given by

$$\hat{\mu}_j = \bar{y}_j, \qquad\qquad j = 1, \ldots, K, \tag{34}$$

$$\hat{\sigma}_{jk} = d_{jk}/N_s - \bar{y}_j \bar{y}_k, \qquad j, k = 1, \ldots, K. \tag{35}$$

Now suppose we have incomplete data p. The E step of the EM algorithm consists in finding expected values of the sufficient statistics:

$$\bar{y}_{ja} = E(\bar{y}_j|p; \mu_a, \Sigma_a), \tag{36}$$

$$d_{jka} = E(d_{jk}|p; \mu_a, \Sigma_a), \tag{37}$$

where μ_a and Σ_a are current estimates of μ and Σ. The M step consists in forming new estimates μ_b, Σ_b by substituting $\bar{y}_{ja}$ and d_{jka} for $\bar{y}_j$, d_{jk} in (34) and (35). It remains to describe the calculation of $\bar{y}_{ja}$ and d_{jka}. This clearly depends on the pattern of missing data. Note that

$$\bar{y}_{ja} = \frac{1}{N_s} \sum_{i=1}^{N_s} E(y_{ij}|p; \mu_a, \Sigma_a)$$

and

$$d_{jka} = \sum_{i=1}^{N_s} E(y_{ij}y_{ik}|p; \mu_a, \Sigma_a).$$

To calculate the terms in these sums, consider unit i with present items p_i and missing items m_i. Since observations are independent, given (μ_a, Σ_a),

$$E(y_{ij}|p; \mu_a, \Sigma_a) = E(y_{ij}|p_i, \mu_a, \Sigma_a) = \hat{y}_{ija} \quad \text{(say)}$$

and

$$E(y_{ij}y_{ik}|p; \mu_a, \Sigma_a) = E(y_{ij}y_{ik}|p_i; \mu_a, \Sigma_a)$$
$$= \hat{y}_{ija}\hat{y}_{ika} + \text{Cov}(y_{ij}, y_{ik}|p_i; \mu_a, \Sigma_a).$$

If y_{ij} is present, that is, belongs to p_i, then y_{ija} is simply the observed value y_{ij}, and $\text{Cov}(y_{ij}, y_{ik}|p_i; \mu_a, \Sigma_a)$ is zero. If y_{ij} is missing, then y_{ija} is the predicted value of y_{ij} from a linear regression of y_j on the variables present in unit i, with intercept and regression coefficients calculated from μ_a and Σ_a. If y_{ij} and y_{ik} are both missing, $\text{Cov}(y_{ij}, y_{ik}|p_i; \mu_a, \Sigma_a)$ is the residual covariance (or if $j = k$, variance) from the regression of y_j and y_k on the variables present in unit i, calculated from Σ_a. Summing over units,

$$\bar{y}_{ja} = \frac{1}{N_s} \sum_{i=1}^{N_s} \hat{y}_{ija},$$

$$d_{jka} = \frac{1}{N_s} \sum_{i=1}^{N_s} \left[\hat{y}_{ija}\hat{y}_{ika} + \text{Cov}(y_{ij}, y_{ik}|p_i; \mu_a, \Sigma_a)\right].$$

Hence, the complete EM algorithm is as follows:

(i)   Calculate initial estimates μ_a and Σ_a.
(ii) Complete the data matrix by calculating

$$\hat{y}_{ija} = \begin{cases} y_{ij} & \text{if } y_{ij} \text{ is present} \\ E(y_{ij}|p_i; \mu_a, \Sigma_a) & \text{if } y_{ij} \text{ is missing,} \end{cases}$$

where $E(y_{ij}|p_i; \mu_a, \Sigma_a)$ is obtained by the linear regression of y_j on variables present in unit i, with coefficients calculated from μ_a and Σ_a.

(iii)   Form means and scp matrix of the completed data matrix; whenever y_{ij} and y_{ik} are missing add to the (j, k)th element of the scp matrix the residual covariance (variance if $j = k$) of y_i and y_k given the variables present in unit i, calculated from Σ_a.

(iv)   Calculate new estimates μ_b and Σ_b from the means and adjusted cross-products matrix, and iterate.

Note that the basic elements of the algorithm are the filling in of the missing values by regression and an adjustment to the cross-products matrix in (iii), and these correspond exactly to Buck's method as described in the previous section. Thus the ML solution is simply an iterative version of that method.

An advantage of the EM algorithm over the method of scoring is that the fitted values at the last step can be used to predict the population totals for the variable t_j,

$$t_j = \sum_{i=1}^{N_s} \hat{y}_{ij} + (N - N_s)\hat{\mu}_j,$$

where $N - N_s$ is the number of units not sampled. Note that since the information matrix is not calculated and inverted, the asymptotic covariance matrix of the estimates is not available. However, for the estimates $\hat{\mu}$ the information matrix has dimensions $q \times q$ and can be formed and inverted as a final step of the algorithm. For estimates of regression coefficients derived from $\hat{\Sigma}$, Beale and Little (1975) suggest an approximate form for the covariance matrix which appears to work quite well in simulations (Little, 1979).

The algorithm has a particularly wide range of applications, since a large variety of analyses are based on functions of the means and covariance matrix. The example of linear regression has already been noted, and other applications occur in discriminant analysis (Little, 1978) and factor analysis.

Nevertheless, application of the algorithm to incomplete data sets where the reduction of data to the means and covariance matrix is not appropriate can give misleading results.

Pregibon (1977) gives an interesting example of this involving agricultural survey data with special zeros. Specifically, in a survey of poultry farms, variables are included which measure quantities of certain varieties of poultry possessed, with the value zero meaning that the particular variety is not farmed. For some farms, values of these variables are missing. The algorithm estimated the mean quantities of each variety of poultry quite well, but failed badly to estimate the conditional mean for farmers who farmed a particular variety. The problem here is that the data really have an analysis of covariance structure with implicit dichotomies defined by zero versus nonzero values of the items. These dichotomies are missing when items are missing, and are not well estimated by the version of the EM algorithm which is based on the erroneous assumption of multivariate normality. Pregibon suggests an alternative imputation strategy which takes into account the special nature of the zeros in the data, and hence performs in a more satisfactory manner. This is discussed in more detail in Chapter 22.

4. CONTINGENCY TABLES WITH PARTIALLY CLASSIFIED OBSERVATIONS

In Section 3 item nonresponse for interval-scaled variables was considered, and any categorical variables were assumed to be completely observed. In this section we consider nonresponse for categorical items.

The joint distribution of a set of r categorical variables is displayed as an r-dimensional contingency table with a cell for each combination of levels. If one or more of the variables is missing for some respondents, the result is a set of partially classified units. In most cross-tablulation packages these partially classified units are omitted from the r-way table, but as in the case of interval-scaled variables this results in a loss of information. Methods which make efficient use of all the available data can be developed by the method of maximum likelihood. (Chen and Fienberg, 1974; Haberman, 1974; Fuchs, 1982). Three examples are given here: the first is a simple case of monotone data where the likelihood factorizes into complete data components. The other two demonstrate the EM algorithm applied to multinomial data.

The form of nonresponse for categorical variables considered here should be distinguished from the problem of contingency tables with *structural zeros*, where particular cells of the table are empty because certain combinations of the variable levels are impossible.

EXAMPLE 9: TWO-WAY CONTINGENCY TABLE WITH ITEMS UNCLASSIFIED BY ONE OF THE VARIABLES.   Cousider two categorical variables y_1, with levels $j = 1, \ldots, J$, and y_2, with levels $k = 1, \ldots, K$. The data consist of n units $\{(y_{i1}, y_{i2}), i = 1, \ldots, n\}$, with y_1 and y_2 recorded, and $n_1 - n$ units $\{y_{i1}, i = n + 1, \ldots, n_1\}$, with y_1 recorded and y_2 missing. The data pattern is thus identical to that of Example 2, except that now the variables are categorical.

The n complete units can be displayed in a $J \times K$ contingency table, with n_{jk} units in the cell, with $y_1 = j$, $y_2 = k$, and $\sum_{j,k} n_{jk} = n$. The $n_1 - n$ units classified by y_1 but not y_2 form a $J \times 1$ table, with m_j units in the cell with $y_1 = j$ and $\sum_j m_j = m \equiv n_1 - n$ (see Fig. 4).

We shall use the standard "plus" notation for summation over subscripts j and k. Let us assume that conditional on the total sample size $n_1 = n + m$, the data if completely classified would have a multinomial distribution with index n_1 and probabilities p_{jk} of being classified in the (j, k)th cell. Thus

$$\theta = (p_{11}, p_{12}, \ldots, p_{JK}); \qquad \sum_{j=1}^{J} \sum_{k=1}^{K} p_{jk} = 1.$$

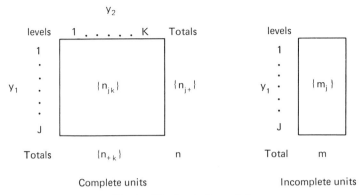

Fig. 4.   *The data in Example 9.*

As in Example 2, we adopt the alternative parameter set ϕ corresponding to the marginal distribution of y_1 and the conditional distribution of y_2 given y_1. The log-likelihood of the data can be written

$$l(\phi; \{n_{jk}, m_j\}) = \sum_{j=1}^{J} (n_{j+} + m_j) \log p_{j+} + \sum_{j=1}^{J} \sum_{k=1}^{K} n_{jk} \log q_{jk}, \qquad (38)$$

where the first term is the log-likelihood for the multinomial distribution of the marginal counts $n_{j+} + m_j$, with index n_1 and probabilities p_{j+}, and the second term is the log-likelihood for the conditional multinomial distribution of n_{jk} given n_{j+}, with index n_{j+} and probabilities

$$q_{jk} = \text{Pr}(y_2 = k|y_1 = j) = p_{jk}/p_{j+}.$$

Thus (38) is a factorization of the likelihood of the form (22), with

$$\phi_1 = \{p_{j+}, j = 1, \ldots, J\} \qquad \text{and} \qquad \phi_2 = \{q_{jk}, j = 1, \ldots, J; k = 1, \ldots, K\}.$$

Maximizing each component separately, we obtain maximum likelihood estimates

$$\hat{p}_{j+} = \frac{n_{j+} + m_j}{n + m}, \qquad \hat{q}_{jk} = \frac{n_{jk}}{n_{j+}},$$

and so

$$\hat{p}_{jk} = \hat{p}_{j+}\hat{q}_{jk} = \left(n_{jk} + \frac{n_{jk}}{n_{j+}} m_j\right) \Big/ (n + m). \qquad (39)$$

Thus, the maximum likelihood estimate effectively distributes a proportion n_{jk}/n_{j+} of the unclassified observations into the (j, k)th cell.

TABLE 4

A Numerical Example of the Data Pattern of Fig. 4

		1	2	3	Total			
X_1	1	20	30	40	90	X_1	1	100
	2	50	60	20	130		2	90
Total		70	90	60	220	Total		190
			Complete Units					Incomplete Units

A simple numerical illustration is provided by the data in Table 4, where X_1 is a dichotomous variable and X_2 is a trichotomy. The marginal probabilities of X_1 are estimated from completely and partially classified units:

$$\hat{p}_{1+} = 190/410, \qquad \hat{p}_{2+} = 220/410.$$

The conditional probabilities of classification for X_2 given X_1 are estimated from the completely classified units:

$$\hat{q}_{11} = 20/90, \qquad \hat{q}_{12} = 30/90, \qquad \hat{q}_{13} = 40/90,$$

$$\hat{q}_{21} = 50/130, \qquad \hat{q}_{22} = 60/130, \qquad \hat{q}_{23} = 20/130.$$

Combining these estimates gives the probabilities in Eq. (39):

$$\hat{p}_{11} = (20/90)(190/410), \qquad \hat{p}_{12} = (30/90)(190/410), \qquad \hat{p}_{13} = (40/90)(190/410),$$

$$\hat{p}_{21} = (50/130)(220/410), \qquad \hat{p}_{22} = (60/130)(220/410), \qquad \hat{p}_{23} = (20/130)(220/410).$$

EXAMPLE 10:   TWO-WAY CONTINGENCY TABLE WITH PARTIALLY CLASSIFIED UNITS FOR BOTH VARIABLES. Suppose that for the two-variable case of Example 9, in addition to the n units classified by y_1 and y_2 and the m units classified by y_1 alone, there are m' units classified by y_2 alone. Thus there are also m'_k, say, observations in category k of y_2 but unclassified by y_1, for $k = 1, \ldots, K$. The total sample size is $n_1 = n + m + m'$. We proceed to describe the EM algorithm for estimating the cell probabilities $\{p_{jk}, j = 1, \ldots, J, k = 1, \ldots, K\}$.

We assume that the hypothetical complete data, with all units classified by y_1 and y_2, are distributed according to a multinomial distribution with index n_1 and probabilities $\{p_{jk}\}$. This belongs to the exponential family of distributions, with natural parameters

$$\{\log(p_{jk}/(1 - p_{jk}))\}$$

and sufficient statistics $\{N_{jk}\}$, the completely classified cell counts. The complete data ML estimates are

$$\hat{p}_{jk} = N_{jk}/n_1 \qquad (j = 1, \ldots, J; k = 1, \ldots, K).$$

Replacing N_{jk} by its expected value given the data $\{n_{jk}, m_j, m_k'\}$ we obtain the E step of the EM algorithm:

$$N_{jka} = E[N_{jk}|\{n_{jk}, m_k, m_k'\}; \{p_{jka}\}]$$

$$= n_{jk} + (p_{jka}/p_{+ka})m_j + (p_{jka}/p_{j+a})m_k', \qquad (40)$$

where $\{p_{jka}\}$ are current estimates of the parameters. Thus the unclassified counts are distributed over the cells according to current estimates of the conditional cell probabilities p_{jka}/p_{+ka} and p_{jka}/p_{j+a}.

Substituting these in the M step we obtain the iterating equation

$$N_{++}\hat{p}_{jka} = n_j + (p_{jka}/p_{+ka})m_j + (p_{jka}/p_{j+a})m_k',$$

which corresponds to the algorithm given by Chen and Fienberg (1974, Eq. (ii)).

The algorithm is illustrated with data from a 2×2 table given in Table 5. Below the data succeeding steps of the algorithm are shown. The left-hand panels show the estimates of the parameters θ from the M step, with initial estimates based on the completely classified units. The right-hand panels indicate how the partially classified units are distributed in the E step of the algorithm, based on Eq. (40). For example, in step 1 the 30 partially classified units with $y_1 = 1$ (marked with a superscript a) are classified according to the conditional probabilities in Eq. (40),

$$\frac{p_{11a}}{p_{1+a}} = \frac{100/300}{(100/300) + (50/300)} = \frac{2}{3}, \qquad \frac{p_{12a}}{p_{1+a}} = \frac{50/300}{(100/300) + (50/300)} = \frac{1}{3},$$

obtained from the first row of the table of probabilities. Thus $(30)(2/3) = 20$ of these units are allocated to the cell $y_1 = 1$, $y_2 = 1$, and $(30)(1/3) = 10$ of these units are allocated to the cell $y_1 = 1$, $y_2 = 2$. Other marginal counts are allocated in a similar way.

The final estimates are

$$\hat{p}_{11} = .28, \; \hat{p}_{12} = .18, \; \hat{p}_{21} = .24, \; \hat{p}_{22} = .30.$$

EXAMPLE 11: THE INDEPENDENCE MODEL. In the previous example, suppose we wish to estimate the parameters of the model where y_1 and y_2 are independent, that is,

$$p_{jk} = p_{j+}p_{+k} \qquad (j = 1, \ldots, J; k = 1, \ldots, K).$$

The complete data sufficient statistics are now the marginal counts $\{N_{j+}, j = 1, \ldots, J\}$ and $\{N_{+k}, k = 1, \ldots, K\}$, and the complete data maximum likelihood estimates are

$$\hat{p}_{j+} = N_{j+}/n_1, \qquad \hat{p}_{+k} = N_{+k}/n_1.$$

For the incomplete data the conditional expected margins are

$$\hat{N}_{j+a} = n_{j+} + m_j + p_{j+a}m', \qquad \hat{N}_{+ka} = n_{+k} + m_k' + p_{+ka}m.$$

TABLE 5

The EM Algorithm for a 2×2 Table with Data Partially Classified[a] on Both Variables

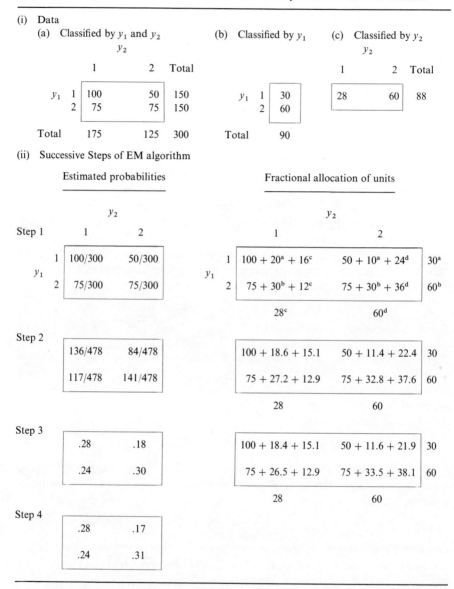

(i) Data

(a) Classified by y_1 and y_2

		y_2 1	2	Total
y_1	1	100	50	150
	2	75	75	150
Total		175	125	300

(b) Classified by y_1

y_1	1	30
	2	60
Total		90

(c) Classified by y_2

	y_2 1	2	Total
	28	60	88

(ii) Successive Steps of EM algorithm

Estimated probabilities

Step 1

		y_2 1	2
y_1	1	100/300	50/300
	2	75/300	75/300

Step 2

	136/478	84/478
	117/478	141/478

Step 3

	.28	.18
	.24	.30

Step 4

	.28	.17
	.24	.31

Fractional allocation of units

Step 1

		y_2 1	2	
y_1	1	$100 + 20^a + 16^c$	$50 + 10^a + 24^d$	30^a
	2	$75 + 30^b + 12^c$	$75 + 30^b + 36^d$	60^b
		28^c	60^d	

Step 2

$100 + 18.6 + 15.1$	$50 + 11.4 + 22.4$	30
$75 + 27.2 + 12.9$	$75 + 32.8 + 37.6$	60
28	60	

Step 3

$100 + 18.4 + 15.1$	$50 + 11.6 + 21.9$	30
$75 + 26.5 + 12.9$	$75 + 33.5 + 38.1$	60
28	60	

[a] The superscripts in the top right-hand panel indicate the allocation of the partially classified margins among the cells of the table. For example, of the 28 units with $y_2 = 1$ (superscript c), 16 are allocated to $y_1 = 1$ and 12 are allocated to $y_1 = 2$.

Hence the EM algorithm is given by

$$Np_{j+b} = n_{j+} + m_j + p_{j+a}m', \qquad N\hat{p}_{+kb} = n_{+k} + m'_k + p_{+ka}m,$$

which simplifies to give

$$\hat{p}_{j+} = \frac{n_{j+} + m_j}{n + m}, \qquad \hat{p}_{+k} = \frac{n_{+k} + m'_k}{n + m'},$$

the intuitively sensible estimates. See Chen and Fienberg (1974, Eq. (15)).

This example is the additive log-linear model for the factors y_1 and y_2, which in the notation of Goodman (1970) would be labeled $\{y_1, y_2\}$. In a series of papers, Goodman has presented a system of hierarchical log-linear models for multiway contingency tables. See, for example, Bishop, Fienberg and Holland (1975). These models are based on Poisson or multinomial sampling, and express the logarithm of the population mean in each cell as linear sum of factors. Sufficient statistics for the models are certain sets of marginal counts of the multiway table. In certain circumstances, including Example 11, complete data maximum likelihood estimates are available in closed form; in other cases an iterative algorithm such as iterative scaling is necessary. The basic equations for these estimates are obtained by setting the set of observed marginal counts which constitute the sufficient statistics equal to their expected values under the model.

The EM algorithm can be used to fit these models in cases where data are partially classified, as discussed by Fuchs (1982). The E step consists in replacing the sufficient observed margins by their conditional expected values given the present data. This effectively distributes unclassified counts across the cells of each margin according to the appropriate conditional distribution, evaluated with current estimates of the parameters. The M step is equivalent to the complete data maximization, and sets the conditional expected margins given the data to the unconditional expected margins under the model.

5. SUMMARY

This chapter has reviewed certain model-based methods for treating non-response which have appeared in the missing values literature. The methods are based on the use of covariate information to improve the estimation of missing values, and as such are relevant to cases where such information exists, either in the form of survey design variables or items variables associated with the item variable which is missing. If, after conditioning on covariate information, the sample of respondents is not a random sample of all individuals in the sample, then alternative methods are required. These are considered in Chapter 21.

Two distinct patterns of nonresponse can be distinguished. For monotone or nested patterns the estimation methods based on normal and multinomial superpopulation models are noniterative and relatively easy to carry out. For other patterns efficient methods of estimation tend to be iterative and more complex.

Two distributions play a key role in applications: the multivariate normal and the multinomial distributions. These often form the basis of the underlying model under which the methods yield maximum likelihood estimates of parameters. The restrictiveness of these models, particularly within a survey context, may lead to the feeling that methods based on them are not appropriate. However, certain standard methods of imputation such as mean imputation and weighting can be regarded as special cases of methods based on the multivariate normal model. Also, more realistic models can be formulated by conditioning on survey design variables used to encode clustering and stratification. Thus the assumptions are not as restrictive as they appear.

The superpopulation model framework provides a useful conceptual basis for evaluating methods for handling nonresponse. As robust superpopulation models are developed for analyzing survey data in the absence of nonresponse, maximum likelihood estimation for these same models with item nonresponse should become increasingly relevant to practical nonresponse problems.

REFERENCES

Afifi, A. A., and Elashoff, R. M. (1966). Missing observations in multivariate statistics, Vol. 1. Review of the literature. *Journal of the American Statistical Association* 61: 595–604.

Afifi, A. A., and Elashoff, R. M. (1967). Missing observations in multivariate statistics, Vol. 2. Point estimation in simple linear regression. *Journal of the American Statistical Association* 62: 10–29.

Afifi, A. A., and Elashoff, R. M. (1969a). Missing observations in multivariate statistics, Vol. 3. Large sample analysis of simple linear regression. *Journal of the American Statistical Association* 64: 337–358.

Afifi, A. A., and Elashoff, R. M. (1969b). Missing observations in multivariate statistics, Vol. 4. A note on simple linear regression. *Journal of the American Statistical Association* 64: 359–365.

Aitchison, J. (1975). Goodness of prediction fit. *Biometrica 62:* 547–554.

Anderson, T. W. (1957). Maximum likelihood estimates for a multivariate normal distribution when some observations are missing. *Journal of the American Statistical Association* 52: 200–203.

Baum, L. E., Petrie, T., Soules, G., and Weiss, N. (1970). A maximization technique occurring in the statistical analysis of probabilistic functions of Markov chains. *Annals of Mathematical Statistics* 41: 164–171.

Beale, E. M. L. (1970). Computational methods in least squares. In J. Abadie (ed.), *Integer and Nonlinear Programming*, pp. 213–227. North Holland: Amsterdam.

Beale, E. M. L., and Little, R. J. A. (1975). Missing values in multivariate analysis. *Journal of the Royal Statistical Society*, Series B, 37: 129–146.

Bhargava, R. (1962). Multivariate tests of hypotheses with incomplete data. Applied Mathematics and Statistical Laboratories, Technical Report 3.

Bishop, Y. M. M., Fienberg, S. E., and Holland, P. W. (1975). *Discrete Multivariate Analysis: Theory and Practice.* Cambridge, Massachusetts: MIT Press.

Buck, S. F. (1960). A method of estimation of missing values in multivariate data suitable for use with an electronic computer. *Journal of the Royal Statistical Society*, Series B, 22: 302–306.

Cassel, C-M., Särndal, C. E., and Wretman, J. H. (1977). *Foundations of Inference in Survey Sampling.* New York: Wiley (Interscience).

Chen, T., and Fienberg, S. E. (1974). Two-dimensional contingency tables with both completely and partially classified data. *Biometrics* 30: 629–642.

Cochran, W. G. (1963). *Sampling Techniques* (2nd ed.). New York: Wiley.

Coleman, J. S. (1961). *The Adolescent Society.* New York: Free Press.

Cox, D. R., and Hinkley, D. V. (1974). *Theoretical Statistics.* London: Chapman and Hall.

Demets, D., and Halperin, M. (1977). Estimation of a simple regression coefficient in samples arising from a subsampling procedure. *Biometrics* 33: 47–56.

Dempster, A. P. (1969). *Elements of Continuous Multivariate Analysis.* Massachusetts: Addison-Wesley.

Dempster, A. P., Laird, N. M., and Rubin, D. B. (1977). Maximum likelihood from incomplete data via the EM Algorithm (with discussion). *Journal of the Royal Statistical Society*, Series B, (39(1): 1–39.

Fuchs, C. (1982). Maximum likelihood estimation and model selection in contingency tables with missing data. *Journal of the American Statistical Association* 77: 270–278.

Geisser, S. (1971). The inferential use of predictive distributions. In V. P. Godambe, and D. A. Sprott (ed.), *Foundations of Statistical Inference*, pp. 459–469. Toronto: Holt, Rinehart, and Winston.

Glasser, M. (1964). Linear regression analysis with missing observations among the independent variables. *Journal of the American Statistical Association* 59: 834–844.

Goodman, L. A. (1970). The multivariate analysis of qualitative data: interactions among multiple classifications. *Journal of the American Statistical Association* 65: 225–256.

Haberman, S. J. (1974). Loglinear models for frequency tables derived by indirect observation: maximum likelihood equations. *Am. Stat.* 2: 911–924.

Haitovsky, Y. (1968). Missing data in regression analysis. *Journal of the Royal Statistical Society* Series B, 30: 67–82.

Hansen, M. H., Madow, W. G., and Tepping, B. J. (1978). On Inference and Estimation from Sample Surveys. *ASA Proceedings of Section on Survey Research Methods*, pp. 82–107 (with discussion).

Hartley, H. O. (1958). Maximum likelihood estimation from incomplete data. *Biometrics* 14: 174–194.

Hartley, H. O., and Hocking, R. R. (1971). The analysis of incomplete data. *Biometrics* 14: 174–194.

Hocking, R. R., and Marx, D. L. (1979). Estimation with incomplete data. *Communications in Statistics*, A8: 12.

Hocking, R. R., and Oxspring, H. H. (1971). Maximum likelihood estimation with incomplete multinomial data. *Journal of the American Statistical Association* 66: 65–70.

Hocking, R. R., and Oxspring, H. H. (1974). The analysis of partially categorized contingency data. *Biometrics*, 30: 469–483.

Holt, D., Smith, T. M. F., and Winter, P. O. (1980). Regression analysis of data from complex surveys. *Journal of the Royal Statistical Society*, Series A 143, 474–487.

Johnson, N. L., and Smith, H. (eds.) (1969). *New Developments in Survey Sampling.* New York: Wiley (Interscience).

Kendall, M. G., and Stuart, A. (1967). *The Advanced Theory of Statistics* (Vol. 2, 2nd ed.). London: Griffin.

Kish, L. (1965). *Survey Sampling.* New York: Wiley.

Little, R. J. A. (1978). Consistent regression methods for discriminant analysis with incomplete data. *Journal of the American Statistical Association* 73: 319–322.

Little, R. J. A. (1979). Maximum likelihood inference for multiple regression with missing values: a simulation study. *Journal of the Royal Statistical Society*, Series B, 41: 76–88.

Lord, F. M. (1955). Estimation of parameters from incomplete data. *Journal of the American Statistical Association* 50: 870–876.

Marini, M. M., Olsen, A. R., and Rubin, D. B. (1980). Maximum likelihood estimation in panel studies with missing data. In *Sociological Methodology*. San Francisco: Jossey Bass.

Matthai, A. (1951). Estimation of parameters from incomplete data with application to design of sample surveys. *Sankhyā* 2: 145–152.

Murray, G. O. (1977). Discussion of paper by Dempster, Laird and Rubin. *Journal of the Royal Statistical Society*, Series B, 39(1): 27.

Orchard, T., and Woodbury, M. A. (1972). A missing information principle: Theory and applications. *Proceedings of the 6th Berkeley Symposium on Mathematical Statistics and Probability* 1: 697–715.

Pregibon, D. (1977). Typical survey data: Estimation and imputation. *Survey Methodology* 2: 70–102.

Press, S. J., and Scott, A. J. (1976). Missing variables in Bayesian regression, Part 2. *Journal of the American Statistical Association* 71: 366–369.

Royall, R. M. (1971). Linear regression models in finite population sampling theory. In V. P. Godambe and D. A. Sprott, (eds.), *Foundations of Statistical Inference*. Toronto: Holt, Rinehart and Winston.

Rubin, D. B. (1974). Characterizing the estimation of parameters in incomplete data problems. *Journal of the American Statistical Association* 69: 467–474.

Scott, A. J., and Smith, T. M. F. (1969). Estimation in multistage surveys. *Journal of the American Statistical Association* 64: 830–840.

Sundberg, R. (1974). Maximum likelihood theory for incomplete data from an exponential family. *Scandanavian Journal of Statistics* 1: 49–58.

Trawinski, I. M., and Bargmann, R. E. (1964). Maximum likelihood estimation with incomplete multivariate data. *Annals of Mathematical Statistics* 35: 647–657.

Wilks, S. S. (1932). Moments and distribution of estimates of population parameters from fragmentary samples. *Annals of Mathematical Statistics* 3: 163–195.

CHAPTER 22

The Nonignorable Case

Roderick J. A. Little

1. CONDITIONS FOR IGNORABILITY OF THE SAMPLING AND RESPONSE MECHANISMS

1.1. Introduction

The crucial issue of nonresponse in sample surveys is the nature of the underlying mechanisms which cause certain values to be missing. Informally speaking, if these mechanisms are unrelated to the values of variables measured in the survey, then the response mechanism can be ignored and the observed values treated as a random subsample of the hypothetical complex sample without nonresponse. Most general methods for dealing with nonresponse at the analysis stage, such as weighting, hot- and cold-deck procedures, and raking effectively make this assumption within strata. The methods in Chapter 21 were also presented within this framework.

If the response mechanism is related to the values of the variables under study, then it is nonignorable, in the sense that methods which do not take this into account are subject to bias.

We begin this chapter by showing how the superpopulation models of Chapter 21 can be extended to model nonignorable response mechanisms. Formal conditions for when the response mechanism can be ignored for likelihood and repeated sampling inferences follow from the general formulation of inference from incomplete data given by Rubin (1976). The discussion given here follows closely that given in Little (1982).

The model is developed in two stages. Within the framework of superpopulation models, inference for sample survey data without nonresponse can itself be viewed as a missing data problem, where the complete data consist of the

INCOMPLETE DATA
IN SAMPLE SURVEYS
Volume 2, Part VI

item values for the whole population, the present data are the sampled values and the missing data are the nonsampled values. This perspective is developed in Section 1.2. The extension to models for sample survey data with nonresponse is then quite straightforward, since item or unit nonresponse is simply incorporated as an additional source of incompleteness. The theory for this extension is developed in Section 1.3.

1.2. Sampling as a Missing Data Problem

As in Chapter 21, we represent the complete data set of population items by the symbol y. For concreteness, we assume that the population consists of N units and that there are K items for each unit, so that y is an $N \times K$ matrix with (i, j)th element y_{ij} representing the jth item for the ith unit, $i = 1, \ldots, N$; $j = 1, \ldots, K$. We also have a matrix of sample design variables z, the values of which are known for each unit in the population.

Let y_s denote the set of sampled items. We define for each item y_{ij} in the population a *sample indicator function*

$$d_{ij} = \begin{cases} 1 & \text{if } y_{ij} \text{ is sampled} \\ 0 & \text{otherwise.} \end{cases} \tag{1}$$

The $N \times K$ matrix of sample indicator functions is denoted d. If only complete units are sampled, d is equivalent to the set of sample labels which arise in the sampling literature. Then we can represent the survey data schematically as in Fig. 1, where the first N_s rows correspond to sampled units, the remaining $N - N_s$ are nonsampled units, and the shaded areas represent data. Note that this corresponds to an incomplete data pattern, the monotone pattern of Example 3.

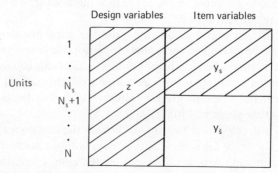

Fig. 1. *The data from a sample survey without nonresponse.*

The superpopulation model treats y and d as realizations of random variables with the following distributions:

(i)   Conditional on the sample design variables z, the population items y have a distribution $f(y|z; \theta)$ indexed by an unknown q-dimensional parameter θ

(ii)   Conditional on z and y, the sample indicator function d has a distribution $f(d|z, y; \phi)$ indexed by an unknown w-dimensional parameter ϕ

These two components induce the joint distribution of y and d, given z, θ, and ϕ:

$$f(y, d|z; \theta, \phi) = f(y|z; \theta)f(d|z, y; \phi). \qquad (2)$$

In the special case of probability sampling, $f(d|z, y; \phi)$ consists of the known sample selection probabilities, and the unknown parameter ϕ can be omitted. A distribution for the design variables may also be specified, but is omitted here since it is not essential to the argument.

The distribution of the data y_s and d is obtained by integrating (2) over the nonsampled items $y_{\bar{s}}$:

$$f(y_s, d|z; \theta, \phi) = \int f(y|z; \theta)f(d|z, y; \phi)\, dy_{\bar{s}}. \qquad (3)$$

In the previous chapter inferences about θ were based on the conditional distribution of y_s given z, obtained by averaging $f(y|z; \theta)$ over the nonsampled items, $y_{\bar{s}}$:

$$f(y_s|z; \theta) = \int f(y|z; \theta)\, dy_{\bar{s}}. \qquad (4)$$

The two distributions (3) and (4) have corresponding log-likelihood functions:

$$l(\theta, \phi; y_s, d|z) = \log f(y_s, d|z; \theta, \phi), \qquad (5)$$

$$l(\theta; y_s|z) = \log f(y_s|z; \theta). \qquad (6)$$

The sampling mechanism is called *ignorable* for likelihood-based inferences about θ if (5) and (6) differ by a quantity which is independent of θ. Then in particular the ML estimate of θ is the same under the full model (3) or the model ignoring the sampling mechanism (4). The following are easily shown to be sufficient conditions for ignorability:

C1.   The log-likelihood of ϕ based on the conditional distribution of given z and y is independent of the nonsampled items y_s. That is,

$$l(\phi; d|z, y) = l(\phi; d|z, y_s). \qquad (7)$$

C2. The parameters θ and ϕ are *distinct*, according to the following definition:

DEFINITION.   Two parameters θ and ϕ are distinct if

(a)   the joint parameter space of θ and ϕ factorizes into the product of the parameter space of θ and the parameter space of ϕ and

(b)   for Bayesian inference, the prior distributions of θ and ϕ are statistically independent.

Different conditions are required if superpopulation inferences about θ based on repeated sampling from the superpopulation distribution (4), ignoring the sampling mechanism, are to be correct. Specifically, we require that the conditional distribution of y_s given z and d derived from (3) be equal to (4). A sufficient condition for this equality is the following:

C3.   The distribution of the sample indicator function d is independent of the population items y. That is,

$$f(d\,|\,z, y; \phi) = f(d\,|\,z; \phi). \tag{8}$$

Condition C3 is stronger than C1, Eq. (7), where the distribution of the sample indicator function can depend on values which have been sampled.

Conditions C1, C2, and C3 are all satisfied for *probability sampling*, where the probability distribution of the sample indicator function is *known* and independent of the population items; that is,

$$f(d\,|\,z, x; \phi) = f(d\,|\,z). \tag{9}$$

The conditions C1 and C2 for likelihood-based inference are also satisfied for sequential sample designs, where the probability of selecting a unit can depend on the values of items for units already sampled. However, these conditions are not necessarily satisfied for purposive and quota sampling which do not involve some form of randomization. The consequence that the usual log-likelihood (6) is not correct for such sample designs provides a strong counterargument to the widely held view that randomization is not relevant to a Bayesian analysis of sample surveys.

1.3.   A Model for Nonresponse

Suppose now that some of the sampled items y_s are missing. For each sampled item y_{ij} we define the response indicator function

$$r_{ij} = \begin{cases} 1, & y_{ij} \text{ responds} \\ 0, & y_{ij} \text{ missing.} \end{cases}$$

Also, let p represent the set of present items for which $r_{ij} = 1$, and m the set of missing items for which $r_{ij} = 0$. For the sample represented in Fig. 1, y_s and r

are $N_s \times K$ matrices. The data in the presence of nonresponse are represented as shaded areas in Fig. 2. The shading suggests a monotone pattern of response for the sampled items, although the formulation applies to any pattern. The observed data consist of (z, d, r, p) and the missing values are contained in $y_{\bar{s}}$ and m.

The response mechanism is modeled by specifying a distribution for the response indicator matrix r. Specifically, we suppose that conditional on z, y, and d, r has a distribution $f(r|z, y, d; \psi)$ indexed by an unknown parameter ψ. The joint distribution of y, d, and r is obtained by combining this distribution with the distribution of y and d from the previous section:

$$f(y, d, r|z; \theta, \phi, \psi) = f(y|z; \theta)f(d|z, y; \phi)f(r|z, y, d; \psi).$$

The distribution of the data $(d, r, \text{and } p)$ given z is obtained by averaging this equation over the nonsampled and missing items:

$$f(p, d, r|z; \theta, \phi, \psi) = \int f(y|z; \theta)f(d|z, y; \phi)f(r|z, y, d; \psi)\, dy_{\bar{s}}\, dm. \qquad (10)$$

For the problems of nonresponse in Chapter 20, inferences were based on the distribution of p given z obtained by averaging $f(y|z; \theta)$ over the nonsampled and missing items:

$$f(p|z; \theta) = \int f(y|z; \theta)\, dy_{\bar{s}}\, dm. \qquad (11)$$

The question now is under what conditions inferences based on (11) are equivalent to inferences based on (10). By direct analogy with the previous subsection, the sampling and response mechanisms are ignorable for likelihood-based inferences if the log-likelihood based on the full distribution (10) and the marginal distribution (11) differ by a quantity which is independent of θ, that is, if

$$l(\theta, \phi, \psi; p, d, r|z) = l(\theta; p|z) + l(\phi, \psi; p, d, r|z). \qquad (12)$$

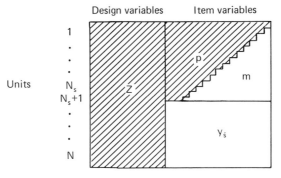

Fig. 2.   *The data from a sample survey with nonresponse.*

Sufficient conditions for (12) are as follows:

C4.　The log-likelihood of the sample indicator function d is independent of the nonsampled items y_s and the missing items m; that is,

$$l(\phi; d \mid z, y) = l(\phi; d \mid z, p). \tag{13}$$

C5.　The log-likelihood of the response indicator function r is independent of the nonsampled items y_s and the missing items m; that is,

$$l(\psi; r \mid z, y, d) = l(\psi; r \mid z, p, d). \tag{14}$$

C6.　The parameters θ and (ϕ, ψ) are *distinct*, according to the definition of the previous section.

Hence, in particular, the probability that an item is sampled or is present cannot depend on the nonsampled items y_s or the missing items m. Alternatively, if inferences about θ are based on the repeated sampling from the superpopulation distribution (11) ignoring the sample design and response mechanism, then we require that (11) equal the conditional distribution of p given z, d, and r derived from (10). Sufficient conditions for this are as follows:

C7.　The distribution of the sample indicator function is independent of the population items y, that is,

$$f(d \mid z, y; \phi) = f(d \mid z; \phi). \tag{15}$$

This condition is identical to condition C3, Eq. (8).

C8.　The distribution of the response indicator function is independent of the population items y, that is,

$$f(r \mid z, y, d; \phi) = f(r \mid z, d; \phi). \tag{16}$$

This condition is considerably stronger than its analog for likelihood-based inferences (14) since the probability that an item is present cannot depend on recorded item values. In some situations it can be weakened. For example, if inferences are restricted to the parameters of the conditional distribution of items u given items v, and if items v are observed for all units in the sample, then it is sufficient that the distribution of u is independent of the population items v. An example of this occurs with the parameters of the regression of y_2 on y_1 in Example 2.

For the remainder of this chapter we shall assume that the sample design is ignorable for inference based on the likelihood or sampling distribution as appropriate, and hence that we can condition on the selected sample d and the design variables z where present. We shall also assume that the parameters of the response mechanism ψ are distinct from the parameters of the superpopulation distribution of y. The key conditions for determining whether the response mechanism can be ignored are C5 and C8, and particular attention is paid to these conditions in the examples of the next section.

2. NONIGNORABLE RESPONSE MECHANISMS FOR A SINGLE-ITEM VARIABLE

2.1. Introduction

The general model of the previous section is now applied to cases with nonresponse confined to a single item variable y. Nearly all of the literature of nonignorable response mechanisms has concentrated on this case, although extensions to multivariate nonresponse are possible in principle.

Since only one variable is missing in the sample, we confine the response indicator variable r to that item. Hence for unit i define the scalar value

$$r_i = \begin{cases} 1, & y_i \text{ present} \\ 0, & y_i \text{ missing.} \end{cases} \tag{17}$$

The probability that $r_i = 1$ can in general depend on the values of y, the values of other observed items w, and the values of unobserved or latent covariates. A convenient formulation is to assume that y_i is observed when another interval scaled variable u_i lies below a threshold value c. The conditional probability that y_i is observed given w_i and y_i is then obtained from the regression of u_i on w_i and y_i. If we make the important assumption that this regression is linear and additive, then we obtain the response mechanism

$$u_i = \alpha_0 + \alpha w_i + \beta y_i + v_i,$$
$$r_i = 1 \quad \text{if and only if} \quad u_i \leq c. \tag{18}$$

Where α_0, α, and β correspond to the parameters ψ in the formulation of the previous section, $E(v_i) = 0$ and v_i is uncorrelated with w_i and y_i. If we also assume that the distribution of u_i and y_i given w_i is normal, then v_i and y_i are conditionally independent given w_i. This is the model proposed by Heckman [1976, Eqs. 7(a), 7(b), and 8]. The conditional probability that y_i is observed is

$$\text{pr}(r_i = 1 | w_i, y_i) = \text{pr}(v_i \leq c - \alpha_0 - \alpha w_i - \beta y_i), \tag{19}$$

which is a monotonic function of w_i and y_i. Two special cases are of particular interest. If u_i and y_i are conditionally independent given w_i, that is, if $\beta = 0$, then the probability (19) depends only on item values w_i which are observed in the sample. Hence condition C5 of the previous section is satisfied and the response mechanism is ignorable for likelihood-based inferences. If $\beta \neq 0$ and u_i and y_i are perfectly correlated given w_i, that is, if $v_i = 0$, then we obtain the case of pure censoring:

$$r_i = 1 \quad \text{if and only if} \quad y_i \leq c_i,$$
$$c_i = \beta^{-1}(u_i - \alpha_0 - \alpha w_i). \tag{20}$$

Two applications of this model should be carefully distinguished. If the censoring points c_i are *known* for all i, then we obtain a case where the response mechanism is not ignorable but is known. In such cases the likelihood function does not involve unknown nuisance parameters associated with the response process, but is a known modification of the likelihood obtained by ignoring the response mechanism. Methods for maximum likelihood estimation for censored data with known censoring points have an extensive literature. See, for example, Kaplan and Meier (1958), Kulldorf (1961), Glasser (1967), Blight (1970), Cox (1972), Dempster, Laird and Rubin (1977, Section 4.2).

For most practical problems of nonresponse, we are in the less fortunate situation where the response mechanism is unknown and not ignorable. For the present model this corresponds to the case where the values of c_i are not known. The response mechanism introduces nuisance parameters (here β, α_0, and α) into the likelihood. The basic difficulty of the nonresponse problem, namely, that the nonrespondents may differ from the respondents in an unknown way, is reflected in the model-based formulation by the fact that although these nuisance parameters modify the likelihood in an important way, information with which to estimate them from the data is very scarce, and estimation is highly dependent on assumptions about the distribution of the hypothetical complete data. This crucial point is illustrated in the examples of the next section.

An alternative formulation of the model given in Eq. (18) is the model proposed by Nelson (1977), who assumed a stochastic censoring point c_i which has a linear regression on w_i. By regressing c_i on both w_i and y_i, Nelson's model can be written in the form

$$c_i = \alpha_0' + \alpha w_i + \beta' y_i + v_i,$$
$$r_i = 1 \qquad \text{if and only if} \quad y_i \geq c_i, \tag{21}$$

where v_i is an independent disturbance. This formulation is identical to Heckman's model (18) with

$$u_i = c + c_i - y_i, \qquad \beta = \beta' - 1, \qquad \alpha_0 = c + \alpha_0'.$$

The condition for ignorability under Heckman's model, $\beta = 0$, is replaced by the condition $\beta' = 1$. Thus Heckman's formulation might be considered conceptually more satisfying since the ignorability condition corresponds to zero conditional association between u and y given w. On the other hand, the Nelson form of the model recognizes more explicitly the relation to censoring models with known censoring points, and related models for limited dependent variables such as those considered by Tobin (1958).

2.2. Examples

EXAMPLE 1: NONRESPONSE FOR A UNIVARIATE NORMAL SAMPLE. Suppose that the hypothetical complete data consist of a random sample of N_s units $\{y_i : i = 1, \ldots, N_s\}$ from a single variable y, where y has a normal distribution with mean μ and variance σ^2. In practice only $n\,(<N_s)$ of the sampled units respond. We define the response indicator function by Eq. (17).

The response mechanism is modeled by specifying a distribution $f(r\,|\,y;\psi)$ for the response indicator function given the partially observed complete data y. We suppose that given values of ψ_0, ψ_1 and y, the event that y_i is observed is independent across units i and has probability

$$\mathrm{pr}(r_i = 1\,|\,y_i) = \Phi(\psi_0 + \psi_1 y_i), \tag{22}$$

where Φ is the cumulative standard normal distribution function. If $\psi_1 = 0$, the distribution of r is independent of the item values and the response mechanism is ignorable. If $\psi_1 \neq 0$, we have a form of stochastic censoring, where the probability of response is a monotone function of the item value.

This is a special case of the response mechanism modeled by Eq. (18). To see this, suppose that is observed when an unobserved or latent variable u lies below a threshold, that is,

$$r_i = 1 \qquad \text{if and only if} \quad u_i < c,$$

where u_i is a unit normal deviate and c is the unknown threshold. If u and y are bivariate normal with means $(0, \mu)$, variances $(1, \sigma^2)$, and covariance β, then the distribution of u_i given y_i is normal with mean $\beta(y_i - \mu)/\sigma^2$ and variance $1 - \beta^2/\sigma^2$. Hence the probability that y_i is observed is

$$\mathrm{pr}(r_i = 1\,|\,y) = \mathrm{pr}(u_i < c\,|\,y_i) = \Phi\left[\frac{c - \beta(y_i - \mu)/\sigma^2}{(1 - \beta^2/\sigma^2)^{1/2}}\right], \tag{23}$$

which equals Eq. (22) with

$$\psi_0 = (c + \beta\mu/\sigma^2)(1 - \beta^2/\sigma^2)^{-1/2}, \qquad \psi_1 = -\beta/\sigma(1 - \beta^2/\sigma^2)^{-1/2}.$$

Note that $\psi_1 = 0$ if and only if $\beta = 0$. That is, the response mechanism is ignorable if and only if u and y are uncorrelated.

Suppose that μ is estimated by $\bar{y}$, the sample mean of the observed units. The expected value of $\bar{y}$ under this model is

$$E(\bar{y}\,|\,r) = E(y_i\,|\,u_i < c) = \mu - \beta\gamma(c),$$

where $\gamma(c) = -E(u_i\,|\,u_i < c) = \phi(c)/\Phi(c)$, and $\phi(c)$ is the standard normal density. Hence $\bar{y}$ is a biased estimate of μ unless $\beta = 0$, and the bias is proportional to the covariance of y and u.

The effect of censoring is illustrated in Table 1. Stem and leaf plots of three sets of data are given: (a) an uncensored normal distribution of 100 observations with parameters $\mu = 0$, $\sigma^2 = 1$, generated from pseudorandom numbers; (b) a subsample of the data in (a) with conditional probability of inclusion (that is, response) given by (23) with $c = 0$, $\beta = 0$; and (c) a different subsample with probability of inclusion given by (23) with $c = 0$, $\beta = .9$. In both (b) and (c) the unconditional probability of response is one-half, and slightly more than half of the original observations are included.

TABLE 1

Stem and Leaf Plots of Distribution of Standard Normal Sample with Stochastic Censoring

	(a) Uncensored sample: $N = 100$	(b) Ignorable censoring mechanism: $Pr(y_i \text{ observed}) = .5$, $N = 52$	(cj) Nonignorable censoring mechanism: $Pr(y_i \text{ observed}) = \phi(-2.05y_i)$, $N = 53$
$-3\frac{1}{2}$	7		7
-3			
$-2\frac{1}{2}$	8		8
-2			
$-1\frac{1}{2}$	57889	578	57889
-1	001111222233	1112233	001111222233
$-\frac{1}{2}$	5556666778888899999	566788899999	555666778888899999
-0	0112222223344	011234	0112222234
$+0$	00112222222233344444	0122222234	012224
$+\frac{1}{2}$	56777778899	677789	
$+1$	0011113444	11144	
$+1\frac{1}{2}$	56778	6	
$+2$	023	02	
$+2\frac{1}{2}$			
$+3$	3		
	Sample mean $= -.03$	Sample mean $= -.11$	Sample mean $= -.81$

In case (b) $\beta = 0$ and hence the response mechanism is ignorable. The sample mean -0.11 is a consistent estimate of the mean of the uncensored distribution, namely, zero. Case (c) is not ignorable, and results in the inclusion of low values of y and the exclusion of high values. The observed distribution is skewed and the sample mean $-.81$ is no longer a consistent estimate of the uncensored mean, zero.

The likelihood of the data takes the form

$$\prod_{r_i=1} f(y_i) \Pr(r_i = 1 \mid y_i) \prod_{r_i=0} \Pr(r_i = 0)$$

$$= \prod_{r_i=1} \sigma^{-1}\phi\left(\frac{y_i - \mu}{\sigma}\right) \Phi\left(\frac{c - \beta(y_i - \mu)\sigma^{-2}}{(1 - \beta^2/\sigma^2)^{1/2}}\right)(1 - \Phi(c))^{N-n},$$

where $N - n$ is the number of missing values. This likelihood can be maximized by iterative methods to obtain ML estimates of the parameters. In this process the ML estimate $\hat{c}$ of c is strongly related to the proportion of missing values, and the estimate $\hat{\beta}$ of β is strongly related to the skewness in the observed values of y.

The ML estimate of the uncensored mean of y can be written as

$$\hat{\mu} = \bar{y} + \frac{N - n}{n} \hat{\beta}\phi(\hat{c})(1 - \Phi(\hat{c}))^{-1}, \tag{24}$$

and is of course a consistent estimate. However, the last term in the expression, representing the correction for the selection bias, is proportional to $\hat{\beta}$, an estimate determined by skewness in the observed values of y. This correction is ill-determined unless the sample size is large, and hence the variance of $\hat{\mu}$ is likely to be considerably greater than that of $\bar{y}$. More crucially, the estimate of β (and hence the correction) is totally dependent on the assumption of symmetry in the uncensored distribution of y. Regardless of sample size, this assumption cannot be contradicted by the observed values, since any skewness in their distribution is attributed to selection bias.

Thus the symmetry implied by the normality assumption in this example has a fundamental bearing on the estimate of the mean. This softness in the model also applies to more complex examples, to be described. Note also that fitted values for the missing items can be calculated as

$$\hat{y}_i = E(y_i|u_i > c) = \hat{\mu} + \hat{\beta}E(u_i|u_i > c) = \hat{\mu} + \hat{\beta}\phi(\hat{c})(1 - \Phi(\hat{c}))^{-1},$$

where $\hat{\mu}$, $\hat{\beta}$, and $\hat{c}$ are ML estimates of μ, β, and c. The last term in this expression represents the adjustment for the stochastic censoring of the item values.

EXAMPLE 2: THE MONOTONE TWO-VARIABLE CASE (EXAMPLE 2 IN CHAPTER 21 CONTINUED). We now add to the previous example a completely observed variable y_1, so that the data consist of y_1 observed for all units in the sample and y_2 (corresponding to y in Example 1), observed for some units and missing for others. This data pattern was considered previously in Example 2, Chapter 21.

Assuming that given the item values the event that y_2 is present is independent across items, there are three response mechanisms of interest. If the conditional probability that y_2 responds given y_1 and y_2 is independent of the values of y_1 and y_2, we have the ignorable response mechanism assumed in Example 2, Chapter 20. If the probability depends on y_1 but not y_2, the response mechanism is ignorable for likelihood-based inferences but not for all sampling distribution inferences. If the probability depends on y_2 but not y_1, or on y_1 and y_2, the mechanism is not ignorable and inference based on the methods of Chapter 21 lead to bias.

It is not difficult to motivate models where the probability that a variable is missing depends on the value of that variable or covariates. For example, suppose that $y_1 =$ age and $y_2 =$ income in a household expenditure survey. If income is not recorded for some respondents, then the probability of response is likely to be related to both age and income. Another example occurs in demographic surveys with $y_1 =$ age, $y_2 =$ the date of a retrospective event such as age at marriage. The probability that y_2 is correctly remembered is often an increasing function of age and the length of interval between the y_2 and the survey date. Hence this probability depends on y_1 and y_2.

For numerical illustrations we shall apply the Heckman model for this data pattern. An unobserved standard normal deviate y_3 is introduced (corresponding to u in the previous example) and we suppose that y_2 is observed when $y_3 < c$, for some unknown threshold c. The response mechanisms distinguished above are modelled by partial correlations between y_3 and the item variables y_1 and y_2.

Suppose that (y_1, y_2, y_3) have a trivariate normal distribution with means $(\mu_1, \mu_2, 0)$ and covariance matrix

$$
\Sigma = \begin{bmatrix} \sigma_{11} & \sigma_{12} & \sigma_{13} \\ \sigma_{12} & \sigma_{22} & \sigma_{23} \\ \sigma_{13} & \sigma_{23} & 1 \end{bmatrix},
$$

and that $\{(y_{i1}, y_{i2}, y_{i3}): i = 1, \ldots, N_s\}$ are a random sample of size N_s from this distribution. The values $\{y_{i1}\}$ are observed for all units, the value y_{i2} is observed when $y_{i3} < c$, for some unknown threshold c, and the values $\{y_{i3}\}$ are not observed. Define as before the response indicator function

$$
r_i = \begin{cases} 1, & y_{i2} \text{ observed} \\ 0, & \text{otherwise,} \end{cases}
$$

$$
r = (r_1, \ldots, r_N).
$$

We first derive the distribution of r. The conditional distribution of y_3 given y_1 and y_2 is normal with mean and variance

$$
E(y_3 | y_1, y_2) = \beta_{31.12}(y_1 - \mu_1) + \beta_{32.12}(y_2 - \mu_2), \qquad \text{Var}(y_3 | y_1, y_2) = \sigma_{33.12},
$$

where $\beta_{jk.kl}$ denotes the coefficient of y_k and $\sigma_{jj.kl}$ denotes the residual variance when y_j is regressed on y_k and y_l.

The probability that y_{i2} is present is

$$
\text{pr}(r_i = 1 | y_{i1}, y_{i2}) = \text{pr}(y_{i3} < c | y_{i1}, y_{i2}) = \Phi(\psi_0 + \psi_1 y_{i1} + \psi_2 y_{i2}), \quad (25)
$$

where

$$
\psi_0 = (c + \beta_{31.12}\mu_1 + \beta_{32.12}\mu_2)\sigma_{33.12}^{-1/2},
$$

$$
\psi_1 = -\beta_{31.12}\sigma_{33.12}^{-1/2},
$$

$$
\psi_2 = -\beta_{32.12}\sigma_{33.12}^{-1/2}.
$$

Hence as in the previous example the probability of response is a transformation of a linear function of the item variables.

2.2.1. Conditions for Ignorability

According to the theory of the previous section, the response mechanism is ignorable for likelihood-based inferences if the expression (25) does not depend on values y_{i2} which are missing. A sufficient (and, in fact, necessary) condition is that $\beta_{32.12} = 0$, that is, the partial correlation of y_2 and y_3 given y_1 is zero. For small sample inferences based on the conditional distribution of the observed items given the response pattern, the response mechanism is ignorable if the expression (24) does not depend on the values of y_{i1} and y_{i2}, which occurs if and only if $\beta_{32.12} = \beta_{31.12} = 0$. Then the paired observations on (y_1, y_2) and the unpaired observations on y_1 are random samples from their complete data distributions, and we have the case described in Example 2, Chapter 21.

2.2.2. Performance of Estimates Which Ignore the Response Mechanism

If the conditions of Example 2, Chapter 20, are correct, that is, $\beta_{31.12} = \beta_{32.12} = 0$, then estimates of the parameters which use all the data are generally preferable to estimates based on the paired observations because they are more efficient. The ML estimate $\hat{\mu}_2$ of μ_2 given in Eq. (21), Chapter 21, is unbiased and can be shown to have variance

$$\text{Var}(\hat{\mu}_2) = \sigma_{22}/n - \sigma_{22}(n^{-1} - N_s^{-1})\left(1 - \frac{n-2}{n-3}(1 - \rho^2)\right), \qquad (26)$$

where n is the number of paired observations and ρ is the correlation between y_1 and y_2 (Morrison, 1971). The variance of $\bar{y}_2$, the sample mean of y_2 from the paired observations, is

$$\text{Var}(\bar{y}_2) = \sigma_{22}/n, \qquad (27)$$

and hence $\text{Var}(\hat{\mu}_2) < \text{Var}(\bar{y}_2)$ unless $\rho^2 \leq (n-2)^{-1}$. In practice, the increase in precision achieved by using $\hat{\mu}_2$ rather than $\bar{y}_2$ is often not great, and $\bar{y}_2$ has the advantage that its sampling distribution is normal for all sample sizes.

The potential gains of using a regression estimate based on all the data rather than discarding the incomplete units are much greater when the assumption $\beta_{32.12} = \beta_{31.12} = 0$ is not valid. We illustrate this by evaluating the bias of $\hat{\mu}_2$ and $\bar{y}_2$ when the response mechanism is not ignorable. These biases are expressed most simply in terms of the regressions of y_1 and y_2 on y_3, rather than the regression of y_3 on y_1 and y_2 used for Eq. (25). Since y_3 has mean zero, we can write

$$E(y_2 | y_3) = \mu_2 + \beta_{23.3} y_3,$$
$$E(y_1 | y_3) = \mu_1 + \beta_{13.3} y_3,$$
$$E(y_2 | y_1, y_3) = \mu_2 + \beta_{21.13}(y_1 - \mu_1) + \beta_{23.13} y_3,$$

where the regression coefficients are standard functions of Σ such that

$$\beta_{23.3} = \beta_{23.13} + \beta_{21.13}\beta_{13.3}. \qquad (28)$$

Equation (28) expresses the path decomposition of the total effect of y_2 on y_3 ($\beta_{23.3}$) into the direct effect controlling y_1 ($\beta_{23.13}$), and the indirect effect through y_1 $(\beta_{21.13}\beta_{13.3})$. The coefficients in this decomposition can be represented in the path diagram[1]

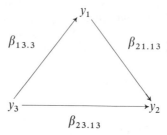

As in Example 1, the sample mean $\bar{y}_2$ has expected value

$$E(\bar{y}_2) = \mu_2 - \beta_{23.3}\gamma(c),$$

where as above $\gamma(c) = \phi(c)/\Phi(c)$. The ML estimate $\hat{\mu}_2$ ignoring the response mechanism has expected value

$$E(\hat{\mu}_2) = \mu_2 - \beta_{23.13}\{\gamma(c) + \Delta\}, \qquad (29)$$

where

$$\Delta = \sigma_{33.1}^{-1/2}E\{(\hat{\mu}_1 - \bar{y}_1) \sum_{\{i:r_i=1\}} \gamma_i(y_{i1} - \bar{y}_1)/ \sum_{\{i:r_i=1\}} (y_{i1} - \bar{y}_1)^2\},$$

$$\gamma_i = \gamma\{[c - \beta_{31.1}(y_{i1} - \mu_1)]\sigma_{33.1}^{-1/2}\},$$

and $\hat{\mu}_1$ is the mean of y_1 based on all the N_s observations.

For small deviations from ignorability the term γ_i is small, and hence the biases of $\hat{\mu}_2$ and $\bar{y}$ as estimates of μ_2 are, respectively,

$$E(\hat{\mu}_2) - \mu_2 \simeq -\beta_{23.13}\gamma(c),$$
$$E(\bar{y}_2) - \mu_2 = -\beta_{23.3}\gamma(c). \qquad (30)$$

As noted in Example 2, Chapter 21, the regression estimate $\hat{\mu}_2$ effectively predicts the values of y_2 for the nonresponding units on the basis of the covariate y_1. Equation (30) suggests that this is an effective way of reducing nonresponse bias if y_1 is chosen so that, when controlled, it reduces the degree of association between y_2 and y_3. This implies that y_1 should be highly correlated with both the latent variable y_3 and the response variable y_2. However, it should also be chosen so that indirect effect of y_3 on y_2 through y_1, $\beta_{21.13}\beta_{13.3}$, has the same sign as the total effect of y_3 on y_2, $\beta_{23.3}$. Otherwise the effect of regressing on y_1 is to *increase* both the association between y_2 and y_3 and the bias of the estimates of μ_2.

A small simulation study from Little (1982) is included to provide a numerical illustration of the performance of $\hat{\mu}_2$ and $\bar{y}_2$ under this model. Bivariate normal

[1] An interesting early conceptualization of nonignorable response mechanisms with the aid of path diagrams is given in Eklund (1960).

samples of 200 units of y_1 and y_2 were generated with zero means, unit variances and correlation ρ_{12}. The latent variable y_3 was created by the regression formula

$$y_3 = \beta_{31.12} y_1 + \beta_{32.12} y_2 + Z(1 - \beta_{32.12}^2 - \beta_{31.12}^2),$$

where Z is an independent standard normal deviate. Hence y_3 is also standard normal, with partial correlations $\beta_{31.12}$ and $\beta_{32.12}$ with y_1 and y_2, respectively.

Thirty data sets were generated for the following values of ρ_{12}, $\beta_{31.12}$, and $\beta_{32.12}$:

$$\rho_{12} = -0.9, -0.6, 0, 0.6, 0.9,$$

$$(\beta_{31.12}, \beta_{32.12}) = (0, 0), (0.6, 0), (0.9, 0), (0, 0.6), (0, 0.9), (0.6, 0.6).$$

Values of y_2 were treated as missing if $y_3 < 0$. This choice of threshold, $c = 0$, implies that the overall probability that y_2 is missing is one-half, and in fact for the 30 data sets generated the number of missing values ranged from 92 to 112 out of 200 units.

Table 2 tabulates estimates $\bar{y}_2$ and $\hat{\mu}_2$ for each data set, together with their theoretical biases as estimates of μ_2, as determined by (30). The coefficients $\beta_{23.3}$ and $\beta_{23.13}$ are obtained by dividing these biases by $-\gamma(0) = -0.7978$. As noted, the expression for the bias of $\hat{\mu}_2$ is approximate if $\beta_{32.12} \neq 0$. Since $\mu_2 = 0$, the estimates of $\hat{\mu}_2$ and $\bar{y}_2$ are in fact deviations from the true population value. The values of $\hat{\mu}_2$ and $\bar{y}_2$ can alternatively be compared with $\bar{y}_{2N_s}$, the sample mean of the hypothetical complete data, which is also included in the table. As indicated, this hypothetical estimate is always unbiased for μ_2. Finally, a problem number is included in the table for reference purposes.

For problems 1–5, $\beta_{31.12} = \beta_{32.12} = 0$ and we have the "random" response mechanism assumed in Example 2, Chapter 21. Both $\hat{\mu}_2$ and $\bar{y}_2$ are unbiased, and have variances given by (26) and (27). Applying these expressions with $\sigma_{22} = 1$, $n \simeq 100$ and $N = 200$, the standard error of $\bar{y}_2$ is .1 and the standard error of $\hat{\mu}_2$ varies from .1 ($\rho_{12} = 0$) to 0.08 ($\rho_{12} = \pm 0.9$). Of course, the gain in precision of $\hat{\mu}_2$ over $\bar{y}_2$ is not evident in Table 2, where only one data set is generated for each problem. However with one exception (problem 2), the estimates $\bar{y}_2$ and $\hat{\mu}_2$ are within two standard deviations of the true value of μ_2.

For problems 6–15, $\beta_{32.12} = 0$, and hence the conditional probability that y_2 is observed given y_1 and y_2 depends on y_1 but not y_2. By the theory of the previous section, the response mechanism is ignorable for likelihood inferences, but not for inferences based on the sampling distribution of the data. Note that $\hat{\mu}_2$ is unbiased, but $\bar{y}_2$ is biased unless $\rho_{12} = 0$, with a bias which increases with ρ_{12}^2 and $\beta_{31.12}$. The regression estimate basically corrects for the bias in the sample mean caused by the response mechanism. The observed values of $\bar{y}_2$ and $\hat{\mu}_2$ reflect these properties: $\hat{\mu}_2$ is indeed closer to the population value of μ_2 except when $\rho_{12} = 0$.

TABLE 2

Estimates of the Mean of y_2 for Selected Response Mechanisms, and Their Predicted Bias

Coefficients of y_3 on y_1, y_2 ($\beta_{31.12}, \beta_{32.12}$)	Correlation of $y_1, y_2 = \rho_{12}$									
	$-.9$		$-.6$		$.0$		$.6$		$.9$	
	Estimate	Bias	Estimate	Bias	Estimate	Bias	Estimate	Bias	Estimate	Bias
$(0, 0)$	Problem 1		Problem 2		Problem 3		Problem 4		Problem 5	
$\bar{y}_{2N_s}$	.03	0	.13	0	.07	0	$-.05$	0	$-.09$	0
$\bar{y}_2$	$-.01$	0	.26	0	.08	0	.06	0	$-.01$	0
$\hat{\mu}_2$	.09	0	.20	0	.08	0	.03	0	$-.08$	0
$(.6, 0)$	Problem 6		Problem 7		Problem 8		Problem 9		Problem 10	
$\bar{y}_{2N_s}$	.02	0	$-.09$	0	$-.05$	0	.06	0	.02	0
$\bar{y}_2$	.54	.43	.10	.29	.06	0	$-.30$	$-.29$	$-.38$	$-.43$
$\hat{\mu}_2$	.13	0	$-.26$	0	.04	0	.01	0	.01	0
$(.9, 0)$	Problem 11		Problem 12		Problem 13		Problem 14		Problem 15	
$\bar{y}_{2N_s}$	.1	0	$-.09$	0	$-.04$	0	$-.05$	0	$-.11$	0
$\bar{y}_2$	.65	.65	.32	.43	$-.02$	0	$-.48$	$-.43$	$-.75$	$-.65$
$\hat{\mu}_2$	$-.04$	0	$-.13$	0	.01	0	$-.26$	0	$-.11$	0
$(0, .6)$	Problem 16		Problem 17		Problem 18		Problem 19		Problem 20	
$\bar{y}_{2N_s}$	$-.02$	0	.01	0	.05	0	$-.06$	0	.10	0
$\bar{y}_2$	$-.45$	$-.48$	$-.44$	$-.48$	$-.33$	$-.48$	$-.53$	$-.48$	$-.37$	$-.48$
$\hat{\mu}_2$	$-.11$	$-.13$	$-.27$	$-.35$	$-.33$	$-.48$	$-.45$	$-.35$	$-.07$	$-.13$
$(0, .9)$	Problem 21		Problem 22		Problem 23		Problem 24		Problem 25	
$\bar{y}_{2N_s}$	.10	0	.04	0	$-.02$	0	.06	0	.08	0
$\bar{y}_2$	$-.63$	$-.72$	$-.77$	$-.72$	.73	$-.72$	$-.72$	$-.72$	$-.69$	$-.72$
$\hat{\mu}_2$	$-.18$	$-.40$	$-.63$	$-.65$	.73	$-.72$	$-.62$	$-.65$	$-.26$	$-.40$
$(.6, .6)$	Problem 26		Problem 27		Problem 28		Problem 29		Problem 30	
$\bar{y}_{2N_s}$	$-.01$	0	$-.04$	0	$-.04$	0	.00	0	$-.01$	0
$\bar{y}_2$	$-.08$	$-.14$	$-.26$	$-.34$	$-.36$	$-.48$	$-.67$	$-.53$	$-.81$	$-.55$
$\hat{\mu}_2$	$-.13$	$-.26$	$-.44$	$-.60$	$-.53$	$-.75$	$-.49$	$-.60$	$-.22$	$-.26$

Problems 16–25 model the less favorable situation where the conditional probability that y_2 is observed given y_1 and y_2 depends on y_2 but not y_1. In these cases the response mechanism is not ignorable and both $\hat{\mu}_2$ and $\bar{y}_2$ are biased. The bias of $\bar{y}_2$ is unrelated to the correlation of y_1 and y_2, and equals the bias of $\hat{\mu}_2$ when $\rho_{12} = 0$. However, when $\rho_{12} \neq 0$, the coefficient $\beta_{32.12}$ is reduced as ρ_{12}^2 increases, and hence the bias of $\hat{\mu}_2$ is inversely related to ρ_{12}^2. The observed values of $\hat{\mu}_2$ and $\bar{y}_2$ confirm that $\hat{\mu}_2$ also reduces the bias in these situations.

Problems 26–29 are interesting, since they illustrate situations where the regression estimate performs worse than the sample mean. The reason is that the magnitude of $\beta_{32.12}$ is greater than the magnitude of $\beta_{32.2}$, or in other words the effect of controlling y_1 is to *increase* the association between y_2 and the missing value generator variable y_3. Consequently the bias of $\hat{\mu}_2$ is greater than the bias of $\bar{y}_2$, and this is reflected in the superior performance of $\bar{y}_2$ in these problems. However such cases are probably uncommon in practical applications. In the last problem, problem 30, $\beta_{32.12} < \beta_{32.2}$ and $\hat{\mu}_2$ is once again closer to zero than the sample mean.

2.2.3. Consistent Estimates of the Parameters

As in the previous example, consistent estimates of the parameters of the model can be calculated. The ML estimates of μ_1 and σ_{11} are clearly given by the sample mean and variance of y_1. For estimates of the other parameters, Heckman (1976) exploits the fact that observed values of y_2 have conditional mean

$$E(y_2 | y_1, r = 1) = \beta_{20.1} + \beta_{21.1} y_1 - \beta_{23.13} \lambda (c^* - \beta_{31.1} y_1),$$

where $c^* = c + \beta_{31.1} \mu_1$ and $\lambda( ) = \phi( )/\Phi( )$. The parameters c^* and $\beta_{31.1}$ are estimated by a probit regression of the response indicator r on y_1. Then values of $\lambda(c^* - \beta_{31.1} y_1)$ can be determined for each observation and consistent estimates of $\beta_{20.1}$, $\beta_{21.1}$, and $-\beta_{23.13}$ obtained by regressing y_2 on y_1 and λ.

This procedure does not give efficient estimates of the parameters. Hausman and Spence (1977) maximize the likelihood directly using an iterative algorithm which is a modified form of the Newton–Raphson algorithm requiring only first derivatives of the likelihood. Empirical results from two applications are given in the next example.

Again, estimation is strongly related to unverifiable assumptions in the model. For example, the ML estimate of the mean of y_2 takes the form

$$\hat{\mu}_2 = \bar{y}_2 + \hat{\beta}_{21.1}(\bar{y}_1 - \hat{\mu}_1) + \frac{1}{n} \hat{\beta}_{32.12} \hat{\sigma}_{22.1} \sum_{r_i = 0} \phi_i/(1 - \Phi_i),$$

where the first two terms have the same form as the ML estimate ignoring the response mechanism, and the third term is an adjustment analogous to that given for the previous example in Eq. (25). The ML estimate of $\beta_{32.12}$, $\hat{\beta}_{32.12}$, which controls the size of the adjustment, is based on the extent to which the data deviate from a normal linear model for the regression of y_2 on y_1. Thus the correction may be reflecting real departures unrelated to the censoring process.

EXAMPLE 3: A straightforward generalization of the previous example is to replace the item y_1 which is observed for all units in the sample by a set of variables. Hausman and Spence (1977) derive the likelihood for this data pattern and apply ML estimation to data on economic characteristics of Canadian industries. Two partially observed items were chosen to demonstrate the model, an index of foreign control in Canadian industry, FSE, which is missing for 24 out of 84 industries; and the cost disadvantage of small firms, DCRC, which is missing for 13 out of 84 industries.

The regression of FSE on the following five regressors was required: the value added per establishment in the industry (VPE), the standard deviation of the value of shipments of firms in the industry (SSI), the proportion of shipments in the U.S. counterpart industry by the largest four enterprises in that industry (US467), the proportion of nonproduction workers in the industry (NPW), and average overhead labor costs in the industry (WNP). Unweighted least squares on the 60 complete units gave the following regression equation:

$$E(FSE) = -.696 - .092\,VPE - 1.13\,SSI + .097\,US\,467$$

$$+ .499\,NPW + .118\,WNP. \tag{31}$$

However, a priori the probability of nonresponse was expected to be inversely related to the value of FSE. Hence the ML procedure was applied. For the probit regression of r on X_1 all five regressor variables defined above were included together with a variable indicating whether the industry sold convenience goods (CON). This yielded the following equation for the regression of FSE:

$$E(FSE) = -.972 - .078\,VPE - .970\,SSI + .077\,US\,467$$

$$+ .704\,NPW + .144\,WNP. \tag{32}$$

Comparison of (31) and (32) indicates considerable differences in the estimated coefficients. Significantly, the predicted means for the 24 missing observations are even more divergent, the least squares equation predicting .2195 and the ML equation predicting .5724. This was consistent with the hypothesized pattern of nonresponse. Also, the estimated partial correlation $\rho_{23.1}$ between FSE and the unobserved nonresponse generator variable X_3 was 0.937, and the likelihood ratio test of the hypothesis $\rho_{23.1} = 0$ (or equivalently, $\beta_{32.13} = 0$) yielded a χ_1^2 deviate of 7.90, significant at the 1% level.

For the other response variable, CDRC, the probability of nonresponse was not expected to be strongly associated with the values of CDRC. The least squares regression of CDRC on SSI, NPW, and average assets per employee

(LAB2C) yielded the equation

$$E(\text{CDRC}) = 1.24 - 1.28\,\text{SSI} - .407\,\text{NPW} - .113\,\text{LAB2C}. \qquad (33)$$

The maximum likelihood procedure gave the alternative equation

$$E(\text{CDRC}) = 1.25 - .124\,\text{SSI} - .408\,\text{NPW} - .103\,\text{LAB2C}. \qquad (34)$$

Comparison of (33) and (34) reveals only slight differences. The predicted means of the missing observations are also close, .941 and 1.10, respectively. Finally, the likelihood ratio test of $\rho_{23.1} = 0$ yielded a χ_1^2 deviate of less than one, and hence there is no evidence of association between the CDRC and the response indicator function after the variables X_1 have been controlled.

The results of applying and estimating the Heckman model appear to accord with intuition in this example. Nevertheless, the sensitivity of the method to unverifiable assumptions, noted earlier for simple cases of the model, remains an issue. In one respect this example differs from earlier cases, namely, the regressions of the response indicator variable and of the dependent variable (FSE or CDRC) involve different sets of covariates. This in effect assumes that certain coefficients from the combined set of covariates are equal to zero in one of the two regressions. This assumption, if justified a priori, will reduce the sensitivity of the method to the other distributional assumptions.

The models discussed here assume a probit specification for the probability of response [cf. Eqs. (22) and (25)]. Other specifications are plausible. For example, Greenlees, Reece, and Zieschang (1982) fit a logit model for the probability of response to income data from the Current Population Survey.

3. NONIGNORABLE MECHANISMS FOR PARTIALLY CLASSIFIED CONTINGENCY TABLES

We have seen that for interval-scaled variables parameters of nonignorable response mechanisms can be estimated from the data, although "heroic assumptions" (to borrow a phrase from Carl Morris) are required. We now consider categorical variables with data in the form of a contingency table with partially classified observations. For the examples discussed in this section, the key parameters of a nonignorable mechanism (that is, parameters which modify the likelihood of the parameters of interest) cannot be estimated from the data; that is, their likelihood is flat. Hence to correct for nonresponse bias these parameters must be estimated from prior information, or uncertainty about them modeled by a prior distribution. The practical difficulties involved in such subjective methods have perhaps inhibited discussion of formal models for nonresponse bias in the literature. Hence the examples provided in this section represent preliminary incursions in largely unexplored territory.

Despite the difficulties, these models are valuable because they provide a framework for formalizing subjective notions about nonresponse bias, and evaluating the sensitivity of estimates to the levels of bias expected. They also ensure that the problems of nonresponse bias are in the open, rather than hidden in simplistic statements about response rates.

Examples 4 and 7 are rare examples in the literature which address the problems of nonresponse bias for categorical data from a formal model-based perspective. Example 5 is a more general formulation of the problem given in Example 7 which approaches estimation in terms of maximum likelihood estimation with the EM algorithm. A simple numerical illustration of the method is given in Example 6.

EXAMPLE 4: A NONIGNORABLE RESPONSE MECHANISM FOR NESTED CATEGORICAL DATA. Stene (1980) presents an example of a nonignorable mechanism for multinomial data, concerning congenital Down's syndrome or mongolism. Offspring can be classified as M (mongols) or P (phenotypically normal). Furthermore, offspring of type P can be classified as having normal chromosomes (N) or as translocation carriers (T). If one parent is type T and the other one is type N. the probabilities that an offspring is M, T or N are p, q, and r, respectively. That is

$$\text{pr}(M) = p, \quad \text{pr}(T) = q, \quad \text{pr}(N) = r, \quad \text{pr}(P) = q + r, \quad p + q + r = 1.$$

The data consist of n offspring. If these were all classified as M, T, or N, they would be regarded as a multinomial sample with probabilities, p, q, and r, and analysis would proceed according to standard theory. However, certain offspring are unclassified, and others are classified as P, but not further classified as T or N. The former are called *missing* observations, and the latter are called *mixed-up* observations.

Let μ and π be the conditional probabilities that individuals belonging to categories M and P, respectively, are classified as such. Let τ and υ be the conditional probabilities that an individual belonging to T and N, respectively, is classified as such, given that the individual is already classified as P. All classifications are assumed to be correct. Then the conditional probabilities of the two varieties of nonresponse are

$$\text{pr}(\text{missing}|M) = 1 - \mu, \quad \text{pr}(\text{missing}|P) = 1 - \pi;$$

$$\text{pr}(\text{mixed-up}|\text{classified } P, T) = 1 - \tau, \quad \text{pr}(\text{mixed-up}|\text{classified } P, N) = 1 - \upsilon.$$

Hence the response mechanism is ignorable if and only if $\mu = \pi$ and $\tau = \upsilon$. In this case we can proceed as in Section 3. The data are monotone with respect to the parametrization

$$p \text{ and } q' = q/(q + r),$$

where q' is the conditional probability of T given P. Thus the likelihood factors; p is estimated by the proportion of completely classified or mixed-up cases which are classified as M, and the likelihood factor q' is estimated by the proportion of cases completely classified and classified as P which are further classified as T.

If $\mu \neq \pi$ and $\tau \neq \upsilon$, then unique maximum likelihood estimates of p and q do not exist, and external information is required about the values of μ, π, τ, and υ.

An interesting aspect of this example is that the conditions for ignorability can be applied independently to the estimation of p and q'. That is, if $\mu = \pi$ but $\tau = \upsilon$, then p is still correctly estimated ignoring the nonresponse mechanism, but q' cannot be estimated without further information. On the other hand, if $\mu \neq \pi$ but $\tau = \upsilon$, then q' is correctly estimated ignoring the response mechanism, but the estimation of p requires further information. This intuitively sensible result is a direct result of the factorization of the likelihood for this monotone data pattern.

EXAMPLE 5:   PARTIALLY CLASSIFIED DATA.   This example presents a general solution of the problem of ML estimation for partially classified data with a nonignorable response mechanism. A reader discouraged by the heavy notation may wish to turn to the numerical illustration in Example 3.

(a)   *Data*   Suppose that N_s units are partially or completely classified by k categorical variables $y_1, \ldots, y_k$, so that y_{ij} is the level of variable y_j for unit i. Complete data for a unit are represented by the vector

$$\mathbf{y}_i = (y_{i1}, \ldots, y_{ik}),$$

which identifies the cell of the crosstabulation to which the unit belongs. Incomplete units are specified by the response indicator function

$$\mathbf{r}_i = (r_{i1}, \ldots, r_{ik}),$$

where r_{ij} takes values 1 or 0 according to where y_{ij} is observed or missing, respectively. The data for unit i consists of $\mathbf{r}_i$ and the values of observed variables $\{y_{ij} : r_{ij} = 1\}$.

(b)   *Model*   We suppose that $\mathbf{y}_1, \ldots, \mathbf{y}_N$ are independently distributed with probabilities given by

$$p(\mathbf{y}) = \Pi_{\mathbf{y}}, \qquad \sum_{\mathbf{y}} \Pi_{\mathbf{y}} = 1.$$

Thus given N_s, the data have a multinomial distribution with parameters $\boldsymbol{\theta} = \{\Pi_{\mathbf{y}}\}$. Suppose that given $\mathbf{y}_1, \ldots, \mathbf{y}_{N_s}$, the response indicators $\mathbf{r}_1, \ldots, \mathbf{r}_{N_s}$ are independently distributed with probabilities given by

$$p(\mathbf{r}|\mathbf{y}) = \phi_{\mathbf{r}|\mathbf{y}}, \qquad \sum_{\mathbf{r}} \phi_{\mathbf{r}|\mathbf{y}} = 1.$$

For the moment we shall describe ML estimation of $\Pi_{\mathbf{y}}$ under the assumption that $\{\phi_{\mathbf{r}|\mathbf{y}}\}$ is *known*.

(c) *ML estimation* We use the EM algorithm to derive ML estimates of $\theta = \{\Pi_y\}$. The complete data ML estimate of Π_y is simply

$$\hat{\Pi}_y = n_y/N_s, \tag{35}$$

where n_y is the number of units i with $y_i = y$.[2] The E step of the EM algorithm calculates for assumed values θ_a of the parameters the conditional mean

$$n_{ya} = E(n_y|\text{data}, \theta_a); \tag{36}$$

the M step calculates new estimates

$$\theta_b = \{\Pi_{yb}\}, \qquad \Pi_{yb} = n_{ya}/N_s.$$

To find n_{ya}, define for each vector y the set of units $\mathcal{M}_y$ which match with y on observed characteristics; that is,

$$\mathcal{M}_y = \{i: y_{ij} = y_{ij} \text{ if } r_{ij} = 1\}$$

Then n_{ya} can be expressed as a weighted sum of matching units,

$$n_{ya} = \sum_{i \in \mathcal{M}_y} p_i(y; \theta_a),$$

$$p_i(y; \theta_a) = p(y_i = y | r_i, i \in \mathcal{M}_y; \theta_a). \tag{37}$$

Note that completely observed units which match on y appear in this sum with weight $p_i(y; \theta_a)$ equal to one. Incomplete units which match on y are included with weights which are calculated by Bayes theorem:

$$p_i(y; \theta_a) = p(y_i = y | i \in \mathcal{M}_y; \theta_a)\phi_{r_i|y} / \sum_{y': i \in \mathcal{M}_{y'}} p(y_i = y' | i \in \mathcal{M}_{y'}; \theta_a)\phi_{r_i|y'} \tag{38}$$

An alternative form of (38) is in terms of the posterior odds that y_i is classified as y rather than y', for two elements y and y' with which the observed characteristics of y_i match:

$$\frac{p_i(y; \theta_a)}{p_i(y'; \theta_a)} = \left[\frac{p(y_i = y | i \in \mathcal{M}_y; \theta_a)}{p(y_i = y' | i \in \mathcal{M}_{y'}; \theta_a)}\right]\left[\frac{\phi_{r_i|y}}{\phi_{r_i|y'}}\right]. \tag{39}$$

That is, the posterior odds of y relative to y' are the product of the conditional odds that y_i matches with y rather than y' given the observed characteristics, with the relative probabilities of obtaining the response pattern r_i for the two matches, y and y'.

In practice the parameters $\{\phi_{r|y}\}$ are unknown, and the sensitive aspect of the method is the specification of the relative probabilities $\{\phi_{r_i|y}/\phi_{r_i|y'}\}$ required to evaluate the distribution (39) for partially classified units. Most discussions of partially classified data assume that the response mechanism is ignorable for

---

[2] We treat here the saturated model where the cell probabilities are unrestricted apart from the fact that they sum to one. For unsaturated models the M step is replaced by the appropriate complete data maximization.

likelihood inferences, which is equivalent to assuming that for all units the probability of response does not depend on missing items. That is,

$$\phi_{\mathbf{r}_i|\mathbf{y}} \text{ is independent of } \{y_{ij} : r_{ij} = 0\}.$$

In this case the second factor on the right-hand side of (39) is one for all $\mathbf{y}$ and $\mathbf{y}'$, and ML estimates can be obtained without further specification of the parameters $\{\phi_{\mathbf{r}_i|\mathbf{y}}\}$. Special cases of the resulting procedure are given in Examples 9 and 10 in Chapter 20.

An alternative assumption which models a simplified form of response bias is that responses are independently distributed across items, that is,

$$\phi_{\mathbf{r}|\mathbf{y}} = \prod_{j=1}^{k} \phi_{r_j|y_j}^{(j)}. \tag{40}$$

Then Eq. (39) reduces to

$$\frac{p_i(\mathbf{y}; \boldsymbol{\theta}_a)}{p_i(\mathbf{y}'; \boldsymbol{\theta}_a)} = \left[\frac{p(\mathbf{y}_i = \mathbf{y} | i \in \mathcal{M}_{\mathbf{y}}; \boldsymbol{\theta}_a)}{p(\mathbf{y}_i = \mathbf{y}' | i \in \mathcal{M}_{\mathbf{y}'}; \boldsymbol{\theta}_a)}\right] \left[\prod_{j:r_{ij}=0} \frac{\phi_{0|y_j}^{(j)}}{\phi_{0|y_j'}^{(j)}}\right]. \tag{41}$$

Hence the parameters $\{\phi_{\mathbf{r}|\mathbf{y}}\}$ enter the calculation only through the relative probabilities that y_j is missing given each value of y_j. For example, if y_j is a dichotomy with values 1 and 2, it is sufficient to specify for that variable the single number

$$\text{pr}(r_j = 0 | y_j = 1)/\text{pr}(r_j = 0 | y_j = 2) = \phi_{0|1}^{(j)}/\phi_{0|2}^{(j)}.$$

By substituting various assessments of the relative probabilities of response for each category, the impact of nonresponse on the final estimates can be assessed.

This formulation is adopted by Pregibon (1977) in an example previously encountered in Chapter 2, Section 3.3. Before outlining that application, we illustrate the algorithm with the 2×2 table previously analyzed in Example 10, Chapter 20, under the assumption that y_1 is twice as likely to be missing when $y_1 = 1$ than when $y_1 = 2$, and y_2 is twice as likely to be missing when $y_2 = 2$ than when $y_2 = 1$. That is, in the notation of Eq. (41),

$$\phi_{0|1}^{(1)}/\phi_{0|2}^{(1)} = 2, \quad \phi_{0|1}^{(2)}/\phi_{0|2}^{(2)} = .5.$$

EXAMPLE 6: A NUMERICAL ILLUSTRATION. TABLE 3A presents partially classified data as in Example 10, Chapter 20. Table 3B presents the steps of the EM algorithm.

The final estimates are

$$\hat{\theta}_{11} = .28, \qquad \hat{\theta}_{12} = .22, \qquad \hat{\theta}_{21} = .21, \qquad \hat{\theta}_{22} = .29.$$

These estimates may be compared with those obtained in Example 10, Chapter 20, assuming the response mechanism ignorable:

$$\hat{\theta}_{11} = .28, \qquad \hat{\theta}_{12} = .18, \qquad \hat{\theta}_{21} = .24, \qquad \hat{\theta}_{22} = .30.$$

Thus the effect of the redistribution of the partially classified observations is to bring closer together the estimates of $\hat{\theta}_{12}$ and $\hat{\theta}_{21}$.

EXAMPLE 7: (PREGIBON, 1977).   In a survey of poultry farms, data are available on r variables $x_1, \ldots, x_r$, where x_j is the count of a particular variety of

TABLE 3

The EM Algorithm for Data in Table 1, Assuming $y_1 = 1$ Is Twice as Likely to Be Missing as $y_1 = 2$ and $y_2 = 2$ Is Twice as Likely to Be Missing as $y_2 = 1$[a]

(a)   Data

(a) *Classified by y_1 and y_2*				(b) *Classified by y_1*		(c) *Classified by y_2*		
		y_2					y_2	
	1	2	Total			1	2	Total
y_1 1	100	50	150	y_1 1	30	28	60	88
2	75	75	150	2	60			
Total	175	125	300	Total	90			

(B) Successive steps of EM algorithm

	Estimated probabilities			*Fractional allocation of units*		
		y_2			y_2	
Step 1	1	2		1	2	
1	100/300	50/300	1	$100 + 15^a + 20.4^c$	$50 + 15^a + 34.3^d$	30^a
y_1			y_1			
2	75/300	75/300	2	$75 + 20^b + 7.6^c$	$75 + 40^b + 25.7^d$	60^b
				28^c	60^d	
Step 2	.28	.21		$100 + 12.2 + 20.3$	$50 + 17.7 + 35.1$	30
	.21	.29		$75 + 16.0 + 7.7$	$75 + 44.0 + 24.9$	60
				28	60	
Step 3	.28	.22				
	.21	.30				

[a] The superscripts in the top right-hand panel indicate the allocation of the partially classified margins among the cells of the table. For example, of the 28 units with $y_2 = 1$ (superscript c), 20.4 are allocated to $y_1 = 1$ and 7.6 are allocated to $y_1 = 2$.

poultry. Values of x_j are missing for some farms. A value zero implies that variety is not farmed, and is considered to have special significance. Accordingly a binary variable y_j is formed, taking value one if the variety is farmed ($x_j > 0$) and zero otherwise ($x_j = 0$). The set of joint levels of $y_1, \ldots, y_r$ forms a 2^r-contingency table, in which farms with values of x_j missing are partially classified. Analysis proceeds in two stages. First, partially classified farms are classified in a cell of the 2^r-table, a procedure which corresponds to imputing zero or one for each missing y_j. Second, in each cell of the filled-in 2^r-table the mean values of items which are farmed are estimated, with missing counts for the incomplete observations filled in by regression. We shall concentrate on the first part of the analysis.

The classification of incomplete observations is based only on the values of $y_1, \ldots, y_r$, and does not involve the known counts x_j. Hence the data used for classification purposes are a special case of the previous example, where all the categorical variables y_j are binary. Classification is achieved by first calculating for each incomplete observation the conditional probability of belonging to cells which match on observed characteristics, as given in Eq. (40). Then the incomplete observation is randomly classified to a cell according to this distribution.

In order to calculate the probabilities in (40), the relative probability of nonresponse for farms with $y_j = 1$ and $y_j = 0$ has to be assessed, for each j. Also an estimate θ_a of $\theta = \{\Pi_y\}$ is required. Pregibon estimates Π_y as the proportion of completely classified observations in the cell with values $\mathbf{y}$. However, this quantity estimates the probability of $\mathbf{y}$ *given that $\mathbf{y}$ is completely observed*, which is not equal to Π_y unless the response mechanism is ignorable for sampling inferences. Hence the resulting estimates are inconsistent. A better procedure is to calculate the ML estimate $\hat{\theta}$ by the EM algorithm, and substitute $\theta_a = \hat{\theta}$ in Eq. (40) to derive the classification probabilities.

4. A PREDICTIVE BAYESIAN APPROACH TO RESPONSE BIAS

An alternative approach to nonresponse bias, proposed by Rubin (1977), is to model the distribution of nonrespondents and respondents with separate parameters, and relate the parameters by a suitable Bayesian prior distribution. The influence of non-response is assessed by a probability interval based on the predictive distribution of the hypothetical complete data statistic given the responding values. The basic idea is contained in the following simple example. The more general case given by Rubin is presented in Example 9.

EXAMPLE 8: In a simple random sample of n units on a variable Y, a proportion p are nonrespondents. The summary statistic of interest is the average value of Y in the sample, which can be expressed as

$$\bar{y} = (1 - p)\bar{y}_\mathrm{R} + p\bar{y}_\mathrm{NR},$$

where $\bar{y}_\mathrm{R}$ is the observed mean of respondents and $\bar{y}_\mathrm{NR}$ is the unobserved mean for nonrespondents. Suppose that values of Y for respondents are normally distributed with mean α_R and variance σ_R^2, and for nonrespondents are normally distributed with mean α_NR and variance σ_NR^2. For simplicity we assume initially that the variances are equal and known, that is, $\sigma_\mathrm{R}^2 = \sigma_\mathrm{NR}^2 = \sigma^2$, and known. Also the respondent and non-respondent values are independent, given α_R, α_NR and σ^2. Hence

$$(\bar{y}_\mathrm{R}|\alpha_\mathrm{R},\sigma^2) \sim N(\alpha_\mathrm{R},\sigma^2/(n - np)), \qquad (\bar{y}_\mathrm{NR}|\alpha_\mathrm{NR},\sigma^2) \sim N(\alpha_\mathrm{NR},\sigma^2/(np)),$$

where $N(\alpha,\sigma^2)$ is the normal distribution with mean α, variance σ^2. Subjective prior notions about the similarity of respondents and nonrespondents are formalized by specifying a prior distribution for α_NR given α_R and σ^2. For the application discussed by Rubin, the normal prior

$$(\alpha_\mathrm{NR}|\alpha_\mathrm{R},\sigma^2) \sim N(\alpha_\mathrm{R},\theta_2^2\alpha_\mathrm{R}^2),$$

for a selected value of θ_2, was considered appropriate. The mean of this distribution, α_R, implies that there is no a priori reason to expect respondents and nonrespondents to differ in expectation. The quantity θ_2 measures the subjective coefficient of variation for the nonrespondents' mean. In particular, it implies that the investigator is 95% sure that nonrespondent mean will fall in the interval

$$\alpha_\mathrm{R}(1 \pm 2\theta_2).$$

If $\theta_2 = 0$, then the distributions of Y for respondents and nonrespondents are equal, and the response mechanism is ignorable.

The impact of nonresponse is assessed by the predictive distribution of $\bar{y}$ given $\bar{y}_\mathrm{R}$ and θ^2, which can be readily shown to be normal with mean $\bar{y}_\mathrm{R}$ and variance

$$\mathrm{Var}(\bar{y}|\bar{y}_\mathrm{R},\theta^2) = p^2\,\mathrm{Var}(\bar{y}_\mathrm{NR}|\bar{y}_\mathrm{R},\sigma^2)$$

$$= p^2\,\mathrm{Var}(\alpha_\mathrm{R}|\bar{y}_\mathrm{R}) + p^2 E\{\mathrm{Var}(\bar{y}_\mathrm{NR}|\alpha_\mathrm{NR})\} + p^2 E\{\mathrm{Var}(\alpha_\mathrm{NR}|\alpha_\mathrm{R})\},$$

where the expectations are over the posterior distribution of α_R given $\bar{y}_\mathrm{R},\sigma^2$. The last term in this equation is independent of the sample size and reflects the uncertainty in the "nonignorable" component of the model. Assuming a flat prior for α_R and substituting for the prior variance of α_NR given α_R and σ^2, we obtain

$$\mathrm{Var}(\bar{y}|\bar{y}_\mathrm{R},\sigma^2) = p^2\{\sigma^2/(np) + \sigma^2/(n - np) + \theta_2^2(\bar{y}_\mathrm{R}^2 + \sigma^2/(n - np))\}$$

$$= p^2\{\sigma^2/(np - np^2) + \theta_2^2(\bar{y}_\mathrm{R}^2 + \sigma^2/(n - np))\}.$$

Hence a subjective probability interval for $\bar{y}$ given $\bar{y}_\mathrm{R}$ and σ^2 is

$$\bar{y}_\mathrm{R} \pm z\sqrt{\mathrm{Var}(\bar{y}|\bar{y}_\mathrm{R},\sigma^2)} = \bar{y}_\mathrm{R} \pm zp\{\sigma^2/(np - np^2) + \theta_2^2(\bar{y}_\mathrm{R}^2 + \sigma^2/(n - np))\}^{1/2},$$

where z is a standard normal deviate. This equation corresponds to Eq. (2.1) of Rubin's paper with $\overline{X}_{NR} = \overline{X}_R, \theta_1 = 0$. The probability of the interval is determined by substituting the appropriate value of z; thus for a probability of 0.95 the value $z = 1.96$ is substituted.

Note that for large n the width of this interval is approximately $zp\theta_2\bar{y}_R$, which is proportional to θ_2 and the proportion of missing values and does not depend on the sample size n. This represents the uncertainty introduced in the non-ignorable component of the model. Expressed as a proportion of the mean, it is obtained by multiplying the prior estimate of θ_2 by z (say, 2.0) and the proportion of missing values.

EXAMPLE 9: A significant development of the previous example is to include q covariates $X = (X_1, \ldots, X_q)$, available for all units in the sample. If Y is linearly related to X in both respondent and nonrespondent populations, we have for the expected values

$$E(\bar{y}_R) = \alpha_R + \beta_R^T \overline{X}_R, \qquad \text{Var}(\bar{y}_R) = \sigma_R^2/(n - np),$$

$$E(\bar{y}_{NR}) = \alpha_{NR} + \beta_{NR}^T \overline{X}_{NR}, \qquad \text{Var}(\bar{y}_{NR}) = \sigma_{NR}^2/(np),$$

where T denotes matrix transpose, $\overline{X}_R$ and $\overline{X}_{NR}$ are the observed means of X in the sample, and α_R, α_{NR}, β_R, and β_{NR} are unknown parameters. To relate the nonrespondent parameters to those of the respondent we assume that conditional on the respondent parameters, the nonrespondent parameters have priors

$$\beta_{NR} \sim N_q(\beta_R, \theta_1^2 \beta_R \beta_R^T),$$

$$\phi_{NR} \sim N(\phi_R, \theta_2^2 \phi_R^2),$$

where $N_q(a, \mathbf{B})$ is the q-variate normal distribution with mean a and covariance matrix $\mathbf{B}$, and $\phi_{NR} = \alpha_{NR} + \beta_{NR}^T \overline{X}_R$, $\phi_R = \alpha_R + \beta_R^T \overline{X}_R$ are parameters representing the adjusted means at $X = \overline{X}_R$ in the nonrespondent and respondent populations. The parameter θ_1 measures a priori uncertainty about the regression coefficients. Writing $\beta_R^{(i)}$ and $\beta_{NR}^{(i)}$ for ith components of β_R and β_{NR}, respectively, the prior implies that the investigator is 95% sure that $\beta_{NR}^{(i)}$ will fall in the interval

$$\beta_R^{(i)} (1 \pm 2\theta_1),$$

for all i. The parameter θ_2 measures uncertainty in the adjusted mean, and corresponds to θ_2 in Example 5 for the case of no covariates. The response mechanism is ignorable for likelihood based inferences if $\theta_1 = \theta_2 = 0$.

Assuming flat prior distributions for ϕ_R and β_R, a subjective probability interval for $\bar{y}$ given the data takes the form

$$\bar{y}_R [1 + h_0 \pm z(\theta_1^2 h_1^2 + \theta^2{}_2 h_2^2 + h_3^2)^{1/2}],$$

where

$$h_0 = pb_R^T(\bar{X}_{NR} - \bar{X}_R)/\bar{y}_R,$$

$$h_1^2 = h_0^2 + (p^2 s_R^2/\bar{y}_R^2)(\bar{X}_{NR} - \bar{X}_R)^T S_{xx}^{-1}(\bar{X}_{NR} - \bar{X}_R),$$

$$h_2^2 = p^2[1 + s_R^2/\{\bar{y}_R^2 n(1 - p)\}],$$

$$h_2^2 = p^2(s_R^2/\bar{y}_R^2)[1/(np - np^2) + (\bar{X}_{NR} - \bar{X}_R)^T S_{xx}^{-1}(\bar{X}_{NR} - \bar{X}_R)].$$

Here b_R and s_R^2 are the slopes and residual variance from the least squares regression of y_R on X_R, and S_{xx} is the sum of squared and cross-products matrix of X for respondents. In particular, the predicted mean is

$$\bar{y}_R(1 + h_0) = \bar{y}_R = pb_R(\bar{X}_{NR} - \bar{X}_R);$$

the last term represents the covariance adjustment for differences in the means of X in the nonrespondent and respondent populations. The width of the interval,

$$\bar{y}z(\theta_1^2 h_1^2 + \theta_2^2 h_2^2 + h_3^2)^{1/2},$$

involves three components. The first, $\theta_1^2 h_1^2$, is the relative covariance due to uncertainty about the equality of the slopes of y on X in the respondent and nonrespondent groups. The term $\theta_2^2 h_2^2$ reflects uncertainty about the equality of the adjusted means for respondents and nonrespondents. The term h_3^2 represents uncertainty introduced by nonresponse which is present even when the respondent and nonrespondent distributions are equal, that is $\theta_1 = \theta_2 = 0$, and the response mechanism is ignorable.

It is instructive to let the responding sample size tend to infinity. The component h_3^2 tends to zero, and the width of the interval becomes $zp\bar{y}_R\{\theta_2^2 + \theta_1^2[b_R^T(\bar{X}_{NR} - \bar{X}_R)/\bar{y}_R]^2\}^{1/2}$, compared with $zp\bar{y}_R\theta_2$ in the previous example. The fact that the interval is apparently larger when covariates are introduced seems contradictory, since the covariance adjustment should reduce uncertainty in the prediction of $\bar{y}$. However, the subjective parameter θ_2 is *not* comparable in the two examples. The covariate adjustment should reduce the differences between the nonrespondent and respondent populations, and this should be reflected in the priors by a smaller value of θ_2 in this example than in Example 8. An unfortunate (but realistic) characteristic of the model is that it does not assess the improvement in prediction achieved by the introduction of covariates, since this depends on the relative sizes of θ_2 in Example 8 and θ_1 and θ_2 in this example, quantities which are assessed without looking at the data.

Rubin illustrates the method with data from a survey of 660 schools, 472 of which filled out a compensatory reading questionnaire consisting of 80 items. Twenty-one dependent variables (y) and 35 background variables (X) were selected.

The dependent variables in the study measured characteristics of compensatory reading in the form of frequency with which they were present, and were scaled to lie between zero (never) and one (always). The restricted scale creates problems for variables with means at the extreme ends of the scale, and consequently we focus attention on seven variables in the middle of the range. The dependent variables chosen here are as follows:

17B: Compensatory reading carried out during school hours released from other classwork

18A: Compensatory reading carried out during time released from social studies, science, and/or foreign language

18B: Compensatory reading carried out during time released from mathematics

23A: Frequency of organizing compensatory reading class into groups by reading grade level

23C: Frequency of organizing compensatory reading class into groups by shared interests

32A: Compensatory reading teaches textbooks other than basal readers

320: Compensatory reading teaches teacher prepared materials

Background variables recorded for respondents and nonrespondents in the study were as follows:

1. Any Title I money
2. Minority race percentage
3. Urbanization code
4. Zip code area income
5. County median income
6. Any compensatory reading program
7. Any Title I money for compensatory reading programs
8. Enrollment
9–14. Parental occupation items
15–17. Percentage of students reading below grade levels
18–22. Parental education items
23. Any other monetary assistance
24–29. Parental race items
30–34. Parental income items
35. Number of rooms in school

Table 4 presents summary statistics $\bar{y}_R$, R^2 (the squared multiple correlation) between Y and X for respondents, h_0, h_1, h_2, and h_3. The values of h_0 represent the proportional adjustments to the means based on the regression on X. These are generally small, although for variable 18B the mean is increased by 6%, suggesting that nonrespondents carry out compensatory reading during time released from mathematics more often than respondents.

The values of h_1, h_2, and h_3 determine the contributions $\theta_1^2 h_1^2$, $\theta_2^2 h_2^2$, and h_3^2 to the squared width of the probability interval. The width of the 95% interval expressed as a percentage of the mean is tabulated in Table 5. The low values

TABLE 4

Summary Statistics for Seven Dependent Variables from School Survey

Variable[a]	$\bar{y}_R$	R^2	h_0	h_1	h_2	h_3
17B	.39322	.54763	.02096	.02647	.28549	.02786
18A	.23132	.54378	.00080	.02300	.28615	.03961
18B	.09067	.53405	.06331	.07749	.28974	.07701
23A	.65796	.54942	.00814	.01020	.28494	.01060
23C	.45240	.59361	.00368	.00679	.28492	.00983
32A	.33968	.66787	.00190	.00394	.28487	.00596
32D	.41489	.57689	.00130	.00334	.28487	.00531

[a] For a description of the variables and the statistics, see text.

of h_1 imply that uncertainty about equality of the slopes of the regressions for respondents and nonrespondents, modeled by the quantity θ_1, has a negligible impact on the interval. The values of h_2 are only marginally greater than the proportion of missing values, $p = .2848$. Thus the contribution to the interval width of uncertainty about equality of the adjusted means in the respondent and nonrespondent populations is represented by $zh_2\theta_2 \simeq zp\theta_2 = .57\theta_2$.

This quantity has a major impact on the interval widths. For example, the effect of increasing the value of θ_2 from 0 to .1 is to triple the interval widths in variables 23A and 23C and to increase the interval widths in variables 32A and 32D by a factor of five. On the other hand, for variables 17B, 18A, and, in particular, 18B the component attributable to residual variance from the regression h_3 is more pronounced, although the other component is still nonnegligible for $\theta_2 \geq .1$. The example illustrates dramatically the potential impact of response bias, and the extent to which it is dependent on quantities (such as θ_1) which cannot be reliably estimated from the data.

TABLE 5

Widths of Subjective 95% intervals of $\bar{y}$ as Percentages of $\bar{y}_R$

| Variable | $\theta_1 = 0$ | | | | $\theta_1 = .4$ | | | |
	$\theta_2 = 0$	$\theta_2 = .1$	$\theta_2 = .2$	$\theta_2 = .4$	$\theta_2 = 0$	$\theta_2 = .1$	$\theta_2 = .2$	$\theta_2 = .4$
17B	5.6	8.0	12.7	23.7	6.0	8.3	12.9	23.6
18A	7.9	9.8	13.9	24.2	8.1	9.9	14.0	24.3
18B	15.4	16.5	19.3	27.8	16.6	17.6	20.2	28.5
23A	2.1	6.1	11.6	22.9	2.3	6.1	11.6	22.9
23C	2.0	6.0	11.6	22.9	2.0	6.1	11.6	22.9
32A	1.2	5.8	11.5	22.8	1.2	5.8	11.5	22.8
32D	1.1	5.8	11.4	22.8	1.1	5.8	11.4	22.8

REFERENCES

Blight, B. J. N. (1970). Estimation from a censored sample for the exponential family. *Biometrika* 57: 389–395.

Cox, D. R. (1972). Regression models and life tables. *Journal of the Royal Statistical Society*, Series B, 34(2): 187–220.

Dempster, A. P., Laird, N. M., and Rubin, D. B. (1977). Maximum likelihood from incomplete data via the EM algorithm (with discussion). *Journal of the Royal Statistical Society*, Series B, 39(1): 1–38.

Eklund, G. (1960). *Studies of Selection Bias in Applied Statistics*. Uppsala: Almquist and Wiksells.

Glasser, M. (1967). Exponential survival with covariance. *Journal of the American Statistical Association* 62: 561–568.

Greenlees, J. S., Reece, W. S., and Zieschang, K. D. (1982). Imputation of missing values when the probability of response depends on the variable being imputed. *Journal of the American Statistical Association* 77: 251–261.

Hausman, J. A., and Spence, A. M. (1977). Non-random missing data. Working Paper, Department of Economics, Massachusetts Institute of Technology, Cambridge, Massachusetts.

Heckman, J. J. (1976). The common structure of statistical models of truncation, sample selection and limited dependent variables and a simple estimator for such models. *Annals of Economic and Social Measurement* 5: 475–492.

Kaplan, E. L., and Meier, P. (1958). Nonparametric estimation from incomplete observations. *Journal of the American Statistical Association* 53: 457–481.

Kulldorf, G. (1961). *Estimation from Grouped and Partially Grouped Samples*. Stockholm: Almquist and Wiksell.

Little, R. J. A. (1982). Models for nonresponse in sample surveys. *Journal of the American Statistical Association* 77: 237–250.

Morrison, D. F. (1971). Expectations and variances of maximum likelihood for the multivariate normal distribution parameters with missing data. *Journal of the American Statistical Association* 66: 602–604.

Nelson, F. D. (1977). Censored regression models with unobserved, stochastic censoring thresholds. *Journal of Econometrics* 6: 581–592.

Pregibon, D. (1977). Typical survey data: Estimation and imputation. *Survey Methodology* 2: 70–102.

Rubin, D. B. (1976). Inference and missing data. *Biometrika* 63: 581–592.

Rubin, D. B. (1977). Formalizing subjective notions about the effect of nonrespondents in sample surveys. *Journal of the American Statistical Association* 72: 538–543.

Stene, J. (1980). Multinomial Sampling with Partially Classified Data. Unpublished manuscript. Institute of Statistics, University of Copenhagen.

Tobin, J. (1958). Estimation of Relationships for Limited Dependent Variables. *Econometrica* 26: 24–36.

PART VII

Bibliographies

Selected Annotated Bibliography

Larry V. Hedges
Ingram Olkin

INTRODUCTION

Early in the study on incomplete data it was decided that a bibliography of published papers in this subject would add to the usefulness of the project. Together with the theory and case study volume, (Volume 1), and the symposium (Volume 3), a bibliography would provide historical perspective and a way for the reader to pinpoint some of the ideas and techniques in the literature. However, a bibliography per se, though useful, does not provide a guide as to content. Several alternatives that would provide more information were considered. Two such alternatives are placing each paper into a set of categories or giving key words and phrases.

It was decided that a more useful guide would be to provide a summary of each paper. In addition, key words and phrases were prepared for each paper and they are listed in a subject index. Consequently, a reader can now look in a subject index for, say, "Nonresponse, adjustment for" and find those papers in the bibliography that deal with this subject.

The choice of the papers came about in an interactive manner. Each member of the panel was asked to list papers of import. Others were added to create a somewhat expanded list. The panel then reviewed the list, suggested emendations, until finally the present set was obtained. It should be noted that the final list is not exhaustive. Rather it contains papers that are of import to the practitioner. There are indeed many other papers dealing with surveys that have not been included.

417

INCOMPLETE DATA
IN SAMPLE SURVEYS
Volume 2, Part VII

Finally, we wish to acknowledge the help of the many students who had a part in the project. In particular, we have a special debt to Carol Tanimoto for her aid in the myriad of details in such a project. We are grateful to Peggy Bander, Ivy Kramer, and Jerri Rudnick for their patience and typing skills.

Afifi, A. A., and Elashoff, R. M. (1966). Missing observations in multivariate statistics. I: Review of the literature. *Journal of the American Statistical Association* 61: 595–604.

This paper provides a survey of methods dealing with missing observations in a regression context. The focus is on the method of least squares and the method of maximum likelihood.

The underlying model is

$$y = v + X\beta + e,$$

where y, v, and e are n-dimensional column vectors, X is an $n \times p$ design matrix, and β is a p-dimensional column vector.

The vector v has identical elements each equal to $\mu_y - \mu_1\beta_1 - \cdots - \mu_p\beta_p$. The random variables $e_1, \ldots, e_n$ have means 0, common variances σ^2, are mutually independent, and are independent of X. Further, it is assumed that all the parameters are estimable.

A brief description of the papers and methods reviewed follows; the specific references are given in the paper by Afifi and Elashoff.

For the method of least squares, papers by Yates (1933), Bartlett (1937), Tocher (1952), and Wilkinson (1958) are discussed. Basically the concern is with estimating the missing observations by least squares. One of the problems noted is computational, and some consideration is given to this aspect. It is noted that computer programs are available that produce least squares estimates.

Distributional aspects of least squares estimates is considered in papers by Pearson (1926) and Srivastava (1960). A subsequent paper by Afifi and Elashoff provides some improvements, especially when the number of complete observations is small relative to the total number of observations.

A variant of least squares in which imputed values for the missing observations are used is then discussed. This method apparently originated with Wilks (1932). Papers by Dear (1959), Matthai (1951), Glasser (1964), and Buck (1960) are discussed in some detail.

The method of maximum likelihood is centered about the normal distribution. In this case papers by Wilks (1932), Edgett (1956), Nicholson (1957),

Anderson (1957), Bhargava (1962), and Trawinski and Bargmann (1964) are reviewed.

Anderson, T. W. (1957). Maximum likelihood estimates for a multivariate normal distribution when some observations are missing. *Journal of the American Statistical Association* 52: 200–203.

The key feature of this paper is to show that maximum likelihood estimates of the parameters of a bivariate normal distribution can be obtained by a conditioning argument.

More specifically suppose that (x_i, y_i), $i = 1, \ldots, n$, are observed from a bivariate normal distribution with means μ_x, μ_y, variances σ_x^2, σ_y^2, and correlation ρ. In addition, $N - n$ observations $x_{n+1}, \ldots, x_N$ are made on x alone. The main point then is to write the joint density of x and y as

$$N(x, y \,|\, \mu_x, \mu_y; \sigma_x^2, \sigma_y^2; \rho) = N(x \,|\, \mu_x, \sigma_x^2) N(y \,|\, v + \beta_{yx} x, \sigma_{y \cdot x}^2), \tag{1}$$

where

$$v = \mu_y - \beta_{yx} \mu_x, \qquad \beta_{yx} = \rho \sigma_y / \sigma_x, \qquad \sigma_{y \cdot x}^2 = \sigma_y^2 (1 - \rho^2).$$

Thus, finding the maximum likelihood estimate of $(\mu_x, \mu_y, \sigma_x^2, \sigma_y^2, \rho)$ is equivalent to finding the maximum likelihood estimate of $(\mu_x, v, \sigma_x^2, \sigma_{y \cdot x}^2, \beta_{yx})$. But the latter can be obtained directly from the representation (1).

A trivariate model in which we observe

$$w_1, \ldots, w_n, \qquad w_{n+1}, \ldots, w_N,$$

$$x_1, \ldots, x_n, \qquad x_{n+1}, \ldots, x_N,$$

$$y_1, \ldots, y_n$$

can be treated in a similar manner. Now the reparameterization is obtained from the conditioning

$$\prod_{\alpha=1}^{n} N(w_\alpha, x_\alpha, y_\alpha \,|\, \mu_w, \mu_x, \mu_y; \sigma_w^2, \sigma_x^2, \sigma_y^2; \rho_{wx}, \rho_{wy}, \rho_{xy})$$

$$= \prod_{\alpha=1}^{n} N(w_\alpha, x_\alpha \,|\, \mu_w, \mu_x; \sigma_w^2, \sigma_x^2; \rho_{wx})$$

$$= \prod_{\alpha=1}^{N} N(w_\alpha, x_\alpha \,|\, \mu_w, \mu_x; \sigma_w^2, \sigma_x^2; \rho_{wx}) \prod_{\alpha=1}^{n} N(y_\alpha \,|\, v + \beta_{yw \cdot x} w_\alpha + \beta_{yx \cdot w} x_\alpha, \sigma_{y \cdot wx}).$$

Two other trivariate models are analyzed by using a conditioning argument. The patterns are

$$x_1, \ldots, x_n, \qquad x_{n+1}, \ldots, x_N,$$

$$y_1, \ldots, y_n, \qquad z_{n+1}, \ldots, z_N$$

and

$$x_1, \ldots, x_n, \qquad x_{n+1}, \ldots, x_{n+m}, \qquad x_{n+m+1}, \ldots, x_N,$$

$$y_1, \ldots, y_n, \qquad y_{n+1}, \ldots, y_{n+m},$$

$$z_1, \ldots, z_n.$$

Particular patterns of missing observations for higher-dimensional samples where the conditioning procedure yields maximum likelihood estimates are discussed.

Bailar, J. C. III, and Bailar, B. A. (1978). Comparison of two procedures for imputing missing survey values, *Proceedings of the Section on Survey Research Methods*, American Statistical Association, pp. 462–467.

Survey data can be viewed as a matrix in which columns correspond to sample cases and rows to survey items. To reduce the effects of item nonresponse, functions of the sample values for other items in the same column, same row, or in both may be imputed for missing values. The widely used hot-deck procedures and the equal-weights procedure, which requires the mean for a subgroup or an adjustment cell to serve as the imputed value, are included in the class of imputation techniques. This paper presents a theoretical basis upon which to compare the first two moments of the estimated row means for the two techniques.

Assume (a) a fixed sample size n, (b) a fixed number m of nonrespondents, and (c) that whether an item is missing is independent of its value; then the estimator of the mean for a particular survey item can be easily shown to be unbiased for both procedures. However, the relation between the variances of the respective estimators relies upon the correlation structure within the rows of the matrix and the position of the missing values. When, in addition to satisfying the above conditions, the elements of the data matrix are independent and identically distributed, it is algebraically shown that except for the trivial cases, the variance of the equal weights procedure is smaller than that of the hot-deck approach. When the assumption of independence and identical distribution is replaced by the assumption of a serial correlation structure, the ratio of the asymptotic variances of the two procedures is derived to permit an objective comparison in a variety of situations. Finally, a minimum variance weights procedure for an arbitrary covariance structure is discussed.

Bailar, B. A., Bailey, L., and Corby, C. (1978). A comparison of some adjustment and weighting
    procedures for survey data. In *Survey Sampling and Measurement*, K. Namboodiri (ed.), pp.
    175–198. New York: Academic Press.

Because of possible biases in collected survey data, an adjustment procedure
to reduce their effect may become necessary. Unit and item nonresponse are
two common sources of such biases. Data adjustment techniques may range
from substitution of other households or persons for missing households or
persons, to regression techniques, to reweighting of the sample cases.

This paper gives a brief description of techniques for sampling in the
household surveys conducted by the Bureau of the Census. A more detailed
description of the Current Population Survey (CPS), the survey on which other
household surveys are patterned, is provided. Included in the description is a
discussion of the CPS estimation process, with special emphasis on adjustment
for nonresponse and undercoverage.

Some theoretical results are given for the comparison of variances for two
methods of imputing for item nonresponse. One method is imputing the sample
mean for a subgroup; the other method is the imputation of a value from a
"close" record.

Finally, a research project underway at the Bureau of the Census is described.
In this project, a comparison of four alternative strategies for adjusting data will
be made with a consideration of costs, complexity, and accuracy. These methods
are: (A) an adaptation of the current procedure, (B) a raking procedure, (C) a
double-sampling procedure, (D) a "no-adjustment" procedure.

Banks, M. J. (1977). A indication of the effect of noninterview adjustment and post-stratification
    on estimates from a sample survey. *Proceedings of the Social Statistics Section*, American
    Statistical Association, pp. 291–295.

Using data from a national survey of medical care use in 1970, the investigation concentrates on (a) adjustments for nonresponse and (b) poststratification
adjustment. Both procedures assume that respondents and nonrespondents
within the same category tend to have the same characteristics. Consequently,
the overall results differ because of different choices of categories. In one
method categories are created by geographic location. The other method uses
information about the reason that no interview was obtained.

The survey itself consists of 11,619 persons in 3,880 households; the data are
results of an interview about the use and cost of health care.

Comparisons are made for four methods: (A) unadjusted, (B) adjusted using
external data, (C) adjusted using geographic information, (D) adjusted using
reason no interview given. For the data shown in the example there was little
difference in the results.

Two poststratification procedures are compared. In each the adjustment of the data is according to the Current Population Survey distribution of households. The first uses race, residence, size, and income; the second uses race, sex, and age. There was some difference in the results between using and not using poststratification, but little difference in the two poststratification methods.

Bartholomew, D. J. (1961). A method of allowing for 'not-at-home' bias in sample surveys. *Applied Statistics* 10: 52–59.

Different sources of bias can occur in surveys conducted by interviewers calling at the homes of respondents. Moser (1958) has distinguished six different sources. The concern in the present paper is with a bias that may result from the respondent being out at the time of the call. Although callbacks help eliminate this bias, these increase the cost and delay the completion of the survey. Thus it would be helpful to have a method for reducing "not-at-home" bias without repeated callbacks.

The essential feature in this paper is to obtain unbiased estimates with only two calls. The assumption made is that essentially all the bias occurs at the first call.

In estimating the proportion in a given class, let the sample be of size N, with N_1 respondents, at the first call, of whom n_1 belong to the given class. In the first call, the interviewer tries to find out from other inhabitants or neighbors when the interviewee is likely to be at home. In the second call, n_2 are in the class out of N_2, which may differ from $N - N_1$. If there is no bias at the second call, an unbiased estimate of the proportion in the class is

$$\hat{P} = \frac{1}{N}\left(n_1 + \frac{n_2(N - N_1)}{N_2}\right).$$

Let $P_r = n_2/N_2$. Then

$$\text{Var}(\hat{P}) = \left(1 - \frac{N_1}{N}\right)^2 \text{Var}(P_r),$$

of which is an unbiased sample estimate is

$$\left(1 - \frac{N_1}{N}\right)^2 \frac{(N - N_1 - N_2)}{(N - N_1 - 1)} \frac{P_r(1 - P_r)}{N_2}.$$

For estimating a mean, let the mean at the first call be a/N_1 and the mean at the second call (assumed essentially random) be b/N_2. Then the estimated mean of the sample is

$$\hat{\mu}_1 = \frac{a}{N} + \left(1 - \frac{N_1}{N}\right)\frac{b}{N_2}.$$

To test whether it is true that most of the bias occurs at the first call, the author takes as his variate the proportion of men, who are known for the whole sample by their Christian names. For four local government surveys the estimated percentages of men in the sample by his method are 49.5, 47.5, 50.8, and 52.3, as against percentages of 52.2, 48.5, 49.6, and 52.3 for the whole sample. In a larger survey by Edwards (1953) the estimated percentage of men by his method was 43.0, as against 43.6 for the whole sample. Thus for this variate at least, the assumption appears to be correct.

Beale, E. M. L., and Little, R. J. A. (1975). Missing values in multivariate analysis. *Journal of the Royal Statistical Society*, Series B, 37: 129–146.

The problem of finding maximum likelihood estimates for the parameters of a multivariate distribution when there are missing observations presents considerable computational difficulty. The concern in this paper is with computational aspects of alternative estimation procedures in multivariate data with missing observations. More specifically, the paper recommends an algorithm due to Orchard and Woodbury (1972), which gives the maximum likelihood estimator in the case of the multivariate normal distribution.

A simulation study is carried out in which six estimators are compared. The data is artificially generated from multivariate normal populations for which missing data is obtained by random deletions. The estimators are

(1)   Ordinary least squares using complete observations only
(2)   An iterative procedure due to Buck (1960)
(3)   A corrected maximum likelihood estimator
(4)   A method that estimates the means, variances, and covariances of the independent variables only by corrected maximum likelihood, uses these to fit missing values of the independent variables, and then uses ordinary least squares on all observations for which the dependent variable is present
(5)   A variant of method (4) in which incomplete observations are given reduced weights
(6)   A combination of methods (3) and (5)

The paper provides a discussion of the missing information principle and a derivation using an approach due to Buck (1960). The idea here is to use complete observations to estimate the means of all the variables and also the covariance matrix. These values are then used to estimate any missing quantities as linear functions of the variables known for this observation.

Based on a simulation the following results were obtained: Methods 2 and 3 consistently beat method 1. Method 3 requires more computing than method 2 and improves on method 2 except for some marginal cases. Method 4 is not recommended. Method 5 is an improvement on method 4, but is less effective than method 3. Method 6 is an improvement on method 5. Thus the two finalist methods are method 6 and method 3. These are quite comparable with each having some virtues.

An analysis of school examination data is provided as an application of the methods.

Birnbaum, Z. W., and Sirken, M. G. (1950). Bias due to non-availability in sample surveys. *Journal of the American Statistical Association* 45: 98–111.

There are a variety of sources of errors in sample surveys. One such is the nonavailability of respondents, which is the focus of this paper.

Consider a population in which an individual, once available, will respond "yes" or "no" to a single question. For a population of size N we introduce the notation

	Response Yes	No	
Available	N_{11}	N_{10}	$N_{1.}$
Nonavailable	N_{01}	N_{00}	$N_{0.}$
	$N_{.1}$	$N_{.0}$	

The purpose of the survey is to estimate $p_{.1} = N_{.1}/N$, the proportion in the population responding yes. The bias b is defined as

$$b = p' - p_{.1},$$

where $p' = N_{11}/N_{1.}$ is the proportion of those responding "yes" among those who are available.

For a sample of size n we have the sample counterpart

	Response Yes	No	
Available	n_{11}	n_{10}	$n_{1.}$
Nonavailable	n_{01}	n_{00}	$n_{0.}$
	$n_{.1}$	$n_{.0}$	

The statistic

$$U = n_{11}/n_{1.}$$

is used to estimate $p_{.1}$. It is shown that

$$EU = p',$$

and for large samples

$$\text{Var}(U) = p'(1 - p')\frac{1}{(n + 1)p_{1.}},$$

where $p_{1.} = N_{1.}/N$.

An error $U - p_{.1}$ is incurred in using U to estimate $p_{.1}$. We wish to choose the sample size n so that this error is controlled, that is,

$$P\{|U - p_{.1}| \leq \delta\} \geq 1 - \alpha. \tag{1}$$

A value of n that satisfies (1) is the smallest integer satisfying

$$n \geq \frac{T_{\alpha}^2}{4\delta(p_{1.}(\delta - 1 + p_{1.}))} - 1. \tag{2}$$

Blight, B. J. N. (1970). Estimation from a censored sample for the exponential family. *Biometrika* 57: 389–395.

The starting point in this study is a random variable X whose distribution belongs to the exponential family. We do not observe X but rather a censored version as follows. The range of X is divided into $k + 1$ nonintersecting sub-ranges $S, S_1, \ldots, S_k$. If X falls in the subrange S, then we are given X itself. But if X falls outside of S, then instead of X we are given the subrange it falls in. Thus in a sample of size N if $n_1, \ldots, n_k$ observations fall in $S_1, \ldots, S_k$, respectively, and if n observations fall in S, then the data consists of $X_1, \ldots, X_n, n_1, \ldots, n_k$.

The likelihood equations for estimating the parameters in the exponential family are obtained, and an iterative procedure for solving for the maximum likelihood estimate is described. On the basis of empirical evidence, it appears that convergence is rapid.

The Fisher information matrix is obtained; this provides some indication concerning precision. An example is used as a basis for making some comparisons on convergence and precision.

Buck, S. F. (1960). A method of estimation of missing values in multivariate data suitable for use with an electronic computer. *Journal of the Royal Statistical Society*, Series B, 22: 302–306.

The goal of this paper is to estimate the covariance matrix in a p-variate population when there are m observations on all p variates plus some additional observations on some of the variates.

Suppose that each of the additional p-variate observations has only one missing element; that is each observation has $p-1$ components. The proposal then is to use the complete sample of m observations and to compute the regression of the $p-1$ variates on the missing variate. Then using the $p-1$ values, the missing observation is estimated from the regression equation. This is done for each of the additional observations.

When there are v $(v > 1)$ missing components, these are estimated from v regression equations using the $p-v$ variates regressed on each of the v missing variates. The critical point is that these v regressions can be obtained by a single operation of inverting the $p \times p$ information matrix based on the complete sample of m observations.

Some bias estimates are presented as well as a data set consisting of 72 samples of sugar beet on which were measured four variates:

x_1 = purity measure, $\qquad x_3$ = noxious nitrogen,

x_2 = sugar content, $\qquad x_4 = K_2O$ content.

The missing data was obtained by choosing 35 measurements at random and deleting these. The result was

43	complete samples
6	samples with x_1 missing
7	samples with x_2 missing
5	samples with x_3 missing
6	samples with x_4 missing
2	samples with x_1, x_3 missing
2	samples with x_3, x_4 missing
1	sample with x_1, x_3, x_4 missing
72	

Estimates of means, variances, and correlations were then made using the 72 complete samples, the 43 complete samples, and imputed values. For this particular experiment there was not much difference in the results, except that using only the complete samples fared worse than all the other procedures.

Chapman, D. W. (1976). A survey of nonresponse imputation procedures. *Proceedings of the Social Statistics Section*, American Statistical Association, pp. 245–251.

Some of the procedures that have been used in surveys to compensate for missing data and resulting biases are discussed. Descriptions of procedures for both item nonresponse and questionnaire nonresponse are included. For item imputation, cold-deck and hot-deck procedures are discussed with some possible variations. The use of data from the current survey is considered an advantage of the hot-deck method.

Procedures identified for use with unit or questionnaire nonresponse are (1) single-weight adjustment; (2) weighting classes; (3) AID programmed procedure to define weighting classes; (4) "raking" or "balancing" procedure; (5) use of regression in weighting adjustments; (6) use in imputation of the amount of effort needed to obtain response; and (7) imputation by substitution of additional selections from the population. Experience is cited for some of the procedures, and some general observations of relative advantages or limitations are made. It is noted that the hot-deck procedure can also be used for questionnaire nonresponse and, conversely, the regression procedure may be more useful in dealing with item nonresponse.

Chen, T., and Fienberg, S. E. (1974). Two-dimensional contingency tables with both completely and partially cross-classified data. *Biometrics* 30: 629–642.

Two-way contingency tables are studied in which some observations are classified by both column and row classifications, and some observations are classified only by row or by column.

More specifically, $x_{ij}(> 0)$ denotes the count in the (i, j)th cell, $i = 1, \ldots, r$, $j = 1, \ldots, c$, and $R_1, \ldots, R_r$ denote additional observations in the rows and $C_1, \ldots, C_c$ denote additional observations in the columns.

The mechanism for generating these observations is as follows. In a firststage each of the N observations is assigned to a cell by a Poisson or multinomial sampling procedure. In the second stage an observation in the (i, j)th cell has a probability λ_{1i} of losing its row identity, and probability λ_{2j} of losing its column identity ($1 \geq \lambda_{1i} + \lambda_{2j}$). In this way we generate surplus marginal totals.

Maximum likelihood estimates are determined for Poisson and multinomial sampling, and approximate chi-square goodness-of-fit tests are given.

One possible mode of analysis is to ignore the surplus observations. Under some conditions in the model this procedure could lead to inconsistent estimates.

The methodology developed is exemplified with data on 456 premature live births, whereby each birth is classified in accordance with a "health" characteristic or a serum bilirium count (indicative of a malfunctioning kidney).

Clausen, J. A., and Ford, R. N. (1947). Controlling bias in mail questionnaires. *Journal of the American Statistical Association* 42: 497–511.

A discussion is provided on how to increase response in a mail questionnaire. A number of general observations are made. For example, reference is made to a study in which, for a population of college alumni, the length (between 10 and 25 pages) of a questionnaire appears to be relatively unimportant.

The authors engaged in a study with veterans using (i) personal and (ii) impersonal salutations with (iii) personal and (iv) facsimile signatures. A fifth group consisted of letters and personal salutations and signatures and sent airmail special delivery. There was little difference between personal versus impersonal salutations or signatures. However, there was a significant increase in the rate of response for the special postage group.

A second study describes an initial mailing and a first and a second follow-up. There were five groups of veterans—two groups of male separatees, female separatees, applicants for educational benefits, and amputees. For each group the percentage returns increased approximately 20% at the first follow-up and another 10% at the second. The final returns varied from 87% to 94%. The number of cases varied from 1594 to 14,606.

A study of National Service Life insured persons is described. Here the interest aspect is modified. Bias due to educational level and employment status is discussed, as well as bias in a homogeneous group. The latter occurs when a survey is conducted on a subject of considerable interest to some members of a group and not to others.

Colledge, M. J., Johnson, J. H., Paré, R., and Sande, I. G. (1978). Large scale imputation of survey data. *Proceedings of the Section on Survey Research Methods*, American Statistical Association, pp. 431–436.

Statistics Canada is involved in a number of large surveys, in particular, the Census of Construction (COC) and the Motor Carrier Freight Survey (MCF). The COC is concerned with about 80,000 businesses in Canada whose primary activity is construction. The MCF has a universe of about 25,000 carriers.

The present paper provides a discussion of imputation procedures, mainly based on rather complicated matching procedures. Using a sample, an analysis was made of the imputation methods. The results were not conclusive, but pointed out potential positive gains.

Cox, B. G., and Folsom, R. E. (1978). An empirical investigation of alternate item nonresponse adjustments. *Proceedings of the Section on Survey Research Methods*, American Statistical Association, pp. 219–223.

This paper provides an empirical investigation of two methods for adjusting for nonresponse: hot-deck and weighting-class procedures. These were compared using data from the National Longitudinal Survey of the High School Class of 1972. The comparisons were made in terms of bias, variance, and mean square error. A sample of size 5854 was selected and 20 key items were chosen for analysis.

In general the hot-deck procedure appeared to reduce, for discrete items, the bias caused by nonresponse. Though there was a reduction in bias, there was an increase in variance. In the case of continuous items, there was no corresponding bias reduction.

Because the response rates in this study were high, there were no significant gains using either imputation procedure. For continuous items, it appeared that weighting-class estimates did yield smaller mean square errors for items with higher nonresponse rates.

Deming, W. E. (1953). On a probability mechanism to attain an economic balance between the resultant error of response and the bias of nonresponse. *Journal of the American Statistical Association* 48: 743–772.

This paper is concerned with a variety of problems. In particular, the purpose is (i) to study the evidence produced by a proposed probabilistic model that permits the calculation of variance and bias of nonresponse and (ii) to further determine the number of recalls required to achieve a specified accuracy at a minimum cost.

The probability mechanism is to divide the population into 6 classes according to the average proportion of interviews that will be successfully completed out of 8 attempts. These classes are designated by 0, 1, 2, 4, 6, 8. (Although the choice of 6 categories is arbitrary, the author asserts that the results remain resistant to the addition of classes.)

Thus, for example, class 0 contains a stubborn core of permanent refusals, whereas class 8 consists of people who 8 times out of 8 are available at home and will respond to questions.

The analysis is based on a multinominal model. A novel part of the analysis is to sort out the observables at each attempt that permits estimation of the parameters. A discussion of the Politz–Simmons plan is given, including an expression for the variance.

Some tables are provided giving expected sizes of samples in the various attempts. Numerical results are then given to an initial sample of size 1000.

For costs of $3 per call for attempt I, $9 per call for later attempts, and $4 per name for the Politz–Simmons plan, a table of costs of interviewing is developed.

For $n = 100, 200, 300, 500, 1000, 2000, 3000, 5000$, and certain costs, numerical values of biases and root mean square errors are provided. These yield a variety of conclusions.

With the level of response assured, the following are sample conclusions. (a) Even with three recalls, a sample bigger than the binomial equivalent of from

300 to 500 for an estimate of any one class is ineffective and uneconomical. (b) High accuracy can be attained only with 4, 5, or 6 recalls, along with an initial sample equivalent to from 800 to 1500 binomial cases.

This paper contains many detailed results. Because of this and the paper's importance, we include the author's summary.

> The author postulates a probability mechanism for the simultaneous production of the bias of nonresponse and for the variance of response. The nonresponse arises from a graded series of classes of the members of the universe to be sampled. The classes range from an impregnable core of no possible response, on up to a class of complete response. Nonresponse arises from two sources, not at home, and refusal. Refusals are of two kinds, permanent and temporary. The variation in the amount of time spent at home, and the variation in the firmness of the temporary refusal, produce the graded series of classes. The bias of nonresponse arises from the variation of any characteristic from one class to another. The variance of response arises from the variation of any characteristics from one member to another within a single class, and from the random variation in the number of responses therefrom.
>
> An increase in the size of the initial sample or a more efficient method of selection will decrease the variance of response, but will have no effect on the bias of nonresponse. Successive recalls, on the other hand, decrease the bias of response, and are more effective than an increase in the size of the sample or a more efficient method of selection in decreasing the root-mean-square error which arises from both nonresponse and from the variation of response.
>
> The results show that without recalls, it is hazardous to put any confidence in the result, no matter how big the sample, even when the variation in the measured characteristic is only two-fold from the class of lowest response to the class of highest response.
>
> With the levels of response assumed here (taken from average urban experience), and with an estimate formed by summing up the initial call and the recalls, the first two recalls effect together about a 50% reduction in the initial bias of nonresponse. Further recalls continue to be productive. In fact, with this method of estimation, each recall added to a sampling plan, even to six recalls, actually increases the amount of information obtained for each dollar expended on interviewing.
>
> Even with three recalls, and with only a two-fold variation from the class of lowest response to the class of highest response, an initial sample bigger than the equivalent of from 300 to 500 binomial cases in any one subclass is ineffective and uneconomical. The apparent precision of a bigger sample is a delusion, as with bigger samples the bias of nonresponse will eclipse the error of sampling unless there are 4, 5, or more recalls. An attempted "complete count" is no exception and often represents an extreme waste of effort.

For high accuracy, a plan that uses the ordinary method of estimation by combining the initial attempt and the recalls must support 4, 5, or 6 recalls, along with an initial sample equivalent to from 800 to 1500 binomial cases.

For any proposed survey, calculations based on rough advance estimates of the constants that appear in the formulas will predict to a useful degree of approximation the biases and the variances to be expected from various types of plans. Figures on costs will then point out which plan is most economical, of those that are possible, for the attainment of a prescribed accuracy.

Where extremely high accuracy is required, the Politz plan with 2000 or more binomial cases becomes competitive in cost with a survey that depends on recalls. In any case, the Politz plan has the advantage of speed and of being able to produce results under circumstances wherein recalls are impossible (for example, listening to a radio program).

The proposed mechanism provides a theory of bias to supplement the theory of sampling. It indicates the possibility of new and more efficient methods of estimation than the simple combination of the initial attempt and the recalls, as it will provide a rational basis for extracting more information from the recalls. It will also point out, for any particular method of estimation, what empirical information will be helpful in the planning of the efficient allocation of effort amongst the initial sample and the recalls.

Dempster, A. P., Laird, N. M., and Rubin, D. B. (1977). Maximum likelihood from incomplete data via the EM algorithm. *Journal of the Royal Statistical Society*, Series B, 39: 1–39.

This paper presents an algorithm that is suitable for the iterative computation of maximum likelihood estimates when there are missing observations. The same algorithm can be modified to find the mode of the posterior distribution in the Bayesian framework. The EM algorithm is a generalization of other algorithms based on the missing information principle of Orchard and Woodbury (1972; see summary in this bibliography.)

The model for missing data is that there are two random variables Y and X, where $Y = y(X)$ is the observed data with missing observations and X is the (unobserved) complete data. Let $f(X \mid \Phi)$ be the density function of X given the vector of parameters Φ. The algorithm proceeds iteratively, each iteration having two steps, an expectation (E) step and a maximization (M) step. The expectation calculated is the expectation of the complete data likelihood function given the incomplete data,

$$Q(\Phi' \mid \Phi) = E[f(x \mid y, \Phi)].$$

The M step consists of calculating the Φ' which maximizes $Q(\Phi' | \Phi^{(p)})$, where $\Phi^{(p)}$ is the value of Φ estimated on the pth step. This maximizing value Φ' is then used as the value of Φ for the $(p + 1)$th step.

For some distributions of X such as many of the common regular exponential family distributions the EM algorithm is particularly efficient since the M step can be made explicit. The authors establish sufficient conditions for convergence and conditions under which each iteration of the algorithm increases the likelihood. They also derive some expressions for the rate of convergence near the limiting value.

Applications of the EM algorithm to missing data problems under multinomial sampling, the univariate normal linear model, and multivariate normal sampling are discussed. Some examples are given of the use of the algorithm for problems in censoring and truncation, finite mixtures, variance component estimation, hyperparameter estimation, iteratively reweighted least squares, and factor analysis.

Durbin, J. (1954). Nonresponse and callbacks in surveys. *Bulletin of the International Statistical Institute* 34: 72–86.

Sample surveys involving interviews conducted in the subjects' homes are often plagued with a large proportion of subjects who are not at home the first time that the interviewer calls. Since there is evidence that the ultimate responses of the part of the sample that is not at home on the first call may differ from the responses of the subjects who are interviewed on the first call, some method of dealing with this form of missing data is essential to avoid biased results. Three basic strategies that have been used to deal with the problem of subjects who are not at home on the first call are

(1) Continue to try to contact the subjects who were not at home on the first call until all subjects can be interviewed (the method of subsampling).

(2) Continue to try to contact only a subsample of the subjects who were not at home on the first call (the method of subsampling).

(3) Weight the obtained responses according to an estimate of the probability that the subject was at home (the method of weighting).

Although the cost of recontacting subjects is generally believed to be much higher than the cost of the original call, data from two British surveys that used multiple recalls suggests that the cost of data obtained after several calls is not much higher than the cost of data obtained on the first call. Thus, the strategy of multiple recalls may be more viable than is usually believed.

The estimator derived by Politz and Simmons (1949; see summary in this bibliography) and based on weighting of responses by the probability that the subjects were at home is analyzed. An expression for the variance of this estimator is obtained and used to compare the weighting procedure and procedures based on recalls or subsampling. The conclusion is that if the probability of being at home is correlated with the variable measured in the survey, the weighting procedure may be more efficient than procedures based on recalls or subsampling. Otherwise the estimators based on recalls or subsampling are more efficient if data derived from the second and subsequent calls are not more expensive than data derived from the first calls. The fact that data derived from recalls are usually more expensive than data derived from the first call makes the weighted estimator preferable in many cases.

Durbin, J. (1958). Sampling theory for estimators based on fewer individuals than the number selected. *Bulletin of the International Statistical Institute* 36: 113–119.

Standard sampling theory assumes that the number of observations in a sample or stratum is fixed in advance. When the sample size is fixed, but there is nonresponse, the actual sample or stratum size n becomes a random variable. When estimates are desired for subpopulations that cut across strata the same problem arises. The standard formulas for the variance of a sample mean when sample sizes are fixed do not apply when sample sizes are random variables.

Since the sample mean is a ratio of the sample total to the sample size, the theory for ratio estimation can be used to obtain an estimate of the variance of a sample mean when sample sizes vary. This paper publicizes a formula due to Yates for the variance of a stratified sample when n is a random variable. Yates's result is extended to the case of multistage sampling, and an estimator for the variance of the mean in such samples is given. Random variation in sample size is shown to increase the variance of the sample mean in the case of stratified samples. Thus the standard (fixed n) estimates of the standard error of the sample mean underestimate the true standard error when there are missing observations. The effect of random n on the variance of estimates obtained from multistage samples is less pronounced than for stratified samples, but it can be large if the proportion of missing data is large.

Durbin, J., and Stuart, A. (1954). Callbacks and clustering in sample surveys: An experimental study. *Journal of the Royal Statistical Society*, Series A, 117: 387–428.

Sample surveys involving interviews conducted in the subjects' homes are often plagued by nonresponse due to subjects who were not at home when the interviewer called. This paper is an experimental study of three commonly used methods of handling nonresponse in such sample surveys.

(1) Recalling by repeated attempts to contact the subject who was not at home on the first call

(2) Reweighting the first call sample by the reciprocal of an estimate of the probability that the subject is at home using a method developed by Politz and Simmons (1949; see summary in this bibliography)

(3) Replacement of those subjects not available after a given number of calls by a quota sample based on information collected by the interviewer during unsuccessful calls

The cost and accuracy of each method of handling nonresponse were compared using two types of cluster sampling and simple random sampling. The experiment was replicated using two sets of interviewers and the variation in answers and response rate between interviewers was examined. The standard for comparison of the methods was the result obtained by allowing the interviewers to use an unlimited number of attempts to contact the subjects in the sample. The response rate using an unlimited number of callbacks was 75–80%.

The results of this study suggest that the data obtained from only the individuals interviewed at the first call was badly biased on some questions. The data obtained after three calls did not appear to be biased. This result appears to validate the common policy of using only three callbacks in sample surveys. The method of replacement of nonrespondents by a quota sample was less accurate than an additional call and had only a slight cost advantage. The replacement of nonrespondents by a quota sample was therefor not recommended. The method of reweighting the data from the first-call respondents by the reciprocal of the estimated probability of being found at home did not perform well. It should be emphasized, however, that the conditions for applicability of the reweighting method were not met in this study. The poor performance of the method is therefore not an accurate indication of the ultimate usefulness of the reweighting method.

Clustering was found to decrease the cost of conducting the survey while increasing the variance of the estimates. For some purposes, the increase in variance due to clustering may more than compensate for the decreased cost. Significant differences were found among interviewers in the response rate that they obtained. Surprisingly, there was no evidence that the responses to questions obtained by different interviewers differed systematically. This suggests that with trained interviewers and random samples, biases introduced by interviewers are insignificant compared with normal sampling variability.

Ericson, W. A. (1967). Optimal sample design with nonresponse. *Journal of the American Statistical Association* 62: 63–78.

A Bayes theory approach to answering the following problem is presented. A simple random sample of *n* elements is selected in order to estimate the population mean μ. Of the n selected elements, r elements respond. Then

(a) Given r responses should one attempt to obtain responses from any of the $n - r$ nonrespondents? If so, how many?

(b) How shall inferences be made concerning μ?

(c) What is the optimal initial sample size n?

The loss function for estimating μ is assumed to be quadratic. The population is partitioned into two strata, respondents (on first contact) with mean μ_1 and nonrespondents with mean μ_2. The unknown population proportions of respondents and nonrespondents are π and $1 - \pi$.

The design is as follows: Choose a sample of size n and an $r \leq n$; obtain values for the r responding elements; choose a follow-up sample of $m \leq n - r$ elements from the nonrespondents. Assume all m individuals respond in the second stage.

A prior distribution ("beta-normal") is assumed for (μ_1, μ_2, π) which implies a prior distribution for μ. It is also assumed that the number of respondents r is a binomial random variable with parameters n and π and that each respondent observation is normally distributed with mean μ and *known* variance σ_1^2. (Similar assumptions may be made directly for the responding sample mean $\overline{X}$.) Also, each of the m follow-up observations is normally distributed with mean μ_2 and *known* variance σ_2^2; the follow-up sample mean is denoted $\overline{Y}_m$.

The total likelihood is available and the conditional distribution of μ_1, μ_2, π given $n, r, \overline{X}_r, m, \overline{Y}_m$, or at least its first and second moments, can be calculated. Similarly, the posterior distribution or lower posterior moments of μ given $n, r, \overline{X}_r, m, \overline{Y}_m$ can be calculated. The optimal estimator of $\hat{\mu}$ is derived. Then the expected value of the loss for given values of m, the size of sample from the nonrespondents, is derived and used to determine the optimal proportion of nonrespondents to be sampled. A table giving this optimal proportion is included.

To derive the optimal size of n, the expected loss is first derived as a function of n, assuming the optimal procedure for selecting the subsample of nonrespondents. Values of the expected loss and n can then be determined using a computer program.

The final discussion concerns the effects of possible response biases introduced as a consequence of the pressures used to persuade previous nonrespondents to respond.

Ernst, L. R. (1978). Weighting to adjust for partial nonresponse. *Proceedings of the Survey Research Methods Section,* American Statistical Association, pp. 468–473.

A common type of partial nonresponse with the Current Population Survey (CPS) is the failure to obtain income data from the respondent. Thus, an imputation process is needed for a group of data items (supplement page of questionnaire), knowing from previous studies that nonrespondents tend to have much larger incomes than respondents. The paper focuses on this particular situation, comparing a procedure of weighting by subclass to the hot deck imputation procedure in use with the CPS in 1973.

Notation and variance formula are provided for the weighting procedure. Use of the formula is outlined in a procedure for dividing into subclasses for weighting. Candidate variables for subclassification are chosen on its basis of maximum reduction in variance and added in a stepwise fashion until the reduction in variance from the previous stage is no longer appreciable.

Programs implementing the above procedure were run through nine stages using as data the March CPS with the income supplement of 1975–77. Using mean total money income, results indicated that this weighting procedure produced a relatively small decrease in variance due to the large CPS sample. Consequently, the procedure for dividing into subclasses was redone with emphasis on reducing bias, the major component of the mean square error in the CPS. Stepwise, variables were chosen by the absolute difference in means between stages. In the second scheme the adjustment to the mean was much greater and it was felt the bias was smaller.

A test of the weighting procedure and comparison with the 1973 hot-deck procedure was carried out by matching CPS participants to Internal Revenue Service records. In comparing wage and salary earnings it appeared that the weighting scheme produces smaller bias than the hot-deck procedure. However, this was believed primarily due to larger number of subclasses used in the weighting scheme. In 1975 a revised hot-deck procedure was introduced into the CPS with vastly more cells. In conclusion, the revised hot-deck procedure was judged preferable to the weighting scheme for the CPS although in surveys with much smaller sample sizes the weighting would be preferable because the survey variance would become more significant.

Fellegi, P., and Holt, D. (1976). A systematic approach to automatic edit and imputation. *Journal of the American Statistical Association* 71: 17–35.

The last stage in processing of survey data, just prior to tabulation, is data editing, that is, determining whether the responses to certain items are consistent with one another. Records that fail the edit because of inconsistent values must be corrected by imputing values that satisfy the edit. This paper proposes a systematic theory of edits that can be implemented on a computer in an efficient way. The editing procedure is specified formally and hence the programming can be made independent of particular edit specifications.

Edit specifications define which combinations of item responses are inconsistent with one another. All edit specifications are shown to be representable in a normal form. Any given set of edit specifications implies additional (implicit) edit specifications. The normal form of edits can be used to obtain the complete set of implicit edits. Given a set of records that fail the editing process, the complete set of edits can be used to determine the minimal set of items that must be changed to satisfy the edit. Hence, the items needing imputation are explicitly identified. Furthermore, the imputation procedure can be specified independently of the particular edit specifications used.

Two hot-deck imputation methods are considered, both of which attempt to preserve (after imputation) the distribution of the items for records that passed the edit. The first method, sequential imputation, is fast and preserves the marginal distribution of the data that passed the edit. The second method, joint imputation, is more time consuming but yields a joint distribution of imputed values that is the same as that of data which passed the original edit. Efficient algorithms for programming the editing and imputation procedure are presented, along with an exemplary set of edits and data.

Implementation of the editing and imputation system at Statistics Canada has yielded a number of practical benefits. Inconsistent editing specifications are detected automatically, and the particular specifications leading to the inconsistency are easily identified prior to actual data processing. The system preserves the theoretically maximal amount of information from each record, while guaranteeing that each record that has been corrected will satisfy the edit constraints. Since the computer programs are based on generalized formal edit specifications, changes of particular edit specifications do not require reprogramming.

Ford, B. L. (1976). Missing data procedures: A comparative study. *Proceedings of the Social Statistics Section*, American Statistical Association, pp. 324–329.

This investigation compares six procedures for imputing missing data in sample surveys where the missing data are not "missing at random." The method used is a simulation based on data from a simple stratified sample of an agricultural survey by the Statistical Reporting Service (SRS) of the U.S. Department of Agriculture (USDA). The six procedures used for imputing missing values were

(1)   The double-sampling ratio procedure

(2)   The double-sampling regression procedure

(3)   A "random" hot-deck procedure, in which a randomly selected reported item was substituted for each missing item

(4)   The "closest" hot-deck procedure, in which the closest reported item was substituted for each missing item

(5)   The "two closest" hot-deck procedure, in which the average of the two closest reported items was substituted for each missing item

(6)   The "class" mean hot-deck procedure, in which the "class" mean was substituted for each missing item

The most important aspect in comparing these missing data procedures was bias in the estimated means (or totals). An analysis of variance shows no significant differences among the estimated means which result in using these procedures. All the procedures reduce the relative bias that results from accepting the mean of the reported data as an estimate of the population mean. This relative bias is a result of the nonresponse rate and the difference between the respondents and nonrespondents for the survey variable. The reduction in relative bias averages 15% and varies from 8 to 26%. Considering the low correlations between the auxiliary and primary variables, this reduction is reasonable. Much larger reductions in bias could be obtained if a control variable could be found with a high correlation with the variable of interest and if that variable could easily be obtained for the entire sample.

An important, though secondary, concern was the estimated variances of the estimated means. The estimated variances of the hot-deck procedures are underestimates of the true variances because they are generally *less* than the estimated variance that result with *no* missing data in the sample. Furthermore, the degree of underestimation *increases* as the relative bias increases. This demonstrates why all of the hot-deck procedures (random, "closest," "two closest," and "class" mean substitution) may be undesirable. There is probably an underestimation of variance in the ratio and regression procedures, but these results show that it is not nearly as large as in the hot-deck procedures.

The conclusion of this investigation is a recommendation of the ratio or regression procedure (the effects of these two procedures being indistinguishable). These theoretical properties of two procedures have been investigated more fully than those of the other procedures. The estimated variances of the estimated means from the ratio or regression procedure also better reflect the true quality of the data than does the hot-deck procedure.

Ford, B. L. (1978). Missing data procedures: A comparative study (Part 2). *Economics, Statistics and Cooperative Service, U.S. Department of Agriculture.*

This study examines six methods for imputing missing values in surveys when the missing data are not "missing at random" and an additional datum (control variable) is available for records with missing data. The context for this study is the U.S. Department of Agriculture (USDA) missing data procedure for list frame surveys, where the statistician edits in values for missing items. The present study uses a simulation based on (artificial) deletion of elements in data from a USDA survey.

The six imputation procedures are

(1)   A hot-deck imputation procedure based on the moving average of randomly selected items with complete data
(2)   The same hot-deck imputation procedure with balanced repeated replications (two replicates per stratum)
(3)   A ratio estimator based on the control variable
(4)   The ratio estimator with balanced repeated replications
(5)   A regression estimator based on the control variable
(6)   The regression estimator with balanced repeated replications

All six procedures rely on control data of high quality and high correlation of control variable and variables to be imputed. The correlations within the data set used in this study are approximately 0.30, but inclusion of artificial control variables provides evidence that correlations need to be about 0.60 before any of the procedures considered produces a notable increase in survey accuracy.

Of the six imputation procedures studied in this experiment, three are slightly superior (have smaller standard errors) if the control variable is highly correlated with the variable imputed. The three procedures are the ratio procedures with balanced repeated replications, the hot-deck procedure, and the hot-deck procedure using balanced repeated replications. These procedures are also recommended because of their simplicity and their statistical efficiency. The balanced repeated replication procedures have the advantage that they provide unbiased estimates of the variance.

Both statistical and nonstatistical considerations are crucial in minimizing the problems of missing data. The first priority in the survey considered herein is the improvement of control data. The quality of the control data in the multiple frame surveys is often unknown. The correlations between control data and reported data should be monitored. Control data which is adequate for stratification may not be adequate for use with a missing data procedure. Research on obtaining and constructing better control variables should also be planned. For example, several control variables may be more efficient than just one.

Ghangurde, P. D., and Mulvihill, J. (1978). Non-response and imputation in longitudinal estimation in LFS (Canadian Labour Force Survey), Household Surveys Development Staff. *Statistics Canada Report* (Feb. 1978).

Since information on households in the selected dwellings for the Canadian Labour Force Survey is collected for a period of 6 months (January–June 1976), the survey is a good source of longitudinal data. The estimates of longitudinal patterns of labor force characteristics is based on the sample of individual rotation groups. The longitudinal study analyzes the demographic and labor force status profiles of longitudinal respondent and nonrespondent, outlines decision rules for imputation at record level, and evaluates the effect of sample increase due to imputation. Finally, it characterizes nonrespondents and obtains an indication of the magnitude of nonresponse bias and rotation group bias of monthly estimates. Detailed tables of household patterns are included in the paper.

Haitovsky, Y. (1968). Missing data in regression analysis. *Journal of the Royal Statistical Society,* Series B, 30: 67–82.

An experimenter wishes to predict y based on $x_1, \ldots, x_p$ using linear regression. If all the measurements on each observation are available, then the solution is given by ordinary least squares. When some of the measurements are missing (assumed to be missing at random) several alternative procedures are considered.

In the first procedure (method 1) the incomplete observations are discarded and then the ordinary least squares solution is applied to the complete observations. (This assumes that there are some complete observations.)

Because the normal equations require covariances, the second procedure (method 2) is based on using all the available data for the computation of each variance and covariance.

To assess these two procedures a Monte Carlo experiment was performed in which missing data were artificially created. Eight sets of regression data (1000 observations) were generated with different deletion patterns and different correlational structure. On the basis of these experiments the author arrives at the conclusion that method 1 is relatively better than method 2.

The MSE can be decomposed into two additive terms: one term accounts for the bias and the other one is the variance when the bias is squared. The difficulty with method 2 is that the inconsistences introduced into the normal equations apparently affects the second term in the MSE and is the more important—even though the bias does affect the inference.

A review of several alternative procedures in the literature is also provided.

Hansen, M. H., and Hurwitz, W. N. (1946). The problem of non-response in sample surveys. *Journal of the American Statistical Association* 41: 517–529.

This paper deals with the initial collection of information in a sample survey by an inexpensive procedure, which results in a certain level of nonresponse, after which a subsample of the nonrespondents is chosen for follow-up by a considerably more expensive data collection procedure that is assumed to obtain a response for each subsampled nonrespondent. The procedure is illustrated by the use of mailed questionnaires as the inexpensive procedure, with personal follow-up and interview of a subsample of the nonrespondents to the mailed questionnaires.

The optimal joint use of the two data collection procedures to achieve a given level of precision is given when the expected nonresponse rate is known approximately in advance of taking the survey, along with approximate unit costs and variances. An approximately optimal procedure is given, also, for the case when the response rate is not known in advance, but will be observed as a result of the initial data collection effort.

The estimated variances can be computed, conditioned on the sizes of sample actually achieved for the respondents and nonrespondents. The formulas are given and illustrated.

An illustration is given to show, for a given degree of precision, the varying sizes of the initial mail sample for different expected response rates, and the rate of field follow-up for the nonresponses. For each response rate, the minimum cost of the survey is computed; this enables the determination of the maximum number of schedules to be mailed independently of the rate of response. For achieving the desired precision, the number to be interviewed then varies with the response rate actually observed.

Derivations are in an appendix. The principal discussion assumes an initial simple random sample. Extensions to stratified and more complex designs, including ratio and regression estimators, are discussed.

Hansen, M. H., Hurwitz, W. N., and Bershad, M. (1961). Measurement errors in censuses and surveys. *Bulletin of the International Statistical Institute* 38: 359–374.

This paper formulates a model for measurement (or response) errors in censuses and surveys, and a joint model for sampling and measurement errors. The paper defines various concepts, including the desired measures to be estimated from the survey, the general conditions under which the survey is taken that may affect the results of a survey, an estimate from a survey trial taken under a set of general conditions, and the biases and total mean square error of a survey estimate reflecting both measurement and sampling errors and various components of these.

Let P_j be the conditional expected value of the possible repetitions of measurements over all possible samples and trials (assumed independent repetitions) of a survey taken under a specified set of general conditions on the jth unit of the population, and let x_{jt} be the observed value of that unit on a particular survey (the tth trial). Then $d_{jt} = x_{jt} - p_j$ is defined as the response deviation for that unit in the survey, and the expected value over all units of

d_{jt}^2 is defined as the simple response variance. The contributions of the simple response variance to survey errors are discussed, and for simple random sampling with replacement, their contributions to survey errors are shown to be appropriately reflected in the usual estimate of the sampling variance.

Intraclass correlations of response deviations arise from differences in performance or interpretation of definitions or questionnaire content in the work of interviewers, or of editors or coders. They also arise from differences in treatment by supervisors, and from other factors. The effects of correlated response errors may be substantial and are not reflected in the usual estimates of sampling variance.

Experimental designs within censuses or sample surveys are described from which approximate estimates can be made of the response variance and its components such as the simple response variance and intraclass correlations of response deviations, including estimates of the intraclass correlations associated with interviewers or processors. In particular, a survey replication method, and a method of interpenetrating samples, are described, together with approximate estimators.

Actual estimates of variance components and biases from a large-scale experiment (that included randomization of interviewer assignments, replicated interviews, and intensive measurements) conducted in connection with the 1950 Census of Population are summarized. The paper concludes with a summary of the implications of these results.

These results greatly influenced census methods in the 1960 and subsequent censuses, including the role of sampling and the development of other major modifications in census methods.

Hanson, R. (1978). The current population survey: Design and methodology. Technical Paper Number 40, U.S. Bureau of the Census, 40: 55–58.

This paper describes the procedure used to prepare the Current Population Survey (CPS) monthly labor force estimates. This involves combining estimates from two sample designs in the 461 Primary Sampling Unit National sample. Several steps are involved in the preparation of the labor force estimates. First, simple unbiased estimates are generated from the survey data, even though eventual estimates will be obtained by a different method. Next, an adjustment is made for missing data (nonresponse) arising from failure to obtain a useable response from a household included in the sample. This adjustment for non-response consists of reweighting the sample using weights determined by the race of the respondent and the residence area of the household.

First-stage ratio estimates are then calculated, based on ratios of 1970 census national totals for selected population categories to the totals for the sample in each primary sampling unit. Second-stage ratio estimates are calculated next.

These second-stage ratio estimates are "based on the ratio of independent estimates of the current population for the month of the interview for age–sex–race groups to the first-stage ratio estimates of totals of these groups from the sample." It is believed that the second-stage ratio estimates are less biased and more precise than the first-stage ratio estimates. These are the final estimates from the given month's CPS.

Composite estimates are calculated using survey data from a previous month's CPS. Seasonal adjustments are applied to some key labor force statistics to adjust for the usual seasonal variations.

Hartley, H. O. (1958). Maximum likelihood estimation from incomplete data. *Biometrics* 14: 174–194.

Although maximum likelihood estimates (MLE) can be computed (in theory) when some observations are missing, the computational aspects can become considerably more complicated. A method is presented whereby missing values are imputed, after which maximum likelihood estimates for a complete sample are computed.

More specifically the procedure operates as follows. Let X be a discrete random variable taking values $x_1, x_2, \ldots$, and let

$$P\{X = x_i\} = f_i(\theta), \qquad i = 1, \ldots.$$

Given a sample of size n, let n_i be the number of observations $x_i, i = 1, 2, \ldots$. However, for some values of i the observations are missing. Let $\mathscr{A}$ and $\mathscr{M}$ denote sets of i for which n_i are "available" and "missing," respectively; of course, $\mathscr{A}$ and $\mathscr{M}$ are complementary sets. The ML equations for estimating θ_t are

$$\sum_{i \in \mathscr{A}} n_i \frac{\partial \log f(i, \theta)}{\partial \theta_t} + \sum_{j \in \mathscr{M}} n_j \frac{\partial \log f(j, \theta)}{\partial \theta_t} = 0.$$

Initial estimates, $n_j^{(0)}$ for $j \in \mathscr{M}$ are used, from which a first estimate $\theta^{(1)}$ of θ is made using the ML equations. Next, estimates $n_j^{(1)}, j \in \mathscr{M}$, are made from

$$n_j^{(1)} = n f(j, \theta^{(1)}) / \left[1 - \sum_{j \in \mathscr{M}} f(j, \theta^{(1)}) \right].$$

The process is now repeated.

For the Poisson distribution empirical evidence in 30 examples indicated that convergence was extremely rapid, provided that the set $\mathscr{M}$ is not too large.

Other examples for the binomial distribution and a Poisson distribution with a censored tail sum are discussed in detail. The latter case is one of severe censoring, and an acceleration procedure is provided to help the convergence.

Computations of variance and covariance estimates of MLE depend on second derivatives of the likelihood function; when observations are missing modifications need to be made. A discussion for obtaining these estimates are provided with details in the case of the Poisson and binomial examples worked out. Another example for the negative binomial with a missing zero class is examined in considerable detail.

Hartley, H. O., and Hocking, R. R. (1971). The analysis of incomplete data. *Biometrics* 27: 783–823.

This article presents a taxonomy of incomplete data problems and investigates maximum likelihood estimation for three of the types of incomplete data problems. The first problem concerns multivariate normal data where N observations consist of p variables each and the observations are normally distributed with mean vector μ and covariance matrix Σ. An observation is incomplete if any of the p variables is missing or if only a linear combination, such as the sum, of some of the variables is known. An iterative procedure for obtaining maximum likelihood estimates for μ and Σ is given. The procedure involves dividing the data into T groups that share the same pattern of incomplete data. In certain special cases, such as $T = 2$, i.e., only two patterns of incomplete data, it is also possible to obtain analytic solutions to the likelihood equations.

The second missing data problem is the case where some observations of a discrete or continuous random variable are not available, but it is known that they fall into specified sets of groups of values. This problem is described as the problem of grouped data. The method for obtaining maximum likelihood estimates from data in which some observations are grouped can be reduced by an iterative procedure to the problem of maximum likelihood estimation in ungrouped data. Some theorems that are conditions for convergence are given along with an example of the method applied to estimation of the parameter of the censored Poisson distribution.

A third type of incomplete data problem considered is when some of the fixed independent variables are missing in regression or fixed effects analysis of variance. In the case of analysis of variance, maximum likelihood estimation leads to an integer programming problem that can be solved iteratively. In the case of regression analysis, an estimate of the values of the missing independent variables can be obtained in closed form.

Heckman, J. J. (1976). The common structure of statistical models of truncation, sample selection and limited dependent variables and a simple estimator for such models. *Annals of Economic and Social Measurement* 5: 475–492.

This paper presents a statistical model for estimation of parameters under a linear model with truncation, limited dependent variables, and nonrandom sample selection. The case of estimation under nonrandom sample selection can be interpreted as estimation when missing data are not missing at random. The model for a random sample may be written for the ith individual as

$$Y_{1i} = X_{1i}\beta_1 + U_{1i},$$

$$Y_{2i} = X_{2i}\beta_1 + U_{1i},$$

where X_{ji} is a vector of fixed variables, β_j is a vector of parameters, and the U_{ji} have zero expectations and are mutually independent.

Estimation of parameters β_1 is considered in two situations when the sample of available observations is not randomly selected. One situation is when Y_{1i} is not observed for all cases but we either know X_{1i} for all observations (a censored sample) or we have observations of X_{1i} only when Y_{1i} is available (a truncated sample). A second situation is when observations of Y_{1i} or X_{1i} or both are available only when Y_{2i} exceeds a fixed but unknown value.

Probit analysis and generalized least squares can be used to obtain consistent estimates of β_1 in the case of censored samples. First, probit analysis is used to estimate the probability that Y_{1j} is observed. Then this probability is used to estimate β_1. A modified version of these estimates are asymptotically efficient. Alternative estimators are also described.

A slightly more complicated procedure can be used to estimate β_1 in the situation where Y_{1i} and X_{1i} are observed depending on the value of Y_{2i}. In this situation asymptotically efficient estimators are not available. An example using real data is given to illustrate these methods.

Hendricks, W. A. (1949). Adjustment for bias caused by non-response in mailed surveys. *Agricultural Economics Research* 1; 52–56.

Complete returns of all mailed surveys are extremely unlikely, and the nonrespondents are usually not a representative sample. Therefore the non-returns in mailed surveys result in bias when estimates are based on the surveys returned. Sending more than one wave of surveys to the sample is one way of increasing response rate, but this seldom completely eliminates nonresponse. The data returned from successive waves of mailed surveys frequently exhibits a trend in responses over successive mailings, however.

This paper proposes a method for using the trend in responses from successive response waves to estimate the response mean corresponding to 100% response. A model is proposed where each individual has a score on the variable X, called "resistance." The resistance for an individual is the number of mailings required before the individual responds by completing and returning the survey. The quantity $\log(X/\overline{X})$ is assumed to be normally distributed in the population with zero mean, where $\overline{X}$ is the average value of resistance for all individuals in the sample. This assumption can be checked in any particular survey by plotting log X versus the standard normal deviate corresponding to the total fraction responding after each response wave. The relation will be linear if the model holds, and the intercept of the line is log $\bar{X}$. The dependent variable is then expanded in a series as a function of X. Inserting $\bar{X}$ into the series gives an expression for the average of the dependent variable over the entire sample including nonrespondents. The method is applied to data from two mailed surveys in North Carolina. Independent estimates of the quantities estimated from the two surveys were available and the techniques proposed appeared to substantially reduce the bias due to nonresponse.

Hilgard, E. R., and Payne, S. L. (1944). Those not at home: riddle for pollsters. *Public Opinion Quarterly* 8: 254–261.

Public opinion and market surveys frequently rely on contacting people in their homes. If some of the individuals selected for the sample are not at home when the interviewer calls, the result is missing data due to these "not-at-homes." If the individuals who are frequently not at home differ from the rest of the sample on the characteristic being measured, then excluding the "not-at-homes" from the sample results in biased estimates.

This paper presents some data from the 1943 Survey of Consumer Requirements, conducted by the Special Surveys Division of the Bureau of the Census for the Office of Civilian Requirements of the War Production Board. In this survey, repeated attempts were made to contact each individual until that individual was finally contacted. A record was kept of the number of calls required before the individual was contacted. It is therefore possible to compare the data collected from individuals who were contacted on the first, second, and third or later calls. These data demonstrate that individuals who are more difficult to contact differ from the total sample on a number of demographic characteristics such as age and the size of their families. The population estimates for some variables based on individuals contacted on the first call are also statistically significantly different than the estimates for the same variables based on individuals contacted in subsequent calls.

Hocking, R. R., Huddleston, H. F., and Hunt, H. H. (1974). A procedure for editing survey data. *Applied Statistics* 23: 121–133.

Sample surveys frequently contain missing responses for items or responses that are judged to be in error by an editing process. When the missing items are missing at random, this paper gives a procedure for maximum likelihood estimation of the mean vector of the survey items and the covariance matrix among the items. The procedure can handle situations where individual items are missing and where the sum of missing items is known.

The data consist of N records with p responses per record. Each record is assumed to be an observation from a p variate normal population with mean μ and covariance matrix Σ. A record is incomplete if any of the p responses is omitted or if only a linear combination, such as the sum, of some responses is available. The records are divided into T groups, each of which has the same pattern of incomplete data. Likelihood equations are derived that link μ and Σ to the data for each of the T groups. The algorithm for estimating μ and Σ starts with an initial estimate of Σ based on cases with complete data and the sample mean and covariance matrix in each of the T groups of records. These estimates are used to obtain an estimate of μ, which is in turn used to estimate Σ. The estimate of Σ from the first iteration is then used as a starting point for a second iteration, and the process continues until convergence is obtained. The procedure also yields estimates of the information matrices for μ and Σ. Except for special cases described by Hartley and Hocking (1971; see summary in this bibliography), there is no proof that the algorithm converges to the maximum likelihood estimates of μ and Σ. In practice the algorithm described converges quickly, and simulations suggest that global maxima of the likelihood function are usually attained.

A computer program, ESTMAT, has been written to implement the procedure described in this paper. Two examples are given to illustrate the use of the procedure with real data.

Hocking, R. R., and Oxspring, H. H. (1974). The analysis of partially categorized contingency data. *Biometrics* 30: 469–483.

One type of missing data problem in contingency tables occurs when some observations of a discrete variable are not available, but it is known that they fall into a specified set or group of values. For example, some particular observations might be known to fall in either row one or row three of the contingency table.

In some cases the partially categorized data may arise because of the nature of the data or because of the data collection procedure. In some cases the experiment may have been designed to yield partially categorized data to reduce the cost of complete categorization. The problem of estimating classification probabilities when the data follow the multinomial distribution and some of the classifications are "missing" in this way is called the "partially categorized" or "grouped data" problem.

This paper presents a method of obtaining maximum likelihood estimates of classification probabilities when the data contains some partially categorized observations. The method involves identifying different patterns of partial categorization as distinct contingency tables related to the full table. The problem is then reduced to combining information from a series of related tables. A system of indicator matrices permits a compact expression of the likelihood equation for the series of related tables. An iterative procedure for solution of the likelihood equation is described, and conditions under which a closed form solution exists are discussed. Likelihood ratio tests for independence of row and column classifications and tests for linear hypotheses about classification probabilities are developed. Four applications of the results of this paper are presented.

Kalton, G. (1982). Compensating for missing survey data. ISR Research Report Series, University of Michigan.

This report is concerned with issues of handling missing data in surveys with a focus on the needs of the Income Survey Development Program (ISDP), which concerned itself with income panel surveys conducted primarily in 1978 and 1979.

The work is divided into a number of major sections or chapters. The first of these discusses the types of nonresponse which occur in surveys: unit and item nonresponse and some of the circumstances in which they arise. The assumptions that are commonly made in nonresponse are also discussed and several criteria for assessing the compensation procedures are proposed. These criteria include the precision of the resulting survey estimators, the ease of estimating the standard errors of these estimators, and the ability of the procedures to generate reasonable estimators for a range of population parameters and missing data models.

Weighting adjustments, which are primarily employed to compensate for total or unit nonresponse, are extensively discussed. Methods covered include weighting the sample to some external source such as a census (as in post-stratification), simple inflation weighting adjustments, weighting different classes of the sample by the inverses of the response rate, and raking ratio estimation.

Imputation methods are discussed extensively as a way for handling item nonresponse. The methods reviewed include deductive imputation, cold-deck and hot-deck imputation, mean value and random imputation within classes, imputation by "statistical" matching, and regression imputation. The discussion focuses on several issues which arise in the use of imputation. Included among these are the effect of imputation on the measures of relations between variables, the need for imputed values to satisfy edit checks, problems of handling records with several missing responses, and the choice of control variables for forming imputation classes.

The results of two simulation studies are presented. These studies make concrete many of the general points made elsewhere. Finally, the report also comments on multiple imputation procedures. In particular, the report deals with the problems of applying these procedures to weighted data sets where the sample units are selected with unequal probabilities. A version of the multiple imputation procedure, termed "repeated replication imputation," is described in an appendix by Kish.

Kanuk, L., and Berenson, C. (1975). Mail surveys and response rates: A literature review. *Journal of Marketing Research* 12: 440–453.

This paper summarizes the results of empirical research on factors that affect response rate to mailed questionnaires. Follow-up questionnaires or mailed reminders are almost always successful in increasing response rate. A very high response rate can be achieved if a large number of follow-up mailings are sent. Preliminary notification that a survey will be forthcoming also increases response rate, particularly if the individuals are notified by telephone. Researchers have also focused on a number of aspects of survey design in addition to follow-ups and advanced notification. Contrary to expectations, research evidence does not support the idea that shorter questionnaires obtain higher response rates. Similarly, there is virtually no evidence that sponsorships of the survey by an official or "respected" agency increases response rates. There is little consistent evidence on the effects of various types of postage used to send surveys, except that the use of special delivery enhances response rate. Personalization of the cover letter by using an inside address or individually signed letter does not seem to increase response rate. It is widely thought that anonymity of responses should increase response rate, particularly to sensitive questions. The experimental evidence indicates that this is not true. A few research studies have examined the effects of the size, color, and method of reproduction used for the questionnaire, but no consistent effects on response rate were found. Several studies indicate that a 25¢ incentive sent with the questionnaire increases the response rate. Larger incentives are found to yield further increases in response rate. The studies that examined the use of deadline dates set for return of the questionnaire did not find an increase in response rate. The use of deadlines did result in earlier return of questionnaires, however.

Another line of research has been the examination of demographic and personality differences between respondents and nonrespondents. Some differences have been found, which suggests that the nonrespondents to mailed questionnaires cannot be considered a random sample from the same population as the respondents.

Kaufman, G. M., and King, B. (1973). A Bayesian analysis of nonresponse in dichotomous processes. *Journal of the American Statistical Association* 68: 670–678.

In a dichotomous process let p_f and $p_u = 1 - p_f$ be the probability of favorable (F) and unfavorable (U) responses, respectively. However, for any particular person there is also a probability of responding (R) or not responding (S), thus generating a double dichotomy:

	Parameters				Sample		
	R	S			R	S	
F	p_{fr}	p_{fs}	p_f	F	n_{fr}	n_{fs}	n_f
U	p_{ur}	p_{us}	p_u	U	n_{ur}	n_{us}	n_u
	p_r	p_s	1		n_r	n_s	n

However, although n_s is observed, the components n_{fs} and n_{us} are not observed.

The problem is to estimate p_f. The analysis is Bayesian and permits us to bypass the difficulty of not observing all the data. An alternative parameterization is used: $p_{r \cdot f}$ and $p_{r \cdot u}$ are conditional probabilities of response given favorable or unfavorable category, respectively; $p_{f \cdot r}$ and $p_{f \cdot s}$ are the conditional probabilities of favorable given response or nonresponse category, respectively.

Using independent beta priors for p_f, $p_{r \cdot f}$, and $p_{r \cdot u}$, with some restrictions on the parameters of the beta density, considerable simplification is accomplished.

Assume that all nonrespondents sampled in a follow-up sample respond. The problem is to determine an optimal sample size n and an optimal follow-up sample size k. In the case of an infinite population, formulas are presented for determining n and k. These are not simple to describe but can be obtained numerically. There is considerable discussion on the exact and approximate solutions, which are illustrated by a numerical example.

King, B. F. (1974). Surveys combining probability and quota methods of sampling. *Proceedings of the Social Statistics Section*, American Statistical Association, pp. 351–356.

A model is assumed in which p primary sampling units (PSUs) are randomly selected and that either full probability or quota sampling or both are applied to the units within each PSU.

The following specification is assumed: for $i = 1, \ldots, p$

$$\tilde{x}_{ij}^u = \mu^u + \tilde{\gamma}_i + \tilde{\varepsilon}_{ij}^u, \qquad j = 1, \ldots, n^u,$$

$$\tilde{x}_{ik}^b = \mu^b + \tilde{\gamma}_i + \tilde{\varepsilon}_{ij}^b, \qquad j = 1, \ldots, n^b,$$

where $\tilde{x}^u$ and $\tilde{x}^b$ represent observations from unbiased (probability) and biased (quota) measurement processes, respectively; $\tilde{\gamma}_i$ is a random effect that depends only on the primary sampling unit. The disturbances $\tilde{\varepsilon}^u$, $\tilde{\varepsilon}^b$, and $\tilde{\gamma}$ are mutually independent. The parameters μ^u and μ^b are the expected values of $\tilde{x}^u$ and $\tilde{x}^b$, respectively; the difference $\mu^u - \mu^b$ is the bias.

A bivariate normal prior is assumed for (μ^u, μ^b), which leads to various posterior analysis formulas. Using cost k_c for setting up the survey, per unit costs k^u and k^b for probability and quota sampling, respectively, a fixed budget is equal to

$$k^* = k_c p + k^u p n^u + k^b p n^b.$$

A discussion of optimal allocation is then provided when there is a fixed budget.

Some comparisons are made to determine when quota sampling should be used, which turns out to be when the process means are correlated.

One of the important consequences of the present development is that it provides a means for determining the effect of various prior assumptions.

Little, R. J. A. (1979). Maximum likelihood inference for multiple regression with missing values: a simulation study. *Journal of the Royal Statistical Society*, Series B, 41: 76–87.

Two commonly used methods for handling data missing at random in multiple regression are least squares estimation using only complete observations and maximum likelihood estimation. This paper compares these two methods of handling missing data when the independent and dependent variables have a joint multivariate normal distribution. The specific model used in the simulation has three independent variables $X = (X_1, X_2, X_3)'$ such that the regression coefficients are $\beta - (\beta_1, \beta_2, \beta_3)$ and the dependent variable Y is given by $Y = \beta X + \varepsilon$, $X \sim N_3(\mu, \Sigma)$, $\varepsilon \sim N_1(0, \sigma^2)$. The simulation used five parameter sets and six patterns of missing X_i values (with $N = 50$ or $N = 100$), each replicated 50 times. Two methods of estimating the covariance matrix of $\hat{\beta}$ were used, one based on the inverse of the information matrix and one based on the weighted sum of cross products matrix.

The analysis of mean square error of regression coefficients showed that maximum likelihood estimation based on all observations produced more accurate estimates than those obtained by discarding incomplete observations. The estimate of the covariance matrix based on weighted sums of cross-products produced better estimates of the variances of the $\hat{\beta}_i$ than did the inverse of the information matrix. Confidence intervals for the β_i based on large-sample normal theory and the former estimate of the variance were quite good when the amount of missing data was not large. When the number of missing observations was relatively large, the use of a distribution with heavier tails in place of the asymptotic normal distribution appeared to yield more accurate inferences. In such cases a t distribution with $N - 4$ degrees of freedom appeared to produce more accurate confidence intervals than the normal. The theoretical efficiency of maximum likelihood based on all data relative to least squares on the complete observations was found to be biased in favor of maximum likelihood, particularly when the sample was small.

Matthai, A. (1951): Estimation of parameters from incomplete data with application to design of sample surveys. *Sankhyā* 11: 145–152.

This paper deals with the estimation of the mean vector in a trivariate normal distribution when observations are missing at random. There are n_{123} observations of (X_1, X_2, X_3); n_{120}, n_{103}, and n_{023} of $(X_1, X_2), (X_1, X_3)$, and (X_2, X_3); and $n_{100}, n_{020}, n_{003}$ of X_1, X_2, and X_3, respectively.

When the covariance matrix is known the maximum likelihood equations can be solved explicitly as a matrix equation. When the covariances are unknown, the author suggests estimating the covariances using all the data available for the particular pairs. This could lead to a nonpositive definite estimate of the covariance matrix.

This paper extends the results of Wilks (1932; see summary in this bibliography) for the bivariate normal case. The more general case can now be resolved numerically; for a general discussion see, e.g., Little (1979; see summary in this bibliography).

Nargundkar, M. S., and Joshi, G. B. (1975). Non-response in sample surveys. Contributed Papers, *40th Session of the International Statistical Institute*, Warsaw, pp. 626–628.

Several procedures are currently used to handle missing data in sample surveys. These approaches include hot-deck methods and various weighting procedures. The disadvantage of all these procedures is that, while they provide estimates of population means, it is extremely difficult to obtain estimates of sampling variances.

This paper provides a new approach to missing data in sample surveys by explicitly considering response to the survey to be a random event. Let U_i be the probability that the ith individual in the population will provide information when selected into the sample. Expressions for the estimate of the mean and the variance of that estimate can be obtained for any sample where U_i and the probability that each individual will be selected into the sample are known. Assuming that the U_i are constant over suitable population subgroups, we can obtain empirical estimates of the U_i. This then permits estimates of the variance of the mean. It is suggested that additional data on response probability in various population subgroups could be collected through experimentation. These data could be used either to increase the precision of survey estimates or to plan more efficient survey designs.

Nelson, F. D. (1977). Censored regression models with unobserved stochastic censoring threshold. *Journal of Econometrics* 6: 309–327.

This paper is concerned with the problem of estimation in the linear model with a censored dependent variable. This is equivalent to a special case of missing observations on the dependent variable in linear regression where the data are not missing at random. The model considered is

$$y_{1t} = \beta_1 X_t + u_{1t},$$

$$y_{2t} = \beta_2 X_t + u_{2t},$$

and

$$Y_t = \begin{cases} y_{1t} & \text{if} \quad y_{1t} \geq y_{2t} \\ 0 & \text{if} \quad y_{1t} < y_{2t}, \end{cases}$$

where Y_t is the censored dependent variable, y_{1t} and y_{2t} are latent (not directly observable) variables, X_t is a vector of observable variables, and u_{1t} and u_{2t} are random disturbances assumed to have the bivariate normal distribution with zero mean and unknown covariance matrix.

Maximum likelihood estimation under this model is considered and various conditions necessary for identification of the likelihood equations are established. Methods for iterative solution of the likelihood equations and methods of generating starting values are discussed. Some special cases considered in detail are when

(1) Y_t and y_{2t} are observed.
(2) y_{1t} is observed and it is known which observations are censored.
(3) Y_t is observed and it is known which of the observations is censored.

The results of a small simulation study are reported to illustrate some results of the method under various conditions and to compare the estimates obtained with the estimates obtained by ordinary least squares regression on the complete observations.

An extensive application of the censored variable models to the estimation of parameters in a variety of economic relations is also given.

Nordbotten, S. (1965). The efficiency of automatic detection and correction of errors in individual observations as compared with other means for improving the quality of statistics. *Bulletin of the International Statistical Institute, Proceedings of the 35th Session*, Belgrade, 41 : 417–441.

Large-scale sample surveys require some procedures for detection and correction of errors in the data before estimates are prepared. This paper reports a simulation study comparing the cost and accuracy of several methods of detecting and correcting errors in survey data. The study uses an actual large data set in which errors are artificially introduced.

The model for the error structure uses several sources of error, including two levels of measurement precision (ideal versus not ideal), changes in the values of measured variables from one time period to another, and the usual sampling variability. Fourteen different sampling and data correction designs were investigated, including various combinations of ideal versus not ideal initial measurements, different methods of detecting missing data, and different methods of imputing corrections. Detailed tables of the results of the simulations are given.

Several conclusions emerged from the study. First, since some measurement methods may yield more precise results, but take a longer time to complete (production time), the production time of a measurement method must be taken into account in planning sample surveys where the variable being measured changes rapidly. Second, automatic detection of errors coupled with precise reobservation of data detected as errors appears to be an efficient method of dealing with very deviant observations if the criteria for detecting errors are set appropriately. Automatic correction of errors by a prespecified algorithm was found to be highly inaccurate in some cases. There was evidence that the correction procedures employed in the study sometimes changed large numbers of valid observations.

Oh, H. L., and Scheuren, F. (1978a). Multivariate raking ratio estimation in the 1973 Exact Match Study. *Proceedings of the Section on Survey Research Methods*, American Statistical Association, pp. 716–722.

When a sample is subject to data not missing at random (coverage errors) but the exact marginal totals for a multiway table are known, it may be desirable to adjust sample data to fit these marginal constraints. One method of adjustment was called raking by Deming and Stephan (1940). The raking procedure begins with a set of constraint equations that say that the sums of the adjusted cell frequencies equal the constrained marginal totals. Each constraint equation is solved in turn to obtain a simple ratio adjustment factor to reweight the sample so that the row total will agree with the known marginal total. After reweighting based on the row constraint equation is solved, and the data is reweighted so that the row total matches the specified marginal total, the process continues iteratively along all dimensions of the table. A cycle of adjustments to each dimension of the table is then repeated until individual cell entries do not change appreciably as a result of reweighting. In practice, only a few cycles of adjustment through each dimension of the table are usually needed to obtain convergence.

The present paper extends the method of raking to the case of multivariate observations on individuals. The method was developed for the 1973 Exact Match Study. The data for each individual was a vector of observations. Thus each cell of the multiway table consists of a vector of counts and each component of the vector must receive the same adjustment. A marginal constraint on each component of the data vector is given. A multivariate raking procedure is given that successively adjusts cell counts for row constraints on each component of the data vector. Similar adjustments are then made on each dimension of the table iteratively. As in the univariate case, iteration continues until the adjusted cell frequencies do not change appreciably.

Oh, H. L., and Scheuren, F. (1978b). Some unresolved issues in raking ratio estimation. *Proceedings of the Section on Survey Research Methods*, American Statistical Association, pp. 723–728.

When a sample is subject to coverage errors, some observations are not missing at random. If exact marginal totals are known for a multiway table based on such observations, raking can be used to adjust the sample data to fit the marginal constraints. The raking adjustment procedure sometimes reduces bias due to coverage errors, and may decrease the variance of the estimates.

Raking begins with a set of constraint equations that equate the row and column sums of adjusted cell entries to the known marginal totals. The row constraint equation is solved and the cell entries are reweighted to give the correct row total. The column constraint equations are then solved, and the data are reweighted again to give the correct column total. The process continues along each dimension of the table. A cycle of reweightings based on constraints due to each dimension of the table continues until the individual cell entries do not change appreciably upon reweighting.

Despite an extensive literature on raking, not much is known about the effect of raking on the mean squared error of surveys when raking is used to control coverage errors (missing data that is not missing at random). This paper reports the results of simulations of raking for control of coverage errors.

For small samples raking increased the variance of estimators as expected, though there was a substantial decrease in variance due to raking in larger samples. Similarly, the larger the number of categories, the smaller the benefit of raking, unless sample sizes were very large. When the sample was subject to nonrandomly missing data (coverage error) the raked estimators had larger variance except when the raked and dependent variables were highly dependent.

Thus it was felt that in typical surveys, with many variables and some coverage errors, raking would decrease the mean squared error of some variables while increasing the mean squared error of others. Under these conditions raking must be employed with considerable care.

Orchard, T., and Woodbury, M. A. (1972). A missing information principle: theory and applications. *Proceedings of the Sixth Berkeley Symposium on Mathematical Statistics and Probability* 1 : 697–715.

This paper contains a presentation of the theory underlying the missing information principle. The missing information principle has been the basis for several algorithms for estimation of parameters when the missing observations are missing at random (see, e.g., Dempster, Laird, and Rubin, 1977, summarized in this bibliography). The missing information principle uses a factorization of the density function $f(X|\theta)$ of the complete data vector X given the parameter θ. Let $X = (Y, Z)$ where Y is observed and Z contains the missing components; then

$$f(X|\theta) = f_1(Y|\theta)f_2(Z|\theta, Y)$$

is a factorization of the density function of X into the marginal density function of Y and the conditional density function of Z given Y. This factorization leads to an analogous factorization of the likelihood $L(X|\theta)$, and expressions for efficient scores $\mathrm{SCO}(\theta|X)$ and the information matrix $J(\theta_j, \theta_k)$ as sums of two components. If $L(X|\theta)$, $L_1(X|Y, \theta)$, and $L_2(Y|\theta)$ are the conditional likelihoods of X and Y, as indicated, then

$$L(X|\theta) = L_1(X|Y, \theta)L_2(Y|\theta),$$

$$\mathrm{SCO}(\theta_j|X) = \frac{\partial \log L_1}{\partial \theta_j} + \mathrm{SCO}(\theta_j, Y),$$

$$J(\theta_j, \theta_k|X) = J(\theta_j, \theta_k|Y) + J(\theta_j, \theta_k; Y|X),$$

where $J(\theta_j, \theta_k; Y|X) = E\{\mathrm{Cov}[\mathrm{SCO}(\theta_j|X), \mathrm{SCO}(\theta_k|X)|Y]\}$ is called the "lost information" due to the missing data. This formulation leads to the equation

$$\mathrm{SCO}(\theta_j|Y) = E[\mathrm{SCO}(\theta_j|X)|Y],$$

which is useful in obtaining maximum likelihood estimates of parameters in the presence of missing observations because it is often easy to calculate the right-hand side even when it is difficult to calculate the left-hand side. The "lost information" is shown to be directly related to increases in the variance of parameter estimates due to missing observations.

Examples of applications of the missing information principle are given in the case of the univariate linear model, estimation of parameters of the multivariate normal distribution, and estimation in problems concerning mixtures of distributions.

Platek, R., Singh, M. P., and Tremblay, V. (1978). Adjustment for nonresponse in surveys. In N. K. Namboodiri (ed.), *Survey Sampling and Measurement*, pp. 157–174. New York: Academic Press.

Generally, the problems due to nonresponse are caused by the differences in characteristics between nonrespondents and respondents. To overcome these problems, attempts are made to obtain some indication of the characteristics of the nonrespondents by such means as follow-up, record substitution, and linkage with other data. The approach used is that of response probability in which each unit has a given probability of responding (if selected). Assuming a complete enumeration, general expressions for the bias and variance of the estimate are developed for any imputation procedure.

A brief discussion is presented on the comparison between these expressions indicating the main factors which affect the nonresponse bias and the variance. Empirical results are given for the Auto Exit Survey and the Canadian Labour Force Survey.

Politz, A., and Simmons, W. (1949). An attempt to get the "not at homes" into the sample without callbacks. *Journal of the American Statistical Association* 44: 9–31.

Missing data often arise in sample surveys because individuals are not at home when the interviewer calls on them. These cases of missing data are called "not-at-homes." The simplest device for dealing with "not-at-homes" is completion of the sample by revisiting, again and again, until the missing individual is found. Repeated revisiting (callbacks) can be quite costly, however, and the number of callbacks is usually limited to some fixed number. The expense of callbacks has led to the use of subsampling of the "not-at-homes" in which only a subsample will be revisited.

This paper develops a method for obtaining estimates of the mean without callbacks. The procedure is based on weighting responses using an estimate of the amount of time that an individual is home. An interview is scheduled for each individual at a random time during the interview period (usually one week). Each individual is interviewed once and information is obtained regarding whether that individual was at home at a specific time during each day of the preceding interview period (usually one week). The survey data from individuals are then grouped according to the percentage of time that the individuals are at home. The sample estimate of the mean is obtained by weighting each group by the reciprocal of the proportion of time that they are at home. A check on the reliability of responses is provided by comparing the actual percentage of the sample found at home versus the percentage estimated from the data collected during the interviews.

Expressions for the variance of the weighted estimate of the mean are derived and a numerical example is given. The weighting method is also compared with the callback method in a hypothetical example. Recommendations are also made on conditions under which the higher costs of callbacks might be justified.

Pregibon, D. (1976). Incomplete survey data: Estimation and imputation. *Methodology Journal of Household Survey Division*, Statistics Canada.

This article discusses a special class of missing data problems in which zeros dominate the multivariate response space—an attribute typical of much survey data. A probabilistic model is introduced that provides reasonable estimates while at the time it maintains the distribution of the data base. This model can also be used to include subjective information into its imputation scheme. Under certain conditions the model reduces to a hot-deck procedure.

The particular procedure makes use of a classifying vector $\mathbf{z}$ for each vector of survey variables $\mathbf{x}$. The ith element $z_i, i = 1, \ldots, n$, of z is defined by

$$z_i = \begin{cases} 0 & \text{if } x_i = 0 \\ 1 & \text{if } x_i \neq 0 \\ 2 & \text{if } x_i \text{ is missing,} \end{cases}$$

where n is the sample size. Using this $\mathbf{z}$ vector, each responding unit is classified into domains (thus, no z_i is equal to 2). Then the units with missing items are classified into domains—a classification which may take into account prior probabilities of whether a missing item is zero or positive. Once all units are classified, missing values are made into a zero if the corresponding z_i of the domain is 0 or a positive number if the z_i of the domain is 1. The exact value of the positive imputations is determined by any procedure of the user's choice as long as only the positive values of the respondents in the domain are used.

Using data from the 1974 Agriculture Enumerative Survey, the author demonstrates the use of this procedure and compares it to (1) a procedure that simply ignores the units with missing data, (2) a method that inflates the estimates given by individual domains to account for the missing data, and (3) a multiple linear regression method. The author hypothesizes that because this procedure uses more information, it will prove to be superior based on eight multivariate criteria that are defined. Given the particular data set used by the author, this method does perform quite well (as does the linear regression method). The real advantage of the method comes in the estimation of subpopulation parameters.

Pregibon, D. (1977). Typical survey data: estimation and imputation. *Methodology Journal of the Household Survey Division* 2: 70–103.

A special class of missing data problems arises when zeros are the predominant response to the survey question but other quantitative responses are possible. This class of survey data is common and is referred to as "typical survey data" in this paper. In this case, methods for imputing missing data which do not make use of the fact that zeros are the most common response are frequently misleading.

This paper contains an exposition of a method for imputing missing values in typical survey data where the missing observations are not missing at random. The imputation procedure imputes values in two stages based on the pattern of missing observations. First, a discrete method is used to determine whether to impute a zero or a nonzero quantitative value in a particular data field. Then if a nonzero quantitative value is to be imputed, a regression imputation is made using data from all observations with the same pattern of missing data. The first-stage procedure for imputing either zeros or nonzero quantitative values utilizes a prior estimate of the probability that a zero value should be imputed for a missing observation. By altering the values of these prior probability estimates, the imputed values will have the same or different joint frequency distributions as the complete data. In particular, this procedure permits imputation of missing data under models in which the data come from a mixture of populations defined by patterns of complete data.

A simulation study comparing the proposed imputation method with several other methods of imputation showed that this method performs comparatively well. It should be recognized, however, that the method proposed was designed for "typical survey data" while the other methods used were developed for imputation in more general situations.

Rao, J. N. K. (1973). On double sampling for stratification and analytical surveys. *Biometrika* 60: 125–133.

A population of size N is to be stratified according to the values of an auxiliary or classification variable x, whose distribution is unknown. A large sample (simple random sampling without replacement) of size n' is taken and according to the observed x, L strata are created with $n'_1, n'_2, \ldots, n'_L$ units, respectively ($\Sigma n'_i = n'$). The sample size n' is sufficiently large so that no n'_i is zero. From stratum k, a subsample of size n_k from n'_k (by simple random sampling without replacement) is taken, and this is true for $k = 1, \ldots, L$.

Denote by $\bar{Y}_h$ the population mean for stratum h and by $\bar{Y}$ the population mean. That is, $\bar{Y} = \sum_1^L (N_h/N)\bar{Y}_h$. To estimate $\bar{Y}$, use

$$\bar{y}^* = \sum_1^L (n'_h/n;)\bar{y}_h,$$

where $\bar{y}_h$ is the sample mean for stratum h. The variance of $\bar{y}^*$ is computed and an unbiased estimator of $\mathrm{Var}(\bar{y}^*)$ derived. Using a cost function, "optimal" sample sizes $n_1, \ldots, n_L$ are determined.

The case $L = 2$ is of special interest since one stratum may be respondents and the other nonrespondents. This case is studied in some detail.

The remainder of the paper deals with a further development of analytical surveys. In particular, the two-factor comparative study of Booth and Sedransk (1969) is considered in detail. Here there are two factors (α and τ), each having two categories, so that we have a 2×2 table:

		Factor τ		
		Cat. 1	Cat. 2	
Factor Category α	1	N_{11}	N_{12}	$N_{1\cdot}$
	2	N_{21}	N_{22}	$N_{2\cdot}$
		$N_{\cdot 1}$	$N_{\cdot 2}$	N

The two categories for each factor are compared via the functions

$$D_\alpha = \frac{N_{\cdot 1}}{N}(\bar{y}_{11} - \bar{y}_{21}) + \frac{N_{\cdot 2}}{N}(\bar{y}_{12} - \bar{y}_{22}),$$

$$D_\tau = \frac{N_{\cdot 1}}{N}(\bar{y}_{11} - \bar{y}_{12}) + \frac{N_{2\cdot}}{N}(\bar{y}_{21} - \bar{y}_{22}),$$

where $\bar{y}_{ij}$ is the population mean for cell (i, j). Unbiased estimates for D_α and D_τ are provided and a prescription for choosing sample sizes.

Rao, P. S. R. S. (1966). A study of call backs in sample surveys. Technical Report No. 10, Department of Statistics, Harvard University, Cambridge, Mass.

Callbacks are one of the most effective means of reducing nonresponse in sample surveys. The literature on the use of callbacks in sample surveys indicates that callback policy is influenced by a number of factors, such as the response of the chosen type of individual, the biases at successive calls, the available budget and planned sample size, the relative cost of making callbacks, and the desired accuracy. Deming (1953) proposed a mathematical model to study the effectiveness of callbacks that included each of these factors.

This paper uses Deming's model (1953; see summary in this bibliography) to present a systematic evaluation of the effects of these factors on callback surveys. The paper relies on data about the response rates and biases of 22 surveys that used callbacks. General advice is given on the number of calls that should be prescribed for a sample survey. For some types of surveys commonly met in practice, an expression is given for obtaining the number of calls yielding highest accuracy for an available budget. A method is also suggested for predicting the number of callbacks required in advance of the actual survey. The extensive tables and analyses of the 22 exemplary surveys are also helpful in judging the typical relative magnitudes of parameters in the Demings model.

Rubin, D. B. (1974). Characterizing the estimation of parameters in incomplete-data problems. *Journal of the American Statistical Association* 69: 467–474.

This paper presents an approach to the problem of estimating parameters of a multivariate data set which contains blocks of observations that are missing at random. "The basic technique is to decompose the original estimation problem into smaller estimation problems by factoring the likelihood of the observed data into a product of conditional likelihoods" with distinct parameters. An algorithm is given to generate a factorization table that summarizes the factorization and distinguishes factors whose parameters can be estimated using standard (complete data) techniques from factors whose parameters must be estimated by special (incomplete data) methods. The factorization table also indicates which rows of the data matrix are relevant for each factor and thus identifies the amount of data available for estimation of each parameter. This factorization table also permits easy identification of any parameters that are inestimable because of the pattern of missing data. It may also suggest which observations to delete or "fill in" so that the data are minimally disturbed and so that standard complete data methods could be used to estimate all parameters.

Several special cases of patterned missing data are discussed. An example of construction and interpretation of a factorization table is given.

Rubin, D. B. (1976). Inference and missing data. *Biometrika* 63: 581–592.

The analysis of a data set with missing observations frequently proceeds with the (sometimes implicit) assumption that the process that caused the missing data can be ignored. The purpose of this paper is to derive "the weakest simple conditions on the process that causes the missing data such that it is always appropriate to ignore this process when making inferences about the distribution of the data." A model for missing data is proposed that relies on the observed values of a random variable and a second random variable that indicates whether a potential observation is actually observed. Formal definitions are given for "the process that causes the missing data" and "ignoring the process that causes the missing data." The terms "data missing at random" and "data observed at random" are also distinguished.

Conditions are obtained so that sampling distributions derived by ignoring the process that causes missing data are the same as distributions obtained without assuming the process causing missing data is ignorable.

Similar results are obtained for direct likelihood and Bayesian inference, i.e., conditions under which ignoring the process causing missing data yields the same conclusions as an analysis using information on the process causing the missing data.

There are two basic conclusions:

(1)   For making sampling distribution inferences about a parameter of the data θ: If missing data are "missing at random" and observed data are "observed at random," then, conditional on the observed pattern of missing data, the same sampling distributions of statistics are obtained whether the process causing missing data is ignored or taken into account.

(2)   For making direct likelihood or Bayesian inferences about a parameter of the data θ: If the missing data are "missing at random" and the parameter of the missing data process is "distinct" from θ, then the same likelihood ratios and posterior distributions are obtained whether the process causing missing data is ignored or taken into account.

Rubin, D. B. (1977). Formalizing subjective notions about the effect of nonrespondents in sample surveys. *Journal of the American Statistical Association* 72: 538–543.

In most sample surveys with missing data, the investigator must make some subjective judgments about the effect of nonrespondents. These subjective judgments are equivalent to hypotheses about the value of the sample statistic that would have been calculated if the nonrespondents had responded. This paper formalizes some aspects of subjective judgments about the effects of missing data. Bayesian techniques are used to produce a subjective probability interval for the sample mean $\overline{Y}$ that would have been observed if all the subjects had responded.

The model is that a variable Y is linearly related to a vector valued background variable X, so that

$$E(\overline{Y}_R) = \alpha_R + \beta_R \overline{X}_R,$$

$$E(\overline{Y}_{NR}) = \alpha_{NR} + \beta_{NR} \overline{X}_{NR},$$

where $\overline{Y}_R$, $\overline{Y}_{NR}$, $\overline{X}_R$, and $\overline{X}_{NR}$ are the observed sample means and background variable means for the respondents and nonrespondents, respectively, and α_R, α_{NR}, β_R, and β_{NR} are unknown parameters. The Y variable is assumed to be normally distributed conditional on X. The parameters α_R and β_R can be estimated from the respondent sample. Two subjective parameters are then introduced to formalize the idea of generating plausible values of α_{NR} and β_{NR}. The subjective parameters are used in conjunction with the observed background (X) data and observed (X, Y) data for nonrespondents to obtain a subjective probability interval for the overall mean $\overline{Y}$. An explicit expression for the subjective probability interval for $\overline{Y}$ is given and a scheme for efficient computation is described. The method is illustrated using data from a survey of 660 schools that includes 188 nonrespondents.

Rubin, D. B. (1978a). Multiple imputations in sample surveys—a phenomenological Bayesian approach to nonresponse. In *Imputation and Editing of Faulty or Missing Survey Data*, U.S. Dept. of Commerce, pp. 1–23.

This paper is an outline of the general phenomenological Bayesian approach to nonresponse in sample surveys. In this approach, the objective is to determine how different the summary statistics based on a survey would have been if the nonrespondents had responded. Since the data from nonrespondents are, by definition, unavailable, the objective is therefore to show how the survey summary statistics change under a variety of reasonable models. The subjective criterion of reasonable models implies the necessity of formulating models in such a way that other investigators can easily understand the models used and judge the appropriateness of the models.

A procedure is suggested that involves imputing many different values for each missing observation. First several reasonable models for the data are selected. Then each model is used to impute a number of different values for each missing observation. The result is a collection of complete data sets, one for each set of imputed values for each model. Each of the complete data sets in the collection is then analyzed, and the resulting summary statistics are tabulated. The summary statistics can then be examined to determine the variability of the summary statistics between and within models. If there is little variability between models, then the investigator may conclude that the survey finding can be sharply defined despite missing observations. On the other hand, if there is substantial variability in results between or within models, then sharp inferences are not possible.

An efficient procedure for specifying different models, storing the collection of data sets with imputed values, and completing a set of analyses is given. A phenomenonlogical Bayesian framework for imputing values is outlined, and some suggestions for classes of reasonable models are discussed.

Rubin, D. B. (1978b). The phenomenological Bayesian perspective in sample surveys from finite populations: Foundations. In *Imputation and Editing of Faulty or Missing Survey Data*, U.S. Dept. of Commerce, pp. 10–18.

This paper is a presentation of the fundamental ideas of the phenomenological Bayesian approach to sample surveys. This approach is phenomenological in the sense that all questions of interest are defined explicitly in terms of observable quantities. In contrast, nonphenomenological approaches define questions of interest partially in terms of inherently unobservable parameters of underlying processes. Specific probability models are used to calculate distributions of observables using Bayes's theorem, but particular models are deemphasized. The sensitivity of inferences to models drawn from a broad range of models that are not contradicted by the data is emphasized. The phenomenological Bayesian approach to sample surveys is also compared with the classical sampling theory approach and other Bayesian approaches.

Precise definitions are given for the notions of sampling mechanism and data recording mechanism in terms of conditional probability distributions. Definitions of ignorable sampling or data recording mechanisms are also given along with some specific examples of ignorable and nonignorable mechanisms. The predictive distribution of a set of missing observations is defined as the posterior distribution of the unknown observations given the known observations and the prior specifications. The concepts of ignorable sampling and data recording mechanisms are used to derive predictive distributions under various conditions of ignorability. The concepts of ignorability are also shown to be related to exchangeability in the conditional distributions of all (known and missing) observations given the sampling and data recording mechanisms. The advantage of ignorable sampling and data recording mechanisms is that they greatly simplify model building for inference. Therefore, since the sampling and data recording mechanisms are under the control of the investigator, these mechanisms should be chosen to be ignorable whenever possible.

Santos, R. L. (1982). Effects of imputation on complex statistics. ISR Research Report Series, University of Michigan.

This report presents the results of theoretical and empirical investigations into the effects of imputation on complex statistics. Particular emphasis is placed on regression statistics.

The investigations were developed to meet the imputation needs of the Income Survey Development Program (ISDP). The ISDP envisioned a large-scale data collection activity in which many panels of information were obtained and which would naturally give rise to a greater amount of missing data then would be encountered in a one-time survey. In consequence, how to handle missing data was considered to be a special concern for this survey.

The report begins with a discussion of the missing data environment in which the ISDP panels were collected. Two model frameworks are developed in order to examine missingness in the ISDP. These models are the missing at random (MAR) and the missing at random within cells (MARC) models. Theoretical results are provided for these models for a simple case in which there are three variables (X, Y, and Z), of which only Y incurs missing data. The focus of this discussion is on the impact of imputation on the covariance between X and Y. The general large sample bias of the usual simple random sample estimators of the covariance is derived for each of a half-dozen different imputation schemes.

The general results often simplify in the cases of MAR and MARC missing data. The main consideration for covariance biases to imputation is whether the variable X or some other variable highly correlated with X is employed in the imputation scheme. (The relative biases are shown to be proportional to the rate of missing data.)

The empirical underpinnings of this work come from the 1978 ISDP panel survey, which is used to illustrate alternatives in two ways. The first study investigates the effects of imputation of missing data for hourly wage rates in the July 1978 questionnaire. The second study investigates the effects of impu-tation of missing data for an aggregate variable (quarterly was income as derived from income records in the April 1978 questionnaire). Overall the results of the empirical investigations are in line with theoretical findings.

Simmons, W. R. (1954). A plan to account for "not at homes" by combining weighting and call-backs. *Journal of Marketing* 19: 42–53.

This paper describes two methods for increasing the accuracy of surveys with missing data that result from subjects being away from home when the inter-viewer calls "not-at-homes." One method for dealing with "not-at-homes" is for the interviewer to call on the subject again (the callback). The callback is there-fore a procedure for obtaining the actual values of missing observations. While repeated callbacks solve the problem of missing data by eliminating missing observations, repeated callbacks can also be quite expensive, depending on the number of callbacks required to obtain the missing observations and the travel time required for interviewers to reach the subjects. A second method for obtaining unbiased estimates of a mean when there are "not-at-homes" was suggested by Politz and Simmons (1949). It is based on weighting according to the percentage of time an individual is at home. In this method, interviews are scheduled at random times during an interview period (typically one week). Respondents are asked whether they were at home during a randomly selected time during each day of the preceeding interview period (typically the previous week). The data for respondents are then weighted inversely according to the number of times that they were home in the previous interview period. This weighting procedure produces unbiased estimates of a mean when the mean differs as a function of the number of days that each respondent is available for interview. The weighting scheme is inexpensive to implement, but a high proportion of "not-at-homes" inflates the variance of the weighted estimates.

A combination of a limited number of callbacks and the weighting scheme is also possible. This combination approach is frequently a good compromise between precision and cost in dealing with the problem of "not-at-homes" in sample surveys. Formulas for the weights and sampling variances of the combination estimators are given. The combination approach is illustrated by application of this method to the Crowell–Collier Automotive Survey of 1953.

Singh, B., and Sedransk, J. (1975). Estimation of regression coefficients when there is nonresponse. Technical Report No. 25, Department of Computer Science, State University of New York at Buffalo.

"Assuming nonresponse, inference concerning the regression coefficients of a multiple linear regression is considered from a Bayesian viewpoint. We exploit a two phase sampling scheme. At each phase the sample design is of the following type: select a random sample of size n with n_1 responses obtained. Then, a subsample of size n_2 ($0 \leq n_2 \leq n - n_1$) is selected from the $n - n_1$ nonrespondents. The objectives are: (1) to obtain the optimal point estimators of the regression coefficients; (2) to ascertain at the second phase of sampling the optimal number of nonrespondents to be subsampled; (3) to determine the optimal overall sample size at the second phase" (authors' summary).

More specifically, suppose for r strata we have a regression model for respondents (R) and nonrespondents (NR)

$$x_j^R = \sum_{k=1}^{r} \beta_k^R z_{kj}^R + \varepsilon_j^R,$$

$$x_j^{NR} = \sum_{k=1}^{r} \beta_k^{NR} z_{kj}^{NR} + \varepsilon_j^{NR},$$

where the ε_j^R and the ε_j^{NR} are independently normally distributed with zero mean and variance $1/h^R$ and $1/h^{NR}$, respectively. Further, it is assumed that the regression coefficient β_k in the entire population is given by

$$\beta_k = \pi\beta_k^R + (1 - \pi)\beta_k^{NR},$$

where π is the population proportion of units in the respondent stratum.

A first-phase pilot random sample of size n' is taken, from which n_1' are respondents. Then a random subsample of fixed size n_2' is selected from the $n' - n_1'$ nonrespondents. Using a locally uniform prior for the βs and h, and a beta-prior for π, the authors are able to minimize a loss function, which leads to an optimal choice for the second phase. This choice is obtained numerically, and an approximation is provided.

Singh, B., and Sedransk, J. (1978a). Sample size selection in regression analysis when there is non-response. *Journal of the American Statistical Association* 73: 362–365.

"When there is substantial nonresponse in a sample survey, a common practice is to select a subsample of the nonrespondents and to obtain the observations from this subsample by using more expensive measurement techniques. It is customary to assume that there are two strata of unknown sizes: Stratum 1 consists of those units who would, if selected in the sample, supply the necessary information without recorse to additional measurement techniques; and stratum 2 is the complementary stratum of nonrespondents."

"A pilot (first-phase) random sample of n' observations is selected from a specified population with n_1' responses obtained. Then, a random subsample of size $n_2' \leq n' - n_1'$ is selected from the $(n' - n_1')$ nonrespondents, and these persons are assumed to respond fully after further inquiry. These data are used to plan the second-phase sample of fixed (but arbitraty) size n. Assuming n_1 responses, a subsample of $n_2 \leq n - n_1$ nonrespondents is selected, and these individuals are assumed to respond fully after further inquiry" (authors' summary).

The assumptions are that there are r independent variables $Z_1, \ldots, Z_r$ used to predict X. However, there are two different regressions, depending on whether the observations are from the set of individuals who would, if sampled, respond (denoted R), or those who are nonrespondents (denoted NR). Thus we have

$$x^R = \beta_0^R + \beta_1^R z_1 + \cdots + \beta_r^R z_r + e^R,$$

$$x^{NR} = \beta_0^{NR} + \beta_1^{NR} z_1 + \cdots + \beta_r^{NR} z_r + e^{NR},$$

where the errors e^R and e^{NR} are normally distributed with zero means and variances τ^R and τ^{NR}, respectively.

The particular context under which this study was made was where X denotes income, Z_1 denotes the extent of participation in a vocational education program, and $Z_2, Z_3, \ldots$ were variables such as race, sex, grades, attitude, etc.

The regression coefficient corresponding to Z_1 was of critical concern, so that inferences about $\beta_1^R - \beta_1^{NR}$ were made.

Another parameter π is introduced in the event that a pooled regression $\pi\beta_j^R + (1 - \pi)\beta_j^{NR}$ is of interest.

The analysis is Bayesian. Independent priors on β, τ, π are assumed, and the posterior distribution of (β, τ, π) given the data is used as the prior for any subsequent phase.

The loss function in estimating $(\beta_k^R, \beta_k^{NR})$ is assumed to be quadratic:

$$L = k_1(\beta_k^R - \hat{\beta}_k^R)^2 + k_2(\beta_k^{NR} - \hat{\beta}_k^{NR})^2 + k_3(\beta_k^R - \hat{\beta}_k^R)(\beta_k^{NR} - \hat{\beta}_k^{NR})$$
$$+ cn + c^R n_1 + c^{NR} n_2 + c,$$

where k_1, k_2, k_3 represent trade-offs among the errors of estimation and sampling costs, C denotes the fixed budget for first-phase sampling, c is the cost of selecting the random sample, and c^R and c^{NR} are the total sampling costs for the respondents and nonrespondents.

The analysis yields an approximate optimal value of n:

$$n \cong \max\left\{\sqrt{\frac{K_1 V' n'}{cn' + c^R n_1'}} - n', 0\right\},$$

where $n_1' V'/n'$ is the per unit variance of β_k^R based on the pilot data. More explicitly,

$$V' = n' v_1' v_1' (S_1')^{kk}/(v_1' - 2),$$

where S_1' is the cross-product matrix of the Z from the respondent group, $(S_1')^{kk}$ is the (k, k)th element of $(S_1')^{-1}$, $v_1' = n_1' - \text{rank}(S_1')$ is the degrees of freedom, and v_1' is the sum of squares of residuals for the respondent group divided by the degrees of freedom.

Singh, B., and Sedransk, J. (1978b). A two-phase sample design for estimating the finite population mean when there is non-response. In N. K. Namboodiri (ed.), *Survey Sampling and Measurement*, pp. 143–155. New York: Academic Press.

Suppose that a population of size N is partitioned into L strata (mutually exclusive and exhaustive) with strata boundaries fixed. The number $N_1, \ldots, N_L$ of population units in the L strata is unknown. If X_{ij} denotes the observation for the jth unit in stratum i, then we define

$$\bar{X}_i = \sum_{j=1}^{N_i} X_{ij}/N_i, \qquad \bar{X} = \sum_{i=1}^{L} \pi_i \bar{X}_i, \qquad \pi_i = N_i/N.$$

The approach taken is that of two-phase sampling, and the analysis is Bayesian In the first phase a simple random sample of size n' is selected and the units are identified as to stratum. Thus there are $n'_1, \ldots, n'_L$ observations in the L strata. Now independent subsamples of size $m'_1, \ldots, m'_L$ are selected, and X is measured.

The treatment focuses on finding the optimal value (or an approximation) of the total sample size in the second-phase sample. In the case of two strata—respondents and nonrespondents—a single-phase design is also studied.

Sirken, M. G. (1970). Household surveys with multiplicity. *Journal of the American Statistical Association* 65: 257–266.

In the conventional survey, each individual is reported by the household of which he is a resident. In a household survey with multiplicity, there is a multiplicity rule stating how elements of a sample unit report for a cluster of units. These clusters may be overlapping. Examples of such multiplicity rules are siblings report each other, adjacent households report each other, households on the same block report each other.

Several alternative models for household surveys with multiplicity are considered for estimating the number of individuals in a population that have a specified characteristic:

(1) Every household in a cluster reports the same individuals with the attribute, and every individual with the attribute is reported by one and only one cluster of households.

(2) Every household belongs to one and only one cluster and no two clusters report the same individuals.

(3) A cluster reports one and only one individual.

In model 1 a household can belong to more than one cluster and a cluster can report more than one individual. In model 2 there is a unique grouping of households into cluster.

For each of these models estimators are defined and their expected values and mean square errors (MSE) are derived. Efficiency computations in terms of the MSE are made.

Although no direct comparisons are made, some general conclusions are drawn. It is noted that estimates based on multiplicity surveys may be subject to larger response errors than in conventional surveys if self-respondents are more accurate than proxy respondents. However, this is not always the case, and it was in reference to population changes that the development of multiplicity surveys occurred. Multiplicity surveys become desirable when the multiplicity rules yield estimates with smaller MSEs than the MSEs of conventional surveys with comparable costs.

Sirken, M. G. (1974). The counting rule strategy in sample surveys. *Proceedings of the Social Statistics Section*, American Statistical Association, pp. 119–123.

In a number of surveys the enumeration units are not identical to the population elements whose parameters are being estimated. For example, the farm may be the population element, whereas an aerial segment is the enumeration unit. Or patients with a disease are the population elements, whereas medical sources are the enumeration units. In such an instance a rule linking the enumeration and population elements is needed. Such a rule is called a counting rule.

Some counting rules link every population element to one and only one enumeration unit. This occurs, for example, where households are the enumeration units and persons are the population elements. Multiplicity rules permit more than one enumeration unit to be linked to the same population element.

This paper provides a discussion of counting rules, giving a variety of examples. Weighting in multiplicity rules is needed in order to account for the multiplicities that occur. Of particular concern are the effects of multiplicity rules on sampling errors, coverage errors, response errors, and survey costs.

Srinath, K. P. (1971). Multiphase sampling in nonresponse problems. *Journal of the American Statistical Association* 66: 583–586.

The analyses in this paper are based on the assumption that each individual in a population of N individuals would not respond to j mail surveys but would respond to the $(j + 1)$th mailing, $j = 1, \ldots, L$. There is also one stratum for individuals who would not respond to the final attempt. The population is then stratified in accordance with the response pattern. Let $N_1, \ldots, N_{L+1} (\Sigma N_i = N)$ be number of individuals in the population in the $L + 1$ strata, and $\overline{X}_1, \ldots, \overline{X}_{L+1}$ the strata means. The problem is to estimate $\overline{X} = (N_1 \overline{X}_1 + \cdots + N_{L+1} \overline{X}_{L+1})/N$.

An initial sample of size n (without replacement) is selected, and suppose n_1 and n_2 represent the number of respondents and nonrespondents, respectively. Two rules for choosing the size of a subsample from the nonrespondent sample are given, namely, $n_2' = n_2/k$ and $n_2' = n_2^2/(k'n + n_2)$, where the constants k and k' are determined as a function of the variance and cost. The relations between the optimal k and k' are $k_{\text{opt}}' = (k_{\text{opt}} - 1)N_2/N$, where N_2 is the number of individuals in stratum 2, i.e., individuals who would not respond to the first attempt but would respond to the second attempt.

A modified version of this model is also considered and illustrated by an example.

Stephenson, C. B. (1979). Probability sampling with quotas: An experiment. National Opinion Research Center, University of Chicago, Chicago, Illinois.

Quota samples that used quota categories based on a few demographic variables and broadly defined geographic regions have been largely replaced by full probability (FP) samples that specify every sampling decision probabilistically. Recently, however, a new sampling method, probability sampling with quotas (PSQ), has been proposed that combines the ideas of full probability sampling and quota sampling. In PSQ sampling, the first stages of the sampling design are defined as in FP samples, but in the last stage, the interviewer uses a well-defined procedure to obtain a quota sample within the last stage sampling unit. In theory, PSQ eliminates any interviewer discretion in the choice of households to receive the interview. Since PSQ samples are often less expensive to obtain than FP samples, the PSQ sampling procedure may be preferable if it does not yield highly inaccurate estimates.

The sampling experiment was performed using data from the 1975 and 1976 General Social Surveys conducted by the National Opinion Research Center. The national sample in these two years was split into two subsamples and both FP and PSQ sampling procedures were used. Consistent differences between the results of surveys based on the two methods were found on the variables of employment status, sex, number of adults in the household, number of persons in the household, and number of persons earning money in the household. In addition, there appeared to be a shift in the subsample distribution of respondents' social, economic, and educational status between 1975 and 1976. This makes replication of estimates of bias estimates on these measures impossible. Except for the variables mentioned, there was no consistent evidence of bias in the PSQ sample as compared with the FP sample.

Substantive conclusions were that PSQ overrepresents large households, while both FP and PSQ tend to underrepresent individuals from large households. The PSQ underrepresents men who are working full-time. Finally, the PSQ sample results in more serious under-representation of difficult respondents, except in the case that this difficulty is purely a function of the neighborhood. In the latter case, PSQ designs ensure that neighborhoods are represented in the desired proportions, but FP sample designs do not.

Thomsen, I. (1973). A note on the efficiency of weighting subclass means to reduce the effects of nonresponse when analyzing survey data. *Statistisk Tidskrift* : 278–285.

This paper is devoted to a study of bias reduction due to nonresponse by weighting subclass sample means to account for different response rates. The analysis is based on a decomposition of the bias into two components: one that arises from the fact that different groups in the population have different response rates, and the other due to the biasing effect of nonresponse within each subgroup.

Two examples are considered in detail: (i) Norwegian Survey of Expenditures 1967; (ii) Norwegian Election Survey 1969. For each the effects of the two components are estimated. Thus, for example, in (ii) it is found that weighting reduces the absolute value of the bias, but that the reduction is negligible. It is also noted that there is little difference in the analysis if three or four subclasses are used.

Tupek, A. R., and Richardson, W. J. (1978). Use of ratio estimates to compensate for nonresponse bias in certain economic surveys. *Proceedings of the Section on Survey Research Methods*, American Statistical Association, pp. 197–202.

Response rates for voluntary business surveys in the United States appear to be declining, in part because many companies have a policy not to respond to voluntary surveys. The percentage delinquent for the Survey of Scientific and Technical Personnel is presented. In each survey industries such as textiles and apparel, and transportation, are classified according to size: small, medium, large, very large. For each entry there are two figures of percentage delinquent— one based on the number of establishments and the other based on total employment of establishments.

Imputation of nonrespondents using ratio estimates and probability proportional to size estimators are reviewed.

Whitmore, W. J. (1976). Mail survey premiums and response bias. *Journal of Marketing Research* 13: 46–50.

It is well documented that the inclusion of a premium does improve the response rate of a mail survey. However, there remains a question as to whether this introduces a bias. The present study addresses this issue.

The study consisted of a sample of 1000 new car purchases; 500 were purchases of the Ford Pinto and 500 of the Volkswagen Beetle. Each member of these two groups was assigned randomly into a premium or a nonpremium group. Thus, there were four groups, each consisting of 250 persons: Pinto premium and nonpremium, and Beetle premium and nonpremium. The premium was an inexpensive key ring.

Two weeks after the initial mailing, a follow-up mailing was sent. The results were

	Responded	Did not respond	Total
Premium	287	213	500
No premium	261	239	500
	548	452	1000

The responses were analyzed across 83 different variables. The overall conclusion was that no systematic bias is produced as a result of inclusion of a premium similar to the one used in this study. This study is at variance with some previous studies in which monetary premiums were used, where differences were found based on income level or social class.

Wilks, S. S. (1932). Moments and distributions of estimates of population parameters from fragmentary samples. *Annals of Mathematical Statistics* 3: 163–195.

This paper is the first one to deal with the problem of missing data. The model is that of a bivariate normal population with means μ_1, μ_2, variances σ_1^2, σ_2^2, and correlation ρ, from which we observe t pairs $(x_1, y_1), \ldots, (x_t, y_t)$, m observations $x_{t+1}, \ldots, x_{t+m}$ on X alone, and n observations $y_{t+1}, \ldots, y_{t+n}$ on Y alone.

Maximum likelihood estimates of the parameters under different assumptions are found:

(1) $\hat{\mu}_1, \hat{\mu}_2, \hat{\sigma}_1^2, \hat{\sigma}_2^2, \hat{\rho}$
(2) $\hat{\mu}_1, \hat{\mu}_2$ when σ_1, σ_2, and ρ are known
(3) $\hat{\sigma}_1, \hat{\sigma}_2, \hat{\rho}$ when μ_1 and μ_2 are known
(4) $\hat{\sigma}_1^2, \hat{\sigma}_2^2$ when μ_1, μ_2, and ρ are known

Fisher's information for one parameter is then extended to the multivariate case and it is shown that the determinant K of the information matrix for maximum likelihood estimates is no larger than the determinant H of the information matrix for any other set of estimates which are asymptotically normal. This suggests a measure of efficiency for any set of estimates, namely, the ratio K/H. For each of the cases (1)–(4), the value of K is determined.

Suppose we are interested in μ_1 only; then we should use a combination of the means $\bar{x} = \sum_1^t x_i/t$ and $\bar{\bar{x}} = \sum_{j=1}^m x_{t+j}/m$. The optimal combination is $\bar{x}_0 = c\bar{x} + (1-c)\bar{\bar{x}}$, where $c = t/(t+m)$; its distribution is obtained and its efficiency is discussed.

Various distributional and moment calculations for some of the estimates are provided.

One particular comparison of estimating σ_1, σ_2, and ρ is of considerable interest. In each case σ_1^2 is estimated from the $a+m$ observations on X, and σ_2^2

is estimated from the $a + n$ observations on Y. Call these estimates $\tilde{\sigma}_1^2$ and $\tilde{\sigma}_2^2$, respectively. To estimate $\rho = \sigma_{12}/(\sigma_1, \sigma_2)$ the estimate $\tilde{\sigma}_{12}$ of σ_{12} is obtained from the complete bivariate sample. The two alternative estimates are (i) $\tilde{\rho} = \hat{\sigma}_{12}/\tilde{\sigma}_1\tilde{\sigma}_2$ and (ii) the usual maximum likelihood estimator based on the complete sample. It is shown that (ii) is more efficient than (i).

Williams, S. R., and Folsom, R. E., Jr. (1977). Bias resulting from school nonresponse: Methodology and findings. RTI Project No. 22U-884, Research Triangle Institute, Research Triangle Park, North Caroline.

The National Longitudinal Study (NLS) of the High School Class of 1977 uses a design with a longitudinal national sample. This sample is to be followed throughout postsecondary eduction and entry into the job market. This paper reports the results of a study of the potential effects of missing data that arose in the Base Year (BY) survey because of noncooperation by some schools, initially selected into the sample. The method used was a comparison of estimates based on the original sample with the so-called best estimates. The best estimates are based on the best currently available data, mostly data that have been obtained by resurveying the "missing schools." These school data were used to estimate the probable bias in estimates of student level variables due to school nonresponse.

The conclusion was that school nonresponse may have "significantly affected many of the statistics developed from the BY survey" (p. 17). The estimated bias was about 5% for many population totals. The results on individual questions indicated that statistically significant bias was found in 14 of 35 questions whose results were reported as proportions. Because of these biases, the confidence statements reported for many of the BY estimates are probably inaccurate.

The initial sampling design used backup schools for each school selected into the sample. If a school failed to respond, the backup school was included in place of the original school. These results suggest that this method cannot be relied upon to produce unbiased estimates. A suggestion is made that future efforts should be placed on obtaining higher initial response rates, rather than using backup schools as a palliative.

Williams, W. H. (1970). The systematic bias effects of incomplete responses in rotation samples. *The Public Opinion Quarterly* 33: 593–602.

Rotation sampling is used in continuing studies where both estimates of change in some characteristic over time and estimates for the current time period of interest are made. Rotation samples involve the retention of some subjects in the sample from one time period to the next and replacement of others. Several surveys using rotation samples have encountered systematic biases among subgroups depending on the number of times a group of subjects appeared in the sample.

Samples with callbacks are similiar to rotation samples if the total collection of respondents after each call is considered a "sample." For example, the first-call respondents all appear in the second-call "sample." Systematic biases in the series of "samples" associated with multiple callbacks have also been encountered in some surveys.

The purpose of this paper is to present a simple model that explains systematic biases in rotation and multiple callback surveys as a function of the probability that an individual in the sample responds. Let p_i and p_i' be the probabilities that responses are obtained from the ith individual in the first and second sample, respectively, and Y_i is the response of the ith individual, assumed to have the same distribution for both samples. Then the approximate expected value of the sample estimates $\hat{Y}$ and $\hat{Y}'$ in the first and second samples are

$$E(\hat{Y}) = \sum_{i=1}^{N} p_i E(Y_i)/\sum p_i, \qquad E(\hat{Y}^i) = \sum_{i=1}^{N} p_i' E(Y_i)/\sum p_i.$$

If Y_i is correlated with $p_i - p_i'$, the change in response probability, then sample estimates can easily change between the first sample and the next, even though the true value of the population mean does not change. In particular, if the probability of a response is monotonically related to the variable of interest, and the probabilities of response differ from one sample to the next, the expected value of the estimator must change from one sample to the next. A numerical example is given to indicate the magnitude of changes that are possible.

Williams, W. H. (1975). The seriousness of selection biases, including non-response. *Proceedings of the American Statistical Association*, Social Statistics Section, pp. 11–15.

In the measurement of physical constants, there is a history of bias that has resulted in many examples of widely inaccurate confidence intervals. Selection bias survey research can have devastating effects on the accuracy of confidence intervals, but this bias receives little attention. This paper describes some aspects of selection bias, which occurs when the sampling plan dictates that population units are to be selected into the sample with one set of probabilities but the actual set of selection probabilities differs from those of the sampling plan.

The magnitude of selection bias can be large, as illustrated in a Bell System study where estimates based on different groups in a rotation sample differed by eight standard errors. Analysis suggests that the difference is due to selection bias. Williams (1970; see summary in this bibliography) showed that selection bias could alter estimates of the employment rate by 4% even when the response rate was 98% for employed persons and 95% for unemployed persons, giving an overall response rate of 98%.

The effects of selection biases are also subtle. For example, consideration of selection bias can lead to the conclusion that the usual multiwave fixed panel design is not optimal for estimating change. Partial or complete replacement of subjects may yield more accurate results (see, e.g., Williams and Mallows, 1970; see summary in this bibliography). Relations between variables are not invariant in different subgroups, and selection bias can change the apparant relations. Some economic data sets used to assess the relation between the amount of risk and the rate of return are used to illustrate the effects of selection bias on estimates of relations.

Increasing the rate of response does not always reduce the effects of selection bias. An example given by Williams (1970) demonstrates that increasing response rate can actually increase the bias. The best remedy for the effects of selection bias is to detect its presence by looking for evidence of unexpected differences in response rates and for correlations between response rates and the variable of interest. Reweighting the sample based on known population parameters or explicitly estimating and correcting for selection bias may then help to correct for the effects of selection bias.

Williams, W. H., and Mallows, C. L. (1970). Systematic biases in panel surveys due to differential nonresponse. *Journal of the American Statistical Association* 65: 1338–1349.

The origin of this study is the attempt to explain certain systematic biases that appear to have no apparent explanation. For example, in a Bell System study, families interviewed for the first, second, and third times appeared to be different with respect to the number of children per family.

In order to clarify some potential sources of these differences, a model with two states "unemployed" and "employed" is considered at two time points:

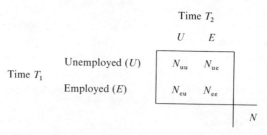

When the sampling begins a third category of "not interviewed" is required, so that the observations can be displayed in a table:

		Time T_2		
		U	E	NI
	Unemployed	F_{uu}	F_{ue}	F_{uo}
Time T_1	Employed	F_{eu}	F_{ee}	F_{eo}
	Not interviewed	F_{ou}	F_{oe}	F_{oo}

Furthermore, define the following probabilities: p_u is the probability that an unemployed person actually appears in the sample at time T_1; p_e is the probability that an employed person actually appears in the sample at time T_1; p_{uu} is the probability that an individual is interviewed at time T_2 given that he was interviewed at time T_1 and was unemployed at both times T_1 and T_2; p_{ue} is the probability that an individual is interviewed at time T_2 given that he was interviewed at time T_1 and was unemployed at time T_1 and employed at time T_2; p_{eu} is the probability that an individual is interviewed at time T_2 given that he was interviewed at time T_1 and was employed at time T_1 and unemployed at time T_2; p_{ee} is the probability that an individual is interviewed at time T_2 given that he was interviewed at time T_1 and was employed at both times T_1 and T_2. Parameters $q_{uu}, q_{ue}, q_{eu}, q_{ee}$ are defined in a manner similar to the p—except that the q are conditional on the individual *not* being interviewed at time T_1.

The expected sample numbers are then computed for the different categories. Using the observed sample numbers, an unbiased estimator of the unemployment rate can be constructed based only on individuals observed at both times. As a consequence of an analysis using this estimator it is found that there will be a change in the observed unemployment rate unless the ratio of the probabilities of interviewing an unemployed to employed person, at time T_1, is the same as the ratio of the corresponding probabilities of time T_2 for persons who were observed at T_1 and whose employment status has changed between T_1 to T_2. More formally, the requirement is that $p_u p_e = p_{eu} p_{ue}$. Furthermore, this change in the observed unemployment rate will occur even though there is no change in the true unemployment case.

The paper continues with this type of analysis using other models.

Wretman, J. (1978). The Swedish data act and imputation for nonresponse. Confidentiality in Surveys, Report Number 30, Department of Statistics, University of Stockholm.

The Swedish Data Act requires that information on Swedish citizens that is kept in any data bank must be "correct." This law has been interpreted as prohibiting the imputation of values to replace missing data in the Swedish Labour Force Survey, since the imputed values would often be "incorrect." The first half of the paper explains the Swedish Data Act and details the arguments for and against imputation.

The second half of the paper examines how the bias and mean squared error of the sample estimate of a population total are affected by two simple imputation techniques and a nonimputation technique for handling missing data. The imputation techniques are mean value imputation and duplication of imputed values from a random sample of values of the respondents.

The estimators are shown to have equal bias, which depends on the mean difference between respondents and nonrespondents. Expressions for the mean squared error of each estimator are reproduced and mean value imputation is shown to have smaller mean squared error than imputation by duplication of values. Expressions for the variance of the estimators based on partially imputed values shows that the usual estimate of the variance may seriously underestimate the variance of the estimator calculated after imputation. This underestimation is most pronounced with mean value imputation.

The conclusion is that since the bias and mean squared error cannot be reduced by either of the imputation techniques, no gain in accuracy results from imputation over reweighting. Imputed values may greatly simplify the data processing and presentation of results, however.

Bibliography on Nonresponse and Related Topics

Edited by

Bengt Bogeström
Monica Larsson
Lars Lyberg

1. INTRODUCTION

A project conducted by Statistics Sweden investigating the problems of nonresponse was recently terminated. One by-product of that work was a bibliography of literature on nonresponse problems and related topics. This bibliography is an excerpt from that more extensive bibliography obtained by omitting all references in the Swedish language.

The references in this bibliography are of three different kinds. First, there are references in which the title gives a definite indication of a treatment of nonresponse problems. Second, there are references in which the title contains a more indirect reference to nonresponse. Titles in this latter category include those containing key words such as "privacy," "respondent burden," "data collection methods," and "incentives." Third, there are items where the type of indications mentioned do not exist, but where inclusion in this bibliography was nevertheless deemed important.

The relevant references were gathered from the following sources.

(1) Ten statistical journals were scanned for the years 1970–1979. They were (1) *Journal of the American Statistical Association*; (2) *American Statistical Association, Proceedings of Social Statistics Section*; (3) *American Statistical*

INCOMPLETE DATA
IN SAMPLE SURVEYS
Volume 2, Part IV

Association, Proceedings of Section on Survey Research Methods; (4) *Bulletin of the International Statistical Institute*; (5) *Review of the International Statistical Institute*; (6) *Sankhyā, Series B*; (7) *Journal of the Royal Statistical Society, Series A*; (8) *Public Opinion Quarterly*; (9) *Applied Statistics*; and (10) *Journal of Marketing Research.*

(2)   In order to cover the years 1940–1969, the bibliography compiled by T. Dalenius and L. Lyberg *Bibliography on Non-sampling Errors* (Institute of Statistics, University of Stockholm, 1971) was scanned, since a subset of the references in that bibliography treat the issue of nonresponse.

(3)   The aforementioned project investigating the nonresponse problems at Statistics Sweden led to numerous contacts with foreign institutes such as the U.S. Bureau of the Census, Statistics Canada, and the National Academy of Sciences, Panel on Incomplete Data. Thus, a number of articles and working papers emanating from these institutions were included.

This bibliography is extensive but by no means complete, since over 100 journals exist that treat statistical matters. However, we think we have achieved good coverage.

It was not possible to categorize the references. Earlier attempts of that kind have not been especially successful. Still, with some patience, the user of this bibliography should be able to locate the articles of his or her interest.

Finally, it should be pointed out that the bibliography is not error-free. We have not been in a position to examine some of the items, primarily some of those excerpted from other reference lists. Consequently, in a few cases, an item may have been included without properly belonging to the issue under study or it may contain errors "inherited" from those other reference lists.

Abbott, L. (1951): A Note on Stimulating Response to Question-naires. American Sociological Review, pp 247-248.

Abernathy, J.R., Greenberg, B.G. and Horvitz, D.G. (1970): Estimates of Induced Abortion in Urban North Carolina. Demography 7, No. 1, pp 19-29.

Abul-Ela, A-L.A. (1966): Randomized Response Models for Sample Surveys on Human Population. Unpublished Ph.D. Thesis, University of North Carolina, Chapel Hill.

Abul-Ela, A-L.A., Greenberg, B.G. and Horvitz, D.G. (1967): A Multi-Proportions Randomized Response Model. Journal of the American Statistical Association 62, pp 990-1008.

Afifi, A.A. and Elashoff, R.M. (1966): Missing Observations in Multivariate Statistics, I: Review of the Literature, Journal of the American Statistical Association 61, pp 595-604.

Afifi, A.A. and Elashoff, R.M. (1967): Missing Observations in Multivariate Statistics, II: Point Estimation in Simple Linear Regression. Journal of the American Statistical Association 62, pp 10-29.

Afifi, A.A. and Elashoff, R.M. (1969): Missing Observations in Multivariate Statistics III: Large Sample Analysis of Sample Linear Regression. Journal of the American Statistical Association 64, pp 337-358.

Afifi, A.A. and Elashoff, R.M. (1969): Missing Observations in Multivariate Statistics IV: A Note on Simple Linear Regression. Journal of the American Statistical Association 64, pp 359-365.

Allen, F.E. and Wishart, J. (1930): A Method of Estimating the Yield of a Missing Plot in Field Experimental Work. J. Agric. Schi. 20, pp 399-406.

Allen, I.L. and Colfax, J.D. (1968): Respondents' Attitudes Toward Legitimate Surveys in Four Cities. Journal of Marketing Research 5, pp 431-433.

Alutto, J.A. (1977): Some Dynamics of Questionnaire Completion and Return Among Professional and Managerial Personnel: The Relative Impacts of Reception at Work Site or Place of Residence. Journal of Applied Psychology 54, pp 430-432.

Alwin, D.F. (1977): Making Errors in Surveys. Sociological Methods & Research, Volume 6, Number 2, pp 131-150.

Alwin, D.F. and Jensen, E.L. (1976): Brief Report on the Combined Use of Mail and Telephone Methods of Data Collection. Unpublished paper.

American Sociological Association (1968): Toward a Code of Ethics for Sociologists. American Sociologist 3, pp 316-318.

American Statistical Association, Census Advisory Committee
(1969): Report of the Subcommittee on Criteria for Surveys
for Other Federal Government Agencies. American Statistician
23, pp 17-19.

American Statistical Association (1974): Report on the ASA
Conference on Surveys of Human Populations. American Statistician 28, pp 30-34.

American Statistical Association (1977): Report of the ad hoc
Committee on Privacy and Confidentiality. American Statistician
31, pp 59-78.

Anderson, J. and Berdie, D. (1975): Effect on Response Rate
of Formal and Informal Follow-Up Techniques. Journal of Applied
Psychology 60, pp 255-257.

Anderson, R.L. (1946): Missing-Plot Techniques. Biometrics
2, pp 41-47.

Anderson, T.W. (1957): Maximum Likelihood Estimates for a Multivariate Normal Distribution When Some Observations Are Missing.
Journal of the American Statistical Association 52, pp 200-203.

Andersson, H. (1975): Estimation of a Proportion Through Randomized Response, Bulletin of International Statistical Institute,
pp 26-29.

Andersson, H. (1979): Nonresponse and Response Probabilities.
Scandinavian Journal of Statistics 6, pp 107-112.

Andreasen, A.R. (1970): Personalizing Mail Questionnaire Correspondence. Public Opinion Quarterly 34, pp 273-277.

Andrews, L. (1974): "Interviewers: Recruiting, Selecting, Training,
and Supervising," in Robert Ferber, ed., Handbook of Marketing
Research. New York: McGraw-Hill Book Co., 2-124-32.

Armstrong, J.S. (1975): Monetary Incentives in Mail Surveys.
Public Opinion Quarterly 39, pp 111-116.

Armstrong, J.S. and Overton, T.S. (1977): Estimating Nonresponse
Bias in Mail Surveys. Journal of Marketing Research 14, pp
396-402.

Arnold, R.G. (1964): The Interview in Jeopardy - A Problem
in Public Relations. Public Opinion Quarterly 28, pp 119-123.

Arora, H.R. and Brackstone, G.J. (1975): The Bias and Variance
of the Raking Ratio Estimator. Technical Report, Statistics
Canada, (unpublished).

Arora, H.R. and Brackstone, G.J. (1977): An Investigation of
the Properties of Raking Ratio Estimators: I. with Random Sampling. Survey Methodology, vol. 3, No. 1, pp 62-83.

Arora, H.R. and Brackstone, G.J. (1977): An Investigation of
the Properties of Raking Ratio Estimators: II. with Cluster
Sampling. Survey Methodology, vol. 3, No. 2, pp 232-252.

Ash, P. and Abramson, E. (1952): The Effect of Anonymity on
Attitude-Questionnaire Response. Journal of Abnormal and Social
Psychology 47, pp 722-723.

Ashraf, A. and Macredie, I. (1978): Edit and Imputation in
the Labor Force Survey. American Statistical Association, Proceedings of the Section on Survey Research Methods, pp 425-430.

Astin, A. and Boruch, R.F. (1970): A 'Link' System for Assuring
Confidentiality of Research Data in Longitudinal Studies. American
Educational Research Journal 7, pp 615-624.

Astin, A.W. and Molm, L.D. (1972): Correcting for Nonresponse
Bias in Follow-Up Surveys. An unpublished manuscript available
from the Office of Research of the American Council on Education,
1 Dupont Circle, Washington, DC.

Atchley, R.C. (1967): Respondents vs. Refusers in an Interview
Study of Retired Women: An Analysis of Selected Characteristics.
Proceedings of the 20th Annual Meeting of the Gerontological
Society 41. Miami, Ohio: Miami University. Also in Journal
of Gerontology 24, 1969, pp 42-47.

Axelrod, M. (1964): An Experimental Attempt to Reduce Field
Costs by Limiting Callbacks and Increasing Cluster Size. American
Statistical Association, Proceedings of the Social Statistics
Section, pp 32-40.

Bachrack, S.D. and Scoble, H.M. (1967): Mail Questionnaire Efficiency: Controlled Reduction of Nonresponse. Public Opinion Quarterly 31, pp 265-271.

Back, K.W. (1960): Comments on Interviewing Reluctant Respondents, with Special Reference to Surveying Human Fertility. Public Opinion Quarterly 24, pp 447-478.

Back, P-E. (1976): Social Research and the Individual's Right to Personal Privacy. In Personal Integrity and the Need for Data in the Social Sciences (T. Dalenius and A. Klevmarken, eds), pp 31-35. Stockholm: Swedish Council for Social Science Research.

Bailar, B.A. (1973): The Effect of Repeated Interviewing. Paper presented at the Conference on Econometrics and Mathematical Economics. Seminar on the Analysis of Panel Microdata, Ann Arbor, Michigan, Apr 5-6, 1973.

Bailar, B.A. (1976): Progress and Problems in the Assessment of Survey Practices. American Statistical Association, Proceedings of the Social Statistics Section, pp 122-129.

Bailar, B.A. (1976): Some Sources of Error and Their Effect on Census Statistics. Demography, Vol. 13, No. 2, pp 273-286.

Bailar, B.A. (1976): The American Statistical Association Examines Survey Interviewing Problems. Paper presented at the annual meeting of the American Association of Public Opinion Research, Ashville, North Carolina, May 13-16, 1976. Unpublished.

Bailar, B.A. (1979): The Evaluation of Sample Survey Data. US Bureau of the Census. Paper prepared for the 1979 meetings of the American Association for the Advancement of Science, Houston.

Bailar, B.A. and Bailar, J.C.III (1979): Comparison of the Biases of the "Hot-Deck" Imputation Procedure with an "Equal-Weights" Imputation Procedure. US Bureau of the Census and National Cancer Institute. Paper presented at the Symposium on incomplete data: Preliminary proceedings, Washington Hilton Hotel on August 10-11, 1979, Washington, DC.

Bailar, B.A., Bailey, L. and Corby, C. (1978): A Comparison of Some Adjustment and Weighting Procedures for Survey Data. Survey Sampling and Measurement, pp 175-198.

Bailar, B.A., Bailey, L. and Corby, C. (1978): A Comparison of Some Adjustment and Weighting Procedures for Survey Data. In: Survey Sampling and Measurement. Edited by N. Krishnan Namboodiri, Academic Press, New York, San Francisco, London.

Bailar, B.A. and Lanphier, C.M. (1978): Development of Survey Methods to Assess Survey Practices. Washington: American Statistical Association.

Bailar, B.A. and Miskura, S. (1979): The 1980 Census Experimental Program. American Statistical Association, Proceedings of the Section on Survey Research Methods, pp 29-38.

Bailar, J.C. (1978): Imputation and Editing of Faulty or Missing Survey Data. US Department of Commerce, Bureau of the Census.

Bailar, J.C. III and Bailar, B.A. (1978): Comparison of Two Procedures for Imputing Missing Survey Values. American Statistical Association, Proceedings of the Section on Survey Research Methods, pp 462-467.

Bailey, L. (1975): Toward a More Complete Analysis of the Total Mean Square Error of Census and Sample Survey Statistics. American Statistical Association, Proceedings of the Social Statistics Section, pp 1-10.

Bailey, L. (1976): Some Aspects of Weighting to Adjust for the Nonresponse Bias of Survey Statistics. Paper presented at the meeting of the Washington Statistical Society, April 14, 1976.

Bancroft, G. (1958): Quality of Census Labor Force Data and Methods of Adjustment. Appendix A of The American Labor Force, New York.

Bankier, M.D. (1978): An Estimate of the Efficiency of Raking Ratio Estimators under Simple Random Sampling. Survey Methodology 4, pp 115-124.

Banks, M.J. (1977): An Indication of the Effect of Non-Interview Adjustment and Post-Stratification on Estimates from a Sample Survey. American Statistical Association, Proceedings of the Social Statistics Section, pp 291-295.

Barabba, V.P. (1974): The Right of Privacy and the Need to Know. American Statistical Association, Proceedings of the Social Statistics Section, pp 33-38.

Barabba, V.P. (1975): The Right of Privacy and the Need to Know. Technical Paper 37 in A Numerator and Denominator for Measuring Change. Washington, DC: US Bureau of the Census, pp 23-29.

Barksdale, W.B. (1975): New Randomized Response Techniques for Control of Nonsampling Errors in Surveys. American Statistical Association, Proceedings of the Social Statistics Section, pp 302-310.

Barnette, W.L. Jr (1950): The Non-Respondent Problem in Questionnaire Research. Journal of Applied Psychology 34, pp 397-398.

Barnoon, S. (1974): Eighty-Two Percent of Doctors do Tests. Lab World, September 1974.

Baron, R.A. (1973): The Foot-in-the-Door Phenomenon: Mediating Effects of Size of First Request and Sex of Requester. Bulletin of the Psychonomic Society 2, pp 113-114.

Barr, A. (1957): Differences between Experienced Interviewers. Applied Statistics 6, pp 180-189.

Bartholomew, D.J. (1961): A Method of Allowing for "Not-at-home" Bias in Sample Surveys. Applied Statistics 10, pp 52-59.

Bauer, R.K. and Meissner, F. (1963): Structures of Mail Questionnaires: Test of Alternatives. Public Opinion Quarterly 27, pp 307-311.

Bauman, L.J., Rodgers, T.F. and Weiss, C.H. (1971): Studies Assessing the Effects of Matching between Interviewer and Respondent. Abstracts of Papers on Respondent-Interviewer Interaction in the Research Interview, pp 12-53.

Baumrind, D. (1971): Principles of Ethical Conduct in the Treatment of Subjects: Reaction to the Draft Report of the Committee on Ethical Standards in Psychological Research. American Psychologist 26, pp 887-896.

Baxter, R. (1964): An Inquiry into the Misuse of the Survey Technique by Sales Solicitors. Public Opinion Quarterly 28, pp 124-134.

Baxter, R. (1969): The Harassed Respondent: I. Sales Solicitation in the Guise of Consumer Research. Chapter 3 in Current Controversies in Marketing, edited by Leo Bogart. Chicago: Markham Publishing Company, pp 23-30.

Baxter, R.E. (1943): Use both Mail-Type Questionnaire and Personal Interviews in Readership Research. Printer's Ink, pp 24-81.

Beach, M.E. (1979): Comparison of CPS Type A Rates Across Strata and Examination of Current CPS Type A Standards. Memo, US Bureau of the Census.

Beach, M.E. (1979): Nonresponse Rates on Current Programs. Memo, US Bureau of the Census.

Beale, E.M.L. and Little, R.J.A. (1975): Missing Values in Multivariate Analysis. Journal of the Royal Statistical Society 37, Series B, pp 129-145.

Bebbington, A.C. (1970): The Effect of Non-response in the Sample Survey with an Example. Human Relations 23, pp 169-180.

Becker, G. and Bakal, D.A. (1970): Subject Anonymity and Motivational Distortion in Self-Report data. Journal of Clinical Psychology 26, pp 207-209.

Becker, T.M. and Meyers, P.R. (1974-75): Empathy and Bravado: Interviewing Reluctant Bureaucrats. Public Opinion Quarterly 38, pp 605-613.

Beilin, H. and Werner, E.E. (1957): Interviewing Availability of a Follow-Up Sample of Rural Youth. Public Opinion Quarterly 21, pp 380-384.

Beller, N.D. (1979): Error Profile for Multiple-Frame Surveys.
US Department of Agriculture Economics, Statistics and Cooper-
atives Service, ESCS-63.

Beller, N.D. (1979): Error Profile-Multiple Frame Designs.
American Statistical Association, Proceedings of the Section
on Survey Research Methods, pp 221-222.

Bennett, C.M. and Hill, R.E. Jr (1964): A Comparison of Selected
Personality Characteristics of Responders and Nonresponders
to a Mailed Questionnaire Study. Journal of Educational Research
58, pp 178-180.

Benson, L.E. (1941): Studies in Secret-Ballot Technique. Public
Opinion Quarterly 5, pp 78-82.

Benson, L.E. (1946): Mail Surveys Can Be Valuable. Public Opinion
Quarterly 10, pp 234-241.

Benson, S., Booman, W.P. and Clark, K.E. (1951): A Study of
Interview Refusals. Journal of Applied Psychology 35, pp 116-119.

Benus, J. and Ackerman, J.C. (1971): The Problem of Non-Response
in Sample Surveys. Chapter 2 of Working Papers on Survey Research
in Poverty Areas. Edited by John B. Lansing, Stephen B. Withey
and Arthur C. Wolfe. Ann Arbor: Survey Research Center, University of Michigan, pp 26-59.

Berdie, D.R. (1973): Questionnaire Length and Response Rate.
Journal of Applied Psychology 58, pp 278-280.

Berdie, D.R. and Anderson, J.F. (1976): Mail Questionnaire
Response Rates - Updating Outmoded Thinking. Journal of Marketing
40, pp 71-73.

Berelson, B. (1966): Privacy in Behavioral Research. Public
Opinion Quarterly 30, pp 457.

Bergman, L.R., Hanve, R. and Rapp, J. (1978): Why Do Some People
Refuse to Participate in Interview Surveys. Statistisk Tidskrift
5, pp 341-356.

Bernstein, M. (1979): Characteristics of Interview and Non-
Interview Cases in the Public Information Campaign Evaluation
Survey in the 1976 Census of Camden, New Jersey. Memo, US Bureau
of the Census.

Berscheid, E., Baron, R.S., Dernier, M. and Libman, M. (1973):
Anticipating Informed Consent. American Psychologist 7, pp
913-925.

Bethlehem, J.G. and Kersten, H.M.P. (1980): Graphical Display
of Non-Response Data. Central Bureau voor de Statistiek, Department of Statistical Methods, PO Box 959, 2270 AZ Voorburg,
Netherlands.

Bevis, J.C. (1948): Economic Incentives Used for Mail Questionnaires. Public Opinion Quarterly 12, pp 493-493.

Bhargava, R.N.P. (1962): Multivariate Tests of Hypotheses with Incomplete Data. Technical Report No. 3, Applied Mathematics and Statistical Laboratories, Stanford University.

Biel, A.L. (1967): Abuses of Survey Research Techniques: The Phony Interview. Public Opinion Quarterly 31, pp 298.

Biemer, P.P. (1978): The Estimation of Nonsampling Variance Components in Sample Surveys. Unpublished Ph.D dissertation, Institute of Statistics, Texas A&M University.

Birch, F. (n.d.): The Effects of Proxy Interviewing. Social Survey Paper. GHS Series No. 3. HM 50, London.

Birnbaum, Z.W. and Sirken, M.G. (1950): Bias Due to Non-Availability in Sampling Surveys. Journal of the American Statistical Association 45, pp 98-111.

Birnbaum, Z.W. and Sirken, M.G. (1950): On the Total Error Due to Non-Interview and to Random Sampling. International Journal of Opinion and Attitude Research 4, pp 179-191.

Bishop, Y.M. and Fienberg, S.E. (1969): Incomplete Two-Dimensional Contingency Tables. Biometrics 25, pp 383-400.

Blankenship, A.B. (1964): Some Aspects of Ethics in Marketing Research. Journal of Marketing Research 1, pp 26-31.

Blass, Goodson, Haas and Higgins (1978): Quality Control for Field Operations in the 1980 Census of Population and Housing. American Statistical Association, Proceedings of the Social Statistics Section, pp 441-446.

Bloomfield, P. (1970): Spectral Analysis with Randomly Missing Observations. Journal of the Royal Statistical Society 32, Series B, pp 369-380.

Blumberg, H.H., Fuller, C. and Hare, A.P. (1974): Response Rates in Postal Surveys. Public Opinion Quarterly 38, pp 113-123.

Blumfield, W.S. (1973): Effect of Appearance of Correspondence on Response Rate to a Mail Questionnaire Survey. Psychological Reports 32, pp 178.

Bobren, H.M. (1962): The Time Order of Response and Non-Response Bias in Mail Surveys. University Microfilms, Inc., Ann Arbor, Michigan, pp 1-69.

Boek, W.E. and Lade, J.H. (1963): Test of the Usefulness of the Post-Card Technique in a Mail Questionnaire Study. Public Opinion Quarterly 27, pp 303-306.

Bogart, L. (1967): No Opinion, Don't Know and May Be No Answer. Public Opinion Quarterly 31.

Bohannon, T.R. (1976): Discriminant Analysis with Missing Data. Ph.D. dissertation, Texas A&M University, College Station, Texas.

Bohannon, T.R. and Smith, W.B. (1976): Classification Based on Incomplete Data Records. American Statistical Association, Proceedings of the Social Statistics Section, pp 214-218.

Bonham, G.S. (1977): Length of Interview: the National Survey of Family Growth. American Statistical Association, Proceedings of the Social Statistics Section, pp 583-588.

Boruch, R.F. (1971): Assuring Confidentiality of Responses in Social Research: A Note on Strategies. The American Sociologist, Vol. 6, No. 4, pp 308-311.

Boruch, R.F. (1971): Educational Research and the Confidentiality of Data: A Case Study. Sociology of Education, Vol. 44, No. 1, pp 59-85.

Boruch, R.F. (1971): Maintaining Confidentiality in Educational Research: A Systematic Analysis. American Psychologist 26, pp 413-430.

Boruch, R.F. (1972): Relations Among Statistical Methods for Assuring Confidentiality of Social Research Data. Social Science Research 1, pp 403-414.

Boruch, R.F. (1972): Strategies for Eliciting and Merging Confidential Social Research Data. Policy Sciences, Vol. 3, No. 3, pp 275-297.

Boruch, R.F. (1976): Costs, Benefits, and Legal Implications of Methods for Assuring Confidentiality in Social Research. In Forschung im Konflikt mit Recht und Ethik, edited by A. Eser and K.F. Schumann. Stuttgart: Ferdinand Enke Verlag.

Boruch, R.F. (1976): Record Linkage in Longitudinal and Correlational Research: Its Justification and Implications for Individual Privacy. In Expanding the Right to Privacy: Research and Legislative Initiatives for the Future, edited by Steven E. Aufrecht. Final conference proceedings of an executive seminar sponsored by the Washington Public Affairs Center, University of Southern California, Washington DC, October 14-15, 1976, pp 59-99.

Boruch, R.F. and Cecil, J.S. (1979): Assuring Confidentiality in Social Research. Philadelphia: University of Pennsylvania Press.

Bourke, P.D. (1974): Multi-Proportions Randomized Response Using the Unrelated Question Technique. Report No. 74 of the Errors in Surveys research project. Institute of Statistics, University of Stockholm.

Bourke, P.D. and Dalenius, T. (1973): Multi-Proportions Randomized Response Using a Single Sample. Report No. 68 of the Errors
in Surveys research project. Institute of Statistics, University
of Stockholm.

Bourke, P.D. and Dalenius, T. (1974): Randomized Response Models
with Lying. Report No. 71 of the Errors in Surveys research
project. Institute of Statistics, University of Stockholm.

Bourke, P.D. and Dalenius, T. (1976): Some New Ideas in the
Realm of Randomized Inquiries. International Statistical Review,
Vol. 44, pp 219-222.

Bostwick, G.L. (1977): Privacy of Personal Information: California
Faces the Issues. Public Affairs Report, Bulletin of the Insti-
tute of Governmental Studies, University of California, Berkeley,
Vol. 18, No. 1, pp 1-6.

Box, M.J. (1971): A Parameter Estimation Criterion for Multiresponse Models Applicable when Some Observations are Missing.
Applied Statistics, Vol. 20, No. 1, pp 1-7.

Box, M.J., Draper, N.R. and Hunter, W.G. (1970): Missing Values
in Multiresponse Non-Linear Model Fitting. Technometrics 12,
pp 613-620.

Boyd, H.W. Jr and Westfall, R. (1955): Interviewers as a Source
of Error in Surveys. Journal of Marketing 19, pp 311-324.

Boyd, H.W. Jr and Westfall, R. (1965): Interviewer Bias Revisited.
Journal of Marketing Research 2, pp 58-63.

Boyd, H.W. Jr and Westfall, R. (1970): Interviewer Bias Once
More Revisited. Journal of Marketing Research 7, pp 249-253.

Brackstone, G.J. and Rao, J.N.K. (1976): Raking Ratio Estimators.
Survey Methodology, Vol. 2, No. 1, pp 63-69.

Brackstone, G.J. and Rao, J.N.K. (1978): An Investigation of
Raking Ratio Estimators. Unpublished Statistics Canada Working
Paper.

Bradburn, N.M. (1978): Respondent Burden. American Statistical
Association, Proceedings of the Section on Survey Research
Methods, pp 35-40.

Bradburn, N.M. and Mason, W.M. (1964): The Effect of Question
Order on Responses. Journal of Marketing Research 1, pp 57-61.

Bradburn, N.M., Sudman, S., Blair, E. and Stocking, C. (1977):
Question Threat and Response Bias. Public Opinion Quarterly
42, pp 221-234.

Bradt, K. (1955): The Usefulness of a Postcard Technique in
a Mail Questionnaire Study. Public Opinion Quarterly 19, pp
218-222.

Brein, M. and Ryback, D. (1970): Stimulus, Respondent, and
Response Characteristics of Social Distance and Self-Disclosure.
Sociology and Social Research 55, pp 17-28.

Brennan, R.D. (1958): Trading Stamps as an Incentive in Mail
Surveys. Journal of Marketing 22, pp 306-307.

Brewer, K.R.W. and Särndal, C.E. (1979): Six Approaches to
Enumerative Survey Sampling. Paper presented at the Symposium
on incomplete data: Preliminary proceedings, Washington Hilton
Hotel on August 10-11, 1979, Washington, DC.

Bridge, G. (1977): Comments on "Respondent Burden" by Bradburn,
N.M.. Memo, Department of Psychology, Teachers College, Columbia
University.

Britton, J.H. and Britton, J.O. (1951): Factors in the Return
of Questionnaires Mailed to Older Persons. Journal of Applied
Psychology 35, pp 57-60.

Brooks, C.A. and Bailar, B.A. (1977): An Error Profile: Employ-
ment as Measured by the Current Population Survey. American
Statistical Association, Proceedings of the Social Statistics
Section, pp 26-34.

Brooks, C.A. and Bailar, B.A. (1978): Nonsampling Errors in
the Current Population Survey as They Affect the Employment
Statistics. Memo, US Bureau of the Census.

Brooks, V. (1947): Can You Trust Mail Questionnaires? Printer's
Ink 220, pp 86-194.

Brown, J.M. (1955): Respondents Rate Public Opinion Interviewers.
Journal of Applied Psychology 39, pp 96-102.

Brown, M.L. (1965-66): Use of a Postcard Query in Mail Surveys.
Public Opinion Quarterly 29, pp 635-637.

Brown, R.V. (1963): Credence Analysis. A Guide to Choosing
Research Strategies. Metra, pp 361-383.

Brown, R.V. (1967): Evaluation of Total Survey Error. Journal
of Marketing Research 4, pp 117-128.

Brown, R.V. (1967): Evaluation of Total Survey Error by Error
Ratio Analysis. Metra, pp 593-613.

Brown, R.V. (1969): Just How Credible Are Your Research Estimates? Journal of Marketing 33, pp 46-50.

Brown, R.V. (1969): Research and the Credibility of Estimates.
Boston: Graduate School of Business Administration, Harvard
University.

Brown, S.W. and Coney, K.A. (1977): Comments on "Mail Survey
Premiums and Response Bias". Journal of Marketing Research
14, pp 385-386.

Brownlee, K.A. (1957): A Note on the Effects of Non-Response
on Surveys. Journal of the American Statistical Association
21, pp 29-32.

Brunner, G.A. and Carrol, S.J. Jr (1967-68): The Effect of
Prior Telephone Appointments on the Completion Rates and Response
Content Patterns in Two Fixed Address Surveys. Public Opinion
Quarterly 31, pp 652-654.

Brunner, G.A. and Carroll, S.J. Jr (1969): The Effect of Prior
Notification on the Refusal Rate in Fixed Address Surveys.
Journal of Advertising Research 9, pp 42-44.

Brunner, G.A. and Carroll, S.J. Jr (1969): Weekday Evening
Interviews of Employed Persons Are Better. Public Opinion Quarterly 33, pp 265-267.

Brunner, J.A. and Brunner, G.A. (1971): Are Voluntarily Unlisted
Telephone Subscribers Really Different? Journal of Marketing
Research 8, pp 121-124.

Bryant, E.C. and Hansen, M.H. (1975): Invasion of Privacy and
Surveys: A Growing Dilemma. In H.W. Sinaiko and L.A. Broedling,
eds., Perspectives on Attitude Assessment: Surveys and Their
Alternatives, Washington DC: Manpower Research and Advisory
Services, Smithsonian Institution, pp 77-86.

Bryant, E.E., Kovar, M.G. and Miller, H. (1975): A Study of
the Effect of Remuneration Upon Response in the Health and
Nutrition Examination Survey - United States. Vital and Health
Statistics, Series 2, No. 67.

Buck, S.F. (1960): A Method of Estimation of Missing Values
in Multivariate Data Suitable for Use With an Electronic Computer.
Journal of the Royal Statistical Society 22, Series B, pp 302-306.

Bugental, J.F.T., Stark, E. and Salmon, C. (1957): An Experiment
on 'Refusal Rates in Relation to Interviewer Approach'. Indian
Journal of Psychology 32, pp 119-124.

Bulmer, M. (ed.). (1979): Censuses, Surveys and Privacy. London:
Macmillan.

Bushery, J.M., Cowan, C.D. and Murphy, L.R. (1978): Experiments
in Telephone-Personal Visit Surveys. American Statistical Association, Proceedings of the Section on Survey Research Methods,
pp 564-569.

Bushkin, A.A. and Schaen, S.I. (1976): The Privacy Act of 1974:
A Reference Manual for Compliance. McLean, Va. System Development
Corporation.

Business Week (1973): The Public Clams up on Survey Takers.
Sept 15, pp 216-220.

Butler, R.P. (1973): Effects of Signed and Unsigned Questionnaires for Both Sensitive and Nonsensitive Items. Journal of
Applied Psychology 57, pp 348-349.

Cahalan, D. (1951): Effectiveness of a Mail Questionnaire Technique in the Army. Public Opinion Quarterly 15, pp 575-578.

Campbell, C. and Joiner, B.L. (1973): How to Get the Answer Without Being Sure You've Asked the Question. American Statistician, pp 229-231.

Campbell, D.T. (1949): Bias in Mail Surveys. Public Opinion Quarterly 13, pp 562.

Campbell, D.T., Boruch, R.F., Schwartz, R.D. and Steinberg, J. (1975): Confidentiality-Preserving Modes of Access to Files and to Interfile Exchange for Useful Statistical Analysis. Evaluation Quarterly, Vol. 1, No. 2, May 1977, pp 269-299. Also Appendix A in Committee on Federal Agency Evaluation Research, Protecting Individual Privacy in Evaluation Research, Washington, DC: National Research Council/National Academy of Sciences.

Cannell, C.F. (1964): Factors Affecting the Refusal Rate in Interviewing. Working paper distributed by the Survey Research Center. Ann Arbor: The University of Michigan.

Cannell, C.F. (1970): Interviewer Performance Over Time: Some Implications for Field Supervision and Training. In C.F. Cannell, K.H. Marquis and A. Laurent: "Studies of Interviewing Methodology - A Summary of Research Conducted for the National Center for Health Statistics" (May 1970).

Cannell, C.F. (1977): A Summary of Studies of Interviewing Methodology. Memo, National Center for Health Statistics.

Cannell, C.F. and Fowler, F.J. (1963): A Comparison of a Self-Enumerative Procedure and a Personal Interview: A Validity Study. Public Opinion Quarterly 27, pp 250-264.

Cannell, C.F. and Fowler, F.J. (1977): Interviewing and Interviewing Techniques; Advances in Health Survey Research Methods; NCHSR Research Proceedings Series, DHEW Publ. No. (HRA) 77-3154.

Cannell, C.F., Fowler, F.J. and Marquis, K.H. (1965): Report on Development of Brochures for Health Interview Survey Respondent. Survey Research Center. The University of Michigan, (mimeo).

Cannell, C.F., Fowler, F.J. and Marquis, K.H. (1968): The Influence of Interviewer and Respondent Psychological Behavioral Variables on the Reporting in Household Interviews. Vital and Health Statistics, US Public Health Service, Washington, DC, Series 2, No. 26.

Cannell, C.F. and Henson, R. (1974): Incentives, Motives and Response Bias. Annals of Economic and Social Measurement 3, pp 307-317.

Cannell, C.F. and Kahn, R.L. (1965): The Collection of Data by Interviewing. In Leon Festinger and Daniel Katz, eds., "Research Methods in the Behavioral Sciences." New York, Holt, Rinehart, and Winston.

Cannell, C.F., Lawson, S.A. and Hausser, D.L. (1975): A Technique
for Evaluating Interviewer Performance: A Manual for Coding
and Analyzing Interviewer Behavior from Tape Recordings of
Household Interviews. Ann Arbor: Survey Research Center, Institute for Social Research, University of Michigan, 1975. pp
138.

Cannell, C.F., Marquis, K.H. and Laurent, A. (1970): Studies
of Interviewing Methodology - A Summary of Research Conducted
for the National Center for Health Statistics.

Cannell, C.F., Marquis, K.H. and Laurent, A. (1977): A Summary
of Studies of Interviewing Methodology. Vital and Health Statistics - Series 2, No. 69; DHEW Publ. No. (HRA) 77-1343.

Cannell, C.F., Oksenberg, L. and Converse, J.M. (1977): Striving
for Response Accuracy: Experiments in New Interviewing Techniques. Survey Research Center, Institute for Social Research,
The University of Michigan. Journal of Marketing Research 14,
pp 306-315.

Cannell, C.F., Oksenberg, L. and Converse, J.M. (1977): Experi-
ments in Interviewing Techniques: Field Experiments in Health
Reporting, 1971-1977. Hyattsville: National Center for Health
Services Research.

Carlsmith, J., Doob, A. and Freedman, J. (1973): Effects of
Sponsor and Prepayment on Compliance with a Mailed Request.
Journal of Applied Psychology, pp 346-347.

Carlson, R.O. (1967): The Issue of Privacy in Public Opinion
Research. Public Opinion Quarterly 31, pp 1-8.

Carpenter, E.H. (1974-75): Personalizing Mail Surveys: A Replication and Reassessment. Public Opinion Quarterly 38, pp 614-620.

Carson, E.M. (1973): Questionnaire Design. Survey Design and
Management Section, Household Surveys Development Division,
Statistics Canada.

Cartwright, A. (1955): The Families and Individuals Who Did
Not Cooperate on a Sample Survey. The Milbank Memorial Fund
Quarterly, Vol. 37, No. 4, pp 347-368.

Cartwright, A. and Tucker, W. (1967): An Attempt to Reduce
the Number of Calls on an Interview Inquiry. Public Opinion
Quarterly 31, pp 299-302.

Cassel, C-M., Särndal, C-E. and Wretman, J.H. (1979): Some
Uses of Statistical Models in Connection with the Nonresponse
Problem. Paper presented at the Symposium on incomplete data:
Preliminary proceedings, Washington Hilton Hotel on August
10-11, 1979, Washington, DC.

Causey, B.D. (1972): Sensitivity of Raked Contingency Table
Totals to Changes in Problem Conditions. Annals of Mathematical
Statistics 43, pp 656-658.

Causey, B.D. (1973): Variance of Raked-Table Entries. Memo, US Bureau of the Census.

Chai, J.J. (1970): The Effects of "Improved" Methods of Collecting Income Statistics on Non-Response Rates - 1969 CPS Experiments. American Statistical Association, Proceedings of the Social Statistics Section, pp 260-264.

Champion, D.J. and Sear, A.M. (1969): Questionnaire Response Rate: A Methodological Analysis. Social Forces, Vol. 47, No. 3, pp 335-339.

Chan, L.S. and Dunn, O.J. (1972): The Treatment of Missing Values in Discriminant Analysis - I. The Sampling Experiment. Journal of the American Statistical Association 67, pp 473-477.

Chan, L.S. and Dunn, O.J. (1974): A Note on the Asymptotic Aspect of the Treatment of Missing Values in Discriminant Analysis. Journal of the American Statistical Association 69, pp 672-673.

Chan, L.S., Gilman, J.A. and Dunn, O.J. (1976): Alternative Approaches to Missing Data in Discriminant Analysis. Journal of the American Statistical Association 71, pp 842-844.

Chapman, D.W. (1974): An Investigation of Nonresponse Imputation Procedures for the Health and Nutrition Examination Survey. Paper prepared for the division of Health Examination Survey, National Center for Health Statistics, HEW, by Westat Research.

Chapman, D.W. (1976): A Survey of Nonresponse Imputation Procedures. American Statistical Association, Proceedings of the Social Statistical Section, pp 245-251.

Chapman, D.W. (1979): The Impact of Substitution on Survey Estimates. Memo, US Bureau of the Census.

Chen, T.T. (1972): Mixed-up Frequencies and Missing Data in Contingency Tables. Unpublished Ph.D. Dissertation, Department of Statistics, University of Chicago.

Chen, T.T. (1978): Log-Linear Models for the Categorical Data Obtained from Randomized Response Techniques. American Statistical Association, Proceedings of Social Statistics Section, pp 284-288.

Chen, T.T. (1979): Analysis of Randomized Response as Purposively Misclassified Data. American Statistical Association, Proceedings of the Section on Survey Research Methods, pp 158-163.

Chi, I-C., Chow, L.P. and Rider, R.V. (1972): The Randomized Response Technique as Used in the Taiwan Outcome of Pregnancy Study. Studies in Family Planning, Vol. 3, No. 11, pp 265-269.

Childers, T.L. and Ferrell, O.C. (1979): Response Rates and Perceived Questionnaire Length in Mail Surveys. Journal of Marketing Research 16, pp 429-431.

Childers, T.L. and Skinner, S.J. (1979): Gaining Respondent Cooperation in Mail Surveys Through Prior Commitment. Public Opinion Quarterly 43, pp 558-561.

Chinnappa, B.N. and Wills, B. (1978): A Study of Refusal Rates to the Physical Measures Component of the Canada Health Survey. Survey Methodology/Techniques d'Enquête 1978, Vol. 4, No 1, pp 100-114.

Chow, G.C. and Lin, A-L. (1976): Best Linear Unbiased Estimation of Missing Observations in an Economic Time Series. Journal of the American Statistical Association 71, pp 719-721.

Chow, L.P. (1973): Memorandum on a New Randomized Response Technique: Multiple Answer Model, Department of Population Dynamics. The Johns Hopkins University, Baltimore, Maryland.

Christenson, J.A. (1975): Procedure for Conducting Mail Surveys. Journal of the Community Development Society 6, pp 135-146.

Chromy, J.R. and Horvitz, D.G. (1974): The Use of Monetary Incentives in National Assessment Household Surveys. American Statistical Association, Proceedings of the Social Statistics Section, pp 171-179.

Chromy, J.R. and Horvitz, D.G. (1978): The Use of Monetary Incentives in National Assessment Household Surveys. Journal of the American Statistical Association 73, pp 473-478.

Clausen, J.A. and Ford, R.N. (1947): Controlling Bias in Mail Questionnaires. Journal of the American Statistical Association 42, pp 497-511.

Clickner, R.P. and Iglewicz, B. (1976): Warner's Randomized Response Technique: The Two Sensitive Question Case. American Statistical Association, Proceedings of the Social Statistics Section, pp 260-265.

Cobb, S., King, S. and Chen, E. (1957): Differences Between Respondents and Nonrespondents in a Morbidity Survey Involving Clinical Examination. Journal of Chronic Diseases 6, pp 95-108.

Cochran, W.G. (1951): Modern Methods in the Sampling of Human Populations. American Journal of Public Health, pp 647-653.

Cochran, W.G. (1968): The Effectiveness of Adjustment by Sub-classification in Removing Bias in Observational Studies. Biometrics 24, pp 295-313.

Cochran, W.G. (1977): Sampling Techniques, Third edition, Chapter 13. New York: John Wiley and Sons.

Cochran, W.G. and Rubin, D.B. (1973): Controlling Bias in Observational Studies: A Review. Sankhya-A 35, pp 417-446.

Coder, J. (1977): Evaluation of Income Reporting on the Survey of Income and Education. Memo, US Bureau of the Census.

Cohen, S.F. and Lipstein, B. (1954): Response Errors in the
Collection of Wage Statistics by Mail Questionnaire. Journal
of the American Statistical Association 49, pp 240-250.

Cole, S. and Altman, M. (1977): An Experiment with Short Forms
in the Annual Survey of Manufactures. US Bureau of the Census.
Prepared for presentation at the annual meeting of the American
Statistical Association, Chicago, Illinois, aug 15-18, 1977.

Colledge, M.J., Johnson, J.H., Pare, R. and Sande, I.G. (1979):
Large Scale Imputation of Survey Data. Survey Methodology 4,
pp 203-224. Also in American Statistical Association, Proceedings
of the Section on Survey Research Methods, 1978, pp 431-436.

Colley, R.H. (1945): Don't Look Down Your Nose at Mail Questionnaires. Printer's Ink 210, pp 104-108.

Colombotos, J. (1969): Personal Versus Telephone Interviews:
Effect on Responses. Public Health Reports 84, pp 773-782.

Colombotos, J., Elinson, J. and Loewenstein, R. (1973): Effect
of Interviewers' Sex on Interview Responses; Research Methods
in Health Care (ed. McKinlay, J.), Selections from Milbank
Memorial Fund Quarterly, New York 1973. Also in Public Health
Reports, Vol. 83, No. 8, 1968, pp 685-690.

Commission on Federal Paperwork (1977): Confidentiality and
Privacy. Washington, DC: Government Printing Office, July 29,
1977.

Committee on Privacy (1972): Report of the Committee on Privacy.
Presented to Parliament by the Secretary of State for the Home
Department, the Lord High Chancellor, and the Secretary of
State for Scotland by Command of Her Majesty. Cmnd. 5012. London:
Her Majesty's Stationary Office, July 1972.

Cooper, G.A. (1948): The Case for Research by Mail - How It
Can Be Used and Improved. Printer's Ink 224, pp 38-39.

Cordell, W.N. and Rahmel, H.A. (1962): Are Nielsen Ratings
Affected by Non-Cooperation, Conditioning or Response error?
Journal of Advertising Research, pp 45-49.

Corey, S.M. (1937): Signed Versus Unsigned Attitude Questionnaires. Journal of Educational Psychology 28, pp 144-148.

Cornfield, J. (1942): On Certain Biases in Sampling of Human
Populations. Journal of the American Statistical Association
37, pp 63-68.

Coupe, J.M. and Forsythe, J. (1966): Mail-Return Rates and
Effect of Mail Follow-up for Nonresponse in the Agriculture
Field Procedure Study. Results Memorandum No. 4, RRB Department
No. 66-66 (67-451 (MRD)). Washington, DC: Bureau of the Census,
11 p. ditto.

Cowan, C.D. (1977): Incentive Effects on Amounts Reported in
an Expenditure Diary Survey. American Statistical Association,
Proceedings of Social Statistics Section, pp 498-503.

Cowan, C.D., Roman, A.M., Wolter, K.M. and Woltman, H.F. (1978):
A Test of Data Collection Methodologies: The Methods Test.
American Statistical Association, Proceedings of the Section
on Survey Research Methods, pp 141-146.

Cox, B.G. and Folsom, R.E. (1978): An Empirical Investigation
of Alternative Non-Response Adjustments. American Statistical
Association, Proceedings of the Section on Survey Research
Methods, pp 219-223.

Cox, E.P., III (1976): A Cost/Benefit View of Prepaid Monetary
Incentives in Mail Questionnaires. Public Opinion Quarterly
40, pp 101-104.

Cox, E.P., III, Anderson, W.T. Jr and Fulcher, D.G. (1974):
Reappraising Mail Survey Response Rates. Journal of Marketing
Research 11, pp 413-417.

Cox, W.E. Jr (1966): Response Patterns to Mail Surveys. Journal
of Marketing Research 3, pp 392-397.

Craig, S.C. and McCann, J.M. (1978): Item Nonresponse in Mail
Surveys: Extent and Correlates. Journal of Marketing Research
15, pp 285-289.

Crank, K.N. (1979): The Use of Current Partial Information
to Adjust for Nonrespondents. US Dept. Agr., Econ. Stat. Coop.
Serv.

Crider, D.M., Villits, F.K. and Bealer, R.C. (1971-72): Tracking
Respondents in Longitudinal Surveys. Public Opinion Quarterly
35, pp 613-620. Also in Sociology and Social Research 58, Oct.
1972, pp 57-65.

Creech, F.R. (1975): Partial- and Non-Response Bias Effects
in a Nationwide Sample. Princeton, New Jersey: Educational
Testing Service.

Crossley, H.M. and Fink, R. (1951): Response and Non-Response
in a Probability Sample. International Journal of Opinion and
Attitude Research 5, pp 1-19.

Crotty, J. (1966): The Utilization of Mail Questionnaires and
the Problem of a Representative Return Rate. Western Political
Quarterly, pp 44-53.

Crowder, E.T. (1944): Centralized Internal Control of Data
Collection by Federal Agencies. Journal of the American Statistical Association 39, pp 155-164.

Cuchman, E.A. and McCandles, B. (1940): Who Answers Questionnaires? Journal of Applied Psychology 24, pp 758-769.

Cunliffe, S.Y. and Goldstein, H. (1979): Ethical Aspects of
Survey Research. Applied Statistics 28, No. 3, pp 219-222.

Curry, J-O.K.J. (1977): The Treatment of Missing Data in Multivariate Analysis. Sociological Methods & Research, Vol. 6,
No. 2, pp 215-240.

Dagenais, M.G. (1971): Further Suggestions Concerning the Utilization of Incomplete Observations in Regression Analysis. Journal
of the American Statistical Association 66, pp 93-98.

Dagenais, M.G. (1974): Multiple Regression Analysis with Incomplete Observations from a Bayesian Viewpoint. Studies in Bayesian
Econometrics and Statistics.

Dalenius, T. (1955): The Problem of Not-at-Homes. Statistisk
Tidskrift 4, pp 208-211.

Dalenius, T. (1957): Sampling in Sweden. Stockholm, Sweden:
Almquist & Wiksell.

Dalenius, T. (1961): Treatment of the Non-Response Problem.
Journal of Advertising Research 1, pp 1-7.

Dalenius, T. (1962): Automatic Estimation of Missing Values
in Censuses and Sample Surveys. Statistisk Tidskrift, pp 395-400.

Dalenius, T. (1962): Recent Advances in Sample Survey Theory
and Methods. Annals of Mathematical Statistics 33, pp 325-349.

Dalenius, T. (1968): Theory and Methods of Descriptive Surveys,
Some Recent Advances. Forskningsprojektet FEL I UNDERSÖKNINGAR,
rapport nr 10, Stockholms universitet.

Dalenius, T. (1974): Ends and Means of Total Survey Design.
University of Stockholm, Stockholm.

Dalenius, T. (1974): The Invasion of Privacy Problem and Statistics Production - An Overview. Statistisk Tidskrift 3, pp
213-225.

Dalenius, T. (1975): Confidentiality in Surveys - A Research
Program. Confidentiality in Surveys, Report 1. Department of
Statistics, University of Stockholm, May 31, 1977. Proceedings
of the Symposium on Statistics and Related Topics, Carleton
University, 36 p. Unpublished.

Dalenius, T. (1977): The Swedish Data Act and Statistical Data.
Report No. 22 of the research project Confidentiality in Surveys.
Department of Statistics, University of Stockholm, Stockholm,
1977. Also in Statistisk Tidskrift 16 (1978), pp 37-45.

Dalenius, T. (1977): Strain at a Gnat and Swallow a Camel:
Or, the Problem of Measuring Sampling and Non-Sampling Errors.
American Statistical Association, Proceedings of the Social
Statistics Section, pp 21-25.

Dalenius, T. (1978): The Swedish Data Act and Statistical Data
- II. Report No. 28 of the research project Confidentiality
in Surveys. Department of Statistics, University of Stockholm,
Stockholm, 1978.

Dalenius, T. (1979): Data Protection Legislation in Sweden:
A Statistician's Perspective. Journal of the Royal Statistical
Society, Series A, 142, Part 3, pp 285-298.

Dalenius, T. (1979): Informed Consent or R.S.V.P. Paper presented at the Symposium on incomplete data: Preliminary proceedings, Washington Hilton Hotel on August 10-11, 1979, Washington, DC.

Dalenius, T. (n.d.): Towards a Survey Measurement System. Forskningsprojektet FEL I UNDERSÖKNINGAR, rapport nr 1, Stockholms universitet.

Dalenius, T. and Lyberg, L. (1971): Bibliography on Non-Sampling Errors in Surveys. Stockholms universitet, statistiska institutionen.

Dalenius, T. and Vitale, R.A. (1974): A New Randomized Response Design for Estimating the Mean of a Distribution. Errors in Surveys Report 78, Department of Statistics, University of Stockholm. Unpublished.

Daniel, W.W. (1975): Nonresponse in Sociological Surveys - A Review of Some Methods for Handling the Problems. Sociological Methods and Research, Vol. 3, No. 3, pp 291-307.

Dawes, R.M. (1974): Guttman Scaling Randomized Responses: A Technique for Evaluating the Underlying Structures of Behaviours to Which People May Not Wish to Admit. Oregon Research Institute, University of Oregon.

Day, G.S. (1975): The Threats to Marketing Research. Journal of Marketing Research 12, pp 462-467.

Day, R. and Wilcox, J. (1971): A Simulation Analysis of Nonresponse Error in Survey Sampling. Combined Proceedings, 1971 Spring and Fall Conferences, American Marketing Association, pp 478-483.

Dear, R.E. (1959): A Principal-Component Missing-Data Method for Multiple Regression Models, SP-86, System Development Corporation, Santa Monica, California.

Deighton, R.E., Poland, J.R., Stubbs, J.R. and Tortora, R.D. (1978): Glossary of Nonsampling Error Terms: An Illustration of a Semantic Problem in Statistics. US Department of Commerce, Statistical Policy Working Paper 4, Dec 1978. Also in American Statistical Association, Proceedings of the Social Statistics Section, 1977, pp 995-1003.

DeLacy, P.W. (1975): Randomized Conditional Response. American Statistical Association, Proceedings of the Social Statistics Section, pp 383-386.

DeMaio, T.J. (1978): Refusals: Who, Where and Why. Paper presented at 1978 Conference of American Association for Public Opinion Research.

DeMaio, T. (1979): Selected Tabulations from the 1977 Privacy and Confidentiality Attitude Survey. Memo, US Bureau of the Census.

Deming, W.E. (1943): Statistical Adjustment of Data. New York: John Wiley.

Deming, W.E. (1944): On Errors in Surveys. American Sociological Review 9, pp 359-369.

Deming, W.E. (1950): Some Theory of Sampling. New York: John Wiley.

Deming, W.E. (1953): On a Probability Mechanism to Attain an Economic Balance between the Resultant Error of Response and the Bias of Nonresponse. Journal of the American Statistical Association 48, pp 743-772.

Deming, W.E. (1954): On the Presentation of the Results of Sample Surveys as Legal Evidence. Journal of the American Statistical Association 49, pp 814-825.

Deming, W.E. (1960): Uncertainties in Statistical Data, and Their Relation to the Design and Management of Statistical Surveys and Experiments. Bulletin of the International Statistical Institute, Tokyo.

Deming, W.E. and Simmons, W. (1946): On the Design of a Sample for Dealers' Inventories. Journal of the American Statistical Association 41, pp 16-33.

Deming, W.E. and Stephan, F.F. (1940): On a Least Squares Adjustment of a Sampled Frequency Table when the Expected Marginal Totals are Known. Annals of Mathematical Statistics 11, pp 427-444.

Dempster, A.P., Laird, N.M. and Rubin, D.B. (1977): Maximum Likelihood from Incomplete Data Via the EM Algorithm, Journal of the Royal Statistical Society, Series B, 39, pp 1-38.

Deutscher, I. (1956): Physicians' Reactions to a Mailed Questionnaire: A Study in Resistentialism. Public Opinion Quarterly 20, pp 599-604.

Dillman, D.A. (1972): Increasing Mail Questionnaire Response in Large Samples of the General Public. Public Opinion Quarterly 36, pp 254-257.

Dillman, D.A. (1978): Mail and Telephone Surveys. The Total Design Method. New York: John Wiley.

Dillman, D.A., Cristenson, J.A. Carpenter, E.H. and Brooks, R.M. (1974): Increasing Mail Questionnaire Response: A Four-State Comparison. American Sociological Review 39, pp 744-756.

Dillman, D.A. and Frey, J.H. (1974): Contribution of Personalization to Mail Questionnaire Response as an Element of a Previously Tested Method. Journal of Applied Psychology 59, pp 297-301.

Dillman, D.A., Gallegos, J.G. and Frey, J.H. (1976): Reducing Refusal Rates for Telephone Interviews. Public Opinion Quarterly 40, pp 66-78.

Dimling, J.A. Jr (1975): Rates of Response in Local Television Research. American Statistical Association, Proceedings of the Business and Economic Statistics Section, pp 86-89.

Dippo, C., Coleman, J. and Jacobs, C. (1977): Evaluation of the 1972-73 Consumer Expenditure Survey. Paper prepared for presentation at the annual meetings of the American Statistical Association held in Chicago, Illinois, August 15-19, 1977.

Dodge, Y. (1975): Estimability Considerations for N-Way Classification Experimental Arrangements with Missing Observations. Bulletin of International Statistical Institute, pp 224-227.

Dohrenwend, B.S. (1970): An Experimental Study of Payments to Respondents. Public Opinion Quarterly 34, pp 621-624.

Dohrenwend, B.S. and Dohrenwend, B.P. (1968): Sources of Refusals in Mail Surveys. Public Opinion Quarterly 32, pp 74-83.

Dommermuth, W.P. and Cateora, P.R. (1963): Can Refusals by Respondents be Decreased? Journal of Marketing 27, pp 74-76.

Donald, M.N. (1960): The Implications of Non-Response for the Interpretation of Mail Questionnaire Data. Public Opinion Quarterly 24, pp 99-114.

Doob, A.N., Freedman, J.L. and Carlsmith, J.M. (1973): Effects of Sponsor and Prepayment on Compliance with a Mailed Request. Journal of Applied Psychology, Vol. 57, No. 3, pp 346-347.

Doob, A.N. and Zabrack, M. (1971): The Effect of Freedom-Threatening Instructions and Monetary Inducement on Compliance. Canadian Journal of Behavioural Science 3, pp 408-412.

Doran, H.E. (1974): Prediction of Missing Observations in the Time Series of an Economic Variable. Journal of the American Statistical Association 69, pp 546-554.

Dorn, D.S. and Long, G.L. (1974): Brief Remarks on the Association's Code of Ethics. American Sociologist 9, pp 31-35.

Doss, D.C., Hartley, H.O. and Somayajulu, G.R. (1978): An Exact Small Sample Theory for Post-Stratification. Paper presented at the American Statistical Association Meeting, San Diego, California, 1978.

Douglas, D.F., Westley, B.H. and Chaffee, S. (1970): An Information Campaign that Changed Community Attitudes. Journalism Quarterly 47, pp 479-492.

Dowling, T.A. and Shachtman, R.H. (1972): On the Relative Efficiency of Randomized Response Models. University of North Carolina Institute of Statistics Mimeo Series No. 811, Chapel Hill, N.C. Also in Journal of the American Statistical Association 70, pp 84-87.

Drane, W. (1975): Randomized Response to More than One Question. American Statistical Association, Proceedings of the Social Statistics Section, pp 395-397.

Drane, W. (1976): On the Theory of Randomized Responses to Two Sensitive Questions. American Statistical Association, Proceedings of the Social Statistics Section, pp 282-285. Also in Communications in Statistics - Theory and Methods, A 5(6), 1976, pp 565-574.

Draper, N.R. (1961): Missing Values in Response Surface Designs. Technometrics 3, pp 389-398.

Draper, N.R. and Stoneman, D.M. (1963): Estimating Missing Values in Unreplicated Two-Level Factorial and Fractional Factorial Designs. University of Wisconsin Technical Report No. 20.

Duncan, J.W. (1975): Confidentiality and the Future of the US Statistical System. American Statistical Association, Proceedings of the Social Statistics Section, pp 59-64.

Duncan, J.W. (1975): The Impact of Privacy Legislation on the Federal Statistical System. Public Data Use, Vol. 3, No. 1, pp 51-53.

Duncan, J.W. (1976): Assessment of Survey Practices and Data Quality - Comments Concerning Statistical Policy. American Statistical Association, Proceedings of the Social Statistics Section, pp 130-132.

Duncan, J.W. (1976): Confidentiality and the Future of the US Statistical System. American Statistician, Vol. 30, No. 2, pp 54-59.

Duncan, R.P. (1979): Survey Quality and Interviewer Attributes. Southern Sociologist, Vol. 10, No. 3, pp 16-21.

Dunkelberg, W.C. and Day, G.S. (1973): Nonresponse Bias and Callbacks in Sample Surveys. Journal of Marketing Research 10, pp 160-168.

Dunlap, J.W. (1950): The Effect of Color in Direct Mail Advertising. Journal of Applied Psychology 34, pp 280-281.

Dunn, J.P. and Hawkes, R. (1966): Comparison of Respondents and Non-Respondents in a Periodic Health Examination Program to a Mailed Questionnaire. American Journal of Public Health 56, pp 230-236.

Dunning, B. and Cahalan, D. (1973): By-Mail vs. Field Self-
Administered Questionnaires: An Armed Forces Survey. Public
Opinion Quarterly 37, pp 618-624.

Durant, H. and Mass, I. (1956): Who doesn't Answer? A symposium
on the problems of bias through nonreturns in questionnaire
surveys and follow-up conducted by post. Bulletin of the British
Psychological Society 29, pp 33-34.

Durbin, J. (1954): Non-Response and Call-Backs in Surveys.
Bulletin of the International Statistical Institute 34, pp
72-86.

Durbin, J. (1979): Statistics and the Report of the Data Protection Committee. Journal of the Royal Statistical Society 142,
Series A, pp 299-306.

Durbin, J. and Stuart, A. (1951): Differences in Response Rates
of Experienced and Inexperienced Interviewers. Journal of the
Royal Statistical Society 114, Series A, pp 163-206.

Durbin, J. and Stuart, A. (1954): Callbacks and Clustering
in Sample Surveys: An Experimental Study. Journal of the Royal
Statistical Society 117, Series A, pp 387-418.

Eastlack, J.O. Jr and Assael, H. (1966): Better Telephone Surveys through Centralized Interviewing. Journal of Advertising Research, pp 2-7.

Eastman, R.O. (1943): Don'ts about Mail Questionnaires. Printer's Ink, pp 24-29.

Eckland, B.K. (1965): Effects of Prodding to Increase Mail-back Returns. Journal of Applied Psychology 49, pp 165-169.

Edgerton, H.A., Britt, S.H. and Norman, R.D. (1947): Objective Differences among Various Types of Respondents to a Mailed Questionnaire. American Sociological Review 12, pp 435-444.

Edgett, G.L. (1956): Multiple Regression with Missing Observations among the Independent Variables. Journal of the American Statistical Association 51, pp 122-131.

Edsall, R.L. (1958): Getting "Not-at-Homes" to Interview Themselves. Journal of Marketing 23, pp 184-185.

Eisen, M. (1976): Analysis of 1972 Administrative Record Evaluation Tables. Memo, US Bureau of the Census.

Eisinger, R.A., Janicki, W.P., Stevenson, R.L. and Thompson, W.L. (1974): Increasing Returns in International Mail Surveys. Public Opinion Quarterly 38, pp 124-130.

Elashoff, J.D. and Elashoff, R.M. (1971): Missing Data Problems for Two Samples on a Dichotomous Variable. Research and Development Memorandum No. 73, Stanford Center for Research and Development in Teaching, Stanford University, Stanford, California.

Elashoff, J.D. and Elashoff, R.M. (1972): Two-Sample Problems for a Dichotomous Variable with Missing Data. American Statistical Association, Proceedings of the Social Statistics Section, pp 223-226.

Elashoff, J.D. and Elashoff, R.M. (1974): Two-Sample Problems for a Dichotomous Variable with Missing Data. Applied Statistics 23, No. 1, pp 26-34.

Elashoff, R.M. and Afifi, A.A. (1969): Missing Observations in Multivariate Statistics, III, IV. Journal of the American Statistical Association 64, pp 337-365.

El-Badry, M.A. (1956): A Sampling Procedure for Mailed Questionnaires. Journal of the American Statistical Association 51, pp 209-227.

Elinson, J. and Haines, V.T. (1950): Role of Anonymity in Attitude Surveys. American Psychologist 5, pp 315.

Ellis, R.A., Endo, C.M. and Armer, J.M. (1970): The Use of Potential Nonrespondents for Studying Nonresponse Bias. Pacific Sociological Review 13, pp 103-110.

Eokler, A.R. and Hurwitz, W.N. (1958): Response Variance and Biases in Censuses and Surveys. Bulletin of International Statistical Institute 36, No 2, pp 12-35.

Erdos, P.L. (1957): How to Get Higher Returns from Your Mail Surveys. Printer's Ink, pp 30-31.

Erdos, P.L. (1957): Successful Mail Surveys: High Returns and How to Get Them. Printer's Ink 258, pp 56-60.

Erdos, P.L. (1974): Data Collection Methods: Mail Surveys. In Robert Ferber, ed., Handbook of Marketing Research. New York: McGraw-Hill Book Co., 2-90-104.

Erdos, P.L. and Morgan, A.J. (1970): Professional Mail Surveys. New York: McGraw-Hill Book Co.

Ericson, W.A. (1967): Optimal Sample Design with Non-Response. Journal of the American Statistical Association 62, pp 63-78.

Eriksson, S.A. (1973): A New Model for Randomized Response. International Statistics Review 45, No. 1, pp 101-113.

Eriksson, S.A. (1975): Randomized Interviews for Sensitive Questions. Ph.D. dissertation, University Institute of Statistics, University of Gothenburg. Gothenburg, Sweden. Unpublished.

Eriksson, S. (1976): Applications of the Randomized Response Technique. Proceedings of a symposium on personal integrity and the need for data in the social sciences held at Hässelby Slott, Stockholm, March 15-17, 1976.

Ernst, L.F. (1978): Weighting to Adjust for Partial Nonresponse. American Statistical Association, Proceedings of the Section on Survey Research Methods, pp 468-472.

Ernst, L.R. (n.d.): Multiple Sampling. Memo, US Bureau of the Census.

Etzel, M.J. and Walker, B.J. (1974): Effects of Alternative Follow-up Procedures on Mail Survey Response Rates. Journal of Applied Psychology 59, pp 219-221.

Evans, F.B. (1961): On Interviewer Cheating. Public Opinion Quarterly 25, pp 126-127.

Fairclough, E.H. (1977): Personal Interviews and Postal Questionnaires: Some Observations and Experiences. The Statistician,
Vol. 26, No. 4, pp 259-268.

Falliher, J.F. (1973): The Protection of Human Subjects: A
Reexamination of the Professional Code of Ethics. The American
Sociologist 8, pp 93-100.

Falthzik, A.M. (1972): When to Make Telephone Interviews. Journal
of Marketing Research 9, pp 451-452.

Falthzik, A.M. and Carroll, S.J. (1971): Rate of Return for
Closed versus Open-Ended Questions in a Mail Questionnaire
Survey of Industrial Organizations. Psychological Reports 29,
pp 1121-1122.

Fay III, R.E. (n.d.): Problems of Nonsampling Error in the
Survey of Income and Education: Content Analysis. Memo, US
Bureau of the Census.

Feild, H.S. (1975): Effects of Sex of Investigator on Mail
Survey Response Rates and Response Bias. Journal of Applied
Psychology 60, pp 772-773.

Feldman, J.J., Hyman, H.H. and Hart, C.W. (1951-52): Interviewer
Effects on the Quality of Survey Data. Public Opinion Quarterly
15, pp 734-761.

Fellegi, I.P. (1972): On the Question of Statistical Confidentiality. Journal of the American Statistical Association 67,
pp 7-18.

Fellegi, I.P., Gray, G.B. and Platek, R. (1964): The Redesign
of the Canadian Labour Force Survey. American Statistical Association, Proceedings of the Social Statistics Section.

Fellegi, I.P. and Holt, D. (1973): A Systematic Approach to
Automatic Edit and Imputation. Bulletin of International Statistical Institute, Vol. 1, pp 290-302.

Fellegi, I.P. and Holt, D. (1976): A Systematic Approach to
Automatic Edit and Imputation. Journal of the American Statistical Association 71, pp 17-35.

Fellegi, I.P. and Sunter, A.B. (1973): Balance Between Different
Sources of Survey Errors - Some Canadian Experiences. Proceedings
of the 39th Session of the International Statistical Institute,
pp 334-335.

Ferber, R. (1948): Which - Mail Questionnaires or Personal
Interviews? Printer's Ink, pp 44-66.

Ferber, R. (1948-49): The Problem of Bias in Mail Surveys:
A Solution. Public Opinion Quarterly 12, pp 669-676.

Ferber, R. (1950): More on Bias in Mail Surveys. Public Opinion
Quarterly 13, pp 193-197.

Ferber, R. (1966): Item Nonresponse in a Consumer Survey. Public Opinion Quarterly 30, pp 399-415.

Ferber, R. and Sudman, S. (1974): Effects of Compensation in Consumer Expenditure Studies. Annals of Economic and Social Measurement 3, pp 319-332.

Ferriss, A.L. (1951): A Note on Stimulating Response to Questionnaires. American Sociological Review 16, pp 247-249.

Fessey, M.C. and Browning, H.E. (1970): Confidentiality of Business Statistics. Statistical News (Central Statistical Office, United Kingdom), No. 10, pp 10.1-10.6.

Field, M. (1974): Nonresponse and the Responsibility of Researchers. Public Opinion Quarterly 38, pp 477.

Fields, C.M. (1977): A Growing Problem for Researchers: Protecting Privacy. The Chronicle of Higher Education, Vol. XIV, No. 10, pp 1 & 15.

Fienberg, S.E. (1970): Quasi-Independence and Maximum Likelihood Estimation in Incomplete Contingency Tables. Journal of the American Statistical Association 65, pp 1610-1616.

Filion, F.L. (1975-76): Estimating Bias Due to Nonresponse in Mail Surveys. Public Opinion Quarterly 39, pp 482-492.

Filion, F.L. (1976): Exploring and Correcting for Nonresponse Bias Using Follow-Ups of Nonrespondents. Pacific Sociological Review 19, pp 401-408.

Fink, R. and Crossby, H.M. (1951): Response and Non-Response in a Probability Sample. International Journal of Opinion and Attitude Research, pp 1-19.

Finkner, A.L. (1950): Methods of Sampling for Estimating Peach Production in North Carolina. North Carolina Agricultural Experiment Station Technical Bulletin 91.

Finkner, A.L. (1952): Adjustment for Non-Response Bias in a Rural Mailed Survey. Agricultural Economics Research 4, pp 77-82.

Finkner, A.L. (1974): Privacy and Confidentiality Discussion. Presented at a meeting of the Census Bureau's Advisory Committee on Small Areas, Washington, DC, November 21-22, 1974.

Finkner, A.L. (1975): The Problem of Respondent Cooperation and Some Census Bureau Experiences. Memo, Marketing Research Association, October 23, 1975.

Finkner, A.L., Morgan, J.J. and Monroe, R.J. (1943): Methods of Estimating Farm Employment from Sample Data in North Carolina. Bulletin no. 75, North Carolina, Agricultural Experiment Station.

Finney, D.J. (1974): Problems, Data, and Inference. Journal of the Royal Statistical Society 137, Series A, pp 1-23.

Fischer, R.P. (1946): Signed Versus Unsigned Personal Questionnaires. Journal of Applied Psychology 30, pp 220-225.

Fitti, J.E. (1979): Some Results from the Telephone Health Interview System. American Statistical Association, Proceedings of the Section on Survey Research Methods, pp 244-249.

Flaherty, D.H. (1979): Privacy and Government Data Banks: An International Perspective. London: Mansell.

Flinn, N. (1976): Respondent Accessibility Study. Paper presented at 1976 Conference of American Association for Public Opinion Research.

Folsom, R.E. Jr (1974): National Assessment No-Show Analysis: A Study of Nonresponse Bias. National Assessment of Educational Progress, January, 1974.

Folsom, R.E. Jr (1974): A Randomized Response Validation Study: Comparison of Direct and Randomized Reporting of DUI Arrests. Final Report 25U-807. Prepared for the Research Center for Measurement Methods, US Bureau of the Census. Research Triangle Park, Research Triangle Institute, North Carolina. Unpublished.

Folsom, R.E., Greenberg, B.G., Horvitz, D.G. and Abernathy, J.R. (1973): The Two Alternative Questions Randomized Response Model for Human Surveys, Journal of the American Statistical Association 68, pp 525-530.

Foradori, G.T. (1961): Some Non-Response Sampling Theory for Two Stage Designs. North Carolina State College. Mimeographed series No. 297, Raleigh, NC.

Ford, B.L. (1976): Missing Data Procedures: A Comparative Study. American Statistical Association, Proceedings of the Social Statistics Section, pp 324-329.

Ford, B.L. (1978): Missing Data Procedures: A Comperative Study (part 2). US Dept. Agr., Econ. Stat. Coop. Serv.

Ford, B.L. (1978): A General Overview of the Missing Data Problem. US Dept. Agr., Econ. Stat. Coop. Serv.

Ford, B.L., Hocking, R.R. and Coleman, A.T. (1978): Reducing Respondent Burden on an Agricultural Survey. American Statistical Association, Proceedings of the Section on Survey Research Methods, pp 341-345.

Ford, N.M. (1967): The Advance Letter in Mail Surveys. Journal of Marketing Research 4, pp 202-204.

Ford, N.M. (1968): Questionnaire Appearance and Response Rates in Mail Surveys. Journal of Advertising Research 8, pp 43-45.

Ford, R.N. and Zeisel, H. (1949): Bias in Mail Surveys cannot be Controlled by One Mailing. Public Opinion Quarterly 13, pp 495-501.

Forsman, G., Lindström, H. and Wretman, J. (1976): Some Aspects on Utilizing Information about Bias in Survey Sampling, Statistisk Tidskrift 3, pp 230-238.

Forsythe, J.B. (1977): Obtaining Cooperation in a Survey of Business Executives. Journal of Marketing Research 14, pp 370-373.

Fox, P.D. (1963): Noncooperation Bias in Television Ratings. Public Opinion Quarterly 27, pp 312-314.

Frankel, L.R. (1960): How Incentives and Subsamples Affect the Precision of Mail Surveys. Journal of Advertising Research 1, pp 1-5.

Frankel, L.R. (1969): Are Survey Data Being Over-Adjusted? Current Controversies in Marketing Research, Markham.

Frankel, L.R. (1969): The Role of Accuracy and Precision of Response in Sample Surveys. Modern Marketing Series 7.

Frankel, L.R. (1976): Statistics and People - The Statistician's Responsibility. Journal of the American Statistical Association 71, pp 9-16.

Frankel, L.R. and Dutka, S. (1979): Survey Design in Anticipation of Non-Response and Imputation. Paper presented at the Symposium on incomplete data: Preliminary proceedings, Washington Hilton Hotel on August 10-11, 1979, Washington, DC.

Frankel, L.R. and Dutka, S. (1979): The Treatment of Non-Response in Marketing Intelligence Surveys. Paper presented at the 42nd Session of the International Statistical Institute, Manila, Phillipines, December 4-14, 1979.

Frankel, M.R. (1971): Inference From Survey Samples: An Empirical Investigation. Institute for Social Research, University of Michigan.

Frankel, M.R. and Frankel, L.R. (1977): Some Recent Developments in Sample Survey Design. Journal of Marketing Research 14, pp 280-293.

Franzen, R. and Lazarsfeld, P.F. (1945): Mail Questionnaire as a Research Problem. Journal of Psychology 20, pp 293-310.

Frazier, G. and Bird, K. (1958): Increasing the Response of a Mail Questionnaire. Journal of Marketing 22, pp 186-187.

Freedman, J.L. and Frazer, S.C. (1966): Compliance Without Pressure: The Foot-in-the-Door Technique. Journal of Personality and Social Psychology 4, pp 195-202.

Freedman, G.H. (1975): Analysis of Interactions in Incomplete Two-Way Tables. Applied Statistics 24, No. 1, pp 46-55.

Freese, J. (1973): The Swedish Data Act. Current Sweden (published by the Swedish Institute), No. 4, pp 1-6.

French, D. (1979): Dealing with the Problem of Incomplete Data in Cycle II of the National Survey of Family Growth. Paper prepared at the request of the NRC Panel on Incomplete Data.

Freund, R.J. and Hartley, H.O. (1967): A Procedure for Automatic Data Editing. Journal of the American Statistical Association 62, pp 341-352.

Friedman, H.H. and Fireworker, R.B. (1977): Effect of Ethnicity of Signature in Mail Surveys. American Statistical Association, Proceedings of the Social Statistics Section, pp 352-353.

Friedman, H.H. and Goldstein, L. (1975): Effect of Ethnicity of Signature on the Rate of Return and Content of a Mail Questionnaire. Journal of Applied Psychology 60, pp 770-771.

Fuller, C.H. (1974): Effect of Anonymity on Return Rate and Response Bias in a Mail Survey. Journal of Applied Psychology 59, pp 292-296.

Fuller, C.H. (1974): Weighting to Adjust for Survey Nonresponse. Public Opinion Quarterly 38, pp 239-246.

Futrell, C.M. and Swan, J.E. (1977): Anonymity and Response by Salespeople to a Mail Questionnaire. Journal of Marketing Research 14, pp 611-616.

Gallegos, J.G. (n.d.): An Experiment in Maximizing Response to Telephone Interviews through the Use of a Preliminary Letter Based on Principles of Exchange Theory. Unpublished Master's Thesis, Washington State University, Pullman, Washington.

Gates, R. and McDaniel, C. (1976): Improving Completion Rates by More Efficient Scheduling of Telephone Interviews. Viewpoints - The Journal for Data Collection 16, pp 8-10.

Gaudet, H. and Wilson, E.C. (1940): Who Escapes the Personal Investigator? Journal of Applied Psychology 24, pp 773-777.

Gaunou, M.J., Nothern, J.C. and Carroll, S.J. Jr (1971): Characteristics of Nonrespondents Among Workers. Journal of Applied Psychology 55, pp 586-588.

Gelb, B.D. (1975): Incentives to Increase Survey Returns: Social Class Considerations. Journal of Marketing Research 12, pp 107-109.

Gerberich, J.B. and Mason, J.M. (1948): Signed Versus Unsigned Questionnaire. Journal of Educational Research 42, pp 122-126.

Gergen, K.J. (1973): The Codification of Research Ethics: Views of a Doubting Thomas. American Psychologist 28, pp 907-912.

Ghangurde, P.D. and Mulvihill, J. (1978): Non-Response and Imputation in Longitudinal Estimation in LFS. Technical report, Household Surveys Development Staff, Statistics Canada.

Giguère, M.A. and Styan, G.P.H. (1974): Multivariate Normal Estimation with Missing Data on Several Variates. Proceedings of the Seventh Prague Conference on Information Theory, Statistical Decision Functions and Random Processes.

Giguère, M.A. and Styan, G.P.H. (1975): Comparisons Between Maximum Likelihood and Naive Estimators in a Multivariate Normal Population With Data Missing on One Variate. Bulletin of International Statistical Institute, pp 303-307.

Glasser, G. and Metzger, G.A. (1970): Measurement and Control of Interviewer Variability. American Statistical Association, Proceedings of the Business and Economic Section, pp 314-317.

Glasser, M. (1964): Linear Regression Analysis with Missing Observations Among the Independent Variables. Journal of the American Statistical Association 59, pp 834-844.

Gleason, C.P. and Bosecker, R.R. (1978): The Effects of Refusals and Inaccessibles on List-Frame Estimates. US Dept. Agr., Econ. Stat. Coop. Serv. 16.

Gleason, E. and Huck, S. (1974): Using Monetary Inducements to Increase Response Rates from Mailed Surveys: A Replication and Extension of Previous Research. Journal of Applied Psychology 59, pp 222-225.

Gleason, T.C. and Staelin, R. (1975): A Proposal for Handling Missing Data. Psychometrika 40, pp 229-252.

Godwin, R.K. (1979): The Consequences of Large Monetary Incentives in Mail Surveys of Elites. Public Opinion Quarterly 43, 378-387.

Goldfield, E.D., Turner, A.G., Cowan, C.D. and Scott, J.C. (1977): Privacy and Confidentiality as Factors in Survey Response. American Statistical Association, Proceedings of the Social Statistics Section, pp 219-231.

Goldstein, H. (1975): Some Problems in Approaches Toward Handling Missing Data in Longitudinal Files. American Statistical Association, Proceedings of the Social Statistical Section, pp 434-436.

Goldstein, H. and Kroll, B.H. (1957): Methods of Increasing Mail Response. Journal of Marketing 21, pp 55-57.

Goldstein, L. and Friedman, H.H. (1975): A Case for Double Postcards in Surveys. Journal of Advertising Research 15, pp 43-47.

Gonzalez, M., Ogus, J.L., Shapiro, G. and Tepping, B.J. (1975): Standards for Discussion and Presentation of Errors in Survey and Census Data. Journal of the American Statistical Association 70, pp 1-23.

Goodman, L.A. (1968): The Analysis of Cross-Classified Data: Independence, Quasi-Independence and Interactions in Contingency Tables with or without Missing Entries. Journal of the American Statistical Association 63, pp 1091-1131.

Goodstadt, M.S., Chung, L., Kronitz, R. and Cook, G. (1977): Mail Survey Response Rates: Their Manipulation and Impact. Journal of Marketing Research 14, pp 391-395.

Goodstadt, M.S. and Gruson, V. (1975): The Randomized Response Technique: A Test on Drug Use. Journal of the American Statistical Association 70, pp 814-818.

Gorden, R.L. (1975): Interviewing: Strategy, Techniques, and Tactics, revised edition. Homewood, Illinois: Dorsey Press.

Gosselin, J-F., Chinnappa, B.N., Ghangurde, P.D. and Tourigny, J. (1978): A Compendium of Methods of Error Evaluation in Censuses and Surveys. Statistics Canada, Published by Authority of The Minister of Industry, Trade and Commerce.

Goudy, W.J. (1976): Nonresponse Effects on Relationships Between Variables. Public Opinion Quarterly 40, pp 360-369.

Goudy, W.J. (1977): Nonresponse Effects: Studies of the Failure of Potential Respondents to Reply to Survey Instruments. Monticello, Illinois: Council of Planning Librarians Exchange Bibliography.

Goudy, W.J. (1978): Interim Response to a Mail Questionnaire: Impacts on Variable Relationships. The Sociological Quarterly 19, pp 253-265.

Gough, H.G. and Hall, W.B. (1977): A Comparison of Physicians Who did or did not Respond to a Postal Questionnaire. Journal of Applied Psychology 62, pp 777-780.

Gould, A.L., Shah, B.V. and Abernathy, J.R. (1969): Unrelated Question Randomized Response Techniques with Two Trials Per Respondent. American Statistical Association, Proceedings of the Social Statistics Section, pp 351-359.

Goulet, W.M. (1977): Efficacy of a Third Request Letter in Mail Surveys of Professionals. Journal of Marketing Research 14, pp 112-114.

Gower, A.R. (1977): Response Incentives Experiment. Quarterly Bulletin of the Methodology Divisions Statistical Services Field, Statistics Canada, No. 23.

Gower, A.R. (1977): The Response Incentives Experiment in the Canadian Labour Force Survey. Survey Methodology/Techniques d'Enquête, Vol. 3, No. 1, pp 84-103.

Gower, A.R. (1979): Non-Response in the Labour Force Survey. Technical memorandum. Methodology Division, Census and Household Surveys Field, Statistics Canada.

Graves, R.B. (1976): Can-Edit, A Generalized Edit and Imputation System in a Data Base Environment. A report to the working party on electronic data processing. Conference of European Statisticians.

Gray, B.H. (1978): Complexities of Informed Consent. The Annals of the American Academy of Political and Social Science, pp 37-48.

Gray, G.H. and Thompson, M.M. (1977): Description of the Survey of Income and Education (SIE) Operations. Memo, US Bureau of the Census.

Gray, P.G. (1957): A Sample Survey with Both a Postal and an Interview Stage. Applied Statistics 6, pp 139-153.

Gray, P.G. and Corlett, T. (1950): Sampling for the Social Survey. Journal of the Royal Statistical Society 113, pp 150-199.

Green, S. (1976): Maintaining High Response Rates in Studies Involving Repeated Personal Interviews. Paper presented at a seminar sponsored by the American Marketing Association, Oktober 7, 1976.

Greenberg, A. and Manfield, M. (1957): On the Reliability of Mail Questionnaires in Product Tests. Journal of Marketing 21, pp 342-345.

Greenberg, B.G., Abernathy, J.R. and Horvitz, D.G. (1969): Application of the Randomized Response Technique in Obtaining Quantitative Data. American Statistical Association, Proceedings of the Social Statistics Section, pp 40-43.

Greenberg, B.G., Abernathy, J.R. and Horvitz, D.G. (1970):
A New Survey Technique and Its Application in the Field of
Public Health. Milbank Memorial Fund Quarterly, Part 2, pp
39-55.

Greenberg, B.G., Abul-Ela, A-L.A., Simmons, W.R. and Horvitz,
D.G. (1969): The Unrelated Question Randomized Response Model:
Theoretical Framework. Journal of the American Statistical
Association 64, pp 520-539.

Greenberg, B.G., Horvitz, D.G. and Abernathy, J.R. (1974):
A Comparison of Randomized Response Designs. In Frank Proschan
and R.J. Serfling, eds., Reliability and Biometry, Statistical
Analysis of Lifelength, Philadelphia: SIAM, pp 787-815.

Greenberg, B.G., Kuebler, R.R. Jr, Abernathy, J.R. and Horvitz,
D.G. (1971): Application of the Randomized Response Technique
in Obtaining Quantitative Data. Journal of the American Statistical Association 66, pp 243-250.

Greenfield, C.C. (1975): On the Estimation of a Missing Cell
in a 2x2 Contingency Table. Journal of the Royal Statistical
Society 138, Series A, pp 51-61.

Greenfield, C.C. and Tam, S.M. (1976): A Simple Approximation
for the Upper Limit to the Value of a Missing Cell in a 2x2
Contingency Table. Journal of the Royal Statistical Society
139, Series A, pp 96-103.

Groves, R.M. (1977): An Experimental Comparison of National
Telephone and Personal Interview Surveys. American Statistical
Association, Proceedings of the Social Statistics Section,
pp 232-241.

Groves, R.M. (1978): An Empirical Comparison of Two Telephone
Sample Designs. Journal of Marketing Research 15, pp 622-631.

Groves, R.M. (1979): Actors and Questions in Telephone and
Personal Interview Surveys. Public Opinion Quarterly 43, pp
190-205.

Groves, R.M. and Cannell, C.F. (1979): Telephone Interview
Introductions and Refusal Rates: Experiments in Increasing
Respondent Cooperation. American Statistical Association, Proceed-
ings of the Section on Survey Research Methods, pp 252-255.

Groves, R.M. and Kahn, R.L. (1979): Surveys by Telephone -
a National Comparison with Personal Interviews. Quantitative
Studies in Social Relations, Academic Press, Inc., New York.

Gullahorn, J.T. and Gullahorn, J.E. (1959): Increasing Returns
from Non-Respondents. Public Opinion Quarterly 23, pp 119-121.

Gullahorn, J.T. and Gullahorn, J.E. (1963): An Investigation
of the Effects of Three Factors on Response to Mail Questionnaires. Public Opinion Quarterly 27, pp 294-296.

Haase, K.W. and Wilson, R.W. (1972): The Study Design of an Experiment to Measure the Effects of Using Proxy Responses in the National Health Interview Survey. American Statistical Association, Proceedings of the Social Statistics Section, pp 289-293.

Hackler, J.C. and Bourgette, P. (1973): Dollars, Dissonance, and Survey Returns. Public Opinion Quarterly 37, pp 276-281.

Haitovsky, Y. (1968): Missing Data in Regression Analysis. Journal of the Royal Statistical Society 63, Series B, pp 67-82.

Hansen, M.H. and Hurwitz, W.N. (1946): The Problem of Non-Response in Sample Surveys. Journal of the American Statistical Association 41, pp 517-529.

Hansen, M.H., Hurwitz, W.N. and Bershad, M.A. (1962): Measurement Errors in Censuses and Surveys. Bulletin of the International Statistical Institute 38, Part II, pp 359-374.

Hansen, M.H., Hurwitz, W.N. and Pritzker, L. (1967): Standardization of Procedures for the Evaluation of Data: Measurement Errors and Statistical Standards in the Bureau of the Census. Bulletin of the International Statistical Institute, Vol. 42, Part I, pp 49-64, Canberra.

Hansen, M.H., Pritzker, L. and Steinberg, J. (1959): The Evaluation and Research program of the 1960 Censuses. American Statistical Association, Proceedings of the Social Statistics Section, pp 172-180.

Hansen, M.H. and Waksberg, J. (1970): Research on Non-Sampling Errors in Censuses and Surveys. Review of International Statistical Institute, pp 317-332.

Hanson, R.H. (1978): The Current Population Survey: Design and Methodology. Technical Paper No. 40, US Bureau of the Census.

Hanson, R.H. and Marks, E.S. (1958): Influence of the Interviewer on the Accuracy of Survey Results. Journal of the American Statistical Association 53, pp 635-655.

Harding, J. (1947): Refusals as a Source of Bias. In: Cantril, H. (editor): Gauging Public Opinion, Princeton.

Harris, J.R. and Guffey, H.J. Jr (1978): Questionnaire Returns: Stamps versus Business Reply Envelopes Revisited. Journal of Marketing Research 15, pp 290-293.

Hartley, H.O. (1958): Maximum Likelihood Estimation from Incomplete Data. Biometrics 14, pp 174-194.

Hartley, H.O. and Hocking, R.R. (1971): The Analysis of Incomplete Data. Biometrics 27, pp 783-823.

Hartley, H.O. and Hocking, R.R. (1971): Incomplete Data Analysis. Presidential invited lecture, ENAR and IMS Meeting, College Park, Pennsylvania.

Hartmann, E.L., Isaacson, H.L. and Jurgell, C.M. (1968): Public Reaction to Public Opinion Surveying. Public Opinion Quarterly 32, pp 295-298.

Hartwell, T.D. and Gaylor, D.W. (1973): Estimating Variance Components for Two-Way Disproportionate Data with Missing Cells by Method of Unweighted Means. Journal of the American Statistical Association 68, pp 379-383.

Haseman, J.K. and Gaylor, D.W. (1973): An Algorithm for Non-Iterative Estimation of Multiple Missing Values for Crossed Classifications. Technometrics 15, pp 631-636.

Hasselblad, V., Creason, J. and Stead, A.G. (1979): Applications of the Missing Information Principle. Paper presented at the Symposium on incomplete data: Preliminary proceedings, Washington Hilton Hotel on August 10-11, 1979, Washington, DC.

Hatchett, S. and Schuman, H. (1975-76): White Respondents and Race-of-Interviewer Effects. Public Opinion Quarterly 39, pp 523-528.

Hauck, M. (1974): Planning Field Operations. In Robert Ferber, ed., Handbook of Marketing Research. New York: McGraw-Hill Book Co.

Hauck, M. and Steinkamp, S. (1964): Survey Reliability and Interviewer Competence. Studies in Consumer Savings, No. 4, Bureau of Economic and Business Research, University of Illinois, Urbana.

Hawkins, D.F. (1975): Estimation of Nonresponse Bias. Sociological Methods and Research 3, pp 461-488.

Hawkins, D.F. (1977): Nonresponse in Detroit Area Study Surveys: A Ten Year Analysis. Working Papers in Methodology No. 8, Chapel Hill, North Carolina: Institute for Research in Social Science.

Hawkins, D.F. (1978): A Bibliography of Studies of Nonresponse in Survey Research. IRSS Technical Papers Number 2, University of North Carolina at Chapel Hill.

Heads, J. and Thrift, H.J. (1966): Notes on a Study in Postal Response Rates. Commentary 8, pp 257-262.

Healy, M.J.R. and Westmacott, M.H. (1956): Missing Values in Experiments Analysed on Automatic Computers. Applied Statistics 5, pp 203-206.

Heath, A.M. (1950): A Demonstration of Bias in a Mail Questionnaire. Printer's Ink, pp 36-37.

Heaton, E.E. Jr (1965): Increasing Mail Questionnaire Returns with a Preliminary Letter. Journal of Advertising Research 5, pp 36-39.

Heberlein, T.A. and Baumgartner, R. (1979): Factors Affecting Response Rates to Mailed Questionnaires: A Quantitative Analysis of the Published Literature. American Sociological Review 1978, Vol. 43.

Hendrick, C., Borden, R., Giesen, M. and Seyfreid, B.A. (1972): Effectiveness of Ingratiation Tactics in a Cover Letter on Mail Questionnaire Response. Psychonomic Science 26, pp 349-351.

Hendricks, W.A. (1949): Adjustment of Data for Non-Response in Mail Surveys. In: The agricultural estimating and reporting service of the United States Department of Agriculture. US Department of Agriculture, Publication Nr 703, pp 31-34.

Hendricks, W.A. (1949): Adjustment for Bias Caused by Non-Response in Mailed Surveys. Agricultural Economics Research 1, pp 52-56.

Heneman, G.H. and Paterson, D.G. (1949): Refusal Rates and Interviewer Quality. International Journal of Opinion and Attitude Research 3, pp 392-398.

Henley, J.R. Jr (1976): Response Rate to Mail Questionnaires with a Return Deadline. Public Opinion Quarterly 40, pp 374-375.

Henson, R., Roth, A. and Cannell, C.F. (1974): Personal vs. Telephone Interviews and the Effects of Telephone Reinterviews on Reporting of Psychiatric Symptomatology. (Research Report.) Survey Research Center, Institute for Social Research, The University of Michigan.

Herriot, R.A. (n.d.): What Split Panel Studies Taught Us about Collecting Family Income Data. Unpublished memo.

Hertel, B.R. (1976): Minimizing Error Variance Introduced by Missing Data Routines in Survey Analysis. Sociological Methods and Research 4, pp 459-474.

Herzog, T. (1978): Imputation Models for Large Scale Surveys. Invited paper, National Center for Health Statistics.

Hesseldenz, J.S. (1976): Determining Validity and Identifying Nonresponse Bias in a Survey Requesting Income Data. Research in Higher Education 5, pp 179-191.

Hewett, W.C. (1974): How Different Combinations of Postage on Outgoing and Return Envelopes Affect Questionnaire Returns. Journal of the Market Research Society 16, pp 49-50.

Hilgard, E.R. and Payne, S.L. (1944): Those Not at Home-Riddle for Pollsters. Public Opinion Quarterly 8, pp 254-261.

Hill, C.J. (1978): A Report on the Application of a Systematic
Method of Automatic Edit and Imputation to the 1976 Canadian
Census. American Statistical Association, Proceedings of the
Section on Survey Research Methods, pp 474-479.

Hill, R.J. and Hall, N.E. (1973): A Note on Rapport and Quality
of Interviewer Data. Southwestern Social Science Quarterly
44, pp 247-255.

Hill, S.L. (1968): Research Note - Increasing the Response
Rate for Structured Interviews in Community Research. American
Behavioral Scientist 11, pp 47-48.

Hill, T.P., Klein, L.R. and Straw, K.H. (1955): The Savings
Survey 1953: Response Rates and Reliability of Data. Bulletin
of Oxford University Institute of Statistics.

Hilmar, N.A. (1968): Anonymity, Confidentiality, and Invasions
of Privacy: Responsibility of the Researcher. American Journal
of Public Health, Vol. 58, No. 2, pp 324-330.

Hinrichs, J.R. (1975): Effects of Sampling, Follow-up Letters,
and Commitment to Participation on Mail Attitude Survey Response.
Journal of Applied Psychology 60, pp 249-251.

Hise, R.T. and McGinnis, M.A. (1974): Evaluating the Effect
of a Follow-up Request on Mail Survey Results. Akron Business
and Economic Review 5, pp 19-21.

Hochberg, Y. (1975): Two-Stage Randomized Response Schemes
for Estimating a Multinomial. Highway Safety Research Center,
University of North Carolina at Chapel Hill. Also in Communications in Statistics 4, 31, pp 1021-1032.

Hochstim, J.R. (1962): Comparison of Three Information Gathering
Strategies in a Population Study of Sociomedical Variables.
American Statistical Association, Proceedings of the Social
Statistics Section.

Hochstim, J.R. (1967): A Critical Comparison of Three Strategies
of Collecting Data from Households. Journal of the American
Statistical Association 62, pp 976-989.

Hochstim, J.R. and Athanasopoulos, D.A. (1970): Personal Follow-
Up in a Mail Survey: Its Contributions and Its Cost. Public
Opinion Quarterly 34, pp 69-81.

Hocking, R.R. (1977): Technical Report on Design of Sample
Surveys to Reduce Respondent Burden. Department of Computer
Science and Statistics, Mississippi State University.

Hocking, R.R. (1979): The Design and Analysis of Sample Surveys
with Incomplete Data: Reduction of Respondent Burden. Paper
presented at the Symposium on incomplete data: Preliminary
proceedings, Washington Hilton Hotel on August 10-11, 1979,
Washington, DC.

Hocking, R.R., Huddleston, H.F. and Hunt, H.H. (1974): A Procedure for Editing Survey Data. Applied Statistics 23, pp 121-133.

Hocking, R.R ar´ Marx, D.L. (1979): Estimation with Incomplete Data. Communic. .ons in Statistics, A8, 12.

Hocking, R.R. and Oxspring, H.H. (1971): Maximum Likelihood Estimation with Incomplete Multinomial Data. Journal of the American Statistical Association 66, pp 65-70.

Hocking, R.R. and Smith, W.B. (1968): Estimation of Parameters in the Multiple Normal Distribution with Missing Observation. Journal of the American Statistical Association 63, pp 159-173.

Hocking, R.R. and Smith, W.B. (1972): Optimum Incomplete Multi-Normal Samples. Technometrics 14, pp 299-307.

Hocking, R.R., Smith, W.B., Waldron, B.R. and Oxspring, H.H. (1969): Estimation of Parameters with Incomplete Data. Themis Report No. 12, Institute of Statistics, Texas A&M University, College Station, Texas.

Holm, S. and Pehrsson, N. (1976): Isotonic Estimation - A Tool of Handling Nonresponse Errors? Chalmers, Dept of mathematics 1976-8.

Holt, D. and Smith, T.M.F. (1979): Post Stratification. Journal of the Royal Statistical Society 142, Series A, pp 33-46.

Hoppe, D.A. (1952): Certain Factors Found to Improve Mail Survey Returns. Proceedings of the Iowa Academy of Science, pp 374-376.

Horowitz, J.L. and Sedlacek, W.F. (1974): Initial Returns on Mail Questionnaires: A Literature Review and Research Note. Research in Higher Education 2, pp 361-367.

Horvitz, D.G., Chromy, J.R. and King, D.A. (1970): Field Evaluation of the National Assessment Household Survey. Unpublished report, Research Triangle Institute, Research Triangle Park, North Carolina.

Horvitz, D.G., Greenberg, B.G. and Abernathy, J.R. (1973): Recent Development in Randomized Response Designs. Proceedings of International Symposium on Statistical Design and Linear Models, Colorado State University, pp 19-23.

Horvitz, D.G., Greenberg, B.G. and Abernathy, J.R. (1975): Recent Development in Randomized Response Designs. In A Survey of Statistical Design and Linear Models. ed. J.N. Srivastava, North-Holland/American Elsevier, pp 271-285.

Horvitz, D.G., Greenberg, H.G. and Abernathy, J.R. (1976): Randomized Response: A Data-Gathering Device for Sensitive Questions. Review of International Statistical Institute, pp 181-196.

Horvitz, D.G., Shah, B.V. and Simmons, W.R. (1967): The Unrelated Question Randomized Response Model. American Statistical Association, Proceedings of the Social Statistics Section, pp 65-72.

House, J.S., Gerber, W. and McMichael, A.J. (1977): Increasing Mail Questionnaire Response: A Controlled Replication and Extension. Public Opinion Quarterly 41, pp 95-99.

Houseman, E.E. (1953): Statistical Treatment of the Non-Response Problem. Agricultural Economics Research 5, pp 12-19.

Houston, M.J. and Ford, N.M. (1976): Broadening the Scope of Methodological Research on Mail Surveys. Journal of Marketing Research 13, November, pp 397-403.

Houston, M.J. and Jefferson, R.W. (1974): On the Personalization - Anonymity Relationship in Mail Surveys - Reply. Journal of Marketing Research 11, pp 112-113.

Houston, M.J. and Jefferson, R.W. (1975): The Negative Effects of Personalization on Response Patterns in Mail Surveys. Journal of Marketing Research 12, pp 114-117.

Houston, M.J. and Nevin, J.R. (1977): The Effects of Source and Appeal on Mail Survey Response Patterns. Journal of Marketing Research 14, pp 374-378.

Hubbard, R.L., Rachal, J.V. and Ginzburg, H.M. (1978): A Preliminary Examination of the Effects of Compensation for Interviews on the Response Quality in a Study of Drug Treatment Programs. American Statistical Association, Proceedings of the Section on Survey Methods, pp 383-386.

Huck, S.W. and Gleason, E.M. (1974): Using Monetary Inducements to Increase Response Rates from Mailed Surveys: A Replication and Extension of Previous Research. Journal of Applied Psychology, Vol. 59, No. 2, pp 222-225.

Huddleston, H.F. and Hocking, R.R. (1978): Imputation in Agricultural Surveys. American Statistical Association, Proceedings of the Section on Survey Research Methods, pp 480-485.

Hughes, D.A. (1978): A Statistical Approach to the Analysis of Item Omission in Mail Surveys. American Statistical Association, Proceedings of the Section on Survey Research Methods, pp 594-598.

Hughes, D.A. (1979): The Correlates of Item Nonresponse in a Large Scale Mail Survey. American Statistical Association, Proceedings of the Section on Survey Research Methods, pp 363-365.

Hulett, D.T. (1975): Confidentiality of Statistical and Research Data. Statistical Reporter, No. 75-12, pp 197-209.

Hunt, M.K. and Turn, R. (1974): Privacy and Security in Databank Systems: An Annotated Bibliography, 1970-1973. Prepared for the National Science Foundation (R-1361-NSF). Rand Corporation, Santa Monica, California, March 1974.

Hutcheson, J.D., Jr and Prather, J.E. (1977): Assessing the Effects of Missing Data. American Statistical Association, Proceedings of the Social Statistics Section, pp 279-283.

Hutcheson, J.D., Jr and Prather, J.E. (1978): Maximizing Response
to Household Income Items: Respondent Selection. American Statistical Association, Proceedings of the Section on Survey Research
Methods, pp 294-296.

Hutcheson, J.D., Jr, Prather, J.E. and Snow, R.E. (1979): The
Effects of Interviewer Characteristics on Item Response. American
Statistical Association, Proceedings of the Section on Survey
Research Methods, pp 372-377.

Hutchinson, G.B. (1962): Evaluation of a Mailed Health Questionnaire. American Journal of Public Health, pp 1894-1917.

Hyman, H.H. (1950): Problems in the Collection of Opinion-Re-
search Data. American Journal of Sociology 55, pp 362-370.

Hyman, H.H. (1954): Interviewing in Social Research. Chicago:
University of Chicago Press.

Hyman, H.H., Cobb, W.J., Feldman, J.J., Hart, C.W. and Stember,
C.H. (1954): Interviewing in Social Research. Chicago: University
of Chicago Press.

Ibsen, C.A. and Ballweg, J. (1974): Telephone Interviews in
Social Research: Some Methodological Considerations. Quality
and Quantity 7, pp 181-192.

I-Cheng, C., Chow, L.P. and Rider, R.V. (1972): The Randomized
Response Technique as Used in the Taiwan Outcome of Pregnancy
Study. Studies in Family Planning 3, pp 265-269.

Inderfurth, G.P. (1972): Investigation of Census Bureau Interviewer Characteristics, Performance and Attitudes: A Summary.
Working Paper 34, US Bureau of the Census.

Ingemarsson, I. (1976): Application of Stochastic Transformation
to Preserve Anonymity in Surveys. Confidentiality in Surveys
Report 18, Department of Statistics, University of Stockholm,
December 20, 1976.

Ireland, C.T. and Scheuren, F.J. (1975): The Rake's Progress.
The George Washington University, Computer Programs for Contingency Table Analysis, pp 155-216.

Jabine, T.B. and Rothwell, N.D. (1970): Split Panel Tests of
Census and Survey Questionnaires. American Statistical Association, Proceedings of the Social Statistics Section, pp 4-13.

Jackson, E.C. (1968): Missing Values in Linear Multiple Descrimi-
nant Analysis. Biometrics 24, pp 835-844.

Jackson, R.M. and Rothney, J.W.M. (1961): A Comparative Study
of the Mailed Questionnaire and the Interview in Follow-up
Studies. Personnel and Guidance Journal 39, pp 569-571.

Jarrett, R.G. (1978): The Analysis of Designed Experiments
with Missing Observations. Applied Statistics 27, pp 38-46.

John, J.A. and Prescott, P. (1975): Estimating Missing Values
in Experiments. Applied Statistics 24, pp 190-192.

Johnson, R.M. (1972): Marginal Weighting. Memo, Market Facts,
Inc..

Jondle, J.A. (1967): New Haven Special Census: Survey of Nonrespondents. New Haven Special Census Results, Memorandum No.
7, RRB Report No. 67-33 (67-423 (MRD)). Washington, DC: US
Bureau of the Census.

Jones, R.G. (1979): An Examination of Methods of Adjusting
for Non-Response to a Mail Survey: A Mail-Interview Comparison.
Paper presented at the Symposium on incomplete data: Preliminary
proceedings, Washington Hilton Hotel on August 10-11, 1979,
Washington, DC.

Jones, R.H. (1962): Spectral Analysis with Regularly Missed
Observations. Annals of Mathematical Statistics 33, pp 455-461.

Jones, W.H. (1979): Generalizing Mail Survey Inducement Methods:
Population Interactions with Anonymity and Sponsorship. Public
Opinion Quarterly 43, pp 102-111.

Jones, W.H. and Linda, G. (1978): Multiple Criteria Effects
in a Mail Survey Experiment. Journal of Marketing Research
15, pp 280-284.

Jordan, L.A., Marcus, A.C. and Reeder, L.G. (1978): Response
Styles in Telephone and Household Interviewing: A Field Exper-
iment from the Los Angeles Health Study. American Statistical
Association, Proceedings of the Section on Survey Research
Methods, pp 362-366.

Josephson, E. (1970): Resistance to Community Surveys. Social
Problems, Vol. 18, No. 1, pp 117-129.

Juster, F.T. (1976): Methodology, Data Quality and Interpretation: Some Notes on Consumer Surveys. Paper prepared for the
Conference on the Economic and Social Outlook.

Kahle, L.R. and Sales, B.D. (1978): Personalization of the Outside Envelope in Mail Surveys. Public Opinion Quarterly 42, pp 547-550.

Kahle, L.R. and Sales, B.D. (1978): Impression Management in Response to a Mail Survey. Paper presented to the Midwestern Psychological Association, Chicago, Illinois.

Kallek, S., Nisselson, H. and Sturdevant, T.R. (1975): Evaluation Studies of the United States Economic Censuses. Paper prepared for presentation at the 40th Session of the International Statistical Institute, Warsaw, Poland, September 1-4, 1975.

Kalsbeek, W.D., Folsom, R.E. Jr and Clemmer, A. (1974): The National Assessment No-Show Study: An Examination of Nonresponse Bias. American Statistical Association, Proceedings of the Social Statistics Section, pp 180-189.

Kalsbeek, W.D. and Lessler, J.T. (1977): Total Survey Design: Effect of Nonresponse Bias and Procedures for Controlling Measurement Errors. Paper prepared for presentation at the Biennial Conference on Health Survey Research Methods, April 1977.

Kanuk, L. and Berenson, C. (1975): Mail Surveys and Response Rates: A Literature Review. Journal of Marketing Research 12, pp 440-453.

Karson, M.J. and Wrobleski, W.J. (1970): A Bayesian Analysis of a Binomial Model with a Partially Informative Category. American Statistical Association, Proceedings of the Business and Economic Statistics Section, pp 532-534.

Kaufman, G.M. and King, B. (1973): A Bayesian Analysis of Nonresponse in Dichtomous Processes. Journal of the American Statistical Association 68, pp 670-678.

Kawash, M.B. and Aleamoni, L.M. (1971): Effect of Personal Signature on the Initial Rate of Return of a Mailed Questionnaire. Journal of Applied Psychology 55, pp 589-592.

Keane, J.G. (1963): Low Cost, High Return Mail Surveys. Journal of Advertising Research 3, pp 28-30.

Kelejian, H.H. (1969): Missing Observations in Multivariate Regression: Efficiency of a First-Order Method. Journal of the American Statistical Association 64, pp 1609-1616.

Kelman, H.C. (1972): The Rights of the Subject in Social Research: An Analysis in Terms of Relative Power and Legitimacy. American Psychologist 27, pp 989-1015.

Kelman, H.C. (1977): Privacy and Research with Human Beings. Journal of Social Issues, Vol. 33, No. 3, pp 169-195.

Kemsley, W.F.F. (1972): Pre-Computer Editing of Budgets for the Family Expenditure Survey. Applied Statistics 21, pp 58-64.

Kemsley, W.F.F. and Nicholson, J.L. (1960): Some Experiments in Methods of Conducting Family Expenditure Surveys. Journal of the Royal Statistical Society 123, Series A, pp 307-328.

Kendall, M.G. and Buckland, W.R. (1960): A Dictionary of Statistical Terms. Oliver and Boyd, Edinburgh.

Kephart, W.M. and Bressler, M. (1958): Increasing the Responses to Mail Questionnaires: A Research Study. Public Opinion Quarterly 22, pp 123-132.

Kerachsky, S.H., Mallar, C.D. and Moran, J. (1979): An Experiment with Payments to Survey Respondents. American Statistical Association, Proceedings of the Section on Survey Research Methods, pp 198-203.

Kerin, R.A. (1974): Personalization Strategies, Response Rate and Response Quality in a Mail Survey. Social Science Quarterly 55, pp 175-181.

Kerin, R.A. and Peterson, R.A. (1977): Personalization Respondent Anonymity and Response Distortion in Mail Surveys. Journal of Applied Psychology 62, pp 86-89.

Kernan, J.B. (1971): Are 'Bulk-Rate Occupants' Really Unresponsive? Public Opinion Quarterly 35, pp 420-422.

Kershaw, D.N. and Small, J.C. (1972): Data Confidentiality and Privacy: Lessons from the New Jersey Negative Income Tax Experiment. Public Policy, Vol. 20, No. 2, pp 258-280.

Kim, J. (1978): Randomized Response Techniques for Surveying Human Populations. Ph.D. Dissertation, Department of Statistics, Temple University, Philadelphia, Pa.

Kim, J. and Curry, J. (1978): The Treatment of Missing Data in Multivariate Analysis. Sociological Methods and Research, Vol. 6, No. 2, pp 215-240.

Kim, J. and Flueck, J.A. (1976): A Review of Randomized Response Models and Some New Results. American Statistical Association, Proceedings of the Social Statistics Section, pp 477-482.

Kim, J. and Fleuck, J.A. (1978): Modifications of the Randomized Response Technique for Sampling Without Replacement. American Statistical Association, Proceedings of the Section on Survey Research Methods, pp 346-350.

Kim, J. and Flueck, J.A. (1978): An Additive Response Model. American Statistical Association, Proceedings of the Section on Survey Research Methods, pp 351-355.

Kimball, A.E. (1961): Increasing the Rate of Return in Mail Surveys. Journal of Marketing 25, pp 63-65.

King, F.W. (1970): Anonymous versus Identifiable Questionnaires in Drug Usage Surveys. American Psychologist 25, pp 982-985.

Kirchner, W.K. and Mousley, N.B. (1963): A Note on Job Performance: Differences Between Respondent and Nonrespondent Salesmen to an Attitude Survey. Journal of Applied Psychology 47, pp 223-224.

Kish, L. (1979): Samples and Censuses. Memo, The University of Michigan.

Kish, L. and Hess, I. (1959): A 'Replacement' Procedure for Reducing the Bias of Nonresponse. The American Statistician 13, pp 17-19.

Kivlin, J.E. (1965): Contributions to the Study of Mail-Back Bias. Rural Sociology 30, pp 322-326.

Klein, D.P. (1970): Determining the Labor Force Status of Men Missed in the Census. Special Labor-Force Report 117. US Bureau of the Census.

Kleinbaum, D.G. (1973): A Generalization of the Growth Curve Model Which Allows Missing Data. Journal of Multivariate Analysis 3, pp 117-124.

Knott, J.J. (n.d.): Major Administrative Record Files: Documentation and Potential Uses. Memo, US Bureau of the Census.

Knox, J.B. (1951): Maximizing Responses to Mail Questionnaires: A New Technique. Public Opinion Quarterly 15, pp 366-367.

Koch, G.G. and Freeman, D.H. Jr (1976): The Asymptotic Covariance Structure of Estimated Parameters from Marginal Adjustment (Raking) of Contingency Tables. Paper presented to the Washington Statistical Society.

Koo, H.P., Ridley, J.C., Piserchia, P.V., Dawson, D.A., Bachrach, C.A., Holt, M.I. and Horvitz, D.G. (1976): An Experiment on Improving Response Rates and Reducing Call Backs in Household Surveys. American Statistical Association, Proceedings of the Social Statistics Section, pp 491-494.

Koons, D.A. (1967): Mail Return Rates and Results of a Preliminary Edit of Four Questionnaires: Second Format Test. RRB Report 67-32, Memorandum 1, US Bureau of the Census, Washington, DC. Unpublished.

Koons, D.A. (1973): Quality Control and Measurement of Nonsampling Error in the Health Interview Survey. Vital and Health Statistics, Series 2, Number 54.

Koons, D.A. (1974): Current Medicare Survey, Telephone Interviewing Compared with Personal Interviews. Response Research Staff Report 74-4. Washington, DC: US Bureau of the Census, Statistical Research Division.

Kovar, M.G. and Wright, R.A. (1973): An Experiment with Alternate Respondent Rules in the National Health Survey. American Statistical Association, Proceedings of the Social Statistics Section, pp 311-316.

Krótki, K.J. and Fox, B. (1974): The Randomized Response Technique, the Interview, and Self-Administered Questionnaire: An Empirical Comparison of Fertility Reports. American Statistical Association, Proceedings of the Social Statistics Section, pp 367-371.

Krótki, K.J. and McDaniel, S.A. (1975): Three Estimates of Illegal Abortion in Alberta, Canada: Survey, Mail-back Questionnaire and Randomized Response Technique. Bulletin of International Statistical Institute, pp 67-70.

Kviz, F.J. (1977): Toward a Standard Definition of Response Rate. Public Opinion Quarterly 41, pp 265-267.

Lagay, B.W. (1969-70): Assessing Bias: A Comparison of Two Methods. Public Opinion Quarterly 33, pp 615-618.

Lamb, C.W. Jr and Stem, D.E. Jr (1978): An Empirical Validation of the Randomized Response Technique. Journal of Marketing Research 15, pp 616-621.

Landsdowne, J. (1970): The Mailed Questionnaire in Panel Research: Some Empirical Observations. Social Forces 49, pp 136-140.

Lanke, J. (1975): On the Choice of the Unrelated Question in Simmons' Version of Randomized Response. Journal of the American Statistical Association 70, pp 80-83.

Lanke, J. (1975): On Non-Respondents Who Turn Out to Be Late Respondents. University of Lund and Lund Institute of Technology Department of Mathematical Statistics, Sweden.

Lanke, J. (1976): On the Degree of Protection in Randomized Interviews. International Statistical Review 44, pp 197-203.

Lansing, J.G. and Eapen, A.T. (1959): Dealing with Missing Information in Surveys. Journal of Marketing 23, pp 21-28.

Lansing, J.B. and Morgan, J.N. (1971): Methods of Data Collection. In Economic Survey Methods, Institute for Social Research (University of Michigan), Chapter 4.

Larson, I. (1970): Increasing the Rate of Return in Mail Surveys: A Methodological Study. Didakametry and Sociometry, Vol. 2, pp 43-70.

Larson, O.N. (1952): Comparative Validity of Telephone and Face-to-Face Interviews in the Reassurement of Message Diffusion from Les-Nets. American Sociological Review 17, pp 471-476.

Larson, R.F. and Catton, W.R. Jr (1959): Can the Mail-back Bias Contribute to a Study's Validity? American Sociological Review 24, pp 243-245.

Laurent, A. (1972): Effects of Question Length on Reporting Behavior in the Survey Interview. Journal of the American Statistical Association 67, pp 298-305.

Laurent, A., Cannell, C.F. and Marquis, K.H. (1972): Reporting Health Events in Household Interviews - Effects of an Extensive Questionnaire and a Diary Procedure; Vital and Health Statistics, Series 2, No. 49, DHEW Publ No. (HSM) 72-1049.

Lazarsfeld, P.F. (1940): The Use of Mail Questionnaires to Ascertain the Relative Popularity of Network Stations in Family Listening Surveys. Journal of Applied Psychology, pp 802-816.

Lazarsfeld, P.F. and Franzen, R. (1943): The Validity of Mail Questionnaires in Upper Income Groups. Time Research Reports, No. 940.

Lebacqz, K. and Levine, R.J. (1978): Informed Consent: Ethical and Legal Aspects. In: Reich, W.T. (Ed.) Encyclopedia of Bioethics. The Free Press, New York.

Legault-Giguère, M.A. (1974): Multivariate Normal Estimation with Missing Data. M.Sc. thesis, Dept. Math., McGill Univ., Montreal.

Lehman, E.C. Jr (1963): Tests of Significance and Partial Returns to Mailed Questionnaires. Rural Sociology 28, pp 284-289.

Leitner, D.W. (1979): If You Want to Know What Factors Influence Response, Why Not Ask? American Statistical Association, Proceedings of the Section on Survey Research Methods, pp 359-362.

Leslie, L.L. (1972): Are High Response Rates Essential to Valid Surveys? Social Science Research 1, pp 323-334.

Lessler, J.T. (1974): A Double Sampling Scheme Model for Eliminating Measurement Process Bias and Estimating Measurement Errors in Surveys. Institute of Statistics Mimeo Series No 949, University of North Carolina, Chapel Hill.

Lessler, J.T. (1976): Survey Designs Which Employ Double Sampling Schemes for Eliminating Measurement Process Bias. American Statistical Association, Proceedings of the Social Statistics Section, pp 520-525.

Lessler, J.T. (1979): An Expanded Survey Error Model. Paper presented at the Symposium on incomplete data: Preliminary proceedings, Washington Hilton Hotel on August 10-11, 1979, Washington, DC.

Lessler, J.T. and Mason, R.E. (1978): Nonrespondent Subsampling Schemes for Longitudinal Surveys. American Statistical Association, Proceedings of the Section on Survey Research Methods, pp 617-620.

Leuthold, D.A. and Scheele, R. (1971): Patterns of Bias in Samples Based on Telephone Directories. Public Opinion Quarterly 35, pp 249-257.

Levine, S. and Gordon, G. (1958-59): Maximizing Returns on Mail Questionnaires. Public Opinion Quarterly 22, pp 568-575.

Leysieffer, F.W. (1975): Respondent Jeopardy in Randomized Response Procedures. Technical Report M338, ONR Technical Report No. 93, Statistics Department, Florida State University.

Leysieffer, F.W. and Warner, S.L. (1976): Respondent Jeopardy and Optimal Designs in Randomized Response Models. Journal of the American Statistical Association 71, pp 649-656.

Lin, P-E. (1971): Estimation Procedures for Difference of Means with Missing Data. Journal of the American Statistical Association 66, pp 634-636.

Lin, P-E. (1973): Procedures for Testing the Difference of Means with Incomplete Data. Journal of the American Statistical Association 68, pp 699-703.

Lin, P-E. and Stivers, L.E. (1975): Testing for Equality of Means with Incomplete Data on One Variable: A Monte Carlo Study. Journal of the American Statistical Association 70, pp 190-193.

Lindsay, E.E. (1921): Questionnaire and Follow-Up Letters. Pedagogical Seminary 28, pp 303-307.

Lindström, H. et al (1979): Standard Methods for Non-Response Treatment in Statistical Estimation. SCB, I/UI, 1979-06-21.

Lindström, H. and Lundström, S. (1974): A Method to Discuss the Magnitude of the Non-Response Error. Statistisk Tidskrift 6, pp 505-520.

Linowes, D.F. (1977): The Privacy Act of 1974: An Assessment. Appendix 4 of the Report of the Privacy Protection Study Commission. Washington, DC: Government Printing Office.

Linsky, A.S. (1965): A Factorial Experiment in Inducing Responses to a Mail Questionnaire. Sociology and Social Research 29, pp 183-189.

Linsky, A.S. (1975): Stimulating Responses to Mailed Questionnaires: A Review. Public Opinion Quarterly 39, pp 82-101.

Linsky, A.S. and Spendlove, G.A. (1967): Note on an Unusually High Response Rate to a Mail Questionnaire. Journal of Health and Social Behavior, pp 146-148.

Little, R.J.A. (1978): Consistent Regression Methods for Discriminant Analysis with Incomplete Data. Journal of the American Statistical Association 73, pp 319-322.

Liu, P.T., Chen, C.N. and Chow, L.P. (1976): A Study of the Feasibility of Hopkins Randomized Response Models. American Statistical Association, Proceedings of the Social Statistics Section, pp 561-563.

Liu, P.T. and Chow, L.P. (1976): A New Discrete Quantitative Randomized Response Model, Journal of the American Statistical Association 71, pp 72-73.

Liu, P.T. and Chow, L.P. (1976): The Efficiency of the Multiple Trial Randomized Response Technique. Biometrics 32, pp 607-618.

Liu, P.T., Chow, L.P. and Mosley, W.H. (1975): Use of the Randomized Response Technique with a New Randomizing Device, Journal of the American Statistical Association 70, pp 329-332.

Locander, W.B. and Burton, J.P. (1976): The Effect of Question Form on Gathering Income Data by Telephone. Journal of Marketing Research 13, pp 189-192.

Locander, W.B., Sudman, S. and Bradburn, N.M. (1976): An Investigation of Interview Method, Threat and Response Distortion, Journal of the American Statistical Association 71, pp 269-275.

Lochner, R.H. and Basu, A.P. (1972): Bayesian Analysis of the Two-Sample Problem with Incomplete Data. Journal of the American Statistical Association 67, pp 432-438.

London Research Bureau Limited (1971): Report on Survey of Public Attitudes to Privacy.

Longworth, D.S. (1953): Use of a Mail Questionnaire. American Sociological Review 18, pp 310-313.

Lord, F.M. (1955): Estimation of Parameters From Incomplete Data. Journal of the American Statistical Association 50, pp 870-876.

Love, L.T. and Turner, A.G. (1975): The Census Bureau's Experience: Respondent Availability and Response Rates. American Statistical Association, Proceedings of the Business and Economic Statistics Section, pp 76-85.

Lovelock, C.H., Stiff, R., Cullwick, D. and Kaufman, I.M. (1976): An Evaluation of the Effectiveness of Drop-Off Questionnaire Delivery. Journal of Marketing Research 13, pp 358-364.

Lowe, F.E. and McCormick, T.C. (1955): Some Survey Sampling Biases. Public Opinion Quarterly 19, pp 303-315.

Loynes, R.M. (1976): Asymptotically Optimal Randomized Response Procedures. Journal of the American Statistical Association 71, pp 924-928.

Lubin, B.E., Levitt, E.E. and Zuckerman, M.S. (1962): Some Personality Differences Between Respondents and Nonrespondents to a Survey Questionnaire. Journal of Consulting Psychology 26, pp 192-197.

Lucas, W.A. and Adams, W.C. (1977): An Assessment of Telephone Survey Methods. Santa Monica, California: The Rand Corporation.

Lueptow, L., Mueller, S.A., Hammes, R.R. and Master, L.S. (1977): The Impact of Informed Consent Regulations on Response Rate and Response Bias. Sociological Methods & Research, Volume 6, Number 2, pp 183-204.

Lundberg, G.A. and Larsen, O.N. (1949): Characteristics of Hard-to-Reach Individuals in Field Surveys. Public Opinion Quarterly 13, pp 487-494.

Lyberg, I., Haglund, T., Lyberg, L. and Wretman, J. (1978): The Allocation of Resources to Production and Control Steps in the Statistical Process. Statistisk Tidskrift 4, pp 253.

Lyberg, L. and Rapaport, E. (1979): Non-Response Problems at Statistics Sweden. American Statistical Association, Proceedings of the Section on Survey Research Methods, pp 348-352.

Lyberg, L. and Rapaport, E. (1979): Contribution to the Debate on the Report "Incomplete Data". SCB, 1979-07-31. The ASA Congress, Washington, August 1979.

Macek, A.J. and Miles, G.H. (1975): IQ Score and Mailed Questionnaire Response. Journal of Applied Psychology 60, pp 258-259.

Madow, L.H. (1977): An Error Profile: Employment as Measured
by the Current Employment Statistics Program. American Statistical Association, Proceedings of Social Statistics Section,
pp 35-44.

Madow, W.G. and Rizvi, M.H. (n.d.): On Incomplete Data: A Review.
Memo, Committee on National Statistics National Research Council.

Maesen, W.A. (1970): A Note on Replication Versus Anonymity
in Field Studies. The American Sociologist, Vol. 2, pp 372-373.

Magid, F.N., Nicholas, G. and Gold, D. (1962): A Mail Questionnaire Adjunct to the Interview. Public Opinion Quarterly 26,
pp 111-114.

Maloney, P.U. (1954): Comparability of Personal Attitude Scale
Administration with Mail Administration With and Without Incentive. Journal of Applied Psychology 38, pp 238-239.

Mandell, L. (1974): When to Weight: Determining Nonresponse
Bias in Survey Data. Public Opinion Quarterly 38, pp 247-252.

Manfield, M.N. (1948): A Pattern of Response to Mail Surveys.
Public Opinion Quarterly 12, pp 493-495.

Manheimer, D. and Hyman, H. (1949): Interviewer Performance
in Area Sampling. Public Opinion Quarterly 13, pp 83-92.

Manheimer, D.I., Mellinger, G.D., Somers, R.H. and Kleman,
M.T. (1972): Technical and Ethical Considerations in Data Collection. In Proceedings of the First International Conference
on Student Drug Surveys, edited by S. Einstein and S. Allen.
Farmingdale, New York: Baywood Publishing Company, pp 205-214.

Market Research Society (1976): Response Rates in Sample Surveys:
Report of a Working Party of the Market Research Society's
Research and Development Committee. Journal of Market Research
Society 18, pp 113-142.

Marquis, K.H. (1977): Survey Response Rates: Some Trends, Causes
and Correlates. Paper presented at the Biennial Conference
on Health Survey Methods, Williamsburg, Virginia, May 1977.

Marquis, K.H. and Cannell, C.F. (1969): A Study of Interviewer-
Respondent Interaction in the Urban Employment Survey. Survey
Research Center, The University of Michigan.

Marquis, K.H., Cannell, C.F. and Laurent, A. (1972): Reporting
of Health Events in Household Interviews: Effects of Reinforce-
ment, Question Length and Reinterviews. Vital and Health Statistics, US Public Health Service, Series 2, No. 45.

Martin, J.D. (n.d.): Mail Questionnaire Response Induction:
A Negative Induction Experiment. Memo, Lakehead University,
Department of Sociology, Ontario, Canada.

Martin, J.D. and McConnell, J.P. (1973): Mail Questionnaire Response Induction: The Effect of Four Variables on the Response of a Random Sample to a Difficult Questionnaire. Social Science Quarterly 51, pp 409-414.

Martin, M.E. (1975): Statisticians and the Confidentiality Issue. Paper presented at the annual meeting of the American Public Health Association, Session on Health Information Privacy and Confidentiality, November 19, 1975, Chicago, Illinois.

Martin, M.E. (1977): Statisticians, Confidentiality, and Privacy. American Journal of Public Health, Vol. 67, No. 2, pp 165-167.

Maslow, A.H. and Sakoda, J.M. (1952): Volunteer-Error in the Kinsey Study. Journal of Adnormal and Social Psychology, pp 259-262.

Mason, W.S., Dressel, R.J. and Bain, R.K. (1961): An Experimental Study of Factors Affecting Response to a Mail Survey of Beginning Teachers. Public Opinion Quarterly 25, pp 296-299.

Massillon, A. (1978): Analysis of the Effect of Color via the Classroom Experiments (Report A6-1). Memo, US Bureau of the Census.

Massillon, A. (1979): Response Research Plans for Questionnaire Experiments in the 1980 Census (revised). Memo, US Bureau of the Census.

Matteson, M.T. (1974): Type of Transmittal Letter and Questionnaire Color as Two Variables Influencing Response Rates in a Mail Survey. Journal of Applied Psychology 59, pp 535-536.

Matthai, A. (1951): Estimation of Parameters from Incomplete Data with Application to Design of Sample Surveys. Sankhyā, pp 145-152.

Mauldin, W.P. and Marks, E.S. (1950): Problems of Response in Enumeration Surveys. American Sociological Review 15, pp 649-657.

May, R.C. (1960): What Approach Gets the Best Return in Mail Surveys? Industrial Marketing 45, pp 50-51.

Mayer, C.A. (1964): The Interviewer and His Environment. Journal of Marketing Research 1, pp 24-31.

Mayer, C.S. (1970): Assessing the Accuracy of Marketing Research. Journal of Marketing Research 7, pp 285-291.

Mayer, C.S. (1974): Data Collection Methods: Personal Interviews. In Robert Ferber, ed., Handbook of Marketing Research. New York: McGraw-Hill Book Co., 2-82-9.

Mayer, C.S. and Pratt, R.W. Jr (1966-67): A Note on Non-Response in a Mail Survey. Public Opinion Quarterly 30, pp 637-646.

Mayer, E.N. Jr (1946): Postage Stamps Do Affect the Results of Your Mailing. Printer's Ink 217, pp 91-93.

McAllister, R.J., Goe, S.J. and Butler, E.W. (1973): Tracking Respondents in Longitudinal Surveys: Some Preliminary Considerations. Public Opinion Quarterly 37, pp 413-416.

McCarthy, P.J. (1947): Characteristics, Proportions and Effects on Sample Surveys of Individuals Who are Difficult to Contact or Who Refuse to be Interviewed. NRC-SSRC Sampling Project, Cornell University, New York, pp 1-42.

McDonagh, E.C. and Rosenblum, L.A. (1965): A Comparison of Mailed Questionnaires and Subsequent Structured Interviews. Public Opinion Quarterly 29, pp 131-136.

McDonald, L. (1971): On the Estimation of Missing Data in the Multivariate Linear Model. Biometrics 27, pp 535-543.

McFarland, B.H. and Fisher, L. (1978): Estimation and Testing in the Missing Data Problem. Presented at the Joint Statistical Meetings (JSM), San Diego.

McGinnis, M.A. and Hollon, C.J. (1977): Mail Survey Response Rate and Bias: The Effect of Home Versus Work Address. Journal of Marketing Research 14, pp 383-384.

McGuire, W.J. (1969): Suspiciousness of Experimenter's Intent. Pp 13-57 in R. Rosenthal and R.L. Rosnow (eds.), Artifact in Behavioral Research. New York: Academic Press.

McKenzie, J.R. (1977): An Investigation into Interviewer Effects in Market Research. Journal of Marketing Research 14, pp 330-336.

Mehta, J.S. and Swamy, P.A.V.B. (1973): Bayesian Analysis of a Bivariate Normal Distribution with Incomplete Observations. Journal of the American Statistical Association 68, pp 922-927.

Mehta, J.S. and Swamy, P.A.V.B. (n.d.): Bayesian Analysis of Bivariate Normal Distribution When Some Observations Are Missing. Report 7117, Department of Economics, The Ohio State University, Columbus.

Meyers, G. (1969): The Elusive Male - Some Methodological Notes on Survey Research Design. Public Opinion Quarterly 33, pp 255-259.

Meyers, S.M. and Oliver, J.D. (1978): Privacy and Hostility Toward Government as Reasons for Nonresponse in the National Medical Care Expenditure Survey. American Statistical Association, Proceedings of the Social Statistics Section, pp 509-513.

Midgley, J. (1968): A Note on Non-response with Reference to a Current Study in the Cape Malay Group. Journal for Social Research 17, pp 39-44.

Miller, H.W., Kennedy, J. and Bryant, E.E. (1972): A Study of the Effect of Remuneration Upon Response in a Health and Nutrition Examination Survey. American Statistical Association, Proceedings of the Social Statistics Section, pp 370-375.

Miller, W.S. and Engquist, E.J. Jr (1942): On the Effectiveness of "Follow-Ups" in Mail Canvasses. Bulletin of the American Statistical Association, pp 189-190.

Mills, R.H. (1968): Nonresponse Rates in Cleveland, 1965. Cleveland Special Census Results Memorandum No. 4 (68-308 (MRD)). Washington, DC: US Bureau of the Census, pp 10.

Mitchell, W. Jr (1939): Factors Affecting the Rates of Return on Mailed Questionnaires. Journal of the American Statistical Association, pp 683-692.

Moore, C.C. (1941): Increasing the Returns from Questionnaires. Journal of Educational Research 35, pp 138-141.

Moore, T.F., Bettin, P., Kostanich, D. and Shapiro, G.M. (1979): Overview of the Current Population Survey Sample Design. American Statistical Association, Proceedings of the Section on Survey Research Methods, pp 121-126.

Moors, J.J.A. (1971): Optimization of the Unrelated Question Randomized Response Model. Journal of the American Statistical Association 66, pp 627-629.

Morgan, J.N. and Sonquist, J.A. (1963): Problems in the Analysis of Survey Data and a Proposal. Journal of the American Statistical Association 58, pp 415-435.

Moriarty, M. and Wiseman, F. (1976): On the Choice of a Randomization Technique With the Randomized Response Model. American Statistical Association, Proceedings of the Social Statistics Section, pp 624-626.

Morris, C.N. (1979): Nonresponse Issues in Public Policy Experiments, With Emphasis on the Health Insurance Study. Paper presented at the Symposium on incomplete data: Preliminary Proceedings, Washington Hilton Hotel on August 10-11, 1979, Washington, DC.

Morrison, D.F. (1971): Expectations and Variances of Maximum Likelihood Estimates of the Multivariate Normal Distribution Parameters with Missing Data. Journal of the American Statistical Association 66, pp 602-604.

Morrison, D.F. (1973): A Test for Equality of Means of Correlated Variates with Missing Data on One Response. Biometrika 60, pp 101-105.

Mortimer, J.T. and Lorence, J. (1977): Locating Respondents and Inducing High Response in a Panel Study. University of Minnesota (Unpublished).

Moye, D. (1976): CPS Reinterview Results from the Listing Check, Check of Noninterview Classifications, and the Household Composition Check for 1975. US Bureau of the Census Memorandum, May 21, 1976.

Mulford, C.L., Klonglan, G.E., Warren, R.D. and Hay, D.A. (1974):
Influence of Attrition Rates of Responses to Mailed Questionnaire
on Measurement and Modeling. Paper presented at the meeting
of the American Sociological Society, Montreal.

Mulford, C.L., Klonglan, G.E., Warren, R.D. and Hay, D.A. (1978):
What Return Rate is Necessary When Using Mailed Questionnaires?
Political Methodology 5.

Mulvihill, J. and Lawes, M. (1979): Imputation Procedures for
LFS Longitudinal Files. Methodology Division Report. Census
and Household Surveys Field, Statistics Canada.

Murthy, M.N. (1979): A Framework for Studying Incomplete Data
With a Reference to the Experience in Some Countries of Asia
and the Pacific. Paper presented at the Symposium on incomplete
data: Preliminary proceedings, Washington Hilton Hotel on August
10-11, 1979, Washington, DC.

Myers, J.H. and Haug, A.F. (1969): How a Preliminary Letter
Affects Mail Survey Returns and Costs. Journal of Advertising
Research 9, pp 37-40.

Namias, J. (1962): A Rapid Method to Detect Differences in Interviewer Performance. Journal of Marketing 26, pp 68-72.

Nargundkar, M.S. and Arora, H.R. (1971): The Raking-Ratio Estimation Procedure for the 1971 Census, Census Division Memorandum. Statistics Canada (unpublished).

Nargundkar, M.S. and Joshi, G.B. (1975): Non-Response in Sample Surveys. 40th session of the ISI, Warsaw 1975, Contributed papers, pp 626-628.

National Center for Health Statistics (NCHS) (1965): Health Interview Responses Compared with Medical Records. Vital and Health Statistics, P.H.S. Publication No 1000 - Series 2 - No 8. Washington, DC: Government Printing Office.

National Central Bureau of Statistics (1977): The National Central Bureau of Statistics and the General Public: The Findings of an Interview Survey Taken in Sweden During the Spring of 1976. National Central Bureau of Statistics, Stockholm.

National Research Council (1979): Privacy and Confidentiality as Factors in Survey Response.

National Research Council, Committee on Federal Agency Evaluation Research (COFAER) (1977): Protecting Individual Privacy in Evaluation Research. Washington, DC: National Research Council/National Academy of Sciences, 1975. Also Appendix A, "Confidentiality-Preserving Modes of Access to Files and to Interfile Exchange for Useful Statistical Analysis," by Donald T. Campbell, Robert F. Boruch, Richard D. Schwartz, and Joseph Steinberg, in Evaluation Quarterly, Vol. 1, No. 2, May 1977, pp 269-299.

Naus, J.I. (1975): Data Quality Control and Editing. Marcel Dekker, Inc., New York.

Naus, J.I., Johnson, T.A. and Montulvo, R. (1972): A Probabilistic Model for Identifying Errors In Data Editing. Journal of the American Statistical Association 67, pp 943-950.

Neter, J. and Waksberg, J. (1965): Response Errors in Collection of Expenditures Data by Household Interviews: An Experimental Study. Technical Paper No. 11, US Bureau of the Census, Washington, DC.

Nevin, J.R. and Ford, N.M. (1976): Effects of a Deadline and a Veiled Threat on Mail Survey Responses. Journal of Applied Psychology 61, pp 116-118.

Newman, S.W. (1962): Differences between Early and Late Respondents to a Mailed Survey. Journal of Advertising Research 2, pp 37-39.

Neyman, J. (1969): Bias in Surveys due to Nonresponse. In: Johnson and Smith (editors): New Developments in Survey Sampling, New York, pp 712-732.

Nichols, R.C. and Meyer, M.A. (1966): Timing Postcard Follow-Ups in Mail Questionnaire Surveys. Public Opinion Quarterly 30, pp 306.

Nicholls, W.L. (1978): Experiences with CATI in a Large-Scale Survey. American Statistical Association, Proceedings of the Section on Survey Research Methods, pp 9-17.

Nisselson, H. and Bailar, B.A. (1976): Measurement Analysis and Reporting of Nonsampling Errors in Surveys. Proceedings of the International Biometric Conference, Boston, pp 301-321.

Nordbotten, S. (1963): Automatic Editing of Individual Statistical Observations. Conference of European Statisticians, Statistical Standards and Studies, No. 2, United Nations, New York.

Nordbotten, S. (1965): The Efficiency of Automatic Detection and Correction of Errors in Individual Observations as Compared with Other Means for Improving the Quality of Statistics. Bulletin of International Statistical Institute 41, pp 417-441.

Nordheim, E.V. (n.d.): Obtaining Information from Nonrandomly Missing Data. Memo, University of Wisconsin.

Norman, R.D. (1948): A Review of Some Problems Related to the Mail Questionnaire Technique. Educational and Psychological Measurement 8, pp 235-248.

Nuckols, R.C. (1964): Personal Interview Versus Mail Panel Survey. Journal of Marketing Research 1, pp 11-16.

Oakes R.H. (1954): Differences in Responsiveness in Telephone vs Personal Interviews. Journal of Marketing 18, pp 169.

O'Brien, D.M. (1977): The Comprehension Factor in Randomized Response. American Statistical Association, Proceedings of the Social Statistics Section, pp 270-272.

O'Brien, D.M., Cochran, R.S., Marquardt, R.S. and Makens, J.C. (1975): Randomized Response vs. Direct Question in a Mail vs. Personal Interview Consumer Opinion Survey. College of Commerce and Industry Research Paper No. 85, University of Wyoming, July 1975, Laramie, Wyoming.

O'Dell, W.F. (1962): Personal Interviews or Mail Panels? Journal of Marketing 26, pp 34-39.

Office of Federal Statistical Policy and Standards (1978): Glossary of Nonsampling Error Terms: An Illustration of a Semantic Problem in Statistics. Statistical Policy Working Paper 4. Washington, DC: Government Printing Office.

Office of Management and Budget (1976): Guidelines for Reducing Public Reporting to Federal Agencies, Clearance of Public Reporting and Recordkeeping Under the Federal Reports Act, revision to Circular A-40, p 4, 1976. Washington, DC: Government Printing Office.

Ognibene, P. (1970): Traits Affecting Questionnaire Response. Journal of Advertising Research 10, pp 18-20.

Ognibene, P. (1971): Correcting Nonresponse Bias in Mail Questionnaires. Journal of Marketing Research 8, pp 233-235.

Oh, H.L. and Scheuren, F.J. (1978): Multivariate Raking Ratio Estimation in the 1973 Exact Match Study. American Statistical Association, Proceedings of the Section on Survey Research Methods, pp 716-722.

Oh, H.L. and Scheuren, F.J. (1978): Some Unresolved Application Issues in Raking Ratio Estimation. American Statistical Association, Proceedings of the Section on Survey Research Methods, pp 723-728.

Oksenberg, L. and Cannell, C. (n.d.): Some Factors Underlying the Validity of Response in Self Report. Memo, Survey Research Center, Institute for Social Research and The University of Michigan, Ann Arbor, Michigan, USA. Also presented at the ISI meeting in New Dehli, 1977.

Oksenberg, L., Vinokur, A. and Cannell, C.F. (1975): The Effects of Commitment to Being a Good Respondent on Interview Performance. Research report, Survey Research Center, University of Michigan.

Oksenberg, L., Vinokur, A. and Cannell, C.F. (1976): The Effects of Instructions, Commitment and Feedback on Reporting in Personal Interviews. Research report, Survey Research Center, The University of Michigan.

Oliver, J.D. (1977): The Design and Methodology of the National
Medical Care Expenditure Survey. National Center for Health
Statistics. Contributed Paper Session, American Statistical
Association, Chicago, Illinois, August 16, 1977, pp 3-25.

O'Neil, M.J. (1979): Estimating the Nonresponse Bias due to
Refusals in Telephone Surveys. Public Opinion Quarterly 43,
pp 218.

Ono, M. (1971): Current Developments on Collecting Income Data
in the Current Population Survey. American Statistical Association, Proceedings of the Social Statistics Section, pp 342-347.

Ono, M. and Miller, H.P. (1969): Income Nonresponses in the
Current Population Survey. American Statistical Association,
Proceedings of the Social Statistics Section, pp 277-288.

Oppenheim, A.N. (1966): Questionnaire Design and Attitude Measurement. New York: Basic Books.

Orchard, T. and Woodbury, M.A. (1972): A Missing Information
Principle: Theory and Applications. Proceedings of the 6th
Berkeley Symposium on Mathematical Statistics and Probability
1, pp 697-715.

Pace, C.R. (1939): Factors Influencing Questionnaire Returns from Former University Students. Journal of Applied Psychology 23, pp 388-397.

Palmer, S. (1967): On the Character and Influence of Nonresponse in the Current Population Survey. American Statistical Association, Proceedings of the Social Statistics Section, pp 73-80.

Palmer, S. and Jones, C. (1966): A Look at Alternate Imputation Procedures for CPS Noninterviews. Memo, US Bureau of the Census.

Pan, J.S. (1950): Social Characteristics of Respondents and Nonrespondents in a Questionnaire Study of the Aged. American Sociological Review, pp 780-781.

Pan, J.S. (1951): Social Characteristics of Respondents and Nonrespondents in a Questionnaire Study of Later Maturity. Journal of Applied Psychology 35, pp 120-121.

Panel on Incomplete Data (1978): Study of Incomplete Data. National Research Council, Washington, DC.

Parsons, C.W. (1975): The Privacy Act of 1974: New Challenges for Public Administration. Prepared for the annual meeting of the American Society for Public Administration, Chicago, April 2, 1975.

Parsons, R.J. and Medford, T.S. (1972): The Effect of Advance Notice in Mail Surveys of Homogeneous Groups. Public Opinion Quarterly 36, pp 258-259.

Parzen, E. (1963): On Spectral Analysis with Missing Observations and Amplitude Modulation, Sankhyā 25, Series A, pp 383-392.

Patrick, C.A. (1978): Discussion of D.B. Rubin's "Multiple Imputations in Sample Surveys - A Phenomenological Bayesian Approach to Nonresponse". American Statistical Association, Proceedings of the Section on Survey Research Methods, p 32.

Patrick, C. (1978): Estimation, Imputation, Randomization and Risk Equivalence. American Statistical Association, Proceedings of the Section on Survey Research Methods, pp 486-491.

Patterson, G. and Herriot, R. (1976): Evaluation of Income Statistics Collected on the Four Questionnaires. 1980 Census National Mail Income Pretest, Results Memorandum No. 4. US Bureau of the Census.

Pattullo, E.L. (1976): Privacy and Our Institutions: Is There an Alternate Route to 1984? Harvard Magazine, pp 14-19.

Pavalko, R.M. and Lutterman, K.G. (1973): Characteristics of Willing and Reluctant Respondents. Pacific Sociological Review 16, pp 463-476.

Payne, S. (1951): The Art of Asking Questions. New Jersey: Princeton University Press.

Payne, S.L. (1956): Some Advantages of Telephone Surveys. Journal of Marketing 20, pp 278-280.

Payne, S.L. (1974): Data Collection Methods: Telephone Surveys. In Robert Ferber, ed., Handbook of Marketing Research. New York: McGraw-Hill Book Co., 2-105-23.

Pearce, S.C. and Jeffers, J.N.R. (1971): Block Designs and Missing Data. Journal of the Royal Statistical Society, Series B, 33, pp 131-136.

Pearl, R.B. (1968): Methodology of Consumer Expenditure Surveys. US Bureau of the Census, Working Paper No. 27, Washington, DC: Government Printing Office.

Pearl, R.B. (1977): The 1972-73 US Consumer Expenditure Survey: A Preliminary Evaluation. Paper prepared for presentation at the Annual Meeting of the American Statistical Association, Chicago, August 1977.

Pearlin, L.I. (1961): The Appeals of Anonymity in Questionnaire Response. Public Opinion Quarterly 25, pp 640-647.

Perrin, E.M. (1945): You're Right, Mr. Eastman: Mail Questionnaires Aren't Worth Their Salt. Printer's Ink 210, pp 102-106.

Perry, N. (1974): Postage Combinations in Postal Questionnaire Surveys - Another View. Journal of the Market Research Society 16, pp 245-246.

Peterson, R.A. (1975): An Experimental Investigation of Mail Survey Responses. Journal of Business Research 3, pp 199-210.

Peterson, R.A. and Bruce, G.D. (1978): Post-Completion Mail Survey Incentives and Data Quality: An Empirical Investigation. American Statistical Association, Proceedings of the Section on Survey Research Methods, pp 599-602.

Philips, W.M. Jr (1951): Weaknesses of the Mail Questionnaire: A Methodological Study. Sociology and Social Research, pp 260-267.

Platek, R. (1977): Some Factors Affecting Non-Response. Survey Methodology Journal (Statistics Canada), Vol. 3, No. 2, pp 191-214.

Platek, R. and Gray, G.B. (1979): Imputation Methodology. Unpublished technical report, Methodology Division, Statistics Canada.

Platek, R. and Gray, G.B. (1979): Methodology and Application of Adjustments for Nonresponse. Presented at the 42nd Session of the International Statistical Institute, Manila, Phillipines, December 4-14, 1979.

Platek, R. and Singh, M.P. (1976): Methodology of the Canadian Labour Force Survey. Statistics Canada, Household Surveys Development Staff.

Platek, R., Singh, M.P. and Tremblay, V. (1978): Adjustments
for Non-Response in Surveys. In Survey Sampling and Measurement,
edited by N.K. Namboodiri, Academic Press, New York, San Francisco,
London. Also in Survey Methodology Journal, Statistics Canada,
1977, Vol. 3, No. 2, pp 1-24.

Pliner, P., Hart, H., Kohl, J. and Saari, D. (1974): Compliance
Without Pressure: Some Further Data on the Foot-in-the-Door
Technique. Journal of Experimental Social Psychology 10, pp
17-22.

Plog, S.C. (1963): Explanations for a High Return Rate on a
Mail Questionnaire. Public Opinion Quarterly 27, pp 297-298.

Politz, A.N. and Brumbach, R. (1947): Can an Advertiser Believe
What Mail Surveys Tell Him? Printer's Ink, pp 48-52.

Politz, A.N. and Simmons, W.R. (1949): Adjustment for Bias
by Nonresponse in Mailed Surveys. Agricultural Economics Research
1, pp 52-56.

Politz, A.N. and Simmons, W.R. (1949): An Attempt to Get the
"Not at Homes" into the Sample Without Call-Backs. Journal
of the American Statistical Association 44, pp 9-31.

Politz, A.N. and Simmons, W.R. (1950): Note on "An Attempt
to Get the Not at Homes into the Sample Without Callbacks".
Journal of the American Statistical Association 45, pp 136-137.

Pollock, K.H. and Bek, Y. (1976): A Comparison of Three Randomized Response Models for Quantitative Data. Journal of the
American Statistical Association 71, pp 884-886.

Pomeroy, W.B. (1963): The Reluctant Respondent. Public Opinion
Quarterly 27, pp 287-293.

Poole, W.K. (1974): Estimation of the Distribution Function
of a Continuous Type Random Variable Through Randomized Response.
Journal of the American Statistical Association 69, pp 1002-1005.

Power, A.P. and Beaumont, J.A. (1975): Anatomy of a Postal
Survey. Statistical News 30, pp 7-11.

Preece, D.A. (1971): Iterative Procedures for Missing Values
in Experiments. Technometrics 13, pp 743-754.

Pregibon, D. (1976): Incomplete Survey Data: Estimation and
Imputation. Methodology Journal of Household Survey Division,
Statistics Canada.

Prescott, J.A.J. and Prescott, P. (1975): Estimating Missing
Values in Experiments. Applied Statistics 24, pp 190-192.

Press, S.J. and Scott, A.J. (1974): Missing Variables in Bayesian
Regression. Studies in Bayesian Econometrics and Statistics,
Amsterdam: North Holland, pp 259-272.

Press, S.J. and Scott, A.J. (1976): Missing Variables in Bayesian Regression , II. Journal of the American Statistical Association 71, pp 366-369.

Pressley, M.M. (1976): Research on Factors Affecting Response Rates of Mail Surveys: A Critically Annotated Bibliography. Greensboro, North Carolina: The University of North Carolina at Greensboro.

Pressley, M.M. and Tullar, W.L. (1977): A Factor Interactive Investigation of Mail Survey Response Rates From a Commercial Population. Journal of Marketing Research 14, pp 108-111.

Price, D.O. (1959): On the Use of Stamped Return Envelopes with Mail Questionnaires. American Sociological Review 15, pp 672-673.

Price, D.O. and Searles, R. (1961): Some Effects of Interviewer - Respondent Interaction on Responses in a Survey Situation. American Statistical Association, Proceedings of the Social Statistics Section, pp 211-221.

Pritzker, L., Ogus, J. and Hansen, M.H. (1966): Computer Editing Methods - Some Applications and Results. Bulletin of the International Statistical Institute, pp 442-466.

Privacy Protection Study Commission (1977): Personal Privacy in an Information Society. Washington, DC: US Government Printing Office.

Proctor, C.H. (1974): What Proportion of Item Non-Response Should Lead to Deleting the Case? American Statistical Association, Proceedings of the Social Statistics Section, pp 404-408.

Proctor, C.H. (1977): Two Direct Approaches to Survey Non-Response: Estimating a Proportion with Callbacks and Allocating Effort to Raise Response Rate. American Statistical Association, Proceedings of the Social Statistics Section, pp 284-290.

Proctor, C.H. (1978): More on Imputing Versus Deleting When Estimating Scale Scores. American Statistical Association, Proceedings of the Section on Survey Research Methods, pp 209-211.

Pucel, D.J., Nelson, H.F. and Wheeler, D.N. (1971): Questionnaire Follow-up Returns as a Function of Incentives and Respondent Characteristics. Vocational Guidance Quarterly 19, pp 188-193.

Raghavarao, D. and Federer, W.T. (1973): Application of BIB
Designs as an Alternative to the Randomized Response Method
in Surveys. BU-490-M, Biometrics Unit, Cornell University.

Rao, J.N.K. (1968): Some Nonresponse Sampling Theory When the
Frame Contains an Unknown Amount of Duplication. Journal of
the American Statistical Association 63, pp 87-90.

Rao, J.N.K. (1974): Raking Ratio Estimators, II. Technical
Report, Statistics Canada, (unpublished).

Rao, J.N.K. (1974): Raking Ratio Estimators, III. Technical
Report, Statistics Canada, (unpublished).

Rao, J.N.K. and Hughes, E. (1979): Comparison of Domains in
the Presence of Nonresponse. Presented at the Symposium on
incomplete data: Preliminary proceedings, Washington Hilton
Hotel on August 10-11, 1979, Washington, DC.

Rao, P.S.R.S. (1966): A Study of Call-Back Policies in Sample
Surveys. Department of Statistics, Harvard University, Technical
Report No. 10.

Rao, P.S.R.S., et al. (1979): Data Collection Methods, Methods
for Handling Missing Data in Surveys-The Theory of Current
Practice. Report of the Panel on Incomplete Data, Committee
on National Statistics.

Rao, P.S.R.S. (1979): Nonresponse and Double Sampling. Unpublished Report.

Rappeport, M.A. (1971): Comments on 'An Experimental Study
of Payments to Respondents'. Public Opinion Quarterly 35, pp
423.

Reamer, F.G. (1979): Protecting Research Subjects and Unintended
Consequences: The Effect of Guarantees of Confidentiality.
Public Opinion Quarterly 43, pp 497-506.

Reaser, J.M., Hartsock, S. and Hoehn, A.J. (1975): A Test of
the Forced Alternative Random Response Questionnaire Technique.
HumRRO Technical Report 75-9. Alexandria, Virginia: Human Resources Research Organization.

Reeder, L.G. (1960): Mailed Questionnaires in Longitudinal
Health Studies: the Problem of Maintaining and Maximizing Response. Journal of Health and Human Behavior 1, pp 123-129.

Reeder, L.G. (n.d.) Recent Literature Concerning the Use of
the Telephone in Survey Research. Institute for Social Science
Research, University of California, Los Angeles.

Reid, S. (1942): Respondents and Non-Respondents to Mail Questionnaires. Educational Research Bulletin 21, pp 87-96.

Reingen, P.H. and Kernan, J.B. (1977): Compliance With an Interview Request: A Foot-in-the Door, Self-Perception Interpretation.
Journal of Marketing Research 14, pp 365-369.

Reinhold, R. (1976): Polling Encounters Public Resistance,
New York Times, October 25, 1976.

Reinmuth, J.E. and Geurts, M.D. (1975): The Collection of Sensitive Information Using a Two-Stage, Randomized Response Model.
Journal of Marketing Research 12, pp 402-407.

Reiss, S.P. (1977): Statistical Database Confidentiality. Confidentiality in Surveys, Report 25, Department of Statistics,
University of Stockholm.

Reuschling, T.L. and Etzel, M.J. (1973): The Disappearing Data
Source. Business Horizons 16, pp 17-22.

Reuss, C.F. (1943): Differences Between Persons Responding
and Not Responding to a Mailed Questionnaire. American Sociological Review 8, pp 433-438.

Reynolds, P.D. (1972): On the Protection of Human Subjects
and Social Science. International Social Science Journal, Vol.
24, No. 4, pp 693-719.

Ridley, J.C., Dawson, D.A. and Bachrach, C.A. (1979): An Assessment of Nonresponse Bias. American Statistical Association,
Proceedings of the Section on Survey Research Methods, pp 353-358.

Roberts, R.E., McCrory, O.F. and Forthofer R.N. (1978): Further
Evidence on Using a Deadline to Stimulate Responses to a Mail
Survey. Public Opinion Quarterly 42, pp 407-410.

Robertson, D.H. and Bellenger, D.N. (1978): A New Method of
Incresing Mail Survey Responses: Contribution to Charity. Journal
of Marketing Research 15, pp 632-633.

Robin, S.S. (1965): A Procedure for Securing Returns to Mail
Questionnaires. Sociology and Social Research 49, pp 24-35.

Robins, L.N. (1963): The Reluctant Respondent. Public Opinion
Quarterly 27, pp 276-286.

Robinson, R.A. (1946): Five Features Helped This Mail Questionnaire Pull 60 to 70 Per Cent. Printer's Ink 214, pp 25-26.

Robinson, R.A. and Agisim, P. (1951): Making Mail Surveys More
Reliable. Journal of Marketing 15, pp 415-424.

Robison, E.L. and Richardson, W.J. (1978): Editing and Impu-
tation of the 1977 Truck Inventory and Use Survey. American
Statistical Association, Proceedings of the Section on Survey
Research Methods, pp 203-208.

Robson, D.S. (1949): Application of W. Hendricks' Method of
Adjusting for Bias in Mail Surveys. Agricultural Economics
Research, pp 52-56.

Rockwell, R.C. (1975): An Investigation of Imputation and Differential Quality of Data in the 1970 Census. Journal of the American
Statistical Association 70, pp 39-42.

Roeher, A.G. (1963): Effective Techniques in Increasing Response to Mailed Questionnaires. Public Opinion Quarterly 27, pp 299-302.

Rogers, T.F. (1976): Interviews by Telephone and in Person: Quality of Responses and Field Performance. Public Opinion Quarterly 40, pp 51-65.

Rollins, M. (1940): The Practical Use of Repeated Questionnaire Waves. Journal of Applied Psychology 24, pp 770-772.

Roscoe, A.M., Lang, D. and Sheth, J.N. (1975): Follow-up Methods, Questionnaire Length, and Market Differences in Mail Surveys. Journal of Marketing 39, pp 20-27.

Rosen, N.A. (1960): Anonymity and Attitude Measurement. Public Opinion Quarterly 24, pp 675-679.

Rosenau, J.N. (1964): Meticulousness as a Factor in the Response to Mail Questionnaires. Public Opinion Quarterly 28, pp 312-314.

Rosenberg, H.H. (1975): The Delicate Balance: Privacy, Confidentiality, and the Public Interest. Presented at the American Public Health Association's annual meeting, session on Health Information, Privacy, and Confidentiality, Chicago, November 19, 1975.

Rosenblatt, R.R. and Kelly, E.L. (1978): A Comparison of the Sensitivity of the Unrelated Question Randomized Response Model with Three Other Data Accumulation Techniques Using Examination Cheating as a Model. American Statistical Association, Proceedings of the Section on Survey Research Methods, pp 356-361.

Rosenthal, R. (1965): The Volunteer Subject. Human Relations 18, pp 389-406.

Ross, L.H. (1963): The Inaccessible Respondent: A Note on Privacy in City and Country. Public Opinion Quarterly 27, pp 269-275.

Rothwell, D. (1963): SORAR Refusal Rates. Memo, US Bureau of the Census.

Rothwell, D. (1976): Critique of Draft (5/3/76) of Opinion Survey in the Privacy & Confidentiality Study. Memo, US Bureau of the Census.

Rothwell, D. (1976): Meeting with Members of League of Women Voters in Baltimore on the Evening of February 5, 1976. Memo, US Bureau of the Census.

Rothwell, D. (1977): Recommendations for Methods Test Program. Memo, US Bureau of the Census.

Rothwell, D. (1977): Respondent Burden. A report held in the Biennial Conference on Health Survey Research Methods at Williamsburg, Virginia, May 6, 1977.

Rothwell, D. (1979): Mock Interview Project Report. Memo, US Bureau of the Census (July 16 and 23, 1979).

Rothwell, D. and Bridge, G. (n.d.): Discussion of Respondent Burden. Memo, US Bureau of the Census and Columbia University.

Rothwell, D. and Massillon, A. (1978): Classroom Experiments Comparing Richmond Dress Rehearsal Census Form with Oakland Test Form and Five Variants (Report A6-2). Memo, US Bureau of the Census.

Rothwell, D. and Massillon, A. (1978): Perceptions of the Richmond Dress Rehersal Census Form in Comparison with Alternative Forms Tested in Classroom Experiments Conducted in the Spring of 1978 (Report A6-3). Memo, US Bureau of the Census.

Rothwell, D. and Massillon, A. (1979): Opinions of Participants in April 1978 Classroom Experiments (Report A6-4). Memo, US Bureau of the Census.

Rothwell, D. and Rustemeyer, A.M. (1979): Studies of Census Mail Questionnaires. Journal of Marketing Research 16, pp 401-409.

Royal Statistical Society (1977): Evidence from the Royal Statistical Society to the Data Protection Committee. Journal of the Royal Statistical Society, Series A, 140, Part 2, pp 210-216.

Rubin, D.B. (1972): A Non-Iterative Algorithm for Least Squares Estimation of Missing Values in Any Analysis of Variance Design. Applied Statistics 21, No. 2, pp 136-141.

Rubin, D.B. (1973): The Use of Matched Sampling and Regression Adjustment to Remove Bias in Observational Studies. Biometrics 29, pp 185-203.

Rubin, D.B. (1973): Matching to Remove Bias in Observational Studies. Biometrics 29, pp 159-183. Correction note: Biometrics 30, pp 728.

Rubin, D.B. (1974): Characterizing the Estimation of Parameters in Incomplete-Data Problems. Journal of the American Statistical Association 69, pp 467-474.

Rubin, D.B. (1976): Comparing Regressions When Some Predictor Values are Missing. Technometrics 18, No. 2, pp 201-205.

Rubin, D.B. (1976): Inference and Missing Data. Biometrika 63,3, pp 581-592.

Rubin, D.B. (1976): Noniterative Least Squares Estimates. Standard Errors, and F-tests for Analyses of Variance With Missing Data. Journal of the Royal Statistical Society, Series B, pp 38.

Rubin, D.B. (1977): Formalizing Subjective Notions About the Effect of Nonrespondents in Sample Surveys. Journal of the American Statistical Association 72, No. 359, pp 538-543.

Rubin, D.B. (1977): The Design of a General and Flexible System for Handling Non-Response in Sample Surveys. Unpublished.

Rubin, D.B. (1978): Multiple Imputations in Sample Surveys - A Phenomenological Bayesian Approach to Non-Response. American Statistical Association, Proceedings of the Section on Survey Research Methods, pp 20-28.

Rubin, D.B. (1979): Illustrating the Use of Multiple Imputations to Handle Nonresponse in Sample Surveys. Presented at the 42nd Session of the International Statistical Institute, Manila, Phillipines, December 4-14, 1979.

Rubin, D.B. (n.d.): Missing at Random - What Does It Mean? Educational Testing Service Research Bulletin, RB-73-2.

Ruckmick, C.A. (1930): The Uses and Abuses of the Questionnaire Procedure. Journal of Applied Psychology 14, pp 32-41.

Russell, S.D., Konrad, R. and Kaluzny, A.D. (1970): Influencing the Respondent: An Experiment in Maximizing the Response Rate of Mail Questionnaires. Sociological Abstracts, pp 22.

Rust, K. (n.d.): Methods of Non-Response Adjustment. Australian Bureau of Statistics, Canberra.

Rustein, D.D. (1969): The Ethical Design of Human Experiments. Daedalus.

Rustemeyer, A. (1977): Toward Development of a Computer-Assisted Telephone Interviewing System. Memo, US Bureau of the Census.

Rustemeyer, A. (1977): Measuring Interviewer Performance in Mock Interviews. American Statistical Association, Proceedings of the Social Statistics Section, pp 341-346.

Rustemeyer, A. and Levine, A. (1977): Report on a Telephone Survey Using Computer Assistance. Memo, US Bureau of the Census.

Rustemeyer, A., Shure, G.H., Rogers, M.S. and Meeker, R.J. (1978): Computer-Assisted Telephone Interviewing: Design Consider- ations. American Statistical Association, Proceedings of the Section on Survey Research Methods, pp 1-8.

Sanchez-Crespo, J.L. (1966): Non-Response in Mass Campaigns of Public Health Programmes, Illustrated by Data From a Tuberculin Survey. Bulletin of World Health Organization, pp 641-645.

Sanchez-Crespo, J.L. (1975): Notes on the Accuracy, Precision and Reliability of Statistical Data. Bulletin of the International Statistical Institute, Warsaw.

Sande, I.G. (1979): Hot Deck Imputation Procedures. Presented at the Symposium on incomplete data: Preliminary proceedings, Washington Hilton Hotel on August 10-11, 1979, Washington, DC.

Sande, G. (1979): Numerical Edit and Imputation. International Association for Statistical Computing, 42nd Session of the International Statistical Institute. December 1979.

Sandström, R. (1977): The Reduction of Refusal Non-Response: An Attempt to Design a Model and Its Application. Paper presented at the ISI meeting in New Delhi.

Sauls, E. and Millar, J.A. (1974): Nonsampling Errors. American Statistical Association, Proceedings of the Social Statistics Section, pp 433-435.

Sawyer, J. and Schecter, H. (1968): Computers, Privacy, and the National Data Center: The Responsibility of Social Scientists. American Psychologist 23, pp 810-818.

Schafer, M.V. and Mills, R.H. (1967): A Comparison of Nonresponse Rates for Selected Characteristics for Cleveland 1965 and 1960. Cleveland Special Census Results Memorandum No. 52, RRB Report No. 66-65 (67-211 (MRD)). US Bureau of the Census.

Schaible, W.L. (1979): Estimation of Finite Population Totals from Incomplete Sample Data: Prediction Approach. Presented at the Symposium on incomplete data: Preliminary proceedings, Washington Hilton Hotel on August 10-11, 1979, Washington, DC.

Scharff, J.A. (1973): Treatment of Nonresponse in Surveys. Bulletin of International Statistical Institute, pp 378-385.

Schaul, R.A. and Hayya, J.C. (1976): An Imputation Procedure for Determining Missing Factor Levels in Analysis of Variance. American Statistical Association, Proceedings of the Social Statistics Section, pp 746-750.

Scheuren, F.J. (1976): Preliminary Notes on the Partially Missing Data Problem: Some (Very) Elementary Considerations. Delivered at the April 1976 meeting of the Social Security Administration's Statistical Methodology Group.

Scheuren, F.J. and Oh, H.L. (1978): Some Unresolved Application Issues in Raking Ratio Estimation. Paper presented at the American Statistical Association Meetings, San Diego, California.

Schewe, C.D. and Cournoyer, N.G. (1976): Prepaid Versus Promised
Monetary Incentives to Questionnaire Response: Further Evidence.
Public Opinion Quarterly 40, pp 105-107.

Schieber, S.J. (1978): A Comparison of Three Alternative Techniques for Allocating Unreported Social Security Income on
the Survey of the Low-Income Aged and Disabled. American Statistical Association, Proceedings of the Section on Survey Research
Methods, pp 212-218.

Schmidt, M. (1975): Interviewing the "Old Old". The Gerontologist
15, pp 6.

Scholl, J.C. and Burkhead, C.E. (1949): Interviewing Nonrespondents to a Mail Survey: An Experiment in Connection With April
1948 Farm Stocks Report. Agricultural Economics Research 1,
pp 16-23.

Schooley, M., Cahoon, L., Ponikowski, C. and Riccini, K. (1979):
Overview of the Current Population Survey Operations and Esti-
mation. American Statistical Association, Proceedings of the
Section on Survey Research Methods, pp 127-132.

Schreiner, I. (1977): CPS Reinterview Results from the Listing
Check, Check of Noninterview Classifications, and the Household
Composition Check for 1976. US Bureau of the Census, Memorandum,
April 27.

Schwanz, D. (1976): Personal Interviewing Techniques Compared
With Mail Interviewing Techniques for a Survey of Personal
Travel. US Bureau of the Census. Prepared for Presentation
to the American Marketing Association, Census Bureau Seminar
on October 8, 1976.

Schwertman, N.C. (1975): The Analysis of Growth Curve Data
With Missing Observations. Presented at the annual meeting
of the American Statistical Association, 1975, Atlanta, Georgia.

Schwertman, N.C. (1978): A Note on the Geisser-Greenhouse Correction for Incomplete Data Split-Plot Analysis. Journal of the
American Statistical Association 73, pp 393-396.

Schwertman, N.C. and Allen, D.M. (1975): The Smoothing of an
Indefinite Matrix With Applications to Growth Curve Analysis
With Missing Observations. University of Kentucky Technical
Report No. 56.

Schwirian, K.P. and Blaine, H.R. (1966-67): Questionnaire Return
Bias in the Study of Blue-Collar Workers. Public Opinion Quarterly 30, pp 656-663.

Schyberger, B.W. (1967): A Study of Interviewer Behavior. Journal
of Marketing Research 4, pp 32-35.

Scott, C. (1961): Research on Mail Surveys. Journal of the
Royal Statistical Society 124, Series A, pp 143-205.

Scott, F.G. (1956-57): Mail Questionnaires Used in a Study of Older Women. Sociology and Social Research, pp 281-284.

Scott, J.C. (1971): Confidentiality and Co-Operation Between Researchers. American Statistical Association, Proceedings of the Social Statistics Section, pp 13-14.

Scott, J.C. (1971): Response Rate Trends 1955-1970, and Response by Season, Size of Place of Residence and Length of Interview. Technical Report 5a, Field Office, Survey Research Center, Institute for Social Research, The University of Michigan, Ann Arbor.

Seitz, R.M. (1944): How Mail Surveys May be Made to Pay. Printer's Ink, pp 17-19.

Selgrade, F.J. (1967): Influence of Direct-Mail Leaflet on Response Rates in X-Areas. New Haven Special Results Memorandum No. 17 (67-439 (MRD)). US Bureau of the Census.

Seligman, C., Bush, M. and Kirsch, K. (1976): Relationship Between Compliance in the Foot-in-the-Door Paradigm and Size of First Request. Journal of Personality and Social Psychology 33, pp 517-520.

Sen, A.R. (1972): Some Nonsampling Errors in the Canadian Waterfowl Mail Survey. J. Wildlife Management 36, pp 951.

Sen, P.K. (1974): On Unbiased Estimation for Randomized Response Models. Journal of the American Statistical Association 69, pp 997-1001.

Sen, P.K. (1975): Asymptotically Optimal Estimators of General Parameters in Randomized Response Models. Bulletin of International Statistical Institute, pp 323-326.

Shannon, J.R. (1948): Percentages of Returns of Questionnaires in Reputable Educational Research. Journal of Educational Research 42, pp 138-141.

Shapiro, G., Scheuren, F., Lock, H. and Vogel, L. (n.d.): A Hot-Deck Application of Multiple Imputations in the CPS Income Supplement. Unpublished working paper of the Social Security Administration, Washington, DC.

Sharp, H. (1955): The Mail Questionnaire as a Supplement to the Personal Interview. American Sociological Review 20, pp 718.

Shearer, P.R. (1973): Missing Data in Quantitative Designs. Applied Statistics 22, No. 2, pp 135-140.

Shimizu, I.M. and Bonham, G.S. (1976): Randomized Response Technique in a National Survey. American Statistical Association, Proceedings of the Social Statistics Section, pp 761-765. Also in Journal of the American Statistical Association 73, pp 35-39.

Short, R.A. (1968): Follow-up Observations - Reasons for Nonresponse in Trenton Dress Rehearsal. 1970 Census 'Dress Rehearsal'
Program Results Memorandum No. 26 (68-407 (MRD)). US Bureau
of the Census.

Shosteck, H. (1978): Defining the Empirical Limits of Response
to Mail Surveys. Unpublished memo, Herschel Shosteck Associates,
Silver Spring, Maryland.

Shosteck, H. (1979): The Empirical Limits of Response to Mail
Surveys. American Statistical Association, Proceedings of the
Section on Survey Research Methods, pp 366-371.

Shosteck, H. and Fairweather, W.R. (1979): Physician Response
Rates to Mail and Personal Interview Surveys. Public Opinion
Quarterly 43, pp 206-217.

Shure, G.H. and Meeker, J. (1978): A Minicomputer System for
Multiperson Computer-Assisted Telephone Interviewing. Behavior
Research Methods & Instrumentation 1978, Vol. 10 (2), pp 196-202.

Shuttleworth, F.K. (1940): Sampling Errors Involved in Incomplete
Returns to Mail Questionnaires. Psychological Bulletin 37,
pp 437.

Shuttleworth, F.K. (1941): Sampling Errors Involved in Incomplete
Returns to Mail Questionnaires. Journal of Applied Psychology,
pp 588-591.

Simmons, W.R. (1954): A Plan to Account for 'Not-at-Homes'
by Combining Weighting and Callbacks. Journal of Marketing
19, No. 1, pp 42-53.

Simmons, W.R. (1970): Response to Randomized Inquiries - A
Technique for Reducing Bias. Presented to the American Society
for Quality Control, Administrative Applications Division Conference, Arlington, Virginia.

Simon, R.E. (1967): Responses to Personal and Form Letters
in Mail Surveys. Journal of Advertising Research 7, pp 28-30.

Simon, R.J. and Simon, J.L. (1974-75): Money Incentives and
Family Size: A Hypothetical-Question Study. Public Opinion
Quarterly 38, pp 585-595.

Singer, E. (1972): Agreement Between 'Inaccesible' Respondents
and Informants. Public Opinion Quarterly 36, pp 603-611.

Singer, E. (1978): Informed Consent: Consequenses for Response
Rate and Response Quality in Social Surveys. American Sociological Review 43, pp 144-162.

Singer, E. (1978): The Effect of Informed Consent Procedures
on Respondents' Reactions to Surveys. Journal of Consumer Research 5, pp 49-57.

Singer, E. and Kohnke-Aguirre, L. (1979): Interviewer Expectation Effects: A Replication and Extension. Public Opinion Quarterly 43, pp 245-260.

Singh, B. (1974): Some Contributions to the Theory of Nonresponse in Sample Surveys from a Bayesian View. Unpublished Ph.D. thesis, Department of Statistics, University of Wisconsin.

Singh, B. (1979): Nonresponse and Double Sampling: The Bayesian Approach. Methods for Handling Missing Data in Surveys - the Theory of Current Practice (Data collecting methods chapter). Report of the Panel on Incomplete Data, Committee on National Statistics.

Singh, B. and Sedransk, J. (1975): Estimation of Regression Coefficients When There Is Nonresponse. Technical Report No. 25, Statistical Science Division, State University of New York at Buffalo.

Singh, B. and Sedransk, J. (1978): A Two-Phase Sample Design for Estimating the Finite Population Mean When There Is Nonresponse. In Survey Sampling and Measurement (Chapter 10), Academic Press, pp 143-155.

Singh, B. and Sedransk, J. (1978): Sample Size Selection in Regression Analysis When There Is Nonresponse. Journal of the American Statistical Association 73, pp 362-365.

Singh, B. and Sedransk, J. (1979): Bayesian Procedures for Survey Design When There Is Nonresponse. Presented at the Symposium on incomplete data: Preliminary proceedings, Washington Hilton Hotel on August 10-11, 1979, Washington, DC.

Singh, J. (1976): A Note on the Randomized Response Technique. American Statistical Association, Proceedings of the Social Statistics Section, pp 772.

Sirken, M.G. and Brown, M.L. (1962): Quality of Data Elicted by Successive Mailings in Mail Surveys. American Statistical Association, Proceedings of the Social Statistics Section, pp 118-125.

Sirken, M.G. and Royston, P.N. (1970): Reasons Death are Missed in Household Surveys of Population Change. American Statistical Association, Proceedings of the Social Statistics Section, pp 361-364.

Siskin, B.R. and Leone, R.D. (1972): A Sample Design for Interviewing a Hard to Locate Population. American Statistical Association, Proceedings of the Social Statistics Section, pp 432-437.

Skelton, V.C. (1963): Patterns Behind Income Refusals. Journal of Marketing 27, pp 38-41.

Sketh, J. and Roscoe, A. (1975): Impact of Questionnaire Length, Follow-Up Methods, and Geographical Location on Response Rate to Mail Survey. Journal of Applied Psychology, pp 252-254.

Sletto, R. (1940): Pretesting of Questionnaires. American Sociological Review 5, pp 193-200.

Sliwa, G. and Tucker, R. (1977): Analysis of Nonresponse Rates
for Various Household Surveys. Memo, US Bureau of the Census.

Slocum, W.L., Empey, L.T. and Swanson, H.S. (1956): Increasing
Response to Questionnaires and Structured Interviews. American
Sociological Review 21, pp 221-225.

Smith, C.C. (1952): Effect of Personal Visits on Response Rates
to Mail Surveys. Agricultural Economics Research 4, pp 126-127.

Smith, L.L., Federer, W.T. and Raghararao, D. (1975): A Comparison of Three Techniques for Eliciting Truthful Answers to Sensitive Questions. American Statistical Association, Proceedings
of the Social Statistics Section, pp 447-452.

Smith, R.E. (1977): Washington Privacy: Interview. The New
Yorker 53, pp 28-30.

Snelling, W.R. (1969): The Impact of a Personalized Questionnaire. Journal of Educational Research 63, pp 126-129.

Snyder, M. and Cunningham, M.R. (1975): To Comply or Not Comply:
Testing the Self-Perception Explanation of the 'Foot-in-the-
Door' Phenomenon. Journal of Personality and Social Psychology
31, pp 64-67.

Som, R.K. (n.d.): On Adjustments for Non-Sampling Errors and
Biases in the Estimation of Vital Rates. (Further details unknown).

Spaeth, M.A. (1977): Recent Publications on Survey Research
Techniques. Journal of Marketing Research 14, pp 403-409.

Speak, M. (1964): Some Characteristics of Respondents, Partial-
Respondents and Non-Respondents to Questionnaires. Occupational
Psychology 38, pp 173-182.

Spiers, E., Coder, J. and Ono, M. (1971): Characteristics of
Income Nonrespondents in the Current Population Survey. American
Statistical Association, Proceedings of the Social Statistics
Section, pp 369-374.

Spiers, E.F. and Knott, J.J. (1969): Computer Method of Process
Missing Income and Work Experience Information in the Current
Population Survey. American Statistical Association, Proceedings
of the Social Statistics Section, pp 289-297.

Sprately, E. (1973): An Analysis of the Efficiency With Which
Health Interview Survey Data Were Collected During the First
Three Quarters of 1972. Unpublished Trainee Report, National
Center for Health Statistics.

Srinath, K.P. (1971): Multiphase Sampling in Nonresponse Problems.
Journal of the American Statistical Association 66, No. 335,
pp 583-586.

Srivastava, J.N. and Zaatar, M.K. (1973): A Monte Carlo Comparison of Four Estimators of the Dispersion Matrix of a Bivariate Normal Population, Using Incomplete Data. Journal of the American Statistical Association 68, pp 180-183.

Stafford, J.E. (1966): Influence of Preliminary Contact on Mail Returns. Journal of Marketing Research 3, pp 410-411.

Stanton, F. (1939): Notes on the Validity of Mail Questionnaire Returns. Journal of Applied Psychology 23, pp 95-104.

Stemp, P. (1976): Non-Response in the Labour Force Survey and Methods of Imputation. Australian Bureau of Statistics, Canberra.

Stephan, F.F. (1942): An Iterative Method of Adjusting Sample Frequency Tables When Expected Marginal Totals are Known. The Annals of the Mathematical Statistical Association 13, pp 166-178.

Stevens, J.A. (1979): Measuring Quality of Personnel Data: The CPDF/OPF Accuracy Survey. Memo, US Office of Personnel Management.

Stevens, J.A. and Bailar, B.A. (1976): The Relationship Between Various Interviewer Characteristics and the Collection of Income Data. American Statistical Association, Proceedings of the Social Statistics Section, pp 785-790.

Stevens, R.E. (1974-75): Does Precoding Mail Questionnaires Affect Response Rates? Public Opinion Quarterly 38, pp 621-622.

Stover, R.V. and Stone, W.J. (1974): Hand Delivery of Self-Administered Questionnaires. Public Opinion Quarterly 37, pp 284-287.

Suchman, E.A. (1962): An Analysis of 'Bias' in Survey Research. Public Opinion Quarterly 26, pp 102-111.

Suchman, E.A. and McCandless, B. (1940): Who Answers Questionnaires? Journal of Applied Psychology 24, pp 758-769.

Sudman, S. (1965): Time Allocation in Survey Interviewing and in Other Field Occupations. Public Opinion Quarterly 29, pp 638-648.

Sudman, S. (1966): New Uses of Telephone Methods in Survey Research. Journal of Marketing Research 3, pp 163-167.

Sudman, S. and Bradburn, N.M. (1974): Response Effects in Surveys: A Review and Synthesis. Chicago: Aldine Publishing Co.

Sudman, S. and Ferber, R. (1971): Experiments in Obtaining Consumer Expenditures by Diary Methods. Journal of the American Statistical Association 66, pp 725-735.

Sudman, S. and Ferber, R. (1974): A Comparison of Alternative Procedures for Collecting Consumer Expenditure Data for Frequently Purchased Products. Journal of Marketing Research 11, pp 128-135.

Sudman, S., Greeley, A.M. and Pinto, L. (1965): The Effectiveness of Self-Administered Questionnaires. Journal of Marketing Research 2, pp 293-297.

Sukhatme, P.V. and Seth, G.R. (1952): Nonsampling Errors in Surveys. Journal of the Indian Society of Agricultural Statistics 4, pp 5-41.

Summers, J.O. (1974): Less Information Is Better? Journal of Marketing Research 11, pp 467-468.

Sundberg, R. (1974): Maximum Likelihood Theory for Incomplete Data from an Exponential Family. Scandinavian Journal of Statistics 1, pp 49-58.

Sundberg, R. (1976): An Iterative Method for Solution of the Likelihood Equations for Incomplete Data from Exponential Families. Communications in Statistics - Simulation and Computation, B5, pp 55-64.

Sunter, A.B. (1975): A Survey Design Strategy for a National Statistical Agency. Invited paper, ISI meeting in Warsaw.

Sunter, A.B. (n.d.): On Non-Response in a System of Surveys. Memo, Statistics Canada.

Sunter, A.B. (n.d.): Response Burden, Sample Rotation, and Classification Renewal in Economic Surveys. Memo, Statistics Canada.

Survey Research Center (1971): Economic Survey Methods. Institute for Social Research, University of Michigan, Ann Arbor.

Swensson, B. (1972): Stratified Randomized Response With the Special Case: A Combined Use of Regular Interview and Randomized Response Interview. Forskningsprojektet FEL I UNDERSÖKNINGAR, Rapport nr 45, Stockholms Universitet, 1972-05-08.

Swensson, B. (1974): Combined Questions - A New Survey Technique for Eliminating Evasive Answer Bias. Forskningsprojektet FEL I UNDERSÖKNINGAR, Rapport nr 70, Stockholms universitet, Statistiska institutionen.

Swensson, B. (1976): Using Mixtures of Techniques for Estimating Sensitive Attributes. Confidentiality in Surveys Report 13. Department of Statistics, University of Stockholm.

Swensson, B. (1977): Survey Measurement of Sensitive Attributes - Some Contributions. Ph.D. thesis, University of Stockholm.

Swensson, B. (1981): A Survey of Nonresponse Terms. SCB, P/STM, Utkast 1981-02-13.

Sydiaha, D., Stewart, A. and Lafave, H.G. (1968): A Study of Mail Questionnaire Technique With Discharged Psychiatric Patients. International Journal of Social Psychiatry, pp 135-140.

Szameitat, K. and Zindler, H.J. (1965): The Reduction of Errors in Statistics by Automatic Corrections. Bulletin of the International Statistical Institute, Proceedings of the 35th Session, Vol. 16, pp 395-417.

Taggart, M. (1967): Characteristics of Participants and Nonparticipants in Individual Test-Interpretation Interviews. Journal of Consulting Psychology 31, pp 213-215.

Tallent, N. and Reiss, W.J. (1959-60): A Note on an Unusually High Rate of Returns for a Mail Questionnaire. Public Opinion Quarterly 23, pp 579-581.

Taeuber, R.C. (1975): The Right of Privacy. American Society for Information Science, Vol. 1, No. 10, pp 17-18.

Tamhane, A.C. (1977): A Randomized Response Technique for Investigating Several Sensitive Attributes. American Statistical Association, Proceedings of the Social Statistics Section, pp 273-278.

Thessin, M.S. (1977): Evaluation of CPS Interviewers for Calendar Year 1974. Memo, US Bureau of the Census.

Thomas, K. and Schreiner, I. (1978): Experimentation in Methods and Measurement of Reinterview. American Statistical Association, Proceedings of the Social Statistics Section, pp 495-498.

Thompson, N.R. (1979): Nonresponse Bias from 'No Answer/Busy' Calls in a Telephone Survey. American Statistical Association, Proceedings of the Section on Survey Research Methods, pp 250-251.

Thomsen, I. (1971): On the Effect of Non-Response in the Norwegian Election Survey 1969. Statistical Review 3.

Thomsen, I. (1973): A Note on the Efficiency of Weighting Subclass Means to Reduce the Effects of Non-Response when Analyzing Survey Data. Statistical Review 4, Swedish National Central Bureau of Statistics, Stockholm.

Thomsen, I. (1975): Evaluating the Efficiency of Two Weighting Procedures To Reduce Non-Response Bias: An Application of Cochran's Non-Response Stratum Approach. Bulletin of the International Statistical Institute, pp 396-401.

Thomsen, I. (1978): A Second Note on the Efficiency of Weighting Subclass Means to Reduce the Effects of Nonresponse When Analysing Survey Data. Statistical Review 3, pp 191-196.

Thomsen, I. and Siring, E. (1979): On the Causes and Effects of Non-Response: Norwegian Experiences. Presented at the Symposium on incomplete data: Preliminary proceedings, Washington Hilton Hotel on August 10-11, 1979, Washington, DC.

Tillery, D. (1967): Seeking a Balance Between the Right of Privacy and the Advancement of Social Research. Journal of Educational Measurement, Vol. 4, No. 1, pp 11-16.

Timm, N.H. (1970): The Estimation of Variance-Covariance and Correlation Matrices from Incomplete Data. Psychometrika 35, pp 417-437.

Tortora, R.D. (1977): Reducing Respondent Burden for Repeated Samples. Agricultural Economics Research 30, 2, pp 41-44.

Tortora, R.D. and Crank, K. (1978): The Use of Unequal Probability Sampling to Reduce Respondent Burden. American Statistical Association, Proceedings of the Section on Survey Research Methods, pp 337-340.

Trawinski, I.M. and Bargmann, R.E. (1964): Maximum Likelihood Estimation With Incomplete Multivariate Data. Annals of Mathematical Statistics 35, pp 647-657.

Tremblay, V. (1973): Characteristics of Persons for Whom Proxy Responses are Obtained in the Labour Force Survey. Preliminary report, Statistics Canada.

Trewin, D. (1977): The Use of Post-Stratification for Adjustment of Non-Response Biases. Paper presented at the 41st session of the International Statistical Institute, New Delhi.

Trewin, D. (1978): Techniques for Adjustment of Non-Response Biases - Some Australian Experiences. Australian Bureau of Statistics, Canberra.

Tupek, A.R. and Richardson, W.J. (1978): Use of Ratio Estimates to Compensate for Nonresponse Bias in Certain Economic Surveys. American Statistical Association, Proceedings of the Section on Survey Research Methods, pp 197-202.

Turner, A.G. (1977): An Experiment to Compare Three Interviewing Procedures in the National Crime Survey. Memo, US Bureau of the Census.

Twedt, D.W. (1963): Why a Marketing Research Code of Ethics? Journal of Marketing 27, pp 45-50.

Tybout, A.M. and Zaltman, G. (1974): Ethics in Marketing Research: Their Practical Relevance. Journal of Marketing Research 11, pp 357-368.

United Nations (1963): Automatic Editing of Individual Statistical Observations. Statistical Standards and Studies, No. 2.

University of Michigan. Institute for Social Research, Survey Research Center (1965): A Report on Respondents' Reading of the Brochure and Letter and an Analysis of Respondents' Level of Information. A report to the National Health Survey of the Public Health Service. Unpublished.

University of Michigan. Institute for Social Research, Survey Research Center (1970): Response Rate Trends 1950-1970, and Response by Season, Size of Place of Residence, and Length of Interview. Unpublished.

US Bureau of the Census (1963): SORAR Refusal Rates. Memorandum from N.D. Rothwell to Joseph Waksberg, June 19, 1963.

US Bureau of the Census (1963): The Current Population Survey Reinterview Program: Some Notes and Discussion. Bureau of the Census, Technical Paper no. 6, Washington, DC.

US Bureau of the Census (1963): The Current Population Survey, A Report on Methodology. Technical Report No. 7, Washington, DC: Government Printing Office.

US Bureau of the Census (1966): Mail-Return Rates and Effect of Mail Follow-up for Nonresponse in the Agriculture Field Procedure Study. Paper prepared by Jill M. Coupe and John Forsythe. AFPS Results Memorandum 4, RRB 66-66.

US Bureau of the Census (1967): A Comparison of Nonresponse Rates for Selected Characteristics for Cleveland, 1965 and 1960. Paper prepared by Margaret V. Schafer and Ruth H. Mills. Response Research Branch Report 66-65.

US Bureau of the Census (1967): Mail Return Rates and Results of Preliminary Edit of Four Questionnaires: Second Format Test. Paper prepared by David A. Koons. Response Research Branch Report 67-32.

US Bureau of the Census (1967): New Haven Special Census: Survey of Nonrespondents. Paper prepared by James A. Jondle. New Haven Special Census Results Memorandum 7, Response Research Branch Report 67-33 (67-423 MRD).

US Bureau of the Census (1967): Test of Two Versions of a 1970 Sample Questionnaire: Follow-up Rates. Paper prepared by Alice Weidner. First Questionnaire Format Test Results Memorandum 2, Response Research Branch Report 67-6 (67-102 MRD).

US Bureau of the Census (1968): Follow-Up Observations - Reasons for Nonresponse in Trenton Dress Rehearsal. Paper prepared by Richard A. Short. 1970 Census "Dress Rehearsal" Program Results Memorandum 26 (68-407 MRD).

US Bureau of the Census (1968): The Current Population Survey Reinterview Program, January 1961 through December 1966. Technical Paper No. 19, Washington, DC.

US Bureau of the Census (1971): Current Population Survey: Interviewers Reference Manual. Ser. CPS 250, Washington, DC: Government Printing Office.

US Bureau of the Census (1971): 1970 Data-Collection Forms and Procedures. US Census of Population and Housing: 1970. Ser PHC(R)-2, Washington, DC: Government Printing Office.

US Bureau of the Census (1972): Investigation of Census Bureau Interviewer Characteristics, Performance, and Attitudes: A Summary, by Gail Poe Interfurth. Working Paper No. 34, Washington, DC: Government Printing Office.

US Bureau of the Census (1972): Who's Home When. Prepared by Dean Weber and Richard C. Burt. Working Paper 37, Washington DC: Government Printing Office.

US Bureau of the Census (1974): Standards for Discussion and Presentation of Errors in Data. Technical Report No. 32. Washington, DC: Government Printing Office.

US Bureau of the Census (1974): Indexes to Survey Methodology Literature. Technical Report No. 34, Washington, DC: Government Printing Office.

US Bureau of the Census (1975): Reinterview Manual. Form 11-56, Washington, DC: Government Printing Office.

US Bureau of the Census (1976): Status of 1980 Census Testing Program. Prepared for use at the Census Advisory Committee Meeting of the American Statistical Association, September 30 - October 1, 1976.

US Bureau of the Census (1978): Imputation and Editing of Faulty or Missing Survey Data. Papers given primarily in the Section on Survey Research Methods at the 1978 Annual Meeting of the American Statistical Association.

US Bureau of the Census (n.d.): Course on Nonsampling Errors. Lectures 1-9, International Statistics Program Center, Washington, DC.

US Bureau of the Census (n.d.): Use of Advance or Preliminary Letters and Inserts. Memo.

US Bureau of the Census (n.d.): Use of Incentives. Memo.

US Department of Agriculture (1975): Maintaining Statistics with Integrity. Proceedings at National Conference of the Statistical Reporting Service, Dulles, Virginia, Feb 1975, pp 59-60.

US Department of Health, Education, and Welfare (1960): US National Health Survey, Co-Operation in Health Examination Surveys. Washington, DC.

US Department of Health, Education, and Welfare (1974): Protection of Human Subjects. Federal Register, Vol. 39, No. 105, May 30, 1974, Part II, 18914-18920. Washington, DC: Government Printing Office.

US Department of Health, Education, and Welfare (1976): The Secretary's Interpretation of "Subject at Risk". Federal Register, Vol. 41, 26572.

US Energy Information Administration (1979): Plans for Meeting the Clearance Conditions. Memo, January 23, 1979.

US National Center for Health Statistics (1971): Effect of Some Experimental Interviewing Techniques on Reporting in the Health Interview Survey. Vital and Health Statistics, Series 2, No. 41. Washington, DC: Government Printing Office.

US National Center for Health Statistics (1975): A Study of the Effect of Remuneration Upon Response in the Health and Nutriton Examination Survey. Vital and Health Statistics, Series 2, No. 76.

US Office of Management and Budget (1975): Privacy Act Implementation. Guidelines and Responsibilities. Federal Register, Part III, Vol. 40, No. 132, 28948-28978. Washington, DC: Government Printing Office.

Veiga, J.F. (1974): Getting the Mail Questionnaire Returned: Some Practical Research Considerations. Journal of Applied Psychology 59, pp 217-218.

Veltman, C.J. (1972): The Resistance of Respondents in Inter-Ethnic Interviewing. Sociology and Social Research 56, pp 513.

Vigderhous, G. (1977): Analysis of Patterns of Response to Mailed Questionnaires. Sociological Methods and Research, Volume 6, Number 2, pp 205-214.

Vidgerhous, G. (1979): Optimizing the Time Schedules and Response Rates in Telephone Surveys - A Study of the Seasonal Patterns. American Statistical Association, Proceedings of the Section on Survey Research Methods, pp 256-261.

Voight, R.B. (1970): Costs, Response Rates, and Other Aspects of Data Collection in the 1970 Census. American Statistical Association, Proceedings of the Social Statistics Section, pp 47-53.

Waisanen, F.B. (1954): A Note on the Response to a Mailed Questionnaire. Public Opinion Quarterly 18, pp 210-212.

Waite, P.J. (1974): An Evaluation of Nonsampling Errors in the Monthly Retail Trade Sales Data. American Statistical Association, Proceedings of the Economic Statistics Section, pp 602-607.

Walker, B.J. and Burdick, R.K. (1977): Advance Correspondence and Error in Mail Surveys. Journal of Marketing Research 14, pp 379-382.

Wallace, D. (1945): Who Answers Mail Questionnaires? Time Research Publication, No. 929.

Wallace, D. (1954): A Case For - and Against - Mail Questionnaires. Public Opinion Quarterly 18, pp 40-52.

Walsh, T.C. (1976): Selected Results from the 1972-73 Diary Survey. US Bureau of the Census. Presented at a seminar sponsored by the American Marketing Association, October 7, 1976.

Walters, J. (1960): Relation Between Reliability of Responses in Family Life: Research and Method of Data Collection. Marriage and Family Living, pp 232-237.

Ware, W. and Caldwell, J.C. (1972): Confidentiality of Privacy and Sensitivity in Household Surveys. Australian Journal of Statistics 14, No. 3, pp 197-203.

Ware, W.H. (1973): Records, Computers and the Rights of Citizens. Report of the Secretary's Advisory Committee on Automated Data System. Washington, DC: Government Printing Office.

Warner, S.L. (1965): Randomized Response: A Survey Technique for Eliminating Evasive Answer Bias. Journal of the American Statistical Association 60, pp 63-69.

Warner, S.L. (1971): The Linear Randomized Response Model. Journal of the American Statistical Association 66, pp 884-888.

Warshaw, L.J. (1976): Confidentiality Versus the Need to Know. Presented at the American Occupational Health Conference, Cincinnati.

Warwick, D.P. and Kelman, H.C. (1973): Ethical Issues in Social Intervention. In Gerald Zaltman, ed., Processes and Phenomena of Social Change. New York: Wiley-Interscience.

Watson, J.J. (1965): Improving the Response Rate in Mail Research. Journal of Advertising Research 5, pp 48-50.

Wayne, I. (1975-76): Nonresponse, Sample Size, and the Allocation of Resources. Public Opinion Quarterly 39, pp 557-562.

Weaver, C.N., Holmes, S.L. and Glenn, N.D. (1975): Some Characteristics of Inaccessible Respondents in a Telephone Survey. Journal of Applied Psychology 60, pp 260-262.

Weilbacher, W. and Walsh, H.R. (1952): Mail Questionnaires and the Personalized Letter of Transmittal. Journal of Marketing 16, pp 331-336.

Wells, D.E. and Andapia, A.O. (1966): On Adoption Proneness and Response to Mail Questionnaires. Rural Sociology, pp 483-487.

Wells, W.D. (1974): Group Interviewing. In Robert Ferber, ed., Handbook of Marketing Research. New York: McGraw-Hill Book Co., 2-133-46.

Wheatley, J.J. (1973): Self-Administered Written Questionnaires or Telephone Interviews? Journal of Marketing Research 10, pp 94-96.

Whitmore, W.J. (1976): Mail Survey Premiums and Response Bias. Journal of Marketing Research 13, pp 46-50.

Whitmore, W.J. (1977): A Reply on 'Mail Survey Premiums and Response Bias'. Journal of Marketing Research 14, pp 388-390.

Wilcox, J.B. (1977): The Interaction of Refusal and Not-at-Home Sources of Nonresponse Bias. Journal of Marketing Research 14, pp 592-597.

Wildman, R.C. (1977): Effects of Anonymity and Social Setting on Survey Responses. Public Opinion Quarterly 41, pp 74-79.

Wilkinson, G.N. (1958): Estimation of Missing Values for the Analysis of Incomplete Data. Biometrics 14, pp 257-286.

Wilkinson, G.N. (1958): The Analysis of Variance and Derivation of Standard Errors for Incomplete Data. Biometrics 14, pp 360-384.

Wilkinson, G.N. (1960): Comparison of Missing Value Procedures. Australian Journal of Statistics 2, pp 53-65.

Wilks, S.S. (1932): Moments and Distributions of Estimates of Population Parameters from Fragmentary Samples. Annals of Mathematical Statistics 2, pp 163-195.

Williams, A.F. and Wechsler, H. (1970): The Mail Survey: Methods to Minimize Bias Owing to Incomplete Response. Sociology and Social Research 54, pp 533-535.

Williams, J.A. (1964): Interviewer-Respondent Interaction: A Study of Bias in the Information Interview. Sociometry 27, pp 338-352.

Williams, S.R. and Folsom, R.E., Jr (1977): Bias Resulting From School Nonresponse: Methodology and Findings. Prepared by the Research Triangle Institute for the National Center for Educational Statistics.

Williams, W.H. (1962): The Variance of an Estimator With Post-Stratified Weighting. Journal of the American Statistical Association 57, pp 622-627.

Williams, W.H. (1968): The Systematic Bias Effect of Incomplete Responses. American Statistical Association, Proceedings of the Social Statistics Section, pp 308-312.

Williams, W.H. (1970): The Systematic Bias Effects of Incomplete Response in Rotation Samples. Public Opinion Quarterly 34, pp 593-602.

Williams, W.H. (1975): The Seriousness of Selection Biases, Including Nonresponse. American Statistical Association, Proceedings of the Social Statistics Section, pp 11-15.

Williams, W.H. and Mallows, C.L. (1970): Systematic Biases in Panel Surveys due to Differential Nonresponse. Journal of the American Statistical Association 65, pp 1338-1349.

Wiseman, F. (1972): Methodological Bias in Public Opinion Surveys. Public Opinion Quarterly 36, pp 105-108.

Wiseman, F. (1973): Factor Interaction Effects in Mail Survey Response Rates. Journal of Marketing Research 10, pp 330-333.

Wiseman, F. (1976): A Reassessment of the Effects of Personalization on Response Patterns in Mail Surveys. Journal of Marketing Research 13, pp 110-111.

Wiseman, F. and McDonald, P. (1978): An Empirical Investigation of Refusal Rates in Consumer Surveys. American Statistical Association, Proceedings of the Section on Survey Research Methods, pp 283-287.

Wiseman, F. and McDonald, P. (1979): Noncontact and Refusal Rates in Consumer Telephone Surveys. Journal of Marketing Research 16, pp 474-484.

Wiseman, F., Moriarty, M. and Schafer, M. (1975-76): Estimating Public Opinion With the Randomized Response Model. Public Opinion Quarterly 39, pp 507-513.

Wiseman, F. and Schafer, M. (1976): Focus Group Interviews With Survey Non-Respondents. Presented at the May 1976 annual meeting of the American Association for Public Opinion Research.

Wish, E.D., Robins, L.N., Helzer, J.E., Hesselbrock, M. and Davis, D.H. (1978): Monday Morning Quarterbacking on Limiting Call-Backs: Evidence From a Panel Study of Veterans. Presented at the Annual Meeting of the American Association of Public Opinion Research, Roanoke, Virginia, June 1978.

Woltman, H. (1979): Status of the 1980 Census Content Error Evaluation Program. Memo, US Bureau of the Census.

Woltman, H. and Bushery, J. (1979): Results of the NCS Maximum Personal Visit - Maximum Telephone Interview Experiment. US Bureau of the Census.

Woodbury, M.A. and Orchard, T. (1972): A Missing Information Principle: Theory and Applications. In: Proceedings of the Sixth Berkeley Symposium on Mathematical Statistics and Probability. Volume I (LeCam L, Neyman J, Scott EL, eds.). Berkeley, University of California Press, pp 697-715.

Woolson, R.F., Leeper, J.D. and Clarke, W.R. (1978): Analysis of Incomplete Data From Longitudinal and Mixed Longitudinal Studies. Journal of the Royal Statistical Society, Series A, 141, Part 2, pp 242-252.

Wotruba, T.R. (1966): Monetary Inducements and Mail Questionnaire Response. Journal of Marketing Research 3, pp 398-400.

Wretman, J. (1978): The Swedish Data Act and Imputation For Nonresponse. Research project Confidentiality in Surveys. Report No. 30, Department of Statistics, University of Stockholm.

Yates, F. (1933): The Analysis of Replicated Experiments When the Field Results are Incomplete. Emp. J. Exp. Agric. 1, pp 129-142.

Yates, P.B. (1975): Implications of the Freedom of Information and Privacy Acts for Voluntary Labor Statistics Programs. American Statistical Association, Proceedings of the Social Statistics Section, pp 217-220.

Yuskavage, R., Hirschberg, D. and Scheuren, F. (1977): The Impact on Personal and Family Income of Adjusting the Current Population Survey for Undercoverage. American Statistical Association, Proceedings of the Social Statistics Section, pp 70-80.

Zarkovich, S.S. (1966): Quality of Statistical Data. Food and Agriculture Organization of the United Nations, Rome.

Zarkovich, S.S. (1967): A System of Statistical Quality Codes. Paper presented at the 36th Session of the International Statistical Institute in Sydney, 1967.

Zdep, S.M. and Rhodes, I.N. (1976-77): Making the Randomized Response Technique Work. Public Opinion Quarterly 40, pp 531-537.

Zdep, S.M., Rhodes, I.N., Schwarz, R.M. and Kilkenny, M.J. (1979): The Validity of the Randomized Response Technique. Public Opinion Quarterly 43, pp 544.

Zimmer, H. (1956): Validity of Extrapolating Non-Response Bias From Mail Questionnaire Follow-Ups. Journal of Applied Psychology 40, pp 117-121.

Author Index

Subject Index

Survey of Consumer Requirements, 446
Swedish Data Act, 477
Swedish Labour Force Survey, 477

T

Transformations of data, 351
Truncation, 444
Two-stage sample design, 326

U

Unconfounded probability sample, 126
Undercoverage, 6, 87
  adjustment for, 421
Underreporting, 87
Unit, 329
Unit nonresponse, 6, 11, 141
Unit substitution method, 332

V

Variance due to responding, 266
Variance of the event of responding, 330

W

Weighting adjustments for nonresponse, 20
  poststratification, 21
  raking, 22
  weighting-class adjustment, 21
  weighting inflation factor, 20
Weighting-class estimation
  variance, 161
Weighting classes, 259
Weighting methods, 7, 316–321, 331
  Bayesian perspective, 8
  randomization theory perspective, 8
Weighting-class estimation, 149–154, 428,
    435, 442, 448, 452, 465
  bias, 150, 160
  mean square error, 151, 153
  replicate variance estimators, 156
  variance, 154

Z

Zero substitution method, 283, 314, 332
  conditions for application, 283